# NOBEL PRIZE LIBRARY

---

*MARTIN DU GARD*

*G. MISTRAL*

*PASTERNAK*

# Nobel Prize Library

PUBLISHED UNDER THE SPONSORSHIP OF THE

NOBEL FOUNDATION & THE SWEDISH ACADEMY

---

*Roger Martin du Gard*

*Gabriela Mistral*

*Boris Pasternak*

---

ALEXIS GREGORY, *New York*, AND
CRM PUBLISHING, *Del Mar, California*

# CONTENTS

# Roger Martin du Gard

## 1937

---

"For the artistic vigor and truthfulness
with which he has pictured human contrasts,
as well as some fundamental aspects of
contemporary life, in the series of novels
entitled *Les Thibault*"

---

*Illustrated by LEFAGES*

# PRESENTATION ADDRESS

## By *PER HALLSTRÖM*

PERMANENT SECRETARY

OF THE SWEDISH ACADEMY

---

THE RECIPIENT of the Nobel Prize in Literature for 1937, Roger Martin du Gard, has dedicated most of his activity to a single work, a long series of novels with the collective title, *Les Thibault* (1922–40). It is a vast work both in the number of its volumes and in its scope. It represents modern French life by means of a whole gallery of characters and analysis of the intellectual currents and the problems that occupied France during the ten years preceding the First World War, a gallery as full and an analysis as complete as the subject of the novel permitted. The work has therefore taken a form especially characterisitic of our era, called the *roman fleuve* in the country of its origin. The term designates a narrative method that is relatively little concerned with composition and advances like a river across vast countries, reflecting everything that is found on its way. The essence of such a novel, in large as well as small matter, consists in the exactitude of this reflection rather than in the harmonious balance of its parts: it has no shape. The river lingers at will and only rarely does the undercurrent disturb the smooth flow of its surface.

Our age can hardly be called calm; on the contrary, the speed of the machines accelerates the rhythm of life to the point of agitation. It is strange, therefore, that in such an age the most popular literary form, the novel, should have developed in a totally opposite direction, and by so doing have become only the more popular. Still, if the novel offered us the satisfying world of fantasy, one could explain this phenomenon in psychological terms as a sort of poetic compensation for the frustrations

[ 3 ]

of daily life. But it is precisely the heart-rending anguish of reality that the novel takes such time to sound and to emphasize.

Nevertheless, the novel is there, with its boundless substance, and the reader finds a certain solace in the heightened awareness which he acquires from the inevitable element of tragedy inherent in all life. With a kind of heroism, it swallows reality in large drafts and encourages us to bear even great sufferings with joy. The reader's esthetic demands will be satisfied in isolated sections of the work which are more condensed and therefore better suited to call forth his feelings. *Les Thibault* does not lack such sections.

The essential characters of the novel are three members of the same family: the father and two sons. The father remains in the background; his passive role, one of weight and massiveness, is presented by a special technique. The two sons and the countless secondary characters of the work are presented in a dramatic manner. Unprepared by anything in the story, we see them before us, acting and speaking in the present; and we are given a detailed and complete description of the setting. The reader must be quick to grasp what he sees and hears, for the capricious and irregular rhythm of life beats everywhere. He is helped in his task by the writer's most perfected tool: the analysis of his heroes' thoughts, expressed beyond words, an insight into the darkness which engenders conscious actions. Martin du Gard goes even further; he shows how thoughts, feelings, and the will can be transformed before becoming words and acts. Sometimes exterior considerations—habit, vanity, or even a simple gaucherie—alter expressions and personality. This examination, at once subtle and bold, of the dynamic processes of the soul obviously constitutes Martin du Gard's most original and most remarkable contribution to the art of characterizing human beings. From the esthetic point of view, this is not always an advantage, for the analysis may appear cumbersome when its results do not seem necessary to the story.

This introspective method is used even for the father's character, but it is less complicated in his case. His personality is already clear-cut and complete at the beginning of the novel, for he belongs to the past. Events of the present no longer affect him.

He is a member of the upper middle class, conscious of his status and his duties, a faithful servant of the Church and a generous benefactor of society, full of prudent advice. He really belongs to a generation before his own, to the France of the July Monarchy; that is why he is to come into more than one conflict with the next generation, in particular with his sons. But this conflict rarely reaches the verbal level, for the old man is too convinced of his proper worth to engage in discussions. Hence the perennial theme of the opposition of youth to age is not specially treated here.

The representative of age appears above all in an attitude of introspection and immutability; he relies heavily and complacently on all that he thinks wise and just. No word can influence him. In the isolation of his life, one might see the whole tragedy of age if he were not himself so completely unaware of the possibility of such a tragedy.

He is characterized rather by comic traits; profounder sentiments are expressed only at the time of his death, in the face of his human destiny. This expression is not direct but results from a strictly objective, concrete description of the long martyrdom of his agony. It is a moving description despite its minute detail. Up to now he had been considered only from without, with the exception of some rare instances when he had revealed what, even in him, was hidden behind the façade he presented to the world.

The difference between him and his oldest son receives little emphasis. Antoine Thibault is a doctor. Entirely absorbed by his profession, his father's moral and ethical points of view are entirely alien to him. Morality is replaced in him by an intense and conscientious devotion to research and to the exercise of his profession. Master of himself, prudent, tactful, he has not the least desire for opposition; he has not even time to think of it. In the novel one witnesses his rapid evolution within prescribed limits. He is a man ambitious for the future. At first he is occasionally a little fatuous, but he soon commands respect by his work.

Antoine becomes a sympathetic representative of the intellectuals of his day, full of ideas, without prejudices in his conceptions, but as a determinist convinced of the inability of the individual to change whatever the general course of events may be. He is not a revolutionary.

Quite different is his brother Jacques, who is several years younger. The latter is too close to the writer's heart to suffer any criticism. He is the hero of the work, and the exterior world is examined and judged according to his ideals. His father's responsibility for his evolution is con-

[ 5 ]

siderable, but actually Jacques, by his whole nature, is destined to be a revolutionary. When the story begins, he is a schoolboy of fourteen in a college run by priests. Although he dislikes and neglects his studies, he commands respect by his intelligence. The catastrophe occurs when he discovers a friend among his schoolmates, and their affection, at this dangerous period of adolescence, takes an exalted and seemingly erotic form. Their feelings are betrayed by their letters, misinterpreted (as, indeed, they are bound to be) by the priests who intervene with disciplinary measures. The strict surveillance and the very intrusion into his emotional private life are an unbearable offense to Jacques. Furthermore, he has to await his father's rage, stirred up by this scandal. His revolt is expressed in action. He carries along his friend in his escape far from all yokes, those he endured and those he feared in a hostile and harsh world. He feels that his whole being, in the grip of romantic poetry and of more dangerous tendencies, is irreconcilable with the real world. Seeking happiness and freedom, the two boys leave for Africa, but their visionary project is destroyed in Marseilles by the efforts of the police who had been alerted.

On his return, his father, in an excess of pedagogic zeal, makes a psychological mistake; he condemns his son to solitary confinement in a reformatory founded by himself. The oppression of this confinement causes Jacques' indomitable personality to emerge even stronger and fiercer. The account of this development is the most moving episode in the work.

After he has been released by his brother's influence, Jacques is permitted to pursue his studies, his only consolation. He does brilliantly and is easily accepted by the Ecole Normale, the supreme goal of all ambitious and talented students and the open door to all top literary or scientific careers. But Jacques cannot be attracted by an official career that for him is only a void and an illusion; he soon sets out for adventure and reality. Once more the boy runs off to Africa, but this time he succeeds and he remains absent from the narrative for a long time.

He is seen again when Antoine discovers his residence—in Switzerland among the revolutionaries—and brings him back to their father's deathbed. He arrives too late for a reconciliation, even if one considered a reconciliation between these two diametrically opposed concepts of life possible. The old man does not recognize him, but Jacques feels a deep sorrow, for he is not one of those people who, obsessed with mankind's future happiness, begin by stifling every trace of humanity in themselves.

Such is the outline of Jacques' inner life as far as it is known. For the rest he remains rather elusive, as before, but we notice the author's great appreciation of his faculties and of his character.

We get to know him fully when the novel approaches its conclusion and at the same time its height of epic grandeur—in the summer of 1914 just before the world catastrophe. Jacques is in Geneva, having left Paris soon after his father's death in order to escape the necessity of inheriting a fortune in a society he scorns. He belongs to a group of socialist and communist reformers whose immediate mission is to halt the threat of war by the revolt of the masses. The description of these agitators is one of the least successful passages in the book; the overall impression, whether intended or not, is that these men are not worthy of their mission.

But Jacques' stature increases in everyone's eyes when he leaves Geneva and returns to Paris to accomplish his mission. His development is moral rather than intellectual; his actions have no great results, but he saves his soul. The description of the last days of July in Paris, with Jacques wavering between hope and despair in this surcharged atmosphere, is a veritable *tour de force* in Martin du Gard's novelistic achievement. The history of this period revives, reawakens, as far as the masses' role is concerned. But, as almost always, the role is not decisive. The masses are impotent, blind, and in this case even less familiar than usual with the game of politics that causes such tragedies. The author himself seems not to be particularly initiated, but he is tolerant and human, and his description, as far as it goes, is truthful.

Against the background of this bewildering anxiety there occurs a brief but highly illuminating episode of a completely different character. Jacques meets again a young girl with whom he had almost fallen in love several years before, but from whom he had run away as he had run away from everything else. This time the true spark is kindled between them. This fatal love story is one of the most significant episodes in the novel; it is profoundly felt and rendered in all its pure beauty precisely because it is restricted to the dimensions that the breathless flight of days imposes on the story. It lasts only a short time, but that is enough to give it a tragic and simple beauty.

When all the political illusions vanish for Jacques at the declaration of war, he recreates for himself a new illusion, born of his despair and of his will to sacrifice. Right at the front lines he tries to ward off the catastrophe by appealing from an airplane to the two opposing armies, seeking to inspire in them a common revolt and a desire to overthrow the powers which hold them captive. Without hesitating he leaves Paris and the woman he loves.

The adventure is stamped with the same schoolboy romanticism and lack of reality as was his first flight out of the world, but Jacques nonetheless carries out his plan with his customary energy. His call for revolution is printed in Switzerland, the airplane and pilot are ready, the expedition begins. It will not last long, for he has hardly flown over the battlefield when the plane crashes and catches fire with its whole load, men and bundles of paper. Jacques himself falls, a heap of bruised and burned flesh, among the retreating French troops. All his perception is restricted to a vague sensation of the bitterness of defeat and to unbearable and infinite physical torments, which are finally relieved by the bullet of a compatriot tired of dragging along this ill-fated person whom he holds to be a spy anyhow.

It is difficult to imagine a bitterer denouement to a tragedy or a crueller irony in a defeat. But Martin du Gard did not direct his irony toward his hero. Perhaps he wanted to show the brutality and the cruelty of world events as opposed to idealistic tendencies. His bitterness is certainly justified here, but the long detailed description of the whole episode becomes almost intolerable in its scrupulous exactitude.

Jacques Thibault, as we finally get to know him, lives in our memory as a heroic figure. Without grandiloquent attitude or word, this upright, silent, and reserved man receives at last the seal of grandeur: grandeur of will and courage. Whenever the novel centers on him, the writer's untiring work achieves persuasive eloquence. After his pointed and skeptical analysis of the human soul, which almost consumes its object with its often extreme exactness in detail, through the most minute realism possible, Martin du Gard finally pays homage to the idealism of the human spirit.

# ACCEPTANCE SPEECH

## By ROGER MARTIN DU GARD

THE PRESENCE of so many illustrious persons assembled under the patronage of His Highness, the Crown Prince, heightens the emotions that I feel at finding myself here and hearing the words of praise that have just been addressed to me. I feel rather like an owl, suddenly roused from its nest and exposed to the daylight, whose eyes, used to the dark, are blinded by dazzling brightness.

I am proud of the exceptional mark of esteem the Swedish Academy has bestowed on me, but I cannot conceal my surprise from you. Ever since I felt your favor lie upon and almost overwhelm me, I have asked myself how to interpret it.

My first thought was of my country. I am happy that in making a *French* author its choice for this year, the distinguished Swedish Academy has thought fit to glorify our French literature in particular. On the other hand, I know some great poets among my compatriots, noble and powerful minds, whom your votes might have chosen with much better reason. Why then am I today in this place of honor?

The demon of vanity, never completely silenced, at first whispered to me some flattering presumptions. I even went so far as to ask myself whether by granting this distinction to the "man without dogma" that I profess to be, the Academy did not wish to emphasize that in this century, when everyone "believes" and "asserts," it is perhaps useful that there should be some who "hesitate," "put in doubt," and "question"— independent minds that escape the fascination of partisan ideologies and whose constant care is to develop their individual consciences in order to maintain a spirit of "inquiry" as objective, liberal, and fair-minded as is humanly possible.

I should also like to think that this sudden honor acknowledges certain principles dear to me. "Principles" is a big word to be used by a man who says that he is always ready to revise his opinions. I must, however, admit that in the practice of my art I have imposed upon myself certain guidelines to which I have tried to be faithful.

I was still very young when I encountered, in a novel by the English writer Thomas Hardy, this reflection on one of his characters: "The true value of life seemed to him to be not so much its beauty, as its tragic quality." It spoke to an intuition deep within me, closely allied to my literary vocation. Ever since that time I have thought that the prime purpose of the novel is to give voice to the tragic element in life. Today I would add: the tragic element in the life of an individual, the tragedy of a "destiny in the course of being fulfilled."

At this point I cannot refrain from referring to the immortal example of Tolstoy, whose books have had a determining influence on my development. The born novelist recognizes himself by his passion to penetrate ever more deeply into the knowledge of man and to lay bare in each of his characters that individual element of life which makes each being unique. It seems to me that any chance of survival which a novelist's work may have rests solely on the quantity and the quality of the individual lives that he has been able to create in his books. But that is not all. The novelist must also have a sense of life in general; his work must reveal a personal vision of the universe. Here again Tolstoy is the great master. Each of his creatures is more or less secretly haunted by a metaphysical obsession, and each of the human experiences that he has recorded implies, beyond an inquiry into man, an anxious question about the meaning of life. I admit that I take pleasure in the thought that, in crowning my work as a novelist, the members of the Swedish Academy wished to pay indirect homage to my devotion to that unapproachable model and to my efforts to profit from the instruction of his genius.

I should like to conclude with a more somber hypothesis, although I am embarrassed to disturb this festive mood by arousing those painful thoughts that haunt all of us. However, perhaps the Swedish Academy did not hesitate to express a special purpose by drawing the attention of the intellectual world to the author of *L'Été 1914* (*Summer 1914*).

That is the title of my last book. It is not for me to judge its value. But at least I know what I set out to do: in the course of these three volumes I tried to revivify the anguished atmosphere of Europe on the eve of the mobilizations of 1914. I tried to show the weakness of the governments of that day, their hesitations, indiscretions, and unavowed desires; I tried above all to give an impression of the stupefaction of the peaceful masses before the approach of that cataclysm whose victims they were going to be, that cataclysm which was to leave nine million men dead and ten million men crippled.

When I see that one of the highest literary juries in the world supports these books with the prestige of its incontestable authority, I ask myself whether the reason may not be that these books through their wide circulation have appeared to defend certain values that are again being threatened and to fight against the evil contagion of the forces of war.

For I am a son of the West, where the noise of arms does not let our minds rest. Since we have come together today on the tenth of December, the anniversary of the death of Alfred Nobel (that man of action, "no mere shadow," who in the last years of his life seems indeed to have put his supreme hope in the brotherhood of nations), permit me to confess how good it would be to think that my work—the work that has just been honored in his name—might serve not only the cause of letters, but even the cause of peace. In these months of anxiety in which we are living, when blood is already being shed in two extreme parts of the globe, when practically everywhere in an atmosphere polluted by misery and fanaticism passions are seething around pointed guns, when too many signs are again heralding the return of that languid defeatism, that general consent which alone makes wars possible: at this exceptionally grave moment through which humanity is passing, I wish, without vanity, but with a gnawing disquietude in my heart, that my books about *Summer 1914* may be read and discussed, and that they may remind all—the old who have forgotten as well as the young who either do not know or do not care—of the sad lesson of the past.

# JEAN BAROIS

## By ROGER MARTIN DU GARD

*Translated by* Stuart Gilbert

[ Excerpt ]

---

## PART I

### I

#### The Will to Live

I

The residence of Mme Barois at Buis-la-Dame, a small French country town some fifty miles north of Paris. The year is 1878.

In Mme Barois' bedroom the curtains are drawn, and behind them the slats of the venetian blinds glimmer black and silver in the moonlight. The room is in darkness but for a pale sheen that floods the parquet, lighting up the hem of a woman's dress and a man's boot softly tapping the floor. There is the sound of two people breathing, two people watching, waiting . . .

Now and again an iron bedstead creaks in the adjoining room, and a child can be heard muttering rambling phrases; one cannot tell if he is delirious or talking in his sleep. The door between the two bedrooms is ajar, and the faint glow of a night light ribbons the slit.

A long silence.

THE DOCTOR, in a low voice: "The bromide's working. He'll have a calmer night."

Mme Barois rises with an effort and tiptoes to the door. Her face is set and haggard as, narrowing her eyes, she peers into the lighted bedroom, her cheek pressed to the doorjamb.

Mme Barois is a tall old woman of an ungainly build and heavy gait. The light from the unshaded night light ruthlessly probes the furrows on her face, the sallow, distended skin; strongly marked shadows emphasize the pouches under her eyes, the sagging cheeks and swollen lips, a double chin. The face suggests an austere, rather grudging kindliness, gentle obstinacy, rigid self-control.

MME BAROIS, in a whisper: "He's sleeping."

She closes the door softly, then lights a lamp and returns to her chair.

THE DOCTOR, placing his hand on his mother's; then, by force of habit, sliding his fingers up to her wrist and half unconsciously feeling her pulse: "You too, Mother, need rest. That long journey was too much for you."

MME BAROIS, shaking her head: "I can feel you're vexed with me, Philippe, for having taken Jean to—to that place."

Dr. Barois is a small wiry man of fifty-six, deft and prompt in his gestures. He has gray hair, a shrewd face, all in acute angles, the nose-bridge like a knife-blade, a moustache tapering to neatly waxed points, a small peaked beard. Sometimes a smile of gentle irony narrows his lips. His keen, restless eyes glitter now and then behind the pince-nez.

MME BAROIS, after a short silence: "Still everybody here agreed it was the best thing to do. And Jean was always pestering me to put his name down; he felt so certain he'd come back cured from Lourdes. All the way in the train he made me keep on telling him the story of Bernadette."

The doctor takes off his pince-nez and blinks at his mother with affectionate, shortsighted eyes. She stops speaking. Their thoughts meet and clash; the years have made a rift between them. After a few moments she continues. "No, it's no use hoping you'll understand. You and I, my son and I, don't understand each other any longer. That's what they've done to you at Paris, to the boy you used to be!"

THE DOCTOR: "Mother dear, I'd rather we didn't talk about that journey to Lourdes. Not that I blame you in the least. Except for having told me of your intention only when it was too late for me to intervene. You see, Jean wasn't fit to undertake a long journey like that, in a slow train, third class."

MME BAROIS: "Aren't you taking too gloomy a view of his condition, my dear? You've seen him as he is tonight, feverish and inclined to be delirious. But you didn't see him as he was this winter."

THE DOCTOR, uncomfortably: "That's so. I didn't see him once this winter."

MME BAROIS, more boldly: "Since he had that attack of bronchitis he's never looked quite himself, that's sure. He was always complaining of a pain—here. But, I can assure you, he didn't look a bit like a sick child. Often in the evening he was in high spirits, almost too high spirits."

THE DOCTOR, putting his eyeglasses on, bending towards his mother, and clasping her hand: "In too high spirits in the evenings, was he? Ah!" He shakes his head. "You forget the past too quickly, Mother."

MME BAROIS, obstinately: "You know my views on the subject, Philippe. Nothing will convince me that your poor dear wife had—what you think. No, it was Paris that killed her, poor thing, as it's killed so many others."

The doctor is hardly listening. The lamplight falls on his mother's hand; he fondles it absent-mindedly. A thick, soft hand, mottled with little brown spots; gnarled fingers. In a sudden throw-back to a trick of childhood he strokes the wedding ring, thinned almost to breaking point, which the swollen joints will keep imprisoned there until the end. And impulsively, perhaps for the first time in his life, seized by a craven desire to weep, to escape, to shut his eyes to the inevitable, he raises to his lips that old hand, changed out of recognition by the years, which none the less he could never confuse with any other. Mme. Barois, somewhat embarrassed, draws her hand away.

MME BAROIS, almost roughly: "Don't forget, for one thing, that Jean takes after *our* family in every way. Why, he's the very image of you, Philippe! Everybody says so. That child has nothing of his mother, nothing!"

A short silence.

THE DOCTOR, moodily, to himself: "I've been so terribly busy all this winter." He realizes that he hasn't answered his mother and turns to her affectionately. "Doctoring is a hard profession, Mother, in cases like mine. Knowing one's son is ill, only a few hours' journey from Paris. And letting all one's days be taken up, hour after hour, by others. And every time one books another appointment, being reminded that it's impossible to keep the page blank even for an afternoon; never having a moment's freedom! Ah, if only I could throw up everything and come to live here with you two!" Peremptorily. "No, of course I couldn't do that. Out of the question." He takes off his eyeglasses, wipes them, ponders for some moments, then replaces them briskly. His voice becomes curt, incisive, professional. "We must keep him under closer observation than ever, night and day, and fight back the disease inch by inch."

Mme Barois makes an incredulous gesture. The doctor stops speaking and throws a quick searching glance at his mother. A momentary indecision—as when, in the course of an operation, he has abruptly to change his tactics. Then his gaze steadies, sharpens; he has fixed on a new plan of campaign.

A long silence.

## II

A week later. Sunday morning.

THE DOCTOR, entering Jean's bedroom: "Good morning, Jean. And how are we this morning? But why's that window shut when it's such a lovely day?" He takes the boy's hands and has him stand facing the light. "Let's see your tongue. Good. Have you been sleeping well this week? Not too well? You're always changing your position in bed, are you? And you wake up because you feel too hot? I see . . ." He pats Jean's cheek. "Now off with your clothes! I want to listen to your chest."

Jean is a pale-faced lad of twelve, with clean-cut but characterless features. His gaze is more distinctive—affectionate, pensive, without gaiety. He has a poor physique; the ribs show as bluish streaks under the thin, pale skin.

THE DOCTOR: "Now let's have a look. Put your back to the wall as you did last time, and let your arms hang loose. Raise your chin, open your mouth. Right." He takes off his glasses. "Now breathe deeply. Again."

As he listens to Jean's chest he puckers up his face and blinks his eyes. The father's keen anxiety, cut off as he is from the world by his short sight and his intense absorption in the sounds he hears, contrasts with the indifference of the boy, who is yawning, gazing listlessly out at the sky. The examination lasts a long time.

THE DOCTOR, quietly: "Thanks, my dear. Put your clothes on again." With an affectionate smile. "Now I'll tell you what we're going to do, old chap. We'll go to the garden, just the two of us, and have a little chat in the sunshine until your grandmother comes back from Mass. What do you say to that?"

JEAN: "Grandma can't have gone yet." Timidly. "It's Whit-Sunday, Papa. I'd have liked—"

THE DOCTOR, gently: "No, Jean, that wouldn't be at all wise. You'd get hot walking, and it must be quite chilly in the church."

JEAN: "But it's so near—"

THE DOCTOR: "And then—I must catch the three o'clock train; I've a consultation this evening, in Paris. And naturally I want to see a bit of you while I am here." In a different tone. "I've some things to say to you, Jean, important things." A short silence. "So, come along!"

The old house owned by the Barois family for many generations stands at the highest point of the town. The main building seems to shore up the church, on whose tower it abuts. Two long wings, roofed with tiles, project towards the street from each end of the main building; they are linked together by a prison-like wall, in which is a spacious gateway. The space thus enclosed is partly courtyard, partly garden. Several times each day the sound of bells plunges down into this echoing sound-trap, making even the walls vibrate.

The doctor leads Jean to a trellised arbor covered with Virginia creeper.

THE DOCTOR, in a tone of forced joviality: "Sit down, old chap. Make yourself comfy. It's nice here, isn't it?"

JEAN, on the brink of tears, though why he doesn't know: "Yes, Papa."

The doctor has his "hospital face," as Jean calls it; the nose-wings wrinkled, eyes probing and intent.

THE DOCTOR, resolutely: "This is what I have to tell you, Jean. Just three words. You are ill." Silence. Jean keeps very still, gazing at the ground. "Yes, you're ill, and more so than you think." Another silence. The doctor keeps his eyes fixed on the boy. "I wish you to realize this, because if you don't make a really big effort to get well, it may become—extremely serious."

JEAN, forcing back his tears: "Then—then I'm not getting better?" The doctor shakes his head. "But I thought, after what happened at Lourdes . . ." He ponders for some moments. "Perhaps it hasn't begun to show yet?"

THE DOCTOR: "I know nothing about what happened at Lourdes. But I do know this: as things stand, as I find you today, you are very, very far from well."

JEAN, with a weak smile: "But—what have I got?"

THE DOCTOR, frowning: "You have—" He hesitates before continuing. "I'd better try to explain, Jean. And listen well to what I'm going to tell you. Your mother —" He takes off his glasses and starts wiping them, fixing his eyes on Jean. "Can you remember your mother at all?" Jean looks uncomfortable and shakes his head. "Your mother used to live here, in the country, before our marriage. She was never very strong, but her health was satisfactory. After our marriage she had

to come to live in Paris, because of me. Your birth was a great strain on her constitution." The doctor takes a deep breath. "It was then she started being ill." He emphasizes the words. "An attack of acute bronchitis, to begin with. Do you know what that is?"

JEAN: "The same as I had?"

THE DOCTOR: "She made a bad recovery. Every night she had fever; she couldn't sleep well and kept tossing about in bed." The boy gives a slight start. "She often had a pain"—deliberately he leans forward and touches Jean's chest—"just here."

JEAN, nervously: "Like me?"

THE DOCTOR: "I did my best to make her look after herself. I told her much the same things as I'm telling you today. But, unfortunately, she wouldn't listen." A short silence. He has to fumble for his words, but his voice never falters. "Your mother, let me tell you, was a good, gentle, saintly woman—and I loved her most dearly. But she was many years younger than I and—very, very religious." Sadly. "I never managed to have the least influence over her. Every day she could see me giving my patients medical advice, and often curing them; and yet she hadn't confidence. And then, of course, she didn't feel really ill. What made things still harder was that I'd just got my post at the hospital, and this took up so much of my time that I couldn't look after her as well as I'd have liked. I wanted her to come and stay here, for the country air, but she refused. She started a cough. There were consultations. But it was too late." A short silence. "Things went very quickly. A summer, an autumn, a winter—by the spring she was no longer with us."

Jean bursts into tears. The doctor observes him with a cool, observant gaze—as when at a patient's bedside he is waiting for an injection to make its effect. Some minutes pass.

THE DOCTOR: "You mustn't take it so hard, Jean. I don't want to make you sad, you know. I'm only trying to talk to you as I would to one of my grown-up patients, because, well—it has to be done. You've inherited from your mother a tendency to have the same illness as she had. A *tendency,* you understand? No more than that. Which means that if you're exposed to certain unfavorable conditions, you may get the same disease. That, my dear boy, is exactly how you stand today. Since last autumn your health has been very poor, and it's high time, yes, high time to—"

In a sudden access of fear Jean slips off the bench and presses himself to his father, who gives him a rather clumsy hug.

THE DOCTOR: "There, there, Jean! There's no need to be frightened. I'm here to look after you."

JEAN, through his tears: "Oh, I'm not frightened really. I've thought of that already—that I was in heaven."

The doctor thrusts him away almost roughly, then makes the boy stand facing him.

THE DOCTOR, vehemently: "There's no question of dying, Jean. What you've got to do is to *live.* You can save yourself if you choose; well, do so!"

Taken aback, the boy stops sobbing and stares at his father. He'd have liked to be drawn up on his father's knees, petted and consoled. But he comes up against the cold gleam of the pince-nez. A new emotion is stirring in him, of fear and vague resentment; but also—such is the ascendancy of intelligence and strength—of perfect trust, of faith.

THE DOCTOR: "You wouldn't know, of course. The human body seems such a beautifully fitted and adjusted mechanism, doesn't it? Well, it's nothing but a vast battlefield, with millions of cells at war, devouring each other all the time. I'll explain it a bit more clearly. Hosts of tiny, harmful germs are attacking us every moment, and amongst them, naturally, are the germs of T.B. You know what T.B. means, don't you?" Jean nods. "Well, these germs always make a dead set at somebody like you, who has a tendency that way. What happens then is simple. If the body's strong, it drives them off; if it's not, they force their way in." He grips Jean's arm and emphasizes every word. "So there's only one way of defeating them: to build up your strength as quickly as possible, so as to get the whip hand again. You can cure yourself, never fear; all you need is to set your heart on being cured. It's a hard task, but you can and *must* see it through. Really it's only a matter of energy and perseverance. *Now* do you understand? All existence is a struggle; life is simply winning through. And you'll soon find you can win through, provided you really and truly make up your mind to do so." Impulsively Jean has come nearer, and is nestling against his father. The doctor puts his arm round the boy's shoulders. "If I could drop my practice for a while, close my surgery, and give all my time to you, I'd pull you through; that I guarantee." Vehemently. "Well, what I cannot do, what I have not the right to do, you can do by yourself, if you'll be guided by me." He looks him in the eyes. "Well, Jean? Will you promise to do as I tell you?"

JEAN, in a rush of emotion: "Yes, yes, Papa. I promise you. I'll start at once. I'll do everything you say." He is silent for some moments, obviously thinking hard. Then, almost as if he were talking to himself, he adds: "And Abbé Joziers will say Masses for me as well. I'll ask him."

THE DOCTOR, gently: "By all means. But that wouldn't be enough. First, there's a lot of spadework to be done, you know, and only you can do it." Jean moves a little away from his father, who goes on speaking in a gravely affectionate tone. "I ask you, my dear boy, to *believe* what I'm telling you. That's the most important thing, really. It was because she lacked confidence that your poor mother died." The boy comes back to him. "You know quite well that I wouldn't for the world cause you pain by what I'm saying; in fact I'm greatly counting on your religious faith to help see you through. But there's a saying which you know: Heaven helps those who help themselves. Pray with all your might, Jean, but never forget that the course of treatment I'm going to prescribe comes first; everything else—yes, even prayer—is of secondary importance." With a fervor that carries conviction. "Yes, my dear boy, if you want to get well you must follow the treatment I'm going to prescribe, I won't say merely with perseverance and good will . . ." In a great peal all the bells of Pentecost acclaim the Elevation. The doctor has to raise his voice, almost to shout, to make himself heard through their throbbing clangor. "I won't say merely with energy; but with enthusiasm, an almost fanatical determination. With a steadfast purpose to regain all the lost ground, to build up new strength, to fight the disease back inch by inch, and to conquer death through your passionate will to live. To live, Jean! Ah, if only you had learned what that really means: to live! Not merely to stay alive, but to go on loving what you love, seeing that sunlight playing on the walls of your old home, and for many and many a year hearing those bells pour their music down, flooding your ears. Just look around. Look at those trees, that golden light, that blue sky, the church tower. Look!" He clasps the boy's shoulders and shakes him. "To *live*, Jean!"

Quivering with excitement, swept off his feet by an uprush of emotion such as he has never known before, the boy gazes rapturously at his father; his cheeks are flushed, his eyes sparkling.

After observing him gravely for a while, the doctor draws Jean towards him. The bells have fallen silent, but for some moments their vibration lingers in the sunlit courtyard before dispersing into the upper air. A long silence follows.

THE DOCTOR, weighing his words: "Three things: food, fresh air, rest. Now, try to fix in your memory what I'm going to say."

### III

The residence of Mme Pasquelin, Jean's godmother, at Buis. A dimly lit sitting-room. Outside the window, snowy winter twilight. Round the fireplace, lit by the firelight, a silent group. Mme Pasquelin is standing, her arm round Jean, who is weeping on her shoulder. Little Cécile is pressing herself to her mother's skirt, unnerved by the sight of Jean's distress, and crushing her handkerchief to her mouth to stifle her sobs.

On the tablecloth lie two crumpled telegrams:

Pasquelin, Buis-la-Dame, Oise. Mother much shaken by journey to Paris. Operation delayed by unforeseen complications. Very anxious. Barois.

Pasquelin, Buis-la-Dame, Oise. Mother died eleven this morning at nursing home without regaining consciousness. Operation impracticable. Break news to Jean very prudently, avoiding any shock.
                                        Barois.

### IV

Three years later. A small tiled room behind the sacristy, dimly lighted by a window facing a high wall. There are two chairs, two praying desks. A crucifix hangs on the wall in front of them.

Abbé Joziers has a young face, with a high, domed forehead from which the fair, close-cropped, curly hair is already beginning to recede. Frank, cheerful eyes tell of sunny, active faith. The impression of severity given by the thin upper lip is corrected by the lower, which is rather plump and often ripples in a somewhat ironic but good-natured smile. Smile and gaze have the genial, if almost aggressive, assurance of those for whom all the problems of this world and the next have definitely been solved, and who feel serenely confident of being the sole and sure repositories of the truth.

After carefully shutting the door, Abbé Joziers turns and stretches both hands towards Jean.

THE ABBÉ: "Well, Jean, old chap, what is it?" He clasps one of Jean's hands. "Do sit down."

Jean Barois is a tall, lithe boy of fifteen with a well-knit body, a broad chest, a long but sturdy neck. He has an energetic face; a square forehead crowned with thick, stiff brown hair. Slotted between the curved, slightly puckered eyelids, which convey his keen attention, the eyes are keen and forth-right; he has his father's piercing gaze. But the lower portion of the face is still quite childish; the mouth especially is hardly formed and seems to change its shape at every moment. The heaviness of the under-jaw is mitigated by the fullness of the chin.

The young face wears a look of dogged resolution, the outcome of a long uphill struggle towards health; three years of stern self-discipline, of alternating hopes and setbacks—with his life at stake. But the battle has been won.

THE ABBÉ: "Well?"

JEAN: "I did a lot of hard thinking, sir, before deciding to take this step. I've wanted to consult you for quite a while, but kept on putting it off. But now . . ."

He is silent for some moments. "There are some things troubling me today, questions to which I don't know the answer. About religion, I mean. All sorts of ideas that never entered my head before. Especially since I started going to Beauvais for those lessons." Hesitantly. "I need someone to discuss them with, someone to explain . . ."

THE ABBÉ, gazing serenely at Jean: "But there's nothing simpler. I'm entirely at your disposal, my dear boy. So there are certain matters which are troubling you? Well, let's hear what they are."

A look of earnestness beyond his years settles on Jean's face. He raises his head a little. The tension of the muscles draws down the corners of his lips, which are shadowed by a faint growth of down. His eyes are fever-bright.

THE ABBÉ, smiling encouragement: "Come along, Jean; out with it!"

JEAN: "Well, sir, to begin with—what exactly are free-thinkers?"

The priest squares his shoulders and replies briskly, without a moment's hesitation. A faint, pleased smile hovers on his lips. The restrained emotion in his voice is characteristic of the man; his teeth are almost clenched, and he stresses certain words out of all proportion to their context or significance.

THE ABBÉ: "You ask what free-thinkers are? Simpletons, for the most part, who imagine that it's possible for us to think freely. To think freely! But only lunatics think freely." He laughs cheerfully. "Am I free to think that five and five make eleven? Or that I can use a verb in the plural after a subject in the singular? Surely it's obvious there are rules which every sane person abides by—of grammar, of mathematics, and of every activity of the mind. The free-thinker fancies he can dispense with rules. But nobody can achieve anything unless he has something solid to build on. To walk you must have solid ground under your feet. And to think coherently you need solid, well-tested principles—which religion, and religion only, can supply."

JEAN, gloomily: "I rather fear, sir, that I've tendencies towards becoming a free-thinker."

THE ABBÉ, with a laugh: "You don't say so!" Affectionately. "No, my dear child, you need have no fears on that score; I'll answer for it. But how could you even dream of such a thing?"

JEAN: "I've changed. Until quite lately I never had any religious difficulties; I'd never have thought of questioning anything, I took it all for granted. But now—now I have strange moods when I try to clear things up in my mind, and then I get into a hopeless fog! It worries me horribly."

THE ABBÉ: "But, my boy, that's perfectly normal." Jean looks surprised. "It's a sort of growing pains. Yes, you're at the age when a youngster really begins his conscious existence, when daily he discovers hosts of things of which he'd had no notion hitherto. You see, he tries to bring to adult life the simple faith of childhood; and, well, they simply don't tally." The shadow is gradually lifting from Jean's face. "It's nothing, really. All that's needed is to get over this difficult phase as quickly as you can, to buttress your faith with solid arguments, and adapt it to your changed conditions. That's where I can help you."

JEAN, smiling: "Only to hear you speak, sir, does me a world of good." More briskly. "But I've another question. Let's take the case of a sin, a sin which has become almost a habit, with which one's quite familiar, but which one's quite determined to stamp out. Well, one prays, one vows to stop it, and all seems for the best. And then, fight as one may, habit proves stronger than the Will of God."

THE ABBÉ: "That, my boy, is why nothing can be more dangerous to faith than a sin that's committed frequently, even a venial sin. It's just these repeated shocks to the religious sentiment that must be avoided at all costs."

JEAN: "I know that. But why should it be impossible not to give way?" The priest smiles indulgently; Jean, absorbed in his thoughts, fails to notice. "I can't understand the reason for these temptations, all these trials of our faith. When one's a child, one finds it quite natural that there should be happy people and unhappy people, healthy people and invalids. That's how the world is, and you take it for granted. But later on, when you begin to think, you're shocked at all the injustice and evil that exist. If only one could say that unhappiness is always a punishment that's deserved, it would be ever so much simpler—but one can't! I know God must have had his reasons for making the world as it is, but really—"

THE ABBÉ: "Ah, but don't forget that God did not create the world as it is now. It is man who by his first disobedience of the order given by his Creator is responsible for all our woe."

JEAN, obstinately: "But if Adam had been perfect, he would never have disobeyed. And, after all, at the beginning of the world, wasn't it God himself who created the serpent?"

No longer smiling, the priest raises a monitory hand. He gazes hard at Jean and, though affectionate, his gaze unconsciously betrays his awareness of his superior position.

THE ABBÉ: "As you can well imagine, Jean, you're not the first to be puzzled by these seeming contradictions. It's our old friend—or, rather, enemy—the Argument from Evil. It has been refuted time and again, and in all sorts of ways. You have done well to tell me of this difficulty of yours. And as you're troubled by the problem, I'll lend you some books on the subject which will set your mind at rest, definitely." Jean says nothing, but he seems a shade disappointed. "But, mind you, I'm not blind to the good side of your indignation. It's only by realizing the suffering that exists on earth that we can strengthen the instinct of charity within ourselves—and none of us can go too far in that direction." He clasps Jean's hand. "You, Jean, are at an age when the heart is opening to new experience and brimming over with compassion. I realize that the first shock of these discoveries may well be very painful; that's why a word of warning cannot come amiss. Beware, my boy, of letting your emotions run away with you; there's much less Evil in the world than, at first sight, you might suppose. Bear this in mind: if the sum of Evil were greater, or even equal to the sum of Good—why, chaos would reign everywhere! But when we look around us, what do we see? A wonderful order prevailing throughout the universe, and making us feel how pitiably small we are. Every day scientific pioneers are making new discoveries, which enable us to appreciate still better the glorious perfection of God's scheme. As compared with that abounding goodness, how trivial, relatively, are the *individual* penalties of sin! Then, again, human sufferings—and I don't deny they exist, alas; how could I, considering that my mission is to treat and, if possible, heal them?—yes, human sufferings, even if they seem unjust, have their value, as one day you'll find out for yourself. It's through them, and through them only, that man can develop the goodness that is in him and make progress on the way of his salvation. And which is it that really matters: this life on earth or the life to come?"

JEAN: "But there aren't only men on earth. The animals—"

THE ABBÉ: "The suffering of every creature is willed by God, my dear Jean; He made it a condition, indeed the prime condition, of life. That thought should be enough to curb your rebellious instincts, whose origin is in poor, human pride. Yes, the existence of that Perfect Being, infinitely good, all-powerful, who created heaven and earth out of nothing, who every day gives us a thousand proofs of his fatherly love for us—his existence is our best assurance of the necessity for evil in this world, which He made as it had to be for our betterment. And even if his purposes seem dark to our imperfect vision, our duty is to bow to his Will—nay more, to will as He does these sufferings we do not understand but which He has thought best for us. *Fiat voluntas tua . . .*"

Jean says nothing; he frowns slightly, trying to take in what the priest has been saying. In the near-by vestry shrill young voices are singing to the accompaniment of a wheezy harmonium.

THE ABBÉ: "To speak quite frankly, Jean, I see in you a slightly, oh, very slightly, exaggerated tendency to introspection." He smiles. "Far be it from me to speak ill of the noble activities of the mind. But, all the same, the longer I live the more I feel that intelligence serves its true purpose only when it is directed to an end outside itself, when it aims at some practical result. Intelligence should inspire and quicken action; indeed, without it, activity is sterile. But, if it does not lead to action, intelligence is futile, like a lamp lit beside a lighthouse, burning itself out in vain!" With deep feeling. "You've come to me, Jean, to ask for guidance. Well, I'll always urge you to act rather than to meditate. By all means cultivate your mind; it's not only permissible to do so, but your duty. But cultivate it with a human end in view. If our Lord has entrusted you with something rather precious, an intelligence above the ordinary, make it bear fruit—but see that the great family to which we all belong profits by it. Don't be like the unprofitable servant who hid his talent in the earth. By all means increase your store, but only so as to share it with others. Try to be one of the givers.

"I have been through the same phase myself. I started dabbling with these so-called 'advanced' theories, but, God be thanked, I very soon saw my mistake. It's through action, through self-devotion and in self-forgetting, that a man can get the best life has to offer, can achieve mental and spiritual health—the one true and never-failing happiness. Believe me, Jean, this happiness, which we sometimes seek so far afield, is really within easy reach; it springs from such natural feelings as love for our fellow men. And all the rest is vanity!

"Drop in at the Church Club one evening; I'll give you the books I spoke of, and then if you'll stay with us for half an hour or so, you will see for yourself"—his eyes light up with pride and happy enthusiasm—"what noble hearts some of our young folk have, and how rewarding it can be to do our very utmost for them." He rises to his feet. "Yes, Jean, that's the one real joy in life: to feel one's doing a little good for one's fellow men and"—he presses his hand to his chest—"imparting to them some of that warmth of heart that God has placed in us—here."

v

The Pasquelins' morning-room; a long narrow room on the ground floor, crowded with old-fashioned furniture. Cécile is by herself, tidying up the disorder her mother left on going out. A dark October evening is closing in. At a sound of footsteps on the pavement outside she runs to the window and waves her hand. A satchel under his arm, Jean is crossing the street. She hastens to the front door to meet him.

Cécile Pasquelin is a tall, slim girl of sixteen; though not pretty, she has the grace of youth, an exceptionally charming carriage of her supple neck and rather narrow shoulders, which now are wrapped in a white woollen shawl. Her head is small and round as an apple; her black, slightly prominent eyes also are very round, and an almost imperceptible squint gives her gaze a strangely tantalizing charm. Her brown hair falls in a fringe over her forehead. She has a well-shaped mouth, with moist, full, mobile lips and short, sharp teeth that flash brilliantly when she smiles. The smile is lighthearted, superficial. Sometimes she drops into a slight lisp.

CÉCILE: "Hurry up, Jean. I'm afraid the milk's nearly cold."

Jean's meal is set ready on a tray. As he takes large bites of his bread and butter, Cécile's eyes are sparkling. She has drawn her stool in front of him and, when their eyes meet, both young people laugh—for no reason, out of mere gaiety of heart.

JEAN: "And now, to work!" He tips out the books in his satchel onto the table. Cécile lights the lamp, draws the curtains, puts a log on the fire, and moves her chair nearer to the lamp.

CÉCILE: "What is it this evening?"

JEAN: "Greek verse." The room is pleasantly warm. A low droning sound comes from the lamp and the fire. There is an occasional rustle of Cécile's dress, or when Jean turns a page. At one moment, when he is doing this and Cécile is examining a stitch at the tip of her knitting needle, Jean looks towards her. There is something in his voice that puzzles her. "Do you know, Cécile, I found something rather—rather striking this morning, in a bit of Aeschylus I was construing. He's talking about Helen, and he

[ 22 ]

says, 'A soul serene as a calm, windless sea.' Fine, isn't it? 'Serene as a calm, windless sea.' "

He gazes at her. She lowers her eyes but says nothing. She is holding her breath—as when in a game of hide-and-seek, you see the one who's "seeking" come quite near, almost brush against you, and then go on, without having noticed. Jean is poring over his Greek text again.

Half an hour later a woman's footsteps clatter on the tiled floor of the hall, and Mme Pasquelin bustles in. She is a small, dark woman, with a sallow complexion and jet-black hair frizzed over the forehead. She has fine eyes, with a suggestion of a squint like Cécile's; a bright, yet gentle gaze; a smiling, slightly pursed mouth. She has once been quite a beauty, and remembers it. Active, loquacious, she is always on the move, chattering away in a shrill voice, with a rather pronounced Picardy accent. Always bursting with energy, she never spares herself; she is always ready to take a hand in any local activity, in organizing or reorganizing the charitable societies of the parish and similar good works.

MME PASQUELIN: "Hard at it, my dears?" Without waiting for an answer she continues. "Do get a proper chair, Cécile; I hate to see you all doubled up on that silly little stool." She goes to the box containing logs. "It's lucky I came; you're letting the fire go out, you two, as usual."

JEAN, getting up to help her: "Don't trouble. I'll put some logs on."

MME PASQUELIN: "No, you'd take too long over it, Jean. It's nearly out." Deftly she flings two logs into the fireplace and draws the metal curtain half-way down, to make the fire draw. Then, straightening up, she unhooks her cape, goes to the window, and pulls the curtains tighter, talking all the time. "Oh, my dears, I

thought I'd never get back home. It's been an awful day, I'm quite worn out. Everything was in such a muddle, I had to lose my temper half a dozen times. That Abbé Joziers is really most exasperating. He talked the Vicar into having the boys' catechism class at half-past nine on Thursday—just the time we'd fixed for the committee meeting of the sewing-bee. I told the Vicar what I thought about it. 'How do you expect me to be at both ends of the town at the same time?' I asked him.—Jean, will you lift the shutter now? The logs have caught. But it's quarter to six, you know. If you want to go with us to Communion tomorrow, you've only just time to make your confession. The Abbé leaves the church at half past, so you'd better hurry up." Jean rises. "Wrap yourself up well. There's a cold wind tonight."

Next day. The seven o'clock Communion is being administered. Mme Pasquelin rises and moves towards the altar, followed by Jean and Cécile. Side by side, with eyes downcast, they slowly walk towards the Holy Table, Abbé Joziers, who is officiating, raises on high the consecrated Host.

ABBÉ JOZIERS, in a contrite voice: *"Domine, non sum dignus.* Lord, I am not worthy . . ."

Cécile and Jean are kneeling, their elbows touching, their ice-cold hands close together under the white cloth. The same faintly morbid yet delicious thrill of awe, a yearning towards the infinite. The priest draws near. In turn, they slowly raise their heads, tremblingly part their lips, then let their eyelids close upon the ecstasy of joy welling up from their hearts.

At this moment they are utterly united; freed from the trammels of their earthly bodies, two young souls rise effortlessly to the supreme pinnacle of love and mingle there, at one with God.

[ 23 ]

## II

## The Symbolist Compromise

*When I was a child, I spake as a child, I understood as a child: but when I became a man, I put away childish things.*

I Corinthians: 13:11

I

Abbé Joziers
  The Presbytery
    Buis-la-Dame, Oise

Paris, January 11

Dear Abbé Joziers: I wish I could send an answer worthier of the trust you place in me. Unfortunately I am unable to give you the reassurance as to my moral welfare that I know you expect. This first term has been unsatisfactory in several ways, and I still feel terribly "lost" in Paris, where everything is so new to me.

However, I have now mapped out my days on lines I mean to keep to. In addition to the preparatory courses at the School of Medicine, I have entered my name at the Sorbonne as candidate for a Natural Science degree, with the result that for some weeks past I have been spending even more of my time in the Latin Quarter. (I hope, dear Abbé Joziers, that what I have written above will not cause you any uneasiness—I may mention, in this connection, that I was greatly touched by the affectionate advice you gave me in your last letter. No, you need have no fears in that respect; thank God, I have enough strength of will, enough idealism, to resist the temptations you had in mind, and in any case—why, surely you have not forgotten the deep and pure emotion that came to me at Buis and is with me still, and the project, so near to my heart, that is at once the great hope of my life, and my safeguard?)

These science courses take up a great deal of my time, but they are a useful complement to my medical studies, and I can't tell you how absorbing I find them. Anyhow, what could I do with leisure, if I had it? As you may know, my father has been appointed to a professorship, and his lecture courses make still more demands on a life that was already crowded and in which, frankly, I have little place.

You will, I am sure, be glad to hear that I have struck up acquaintance with a young Swiss priest, Schertz by name, who has come to get a Paris degree with a view to teaching natural history in his own country. He is very keen on biology; we work in the same laboratory, and I greatly benefit by his assistance and companionship. These studies are absolutely fascinating; I can't quite analyze my reactions as yet, but some of the lecture courses literally "go to my head." Indeed, I think these first contacts with science bring on a sort of dizziness—when one begins, even in a dim way, to glimpse some of those stupendous laws of nature that govern the vast complexity of the universe.

As you advised me to do, I am constantly trying to gain a deeper insight into this universal order, and to confirm still more my veneration of its divine Creator. But you cannot imagine how much I miss your infectious optimism, and I can only hope that Abbé Schertz's friendship may compensate to some extent. His natural high spirits and his zest for work vouch for a robust faith which may very well help me to recover my moral balance. For I need help of that kind; in the last few weeks especially, I have been through moments of most harrowing depression.

Forgive me once again for distressing you with "confessions" of this order, and please believe me, always your affectionate and loyal pupil,

Jean Barois

II

Dr. Barois' dining-room. Dinner has just ended, and the doctor rises from his seat.

THE DOCTOR: "You will excuse me, Monsieur Schertz, I hope." Jean and the Abbé, too, have risen to their feet. "I have to be at Passy at nine, for a consultation. It has been a great pleasure to me, making your acquaintance, and I'm sorry the time has been so short. So good night, Jean. And I hope, Monsieur Schertz, that you will come again." He smiles. "Believe me, I set great store on that paradoxical theory of mine: that one should act first, and reflect at leisure! Young people nowadays think too much, and, as they've no experience of action, don't think straight."

Jean's bedroom. His friend the Abbé is seated in a low armchair, his legs crossed, his elbows resting on the arms of the chair and his hands clasped under his chin.

Abbé Schertz is a man of thirty-one, with a long, flat body whose angularity is emphasized by his tight-fitting cassock. He has big, sinewy arms, sedately measured gestures. His face is broad and bony, his complexion pale, and the slope of his forehead is accentuated by the way he has of brushing his black hair straight back from his brows. The scantiness of the eyebrows makes the clean-shaven face look still more glabrous. The massive bony structure of the brows juts out over pale, keen eyes with greenish pupils, slotted between jet-black eyelashes. Schertz has a long nose, with a deep, mobile furrow extending to the cheekbone on each side; thin lips that sometimes set in a hard line and turn quite white. His manner is earnest, almost prim, but pleasant. He is inclined to indulge in long phrases and expressions not in current use; in fact he gives the impression of thinking in a foreign language and translating his thoughts.

Jean is sitting on his desk, swinging his legs.

JEAN: "I'm glad you got on with my father. I'm extremely fond of him." He smiles. "Do you know, I once used to be scared of him!"

SCHERTZ: "You cannot mean it!"

JEAN: "Yes, he overawed me. But, really, I knew him so little—until these last few months, when I've been living with him. Ah, how a profession like his ennobles a man!"

SCHERTZ: "Ah, yes, indeed he has a noble character, you feel that at once; but, mind you, it isn't owing only to his profession. Otherwise every doctor—"

JEAN: "Naturally. I grant you that, in my father's case, there must have been a natural predisposition. What I meant was that he hasn't the support of religion."

SCHERTZ, with sudden interest: "Ah? As a matter of fact I'd suspected as much."

JEAN: "My father came of a fervently devout family and was given an education on purely Catholic lines. All the same, for many years I believe, he has never put his foot inside a church."

SCHERTZ: "And given up believing too?"

JEAN: "I think so. As a matter of fact he has never discussed these things with me. Only—well, one can read between the lines, of course. And naturally . . ."

SCHERTZ: " 'And naturally . . .' What were you going to say?"

JEAN, after a brief hesitation: "I wanted to say that Father's profession, when you think of it, is almost bound to weaken faith." Schertz makes a gesture of surprise. "Because of the hospital work, for one thing. Try to imagine what it must mean to a thoughtful man whose sole duty every day from morn to eve is to minister to human suffering. What opinion must he have of God?" Schertz is silent. "Do I shock you?"

SCHERTZ: "Not in the least. You interest me. Of course it's simply the old Argument from Evil."

JEAN: "A very cogent argument."

SCHERTZ: "As you say, very cogent."

JEAN: "And one which, so far, even our greatest theologians have never seriously refuted."

SCHERTZ: "Never."

JEAN: "What! You agree to that?"

SCHERTZ, smiling: "But how could I do otherwise?"

Jean puffs at his cigarette without speaking. Then abruptly he throws it into the fireplace and looks the Abbé in the eyes.

JEAN: "Well, you're the first priest I've ever heard say a thing like that."

SCHERTZ: "Have you ever put the question bluntly to another priest?"

JEAN: "Oh, often."

SCHERTZ: "Well?"

JEAN: "I was given every conceivable answer. That I was too sensitive, too squeamish. That I had a rebellious spirit. That Evil is a necessary condition of Good. That trial and temptation are needed for the betterment of man. That, beginning with man's first disobedience, God willed that Evil should exist, and we must will it with him."

SCHERTZ, smiling again: "Yes? Anything else?"

JEAN, shrugging his shoulders scornfully: "Words! Just words! Arguments that were hardly even specious." Schertz throws a quick glance at Jean; then his face clouds over and he refrains from looking up. "If we go to the heart of the matter we come up against a fallacy. I'm asked to believe in the power and the goodness of God on the strength of the order reigning in the universe. The moment I point out the many imperfections in this order, I am forbidden to criticize it because it is the work of God. A flagrant begging of the question!" He takes some steps before continuing, in a louder tone: "The result is that I've never

been able to reconcile those two affirmations—that God is the sum of all perfection, and that this world of ours, with all its imperfections, was created by him."

He halts in front of the Abbé, fixing his eyes on him, but Schertz looks away. There is a short silence. At last their eyes meet; Jean's are dark with an unspoken question, and the Abbé cannot altogether evade their appeal.

SCHERTZ, with an uncertain smile: "So you too, Jean, are troubled by these tremendous problems? I'm sorry to learn that."

JEAN, fretfully: "How can I help it? I assure you I'd far rather not be obsessed by them like this. But . . ." He paces around the room, his hands in his pockets, sometimes shaking his head, as if continuing the discussion in his mind. He is wearing an even stubborner look than usual; his brows are puckered by the stresses of a pent-up emotion that sets his lips in a hard, tormented line. "Listen, Schertz! Just now you were speaking of my father. Well, there's something that always rather shocked me, even when I was a small boy. It was that anyone could dare to condemn a man like him, on religious grounds, just because he never set foot inside a church or partook of the Sacrament at Easter. At home, at Buis I mean, they take a very severe view of his conduct."

SCHERTZ: "Because they don't understand him, obviously."

JEAN, with an air of surprise: "But surely as a priest you too should condemn him?" Schertz makes a noncommittal gesture. "Personally, I've always, *always* refused to do so; all my instincts rebelled against it. Why, a life like Father's is—is one long aspiration towards everything that's noble and sublime. How could anyone find fault with it, on religious grounds? No, it's preposterous! A life like his, you know, is something apart from all that; it's above—"

He breaks off abruptly, takes a few steps, then halts and faces the Abbé with a look of acute distress. And his voice too betrays profound despondency. "And then, old chap—oh, what a dreadful thing it is to think that a man like my father is an agnostic! That others like him are agnostics! And yet they aren't savages, are they? They were brought up in our religion, have once been practicing—some of them devout—Catholics. And yet one day, deliberately, they discarded the religion of their youth. It makes you think, doesn't it? One tells oneself, 'I believe, and they do not believe. Which is right?' And then one can't escape an insidious afterthought: 'That remains to be seen.' Once that stage is reached one's peace of mind is wrecked. 'That remains to be seen.' That thought is the first accursed step on the path that leads to atheism."

SCHERTZ, earnestly: "Ah, but wait a bit! You've stated the case wrongly, and you're falling into a very grave error. It's true that men of your father's stamp may repudiate the tenets of the Church as we find them today. But be assured that the power within them that makes for goodness and nobility is exactly the same as what we find in the best of priests, the very best."

JEAN: "So there are two ways of being a Christian?"

SCHERTZ, who has let the discussion take him further than he intended: "Well—er—that's not impossible."

JEAN: "And yet, when all is said and done, there *should* be only one way."

SCHERTZ: "Certainly. But don't forget that, underlying all these differences of opinion—which are mostly on the surface and mean far less than you suppose—yes, underlying these, there's always the same thing, the same aspiration towards infinite goodness, perfect justice." Jean gazes at him without speaking. A long silence. Schertz seems ill at ease. "Do you know, I rather like the smell of that tobacco? I'll make an exception and have a cigarette, if you . . . Thanks, old chap." He is determined to give a new turn to the conversation. "I've brought those lecture notes you asked for—the preliminary course."

Jean takes the notebooks and flutters the pages absent-mindedly.

Some days later. The Abbé's bedroom in a quiet boarding-house giving on the Saint Sulpice square.

SCHERTZ, springing up from his chair: "Ah, a pleasant surprise!"

JEAN: "I thought I'd drop in for a chat before we go to the Sorbonne."

The Abbé moves the books off the solitary armchair. Smiling, Jean wanders round the room. There is a small desk, a large deal table for experiments, with an array of bottles, jars, a microscope. On the walls hang anatomical plates, a portrait of Pasteur, a panoramic photograph of Berne, a crucifix.

JEAN, laughing: "Really, it beats me how you can live in this atmosphere!"

SCHERTZ: "Sorry! It's my sulphuric acid, I expect."

JEAN: "No, I didn't mean it literally. But I often wonder how a priest can live in this scientific atmosphere."

SCHERTZ, coming nearer to Jean: "Why shouldn't he?"

JEAN: "Well, even I—and remember I'm not a priest—find it hard to breathe in, terribly hard." Behind his smile lurks an unvoiced sadness. "Ah, one day I really must have a good long talk with you, make a clean breast of my troubles."

SCHERTZ, pensively: "Yes, why not?" He glances round the room, then fixes his gaze on Jean's eyes, as if to probe their secrets. After a while he lowers his eyes; he is thinking deeply. "You really want to do that?" They gaze at each other in silence, conscious of a tension in the air. It is impending, and they know it: one of those memorable hours when two young men, in the protective warmth of friendship, unburden their hearts to each other, mingling their thoughts without reserve, in perfect trust. Schertz's voice is very gentle as he asks: "What exactly is wrong, Jean?"

JEAN, emotionally: "Everything! I'm up against a—a most damnable moral crisis!"

SCHERTZ: "Moral?"

JEAN: "Well, let's say religious."

SCHERTZ: "How long have you been feeling like this?"

JEAN: "Oh, ever so long. Long before I was aware of it. Why, for several years, I should say, I've had to struggle—yes, fight really hard—not to lose my faith."

SCHERTZ, promptly: "No, not your faith. Only the unthinking, credulous faith of a child—which is a very different thing."

JEAN, following up his thoughts: "I didn't fully realize this until a few months ago. It's Paris, perhaps; the atmosphere of Paris. And especially the atmosphere of the Sorbonne, of those lecture rooms where all the great laws of the universe are analyzed—without once mentioning the name of God."

SCHERTZ: "His name isn't mentioned, yes; but they're talking of Him all the time."

JEAN, bitterly: "I used to talk of Him more openly, not just by—by implication."

SCHERTZ, with a smile of encouragement: "The first thing is, obviously, for us to understand each other—to get the background clear." Shyly. "I might be able to help you, old chap, only really I know so little of your religious life. How exactly do you stand at present?"

JEAN, despondently: "I wish I knew! Really, I'm all at sea. All I know is that things are as bad as they can be, with me." The Abbé has settled into a chair, crossed his legs, and is leaning forward,

his chin propped on his locked fingers. "I'm torn between conflicting tendencies, and my mind's in a fiendish turmoil, all the more exasperating because *once* I had the peace of mind—that sort of comfortable warmth—which comes of believing simply, trustingly. I assure you I haven't done anything to bring myself to this pass. Quite the contrary; I always forbade my rational self to meddle with such questions. But I can't keep it under control any longer. Objections, doubts, are piling up around me; almost daily I run up against a new one. And I've been forced to recognize that there's not a single article of Catholic doctrine that isn't riddled with contradictions, in the light of our present knowledge." He takes a magazine from his pocket. "Look! Have you come across this? An essay by Brunois, 'The Issues between Faith and Reason'?" Schertz shakes his head. "This came into my hands by chance not very long ago. Until then I'd never had an inkling of what was being done nowadays in the field of biblical research, or of the attacks that were being launched by competent historians. It came as a shock—and a revelation!—when I read that article. I learned all sorts of facts that were quite new to me. For instance, that the Gospels were written between the years sixty-five and one hundred; which means that the Church was founded, and could carry on, without them. Think of it! Over sixty years after Christ's birth! It's much as if, in our day, someone wanted to write down Napoleon's words and deeds, without a single written document to go on, only vague memories and anecdotes. And that's the sort of book it is, the Book of Books, whose absolute accuracy no Catholic must call in question." He turns some pages of the magazine.

"The writer goes on to say that Jesus never believed himself to be a God, or the founder of a religion, or even a prophet, until quite near the end of his life, when he was infected by the credulity of his disciples.

"That a very long time elapsed before the doctrine of the Trinity took shape, and several Councils had to be convened before Christ's dual nature was established and the distinction drawn between his human and his divine personalities. It comes to this: years of intense controversy were needed to establish this vital article of Christian faith and to link it up, more or less satisfactorily, with Christ's teachings. You'd never guess this from the catechism; that doctrine of the Trinity is one of the first things we are told to believe in, and we're asked to regard it as an elementary, quite simple truth, directly revealed by Christ himself, and so self-evident that it has never been called in question by anyone." He turns some more pages.

"Here's another passage, about the Immaculate Conception. The writer tells us this is an almost modern notion, which took its rise as late as the twelfth century. Two mystically minded English monks were responsible for it. It was not discussed or formulated until the thirteenth century. And its starting point was an absurd mistake made by some Greek translator who used the Greek word παρθένος a maiden, when translating an ancient Hebrew word which simply described Mary as 'a young woman.'

"Ah, I see you're smiling! Then you knew about it already?" Crestfallen. "So of course you can't really understand the effect that information of this sort produced on me—it was like a bolt from the blue. Mind you, I'm still wondering if it's trustworthy." Schertz nods. "But the really amazing thing is that an article like that should appear, with all its details, over the signature of so well-known and cautious-minded a scholar as Brunois. In fact what startled me most was the tone of the article. The points I've mentioned

come in quite incidentally, in support of Brunois' main argument. They are introduced without a word of comment, as if they were matters of common knowledge, facts of history that have been cleared up once for all. The writer does no more than give a few references so as to let ignoramuses like myself know where to find the authorities for the points he takes for granted. I mention this particular article because it's just come to my notice. But, on all sides, in every field of knowledge, I keep running up against anti-Christian arguments of this kind. Am I to believe that all modern knowledge is in flat contradiction to our faith?"

SCHERTZ, affectionately: "But, my dear Jean, I thought you were in contact with an abbé at Buis—a very learned priest, I gathered?"

JEAN: "Learned? I wonder! He's a man of action, a saint who's never had a qualm of doubt and, if he were to have one, would quickly overcome it by plunging into some activity." With a rather bitter smile. "He lent me some books on theology."

SCHERTZ: "Yes? Did they help?"

JEAN, shrugging his shoulders: "I found in them a lot of specious, purely verbal arguments, put forward as if they were unassailable, which a moment's serious thought exploded like so many toy balloons. They'd convince only those who were convinced already. Am I shocking you?"

SCHERTZ: "Not a bit. On the contrary, I understand your difficulties quite well."

JEAN: "But—"

SCHERTZ: "Better than you can possibly imagine." Jean begins to make a gesture of amazement, which Schertz checks with a wave of his hand. "But that can wait. Please go on with what you have to tell me."

JEAN: "Well—really that's all. Whenever I try to argue it out with myself, in the hope of strengthening my faith—indeed, every time I lay a finger on what's troubling me—I find I deal another blow to all that I believed in. Yes, it's just by trying to prove one's faith that one undermines it, as I've learnt to my cost. No, there's nothing to be done about it; my faith is crumbling away, bit by bit."

SCHERTZ, quickly: "No, no! I'm certain that's untrue."

JEAN: "Oh, I assure you I'd do anything to keep my faith." In a tone of utter hopelessness. "There may be people who can do without religion. I'm not one of them. I need it, yes, I *need* it, just to live—as I need food and sleep. Without religion I'd be—oh, I don't know how to describe it!—like a tree whose roots had no earth to feed on, starved. I'd lose everything that counts in life. You see, old chap, I know myself for a Catholic, in every fibre of my being. And now that I have to struggle so fiercely to keep my faith, I feel this even more strongly. All I think, all I desire, and all I do is conditioned by the religious instinct; it's ingrained in my nature, and if I were to lose it my whole life would founder in a sort of quicksand of—of incoherency."

SCHERTZ: "But surely this religious crisis you're living through has periods of respite? Surely there still are days when you can draw near to God?"

JEAN, uncertainly: "I don't quite know how to put it. At bottom, I don't actually feel that I'm drifting away from God, even when my faith is at its lowest ebb." He smiles. "No, I can't explain it, I'm afraid." The Abbé makes a gesture that seems to indicate he understands it very well. Jean ponders for some moments before continuing: "Really, what makes it all so terribly difficult is this: in the Catholic religion everything hangs together—faith, doctrines, morality, our contacts with God through prayer; they're an indivisible whole, you see."

Schertz shakes his head, but Jean fails to notice this. "And so, if one rejects even the smallest part, one loses all."

The Abbé rises and takes some steps, his hands locked behind his back. When he speaks, emotion makes him stumble over his words, as if he were translating laboriously.

SCHERTZ: "Ah, old chap, but what a tragic age is this in the religious life of mankind!" He halts in front of Jean and gazes at him earnestly. His tone grows steadier as he continues: "Now, shall we try to put it in a nutshell? On one side you have your intellect, which boggles at certain points of dogma or frankly rejects them. On the other side, you have your religious sensibility—it's very active in your case, I think—which, if I may put it so, has tasted God and cannot do without him."

JEAN: "Exactly. Not to mention an instinctive fear, which has its origins in my childhood and, most likely, in heredity as well—the dread of losing my faith."

SCHERTZ: "Yes . . . Do you know, it's much like a phase I went through myself?"

JEAN: "You too! When was that?"

SCHERTZ: "Just after I'd left the Training College."

JEAN, eagerly: "Yes? And now?"

SCHERTZ, smiling and pointing to his cassock: "You can see for yourself." Jean seems about to put a question, but Schertz waves it aside. "Mind if I tell you of my own experience?" Jean gives him a grateful smile, and the Abbé settles down in his armchair, resting his chin on his locked hands, knitting his brows, a faraway look in his eyes. "Until I was ordained I'd never studied science seriously, though I always had leanings towards it. So, once I'd taken Orders, I took it up as my special study. Looking back, I can see exactly what happened to me; and many others, I know, have had the same experience. How exciting it is, one's first contact with the scientific method! It comes like a revelation and breaks on you like a great wave, sweeping you off your feet. You feel as if your brain had been scoured clean, made ready for anything! And then a day comes when you look back on the past—and everything's changed. All those familiar things you took for granted—it's as if you were seeing them now for the first time. You analyze them, test them. And from that day there's no escape; you can't stop analyzing. Isn't that so? Well, that's what the discovery of the scientific method does for you."

JEAN: "Yes, it sweeps one off one's feet."

SCHERTZ: "Mind you, I never suspected it was as definite as that. I thought I could always beat a retreat, if needed. So I put my books back on the shelves and betook myself to the monastery at Bürgen. For—for—" He cannot find the word.

JEAN: "A retreat?"

SCHERTZ: "Yes, a retreat. I spent five winter months there. At first I sought help from the Fathers, some of whom were highly educated men. But they merely made categorical statements, whereas I wanted to—to discuss. In fact we were at cross-purposes. They always ended up by smiling serenely and reminding me that nothing was impossible to God. And, of course, there was no answering that! I remember one of them saying to me, 'The amazing thing is that, with ideas like yours, you haven't lost your faith.' That set me thinking. It was so; my faith hadn't wavered once. Just as you were saying about yourself a moment ago, I had a conviction, a positive conviction, that nothing essential had changed in me. So I couldn't feel remorse. All I knew was that I was in the

grip of something stronger than my will, and, moreover, something of a very lofty order and worthy of respect. So what was I to do? I tried to compromise—"

JEAN, shaking his head: "A dangerous way out."

SCHERTZ: "I was forced to recognize that it was no use struggling; the case for science was too strong. And I refused to resort, as some intellectual priests resort, to half-hearted concessions that don't go far enough. No, I preferred to give ground boldly, to be honest with myself—with the feeling deep down in my consciousness that God would not have me do otherwise." He is silent for some moments. "So I left Bürgen, returned to Berne, and tried, with the help of books and meditation, to solve my problems." He smiles. "Ah, old chap, when you come to think of it, those two opposing forces—how unevenly matched they are! On one side you have the enemies of the Church—I'm thinking only of men of real learning, who have made their mark—and, on the other, our defenders of the faith, who do nothing but declaim, parade hoary old arguments, and wind up by threatening to excommunicate you. Try as one may, there's no doubt which group inspires more confidence. Really, the standpoint of the Holy See passes one's understanding. They inveigh against science without knowing the first thing about it. And they're ignorant of even the most elementary rules of thinking; all rational discussion is ruled out. They make the most extravagant assertions, with the result that they cut the ground under their own feet. It took me two years to arrive at this conclusion, but they weren't wasted. Thanks to those two years' strenuous thinking I've regained my peace of mind—for good."

JEAN: "Your peace of mind!"

SCHERTZ, leaning forward, obviously wishing Jean to pay particular attention to what he is going to say: "I discovered, my dear Jean, that in the matter of religion we have to draw a clean-cut line between two totally distinct elements. One of these is our religious sentiment, pure and unsophisticated, which amounts to what I'd call a pact with the Divine Being; it includes, too, the personal, direct relations existing between God and all whose souls are drawn to Him. The second element is what I'd call dogmatic; it includes hypotheses made by theologians about God and all the relations—not personal, but ritual—between man and God. Do you follow?"

JEAN: "Yes."

SCHERTZ: "Well, only one of these elements is appropriate to our modern religious sensibility, and it's the first—one's personal relationship with God."

JEAN: "How can you speak of *modern* religious sensibility? Surely religion isn't something that follows the fashion like—like women's dresses?"

SCHERTZ: "Ah, that's only a manner of speaking. Religion may not follow fashion, but it keeps step with the moral progress of mankind. Here's an example. Don't you agree that the men of the Middle Ages owed much of the robustness of their faith to an absolutely literal interpretation of the dogmas of the Church? Well, that's not the case today. Far from it; you've only to look at the Catholics of our generation, those who are really devout. Many of them don't know the first thing about religious theory; they give the dogmas second place—and they're no worse Catholics for that.

"Let me sum up what I've been saying. With you, with myself, with a great many fellow Christians, that first element, personal faith, is intact. It's the belief in dogma that is tottering, and we can't do anything about it. The Roman Catholic religion, as at present formulated, has features that can hardly be accepted by many enlightened minds; and not at all by those who have studied deeply as well as widely. The God it sets up is too narrowly human; that belief in a personal God, rather like an earthly king, or a celestial artisan who put the universe together—no, it's asking too much! That sort of religion doesn't meet our needs, it doesn't satisfy our—how shall I put it?—craving for perfection.

"Human beliefs, like everything else, are subject to the laws of evolution; they steadily progress from the less good to the better. So obviously it's essential that religion should adjust itself to the modern mind. And Rome is making a mistake in opposing this adjustment."

JEAN, excitedly: "Yes! But when you blame the Church today, as you've just been doing, how can you feel sure it's you who are right? Mightn't it simply be that you—"

SCHERTZ, cutting in: "Wait! Don't forget that in every man's belief, even if we grant its divine origin, there is bound to be a subjective element. People are only just beginning to allow for this. It's only quite recently that orthodox believers have admitted that some of the stories in the Old and New Testaments are to be taken in a figurative sense. Here are some examples. Christ's descent into the nether regions, his being led by Satan to a mountain-top. No serious-minded theologian would dare to say, 'That mountain had a physical existence; that descent took place in the literal sense.' No, what he'd say today is, 'Those passages have a figurative meaning.'

"Well, that sort of mental honesty—which calls what is obviously symbolic by its proper name: a symbol—that's what is needed by people like you and me. But we must not apply the principle reluctantly and half-heartedly, like those orthodox theologians who apply it only to biblical legends which are quite plainly mythical. No, we must apply it to each and every statement of fact, when the modern mind cannot admit its credibility. And there, Jean, you have the solution of all your difficulties."

There is a long silence. Jean is lost in thought but does not shift his gaze from the Abbé's forceful face.

SCHERTZ: "And don't forget, old chap, that before many years are out all theologians of any intellectual standing will have reached these conclusions; in fact they'll be amazed that nineteenth-century Catholics managed to believe so long in the literal truth of those poetic legends. 'They are splendid visions,' I can hear them saying; 'stories full of messages for us—but their content is ideal. The evangelists accepted them uncritically, and the early Christians could do the same, owing to their lack of mental training, and their credulity.' "

JEAN: "But you can't have it both ways, surely? Either the dogmas of the Church are true or else they're—worthless!"

SCHERTZ: "Ah, no indeed! Truth and reality, they're different. Many people, I know, share your difficulty. But when you say 'truth' you're thinking of 'authenticity,' which isn't the same thing. We should concentrate on the truth, not of the literal facts, but of their moral significance. We can admit the eternal verities that underlie the mysteries of the Incarnation and the Resurrection without admitting that these were concrete events, authentic in the historical sense, like the defeat at Sedan or the founding of the French Republic." The Abbé rises, walks round the table, and takes his stand facing the chair in which Jean is seated, pondering deeply. The young priest is deeply moved; the look of rather formalistic gravity has left his face, his eyes glow with a compelling fervor of which Jean had not believed him to be capable. Schertz points to the crucifix. "When I'm kneeling there, in front of the cross, and I feel my love for Jesus surge up from the depths of my being like a great wave, and I hear myself say 'My Redeemer . . . !'—oh, I can assure you it's not because I'm meditating on the doctrine of the Redemption like a boy learning his catechism. No, but I'm thinking—and, *ach,* how *wundervoll* it is!—of all that our Lord did for mankind. I remind myself how all that's best in man today, and all the splendid hopes we place in the man of tomorrow, come from Him alone. And then my doubts are stilled and I bow down before our Redeemer, the divine symbol of self-sacrifice and perfect goodness; of the suffering, willingly accepted, that washes away guilt. And every morning, when I kneel at the altar to partake in the Eucharist, my emotion is so intense that I seem to feel the Real Presence, and throughout the day that sense of strength and uplift never leaves me. Yes, what is the Eucharist but a symbol of the divine grace acting on my soul? But my soul calls for it, craves for it, with an almost physical hunger!"

Jean is still thinking hard; the extreme emotion behind his friend's words has raised in him the spirit of contradiction; his voice is even calmer than before.

JEAN: "I see what you mean. Still, surely an ordinary Catholic who is firmly convinced of the literal truth of the Incarnation and the Real Presence puts far more fervor into his prayers and his attendance at the Holy Table than you can ever put, with your—your reservations."

SCHERTZ, vehemently: "I don't agree! The one thing that matters is to extract for ourselves the truth that best suits our needs, and to cling to it. Let me make myself clearer. Our intellect rebels against certain points of dogma; that's a fact we must accept. But the symbol we extract from it is clear, self-evident; it satisfies our reason and furthers our spiritual well-being. So how can we hesitate?"

[ 33 ]

JEAN: "But surely if you strip Christian doctrine of its traditional forms it loses much of its efficacy? Christianity is, and has always been, a doctrine. 'Go ye, therefore, and teach all nations . . .' It's the acceptance of this doctrine in its entirety that makes the Christian."

SCHERTZ: "And that's the very reason why it's so needful today to modify the form—not the substance, mind you!—of Christian doctrine. History teaches us that through the centuries the dogmas have been constantly changing, expanding, keeping step, in short, with the evolution of mankind. That, indeed, was the condition of their vitality. Why, then, keep them hidebound, swathed like mummies in the trappings of tradition? It's obvious that traditional religion doesn't meet the requirements of modern thought, so why shouldn't we exercise the same rights as the theologians of the Early Church and adjust the dogmas to contemporary needs?" The Saint Sulpice clock strikes four. The Abbé rises and lightly taps Jean's shoulder. "But we must have another talk about these problems."

JEAN, who has been gazing into the middle distance, seems to come out of a dream: "Really, it's all very difficult. I'd got so used, you see, to regarding the traditional forms of our religion as—as absolute values. And, frankly, there's a lack of coherence in the religion you've been describing that goes against the grain, so far as I'm concerned."

SCHERTZ, buttoning his overcoat: "It takes all sorts to make a world, you know. And, considering how different men are from each other, isn't it only to be expected that they should worship the same God in different ways?" He smiles. "Well, we'd better make a move, hadn't we? My advice, old chap, is to let these problems settle themselves. And remember St. Paul's admission: 'Now we see in a glass darkly. . . .'"

They go downstairs and walk in silence for some minutes towards the Sorbonne.

JEAN, abruptly: "But really one must be logical. Why do you persist in observing the rites of the Church when, on your own showing, they have only a symbolic value?"

Schertz stops walking, jerks his chin out of his upturned coat-collar, and fixes his eyes inquiringly on Jean's face, as if he doubts whether his friend is speaking seriously. Then a look of sadness comes over his face.

SCHERTZ: "Ah, I see! You haven't understood me." He reflects for some moments; then, weighing his words, continues: "My answer's this: because it would be sheer folly to cut oneself off from that fountain of living water, religious practice. It's far better to act as if religion were true in every detail; because it *is* true—in depth. Take prayer, for instance; how marvelous is the spiritual uplift it can give us!"

JEAN: "So, on your view, there's no need for set phrases or a ritual?"

SCHERTZ: "No need? Quite the contrary. Those set phrases and the rites of the Church are the best vehicles for the divine message, and none of us, even the most independent-minded, can afford to dispense with them. But each of us should interpret them for himself, according to his spiritual state, and use them according to his need."

JEAN: "In fact, we might as well turn Protestant!"

SCHERTZ: "Certainly not! An individualist, not to say anarchist, religion like Protestantism leaves us unsatisfied; whereas an organized, social, and—how shall I put it?—communalized religion like ours—that's just what human nature needs."

JEAN: "In other words, free-thinking, pure and simple?"

SCHERTZ: "No, my friend. We Catholics will never have the right to make that break with our religion."

JEAN: "The 'right'?"

SCHERTZ, gravely: "We have no right to sever ourselves from the body of our fellow Christians. How did religion build up its undeniable social virtues? By the combined efforts of all believers. Well, to stand aloof is to act like an individualist."

JEAN: "But surely your whole attitude is individualistic!"

SCHERTZ, frankly horrified: "Oh, no indeed! You're quite mistaken. I say that a man can choose his symbols according to his personal stage of development, but never forgetting that every symbol he adopts has its counterpart among the symbols adopted by the masses. That's how we keep in touch with our fellow men—the right kind of individualism."

Jean says nothing. There is a short silence before Schertz continues: "Think, Jean, of all it means, the Catholic religion. Remember that for countless human beings it is the only window opening on the spiritual world, and that so many, perhaps the majority, cannot see further than the simple picture they have formed of it. Don't you understand how wrong it would be for you to cut yourself off from them? The truth is that all varieties of religious experience have a common source; a sort of impassioned appeal or a yearning of the soul towards the infinite. And in God's eyes we are all alike.

"Do as I do. I don't shut my eyes to the difficulties inherent in religious faith today; but I don't dwell on them either. 'Pray to thy Father which is in secret . . .' I know that all human organizations have defects. But I think that, for the majority, Catholicism is vastly superior to other persuasions, because it is literally, in the fullest meaning of the word, an association. And I accept the observances it enjoins because, for one thing, I find in them a source of spiritual strength that I could find in no other per-suasion, and also because without them Catholicism would lose that religious solidarity which is necessary to so many souls."

The Abbé falls silent. They now are in the Sorbonne, threading their way along a corridor crowded with students.

Jean is trying to set his thoughts in order: One thing's certain; I must think this matter out. Until now I've tried to keep myself from thinking; I believed there was nothing to be gained by brooding on these problems. There I was mistaken. One can't put the clock back and return to the simple faith of one's childhood. So the only thing to do is to go forward; and there must be a way of straightening out the tangle; Schertz, anyhow, seems to have done so. Only I realize I don't know the first thing about all this—and without *knowing* I'll never make any headway. Yes, I must get down to essentials. The dogmas especially. So far I've concentrated on externals only: the rites and so forth. But Schertz always insists on what underlies these, the solid core. And hitherto the outer husk of forms has hidden from me the solid core. So it's for me now to dig down to the level at which the claims of human reason and religious dogma are reconcilable; that's obvious. There lies my only chance of regaining my peace of mind.

### III

Abbé Schertz
  Professor of Biological Chemistry
    The Catholic Institute
      Berne

                    Paris, Easter Monday

My dear Hermann: I needn't say how much I appreciate your concern about my father's health. Happily it is improving. But he has had to give up his consulting days and lecture courses, and he confines himself to his hospital work in the mornings. Even that, really, is too much for him. However, his colleagues say that if he takes great care of himself there is no reason to fear a relapse, anyhow for several years.

This letter is shockingly belated, but I hope you will forgive me; I have been so busy all this winter. Your letters are an unfailing pleasure; they bring back those happy evenings of two years ago, our endless confabulations, our readings aloud. Only it saddens me to feel them so remote. Not that the good effects of your influence have worn off. Have no fear, old chap; I feel assured that you have laid the spectres of my doubt forever, and I shall owe you gratitude all my life long for the comprehensive, tranquil faith I now possess; the solidly based yet tolerant faith a man can depend on, come what may. But once one is caught up as I am in the study of medicine, there's no escaping its grip; I hardly ever open a book that isn't a medical textbook.

I have even less time available, as I have made a point of keeping to my study of natural science as well. It's a field of research that has always fascinated me—vastly more than medicine— and I shan't be satisfied with a mere pass degree! My chief is pressing me to take the Senior Medical exam next year; but I would rather concentrate on the Teachers' Final. Of course a medical career seems indicated in my case; but a professorship in science would be more to my taste—only I recognize that, as a career, it's somewhat chancy. So I hardly know what to decide. As you are aware, I have not only myself to think about, and my decision will affect another's life. But all this indecision is very trying and, for obvious reasons, I can't discuss my perplexities with anyone else.

I was most pleased to learn that you have now been given a post after your own heart. My one regret is that you get so few vacations and the prospects of seeing much of you in the future seem more than slender. Indeed, I can't repress a selfish grievance against this new appointment which separates us so effectively.

However, let me say *au revoir,* old chap, and hope that somehow, somewhen, we may meet again. Please send me one of your long, ever-welcome letters in reply.

Ever yours,
Jean Barois

### III

## The Ring

### I

The close of a May afternoon. As Jean enters the small flat where he has been living since his father moved from Paris to Buis, he picks up a letter pushed under his door. It is from Mme Pasquelin.

Buis-la-Dame,
Sunday, May 15

My dear Jean: I have no idea what your father says in his letters about his health, but, personally, I am definitely worried; in my opinion he is in a bad way.—

Jean's shoulders sag. He almost wishes now that he had left the letter unopened.

—He has changed greatly since last spring, and especially since he had that attack, slight though it was, last month, and he is continuing to lose weight. The cheerfulness he showed all through the winter has left him, and he has practically given up following his treatment. He says he's "done for," there's no hope of his recovering. It is heart-rending to see a man who used to be so active doing nothing all day, mewed up by himself with a man-servant in that big house which has so many memories for us all. We wanted him to come to live with us—the garden would have been a godsend to him—but he refused to budge.

All this is very sad, my dear Jean; but I felt I should speak to you frankly.

Jean's hands are beginning to tremble, his eyes are misted.

I fear we must now face the fact that your father may not recover; that is why I am writing. I know how deeply you and your family felt his indifference to religion and, as we are his oldest friends and neighbors, I consider it our duty to try to remedy this sad state of affairs. So whenever I am with your father, I make a point of bringing the conversation round to this subject—for him so all-important. You, dear Jean, must help us by referring to it—discreetly, of course—in your letters.

His arms droop wearily; a vague resentment simmers in his mind. He skips a page, and his eyes fall on the words, "Cécile is quite well . . ." He glances towards the mantelpiece. Her photograph is gone! Then he remembers: Ah, yes, I put it away when Huguette started coming . . . It's six. She'll be here any moment now.

An acute discomfort seizes him; Cécile and Huguette mingle in his thoughts, their faces blurred together. He pulls himself up sharply. No, it can't go on like this. And suddenly, in a flash of intuition, he realizes that "it" is finished. The only reason for its lasting so long was that he'd never given it serious thought.

Cécile is quite well, though she has filled out a little lately, and this has tired her, I think. Several afternoons a week she takes her sewing over to your father's and stays quite a long while with him. She too does her best to direct the conversation to . . .

Jean frowns again. A picture has risen before him of the doctor lying on the sofa in front of the fireplace. Dusk is falling. Cécile is seated at the window, the small, slightly prominent forehead bent above her needlework, while she weaves into her chatter phrases she and her mother have thought up in advance. An odious picture!

He mutters, "Why should Cécile be dragged into it?" Rising, he walks to his desk and, unlocking a drawer, takes out Cécile's photograph, then studies it in the lamplight. An old, slightly faded photograph, it shows her seated in a high-backed chair, her hands folded in her lap, her head inclined a little to one side. Her eyes are smiling, and her hair is dressed as in her early girlhood with a big bow behind her neck. As he gazes, Jean feels his emotion rising: No, nothing's changed. There's only Cécile—nothing else, nobody else matters.

Poor little Huguette! Still he can smile when he thinks how little she will feel it when he breaks the news: It's over. Let's take up our lives again as they were before we met. I'm returning to the girl who has never lost her place in my heart.

Half an hour later. The ferrule of a parasol taps the door. Huguette is wearing a flimsy dress, a lavishly beflowered picture hat.

HUGUETTE: "Sorry, darling, if I'm late. Well? Aren't you going to kiss me? Oh! Mind my hat!" He seems to be seeing her, for the first time, in perspective, and feels hardly a trace of emotion. She has dropped her parasol on the bed and is slowly peeling off her gloves. "I'm dreadfully sorry, dear, but I can't dine with you tonight. I've just seen Simone at Vachette's, with her new boy—you know who I mean. He's got three stalls for the show at the Cluny and we're dining together first. Not too vexed, darling?"

JEAN: "Not a bit."

She comes towards him. The light from a lamp on a low table plays on the silken ripples of her skirt. Her bare hands and slightly parted lips glimmer an invitation, and in a sudden uprush of desire he pictures her body, satin-smooth, accessible. Taking her in his arms, he buries his face in her hair and thinks: No, it can't end like this—just one night more, and tomorrow, tomorrow . . .

HUGUETTE, wriggling free, laughing: "Just a moment, dear. I must wash my hands."

He watches her run to the wash-stand, carefully roll up her sleeves, and, with a familiar gesture, slip off her rings and drop them tinkling into an ash tray. Suddenly his passion changes to antipathy. How she seems at home here! No, it can't go on. I've got to make a break with her, escape. At once. Tonight. Now that his resolve is made, he feels relieved, clear-headed, and can observe her critically. At this moment, scrutinizing her nails, her forehead puckered, she is almost ugly. Yes, all is over, irrevocably; something has snapped, beyond repair.

HUGUETTE: "You'll see me to my bus, won't you?"

They go out together. The Rue de Rennes, at seven, is crowded with people from the suburbs hurrying to catch their trains at the Montparnasse station. Jean walks in front, to force a way through the crowd.

HUGUETTE: "There's my bus. So that's fixed up? If you don't meet me after the show, I'll go straight home. Bye-bye, darling. Oh, damn! It's starting!"

She dashes forward, elbowing her way to the forefront. He follows the slim black form with his eyes, sees her spring onto the moving step and scooped up by the fatherly conductor's arm. The bus recedes into the darkness, spangled with lights.

Jean shivers slightly and remains standing at the bus-stop, beside a café terrace. A sour smell of absinthe fills the air, people are streaming past, paper-boys crying the evening news.

II

Cécile is standing at the window of the doctor's house at Buis, gazing out into the courtyard. Jean and Mme Pasquelin have just appeared in the gateway. On catching sight of them, Cécile steps back hastily, in a sudden access of shyness; they mustn't guess her eagerness. But she continues watching, at a little distance from the window. "He hasn't changed," she murmurs to herself as she sees Jean walking briskly up to the front door. He roves the house-front with his gaze, which comes to a sudden halt when it falls on the closed shutters of his father's bedroom.

Cécile runs out into the hall. Leaning against the banister, she listens in frozen stillness to the sound of hurried footfalls on the steps. Then Jean flings the door open and stops short. His face is very pale, there is no joy in the look he gives her, only intense anxiety.

CÉCILE: "He's upstairs—sleeping."

JEAN: "Ah, he's sleeping." The strained look leaves his face, and now he gazes fondly at Cécile, holding out his hand. Full of tenderness, his eyes respond to the girl's timid smile of welcome.

MME PASQUELIN, opening the drawing-room door: "We'd better stay here for a bit since he's sleeping." Suddenly Jean thinks: The way they say "he"! Not "your father" or "the doctor." Remoteness. Yes, my father's dying. "Sit down, Jean. I've had the drawing-room opened again, and we always sit here so as not to disturb him when we talk. These last few nights I've slept in your poor grand-mother's bedroom so as to be nearer, in case . . ." She has remained standing. Now she casts an affectionate glance at the two young people. "Stay here, my dears, I'm going upstairs. I'll come and tell you, Jean, when your father wakes up." In the doorway she looks round and says to Jean, almost shyly: "Cécile's very pleased to see you again, I know."

Jean and Cécile are alone. There are some moments of silence and constraint. Cécile is gazing at the carpet, one hand resting on a low table, the other on her blouse, nervously toying with a needle she stuck in it without thinking, when she was at her sewing. Jean goes up to her and clasps her hand.

JEAN: "Ah, Cécile, it's a cruel price we're paying for the joy of being together again today."

Raising tear-dimmed eyes, she presses a finger to her lips. He mustn't speak; no words can express . . . Their shyness overrules emotion; each is wondering if this joy in their reunion doesn't fall short of their expectation. Jean leads her to the sofa. She sits there very straight, breathing rather quickly. He still holds her hand. Neither moves. There is a long silence, tense with unspoken thoughts.

Jean hears footsteps overhead. I won-der how I'll find him. Greatly changed, no doubt. And he conjures up his father's face: the shrewd, incisive gaze, the lips imperious even when they kissed, the smile, self-confident and sometimes ironical, but how full of secret kindliness!

He looks at the drawing-room furni-ture, and everything evokes a memory of his childhood. That was the chair in which Grandma sat, the evening when . . . And now she's dead. Soon I'll be saying, "My father *used* to live here, *used* to sit in that chair." And some day others will be saying, "Jean Barois lived here; he *used* to . . ." He shivers.

In his musings he has forgotten the warm, vital presence beside him. Now, suddenly, the thought of her trust in him strikes through his sombre mood, quickening his pulses. He raises the moist, yielding hand he has been clasping to his lips, several times—almost rever-ently at first, pensively; then with grow-ing ardor, and a surge of joyful emotion sweeps him off his balance.

Cécile raises her head, then gently lets it sink upon Jean's shoulder, her eyes closed in a happy daydream. Tenderly he seals the soft eyelids with a long kiss.

Footsteps; a door creaks. Cécile opens her eyes and moves away from Jean.

MME PASQUELIN: "Jean, your father's awake now."

The doctor's bedroom. Mme Pas-quelin opens the door softly, then draws back. Jean pauses on the threshold for a moment, a moment of lacerating appre-hension. Then, as he enters the room alone, an easing of the tension comes with the sight of his father's smile.

The sick man is propped on pillows, his arms stretched out; he has not changed greatly, though his breathing is terribly labored. Still smiling, he watches Jean approach.

THE DOCTOR, in a hoarse whisper: "I'm in a bad way, as you see. In a very bad way, I fear." He moves his arm, and his face, and passionately he draws his hand. The doctor grasps it; then a shadow like a presage of death falls on his face, and passionately he draws his son's hand, his arm, his body, down to-wards the bed. "My son!" His voice breaks on a sob. Pressing the young man's head between his palms, he sees only the face of long ago, a child's. He strokes it feverishly, presses it with this side and that against his stubbly cheeks. "Ah!" With a short sigh he sinks back upon the pillows. He signs to Jean to wait, not to call for help; it will pass . . . Then, his eyes closed, his lips half parted, his fists clenched on his heart to quell its turmoil, he remains quite still.

Jean gazes intently at his father. With his grief mingles a curious perplexity. Why is it he looks so different? Because he's got so thin? No, it's something more. But what?

A little color comes back to the sick man's cheeks; he opens his eyes. When he sees Jean his brows grow furrowed, his lips tighten. Then his features relax, and tears well up in his eyes.

THE DOCTOR: "My dear boy! My own dear son!"

The sight of his father's tears, the forlorn affection of his voice, make Jean strangely ill at ease. Is nothing left of the man his father was? Some minutes pass, and with them Jean's grief recedes; for life is stronger than death. Unsummoned, thoughts of Cécile have crossed his mind, a memory of the way she looked at him just now. And he feels an uprush of desire, no less compelling for its immateriality; the yearning for some ecstatic mingling of their souls, an interpenetration of their thoughts and dreams. And he still can feel on his lips that silken softness of her eyelids. A sudden zest for life courses through him, and with it a fretful impulse to escape this stagnant, thwarting atmosphere of death. But abruptly his mood changes, he feels his face reddening with shame.

The doctor wipes the tears off his cheeks, and his eyes settle on his son.

THE DOCTOR: "Tell me, Jean. They asked you to come, didn't they? . . . Yes, yes, I know. . . . Who was it? The doctor? No? . . . Your godmother then?" Jean shakes his head evasively. The doctor's voice hardens; all sentiment has left it. "They were quite right. I haven't far to go. In fact I was expecting you." Overcome by emotion or, perhaps, to keep himself in countenance, Jean bends over the hand lying limply on the counterpane and presses his lips to it.

The doctor withdraws his hand and uses it to raise himself onto his elbows; his look is earnest, he has something to say that cannot be postponed. "Yes, I was expecting you to come. Now, listen, my dear boy. I haven't much to leave you." Jean does not take his meaning for a moment. Then he makes a protesting gesture. The sick man slowly raises his head to show that he is getting tired, has more to say, and must not be interrupted. He speaks in short phrases, his eyes closed, as if reciting something learnt by rote. "I might have left you more, but I somehow muddled things. Anyhow, you'll have enough to live on. And an untarnished name, I hope; that's something.

"Now listen carefully. Cécile and you—you have—an understanding, haven't you?" Jean gives a slight start. The doctor smiles affectionately. "Yes, she told me about it. She's a dear girl and will make you happy. I'm very glad. . . . And it's up to you, Jean, to make her happy—so far as you can. It's not so easy. You'll see. We may try to understand women, but it's beyond us, really. We must accept the fact that they're different. Quite different from us. And that alone makes it hard enough. Your mother—I feel I was much to blame." A long silence. "Next—about your health, Jean. You know how it is with you. And, of course, you didn't do your military service. That was just to be on the safe side. Anyhow, you're completely cured; you can take that from me. I assured your godmother there was nothing to be feared now—and I meant it. Still, my dear boy, you'd do well to think about your health now and again, and take care not to overwork, especially later on when you are in your forties. That'll always be your weak point. You'll promise me, won't you? Good." He smiles contentedly. "Don't forget what I've been saying. That's all." He lowers his head to the pillows and straightens out his arms with a sigh of relief. But a moment later another thought comes to him, and he opens his eyes again. "Your godmother has been most kind to me, you know. She has done much, I can't tell you how much, for me. She'll let you know, of course." However, he cannot resist the temptation of announcing it himself. A smile comes to his face; first a mere ghost of a smile that glimmers through the veil of suffering; then gradually it develops, lighting up his eyes, his forehead, the whole face—and there is something almost childish in its happy plenitude. He beckons to Jean to come nearer, and Jean bends over the bed. Putting his arm round Jean's neck, the doctor draws Jean's head down near his lips. "Jean, hasn't your godmother told you anything? No? The Abbé came here yesterday." With the air of imparting a momentous secret. "I made my confession." He moves Jean's head a little back so as to savor the effect of this announcement on his face. Then again draws Jean's face near his. "I'd intended to receive the Sacrament today, but when I learnt that you were coming I postponed it. So tomorrow you and I, all of us together . . ." Jean straightens up; he tries to conjure up a look of pleased surprise, but has to turn away. A vague but poignant feeling of disappointment has come over him. The doctor is gazing straight in front of him, with a hint of fear in his eyes. "You know, my dear boy, people may say what they like, but"—he shakes his head—"that unknown quantity—it's a terrible thing to face."

Next day. The doctor's bedroom; a bleak, austere room on the second floor. The Communion service is over. Not wishing to betray her emotions, Mme Pasquelin is busy setting in order the chest of drawers, which has served as an altar. The sick man is sitting up, propped by pillows. The morning light streaming in through the window obliterates his features but harshly emphasizes the whites of his eyes. His head is drooping, his hair tousled, his beard unkempt; his cheeks are cadaverously sunken. Without the pince-nez his gaze is vacillating, but lit with a dim, almost childish rapture.

Cécile and Jean stand at the bedside. This morning their love oppresses them no longer; it has the tranquillity of something solid and perdurable. Each has the certitude of loving for the first—and the last—time.

There has been a remarkable change in the invalid's condition overnight. The strained look has left him and given place to one of infinite repose—which, welcome though it is, alarms them. The dying man's wandering gaze strays over them, lingers, and moves again, but they do not feel its impact. It glides indifferently by, as if it were focused across walls and window on the blue beyond. Then a forced smile—affectionate, yet what worlds away!—forms on the wasted face.

THE DOCTOR, in a toneless but quite clear voice: "So you're there, both of you, my dears. I'm glad, very glad. Give me your hands." The smile grows rigid, conventional. He seems to be playing a part, and in haste to get it over. Gathering their hands in his, he fondles them. Mme Pasquelin has halted at the foot of the bed, a new look on her face. The doctor gazes at her. "Don't you agree? Nothing could be better. Our two dear young people . . ."

Cécile bursts into tears and moves to her mother, who takes Jean's hand and draws him, too, beside her. Unmoving, linked together, they call to mind a statuary group.

The doctor's gaze hovers for a moment on Cécile and on her mother; then abruptly he fixes his eyes on Jean, with a look of unconcealed aversion, a keen flash of rancor, which quickly softens to one of harrowing entreaty; that too dies out almost at once. Jean has guessed the thought behind that look: You will go on living, while I . . .

A boundless compassion fills his heart; if only it were in his power to confer that new lease of life! Impulsively he moves away from the two women and bends over the livid face. But the dying man makes no movement. That mask of unperturbable aloofness has returned to his face, and some moments pass before he is conscious of Jean's kiss. Then with an effort he conjures up a fleeting smile, but his eyes betray no human feeling.

Jean turns and walks toward Cécile, his arms outstretched.

### III

M. Jean Barois
    Buis-la-Dame, Oise
        Berne, June 25
Dear old chap: The sympathy I so naturally expressed in your bereavement certainly did not deserve so kind and affectionate a letter as the one that has just reached me. I thank you for it, dear Jean, from the bottom of my heart. I was particularly touched by the trust you show in me, when you ask my advice about the serious problem you mention in your letter, and I am glad to be able to give you an unequivocal answer.

Quite definitely I do not think that on religious grounds there is any obstacle whatever to your marriage with Mlle Pasquelin. I can see that the rather primitive nature of her faith and the excessive importance she attaches to religious observances have given you pause. But, frankly, I cannot understand you. Fundamentally religious emotion is always one and the same; there's little point in analyzing the different forms it may as-

sume. At a certain level, the highest, all aspirations towards God meet and are united, however different their starting points may be.

You say that if she knew your present feelings about religion, she would break off the engagement. That may well be so. But it would be owing to a mere error of judgment on her part.

So, in my opinion, it would be a great mistake to broach this subject with her. She would certainly fail to grasp the distinction you draw between conventional faith and the moral and human basis of the religious feeling. And, like the simple soul she is, she would be deeply shocked. You would merely be inviting catastrophe by any such ill-timed sincerity— quite uncalled-for as things stand. Thanks to your education and your logical mind, you have risen above the purely instinctive type of faith, and it's for you alone to make, in full awareness, this decision which concerns her happiness and yours, and to shoulder full responsibility.

And, really, there is so little for you to fear. You seem to forget how much she and you have in common: the same heredity, the same upbringing—fundamentals, these! Moreover, your own temperament is so intrinsically religious that you should never have any difficulty in keeping in harmony, indeed in sympathy, with the state of mind of your wife-to-be. She too will evolve, and thus the rift between you will gradually close, not widen.

I felt thoroughly convinced of this on reading your description of the Communion service at the death-bed of that noble man, your father. When you two were kneeling, side by side, each believed in something different; she in the Real Presence of Christ's body, you in the symbol of His superhuman love. Yet suddenly, in the same thrill of emotion, these different conceptions were lifted onto a higher plane in which they fused, became one, and your two souls were no longer separated. And thus it will be in your future life together.

Forgive me, my dear Jean, for the seeming presumption of giving you advice on so delicate a matter. But for so many years I have had the honor of being your confidant that I am in a position to gauge the depth of your feelings for Mlle Pasquelin, and their loyalty. It would be a grievous mistake if, in deference to any exaggerated scruple, you frustrated the happiness which both of you deserve.

With much affection and in all sincerity,

Yours,
H. S.

## IV

## The Chain

*Marriage is a danger only to the man who has ideas.*

Herzog

I

Abbé Schertz
Professor of Biological Chemistry
The Catholic Institute
Berne

My dear Hermann: You were quite right to reproach me with my long silence. But, happily, your letter shows that your affection has not been impaired by my remissness—and that, for me, is the chief thing.

First of all, I must thank you for the concern you show for my wife's health. I have been most anxious about it throughout the last two years; her accident had more serious consequences than I could have believed possible when I wrote to tell you of it. It led to all sorts of complications, and even after eighteen months' treatment she is still in very poor health; so much so that we may have to abandon any hope of ever having a child.

It has been a terrible ordeal for her and has badly shaken her morale.

But don't imagine I am trying to excuse the rarity of my letters on the strength of my domestic anxieties. Often and often I have settled down to write to you and abandoned the idea when I realized how far afield I had traveled from the religious convictions we used to share, and how difficult and distasteful would be the task of explaining this to you. Still, I feel I must bring myself to it, and we are both of us capable—don't you agree?—of keeping our friendship intact, whatever our differences of opinion.

My religious life falls into three distinct phases.

The first ended when I was seventeen and it dawned on me that there were anomalies in "revealed" religion; when I learnt that doubt was not the outcome of a perverted imagination, nor something one can dispel with a brisk shake of the head, but an obsession as compelling as truth itself. It is like a surgical syringe thrust deep into the heart of faith, draining its lifeblood away, drop by drop.

Then, when at twenty I made your acquaintance, I clung desperately to your broad-minded interpretation of Catholicism. You remember, my dear Hermann, how eagerly I grasped at the solutions you proposed to me? To you I owe some years of real peace of mind. And my marriage, to begin with, consolidated your work; those daily contacts with my wife's whole-hearted faith deepened my respect for religion under all its aspects. Your symbolistic interpretation provided exactly the compromise needed, and enabled me to live in close communion with an orthodoxy at whose cast-iron dogmas my intellect persistently balked.

But this peace was only superficial. Beneath the surface a ferment of resistance was developing. Still, even now I cannot see clearly what it was that made the old doubts surge up again.

Of course the position we took up could not be durable. Those symbolistic interpretations are based on far from solid ground and provide only a temporary halting place. By dint of stripping Catholic tradition of all that is no longer acceptable to the modern mind, we soon reduce it to nothingness. Once you admit that the literal meaning of the articles of faith can be discarded—and can a really thoughtful mind do otherwise than discard it?—you open the door to every variety of mental independence: free inquiry and, in the long run, free-thinking.

Surely you too have realized this? I can't conceive that you can still be satisfied, morally or intellectually, by a compromise so arbitrary and so vulnerable. It's a mere playing on the natural meanings of words; a subterfuge. Your link between the present and the past was too precarious; how can a man stop half-way on the road to freedom? To seek to retain the Catholic religion for the sake of its sentimental appeal and the time-proved social values it stands for is the conduct not of a believer but of a dilettante with a taste for folklore! Far be it from me to deny the historical importance of Christianity; but, if we are to be honest with ourselves, we must own that nothing vital can any longer be extracted from its doctrines—by those, anyhow, who refuse to allow their intellect to be befogged.

Thus I soon discovered that the faith of my childhood—a faith "bred in the bone" in my case—which I had so long regarded as the mainstay of my life, had gradually receded from me. And it is one of the many blessings I owe to your influence on the course of my mental development that, thanks to you, my transi-

tion to absolute denial was not so painful as it might have been. Yes, it is to you I owe it that now at last I can analyze so dispassionately those extinct dogmas which meant so much to me in my early life.

But I must allow also for the influence that my present duties at Wenceslas College have had, if indirectly, on the readjustment of my belief. This may seem paradoxical, considering that the College is under clerical control. However, the professors are selected by the University, the teaching is, on the whole, remarkably free, and the lecture courses I give are not subjected to any sort of censorship.

When I put in for this professorial post I had only the vaguest notion of the difficulties ahead. For one thing, I had little or no experience of public speaking. But from the very first lecture I felt a ripple of attention—you must know what I mean; it's unmistakable—pass through the group of students attending my course.

This is the second year, and their interest shows no sign of flagging. I give them all my time and—I can honestly say it—the best of myself. Whatever my daily research work and my private meditations bring me goes into my lectures. I want all the young people who attend them to get from their brief contact with myself something more than a mere smattering of scientific fact. My great hope is to raise their moral level, to uplift their personalities, and to leave a permanent imprint on these young minds that are so malleable. And I really believe that I am getting results not unworthy of the tremendous effort I am putting forth.

So you see my post isn't quite what you seem to think, when you ask me if my duties leave me time to work on my own account. For me it's not in the least a "job" to be done; it is the greatest joy of my life and a consolation for my troubles. (I prefer to say little of the rift that my emancipation has created in my married life, but you can easily guess that I am not spared afflictions of this order.)

So there, my dear Hermann, you have my present existence. And yours—how goes it with you? I greatly hope that I have not distressed you by unburdening myself so frankly in this letter. After all, I have only given practical application to a passage in St. Luke that you know well: "And no man putteth new wine into old bottles; else the new wine will burst the bottles. . . . But new wine must be put into new bottles; and both are preserved."

With very affectionate greetings,

Yours as ever,

Jean Barois

M. Jean Barois
    Professor of Natural Science
        Wenceslas College, Paris

My very dear Jean: I can hardly tell you how amazed I was by your letter, and how profoundly distressed. What suffering you must have gone through before coming to your present state!

But I have not lost faith in your discernment and I believe that some day or other you will come back to a less extremist view. I grant that for men like us, who have no longer the simple faith of earlier days, only two ways lie open: either that of a moral anarchy, unguided by any rules or restrictions whatsoever; or that of a symbolistic interpretation, which reconciles tradition and the modern mind and enables them to abide by and in that noble institution, the Catholic Church. Our religion is the only organization which offers the ideals you and I stand for their full scope, and the only one to confer objective validity on the moral law in which we both believe. No branch of science, no philosophy, can provide any satisfactory argument enforcing the idea, for instance, of duty.

But religion *does* provide such arguments.

Why, then, kick against the pricks and try to break loose from any form of authority?

Like you, I refuse to believe blindly— but is that any reason to reject Catholicism altogether? Was it not Renan himself who advised us "to retain all that part of Christianity which a man can endorse without believing in the supernatural?"

Reading your letter, I much regretted that your friend Abbé Joziers is now abroad on missionary work. This is, I feel, a great loss for you. I know how narrowly orthodox his views are, but he would have realized the critical phase you are going through, and affection would have prompted him to come to your aid in an effective way.

I too, my very dear friend, would like to come to your aid, as I did once before, and I hope you will not spurn my helping hand. In this hope, and with unchanged affection, I am,

As ever yours,

Hermann Schertz

P.S. Your quotation from the Gospel of St. Luke was incomplete; you omitted the last and all-important verse: "No man also having drunk old wine straightway drinketh new: for he saith, The old is better."

Abbé Schertz
    Professor of Biological Chemistry
        The Catholic Institute
            Berne

My dear Hermann: You liken my emancipation to the conduct of a small boy in revolt against an irksome disciplinarian. But, though I admit that since my marriage I have come into more direct and frequent contact with the exigencies of strict Catholicism, I can honestly assure you that I was not swayed by any personal emotion when I resolved to discard for good such remnants of Catholicism as lingered on in my mentality.

You are hoodwinking yourself, I fear, when you interpret on lines that make it palatable to you personally a religion which has given clean-cut definitions of its tenets, and expressly condemns any interpretation such as you propose. For, nothing if not logical, and shrewdly strict in its prohibitions, the Church has never failed to banish from the fold in which you claim a place such lukewarm believers as we were, you and I—and you still are.

The assured tone of your letter justifies me in reminding you of some phrases in the *Dei Filius* ordinance of the 1870 Vatican Council, which seem to me to fit your case. They run thus:

"If any man does not accept as sacred and canonical in their entirety and in all their parts the Books of the Scriptures (as enumerated by the Council of Trent), or denies that they were divinely inspired: let him be anathema.

"If any man declare that miracles cannot take place and therefore all accounts of miracles, even those in the Holy Scriptures, should be accounted myths or fables; or that miracles can never be positively verified and the origin of the Christian religion is not validly demonstrated by them: let him be anathema.

"If any man say that circumstances may arise under which, in view of the progress of science, he may be led to assign to the dogmas of the Church a meaning other than that which the Church has assigned and now assigns to them: let him be anathema."

And, lastly, this passage, which is clear as crystal:

"For the doctrine of the true faith revealed by God was not bestowed as a philosophical instrument for the betterment of the human intellect, but has been committed, as a divine endowment, to the Bride of Christ, that the Church

may be faithfully guarded and taught infallibly. Wherefore it behooves us ever to conserve the meanings which our Holy Mother Church has assigned, once for all, to the sacred dogmas, and never to deviate from them at the behest of an intelligence claiming to be superior to them."

Thus inexorably, my dear Hermann, the Church excludes us from her pen. Why, then, prompted by some sentimental affection (unreciprocated, to all intents and purposes), cling to that aged foster mother, who has no further use for us and regards the efforts we make to stand by her as so many crimes! You'll find out one day that you have made only half your progress towards the light, and boldly, swiftly, you will take the few remaining steps.

Then you will find me waiting for you, outside the pen, in the clear light of day.

Your ever affectionate friend,

J. B.

## II

A bedroom. The dawn is rising. Opening his eyes, Jean blinks at the strip of light between the curtains.

JEAN, sleepily: "What's the time?"

CÉCILE, in a clear, composed voice: "Half-past six."

JEAN: "Only half-past six! Did you sleep badly?"

CÉCILE: "No, darling." He smiles vaguely by way of answer and settles down into the bed. "It's Saturday. You've no lecture this morning, have you?"

JEAN: "No."

CÉCILE, affectionately: "Darling, there's something I want to ask you."

JEAN: "Yes? Ask away."

A short silence. She nestles up to him, as in the past, presses her face against his shoulder, and remains thus, without moving.

CÉCILE: "Listen . . ."

JEAN: "Well . . . ?"

CÉCILE: "Please promise not to be angry. Don't get in one of your cruel moods."

Jean props himself on his elbow and gazes at her fretfully. Only too well he knows that obstinate look in her eyes, masked though it is by tenderness.

JEAN: "Well, what is it now?"

CÉCILE: "Oh, if that's how you feel—"

JEAN: "What do you know about how I feel? Tell me what you want. Out with it!"

CÉCILE: "You can't refuse me this."

JEAN: "But what is it?"

CÉCILE: "Well—I'm doing a novena. You know that, don't you?"

JEAN, gloomily: "No."

CÉCILE, taken aback: "What? You didn't know it?"

JEAN: "You never told me."

CÉCILE: "But you must have noticed, surely?"

JEAN, icily: "A novena. I see. What's it for? Ah, yes, I understand. To have a baby. So you've come to that!"

CÉCILE, with sudden passion, bringing her face close to his: "Oh, please, darling, don't say anything more, don't try to stop me. You see, I'm positive my prayers will be heard. Only, I'd like you too. . . . Really, I'm not asking very much of you; only to come with me this evening to Notre Dame des Victoires. It's the last day, the ninth, of my special intercession, and . . ." She moves away a little and looks at Jean, who shakes his head sadly.

JEAN, gently: "You know quite well—"

CÉCILE, putting her fever-hot hand on his lips: "No, no! Don't say any more."

JEAN: "—that it's out of the question."

CÉCILE, losing self-control: "Can't you keep quiet? Don't say anything yet." She presses herself to him. "Surely you can't refuse me *that*? I'm asking so little, and think what it would mean to us, to you and me, to have a child. All I ask is for you to come to church with me; you needn't say a word, or do anything at all. So there's no need to answer. Of course you'll come."

JEAN, frigidly: "No. I can't do that." A short silence. Cécile is weeping. Jean turns on her irritably. "Oh, for goodness' sake, stop crying; tears won't help." She tries to restrain her tears. Jean holds her wrists. "But can't you understand what you want to make me do? Are you so blind that you can't see the—the *ugliness* of what you're proposing?"

CÉCILE, in a choked voice: "But what can it matter to you? Oh, Jean, won't you—just to please me?"

JEAN: "Do try to think seriously for just a moment. You must know quite well that I don't believe those prayers and candles and all the rest of it are the slightest use. Do you want to coerce me into acting a part, playing the hypocrite?"

CÉCILE, sobbing: "But what harm can it do you? You'd only be doing it to please me."

JEAN: "How could you suppose that I'd agree? Surely you can realize that, in asking me to do a thing like this—after all the painful discussions we've had on these subjects—you're—you're simply lowering us, both of us, by the mere suggestion?"

CÉCILE, whimpering: "Just to please me, darling."

JEAN, roughly: "No!" Cécile gazes at him with distraught eyes. Neither speaks for some moments. "I've explained it to you dozens of times. What's best, what's cleanest, in me is precisely this honest doubt of mine. It's just because I attach so much importance to all professions of faith that I can't make a dishonest show of one to please you. But of course it's no good; you'll never understand the first thing about my feelings on the matter."

CÉCILE, impulsively: "But, Jean, at that time there won't be a soul in church who knows you."

For a moment Jean fails to grasp her meaning and stares at her in bewilderment. Then a look of keen distress crosses his face.

JEAN: "So you, of all people, think an argument like that can weigh with me!" They remain lying side by side, feeling the warmth of each other's nearness, yet utterly remote in thought, estranged. "Do, please, try to understand. This nine days' devotion of yours is your affair; I'm not trying to prevent it, I only refuse to take part in it. Surely I have a right to do that."

CÉCILE, obstinately: "You're always talking about your rights; why not talk about your duties for a change? You have a duty towards me. No, it's no good my trying to explain; nothing would make you understand. But you absolutely *must* come to church with me this evening or—it's all no use."

JEAN: "Really, my dear, that's sheer nonsense. If you drag me there against my will, whom do you suppose you'll be deceiving?"

CÉCILE: "Jean, I implore you, do please come with me this evening."

JEAN, springing out of the bed: "No, I won't! I *will not!* I don't meddle with your beliefs, and you might leave me free to act according to mine."

CÉCILE, with cry of protest: "Oh! But—but it's not the same thing at all!"

JEAN, gazing down at Cécile, who is sobbing passionately: " 'It's not the same thing!' Yes, that's the source of all our troubles. Never will you bring yourself to respect what you do not understand." He raises his hand. "Anyhow, you can do me the justice of admitting that I never tried to shake your faith by any word I've said. But really, my dear Cécile, there are moments when you make me so angry that I wish you could feel a twinge

of doubt one day—just enough to make you a bit less cocksure, less inclined to lay down the law, because you think *your* truth is absolute, infallible!"

His eyes fall on a cheval-glass and he catches sight of his reflected self: barefooted, tousle-headed, hurling denunciations at the tumbled bed. As much disgusted with himself as with Cécile, he flings out of the bedroom, slamming the door.

Jean is alone in his study. Notes are scattered about the desk at which he is sitting. He writes a full page without looking up, then petulantly drops his pen. Try as he may, he cannot settle down to his work; the ideas keep floating away, just out of reach.

It's ridiculous, he thinks. But this morning I can't get down to it at all. And all because of that ridiculous business about the novena—that nine days' wonder! Thrusting aside his notes, he ponders for some moments. No, it would be too damn silly! All the future hangs on incidents like these; I must keep my freedom of action, that's essential. And if I give in today, tomorrow there'll be something else. Out of the question.

He rises to his feet, his nerves on edge, walks to the window, and, folding his arms, gazes vaguely at the rain-blurred sky. But what can she expect to gain by her precious novena? Does she seriously think that her prayers will have some sort of action on God's will? It's all too childish for words! Really, her brand of faith would be worthier of Abbé Joziers' savages. That nine-days' intercession, that mystic number nine! I suppose she's got hold of some formulary for the use of barren women. Fantastic!

He shrugs his shoulders, goes to the bookcase, and seems to be searching for some book. "To thine own self be true." Women don't understand that kind of loyalty. "But what harm can it do you?

[ 48 ]

Just to please me, darling." Self-respect, personal dignity mean nothing to them.

Taking out a book at random, he goes back to his chair.

Luncheon time. Jean takes his seat at the table by himself. He thinks: She'll stay in her room, sulking. She hopes I'll let myself be worked on by her childish antics. In a sudden burst of anger: Oh, damn it, things can't go on like this!

Cécile enters. At the sound of the opening door Jean looks up. He sees a pathetic little face, tear-stained, haggard, leaden-hued. And all his resentment is effaced by an uprush of pity, the pity one feels for a child who has done wrong and is wholly irresponsible; a vast compassion welling up from the depths of his instinctive self, almost a resurrection—but how pallid, joyless!—of the dead love of earlier days.

Quietly, without the least hint of play-acting, she sits down at her usual place. When the maid comes in, she murmurs something about a violent headache. She forces herself to make a show of eating. Long silences.

Jean steals glances at her; observes the clean-cut, wilful curves of the bowed forehead; the swollen eyelids, dry and red; the puffy lips and mouth cruelly disfigured by suffering. And what he sees appals him. I'm torturing her. Whether rightly or wrongly matters little. She is suffering because of me, and it's abominable. Oh, what's the use of trying to make her understand? All I'll ever do is to hurt her. It would be better to give in than to go on torturing her—to no end. After all, what is she asking of me? Little more than what I've often done this summer, when I went with her to Mass on Sundays. So much the worse for her if she can't see the silliness, the ugliness, of what she wants to force me into doing now. No, there's no point in holding out; let her have her way.

A marvelous feeling of relief comes over him, now he has made this decision. There is an almost sensual pleasure in escaping from his egoism, proving himself the better of the pair, the one who understands, forgives—and yields. His eyes grow gentle as he gazes at her. She is eating her meal, like a docile child, without raising her eyes from the plate.

She looks pretty like that, across her tears. But really it's a rotten thing to do, to make a woman cry. Father used to say, "Women are different, and we're much too apt to forget this." He was right. All that comes of treating them like equals is needless suffering. What's happened to Cécile and myself proves how right he was. We must avoid all that makes for estrangement and try our best to cultivate what draws us together. Yes, but for that to be feasible, one would need to be *still* in love.

He rises. Cécile has been waiting, aloof, her eyes fixed on the tablecloth. He thinks: She'll hurry back to her room. I'll follow and tell her that I consent. But, as usual, Cécile goes to Jean's study, where the coffee awaits them. She stands beside the tray, her arms limply drooping.

Jean goes towards her. It has cost him a great struggle with himself; he has had to trample underfoot something of his self-respect, his conscience, and perhaps his future. But he is counting on the coming joy. She will fling herself on his breast, smiling through tears; he will be repaid by the sudden light of gratitude in her eyes. Bending towards her, he puts his arm round her waist. She accepts the contact passively.

JEAN, with a slight tremor in his voice: "Listen! It's all right; I'll come with you this evening, wherever you want. If only you'll not cry any more."

She frees herself and thrusts him roughly away.

CÉCILE: "Ah, I can feel it; I know you

[ 49 ]

will always, *always*, be my enemy." He stares at her, dumbfounded. "I know too that we shall have to separate one day—in a year's time, in ten years' time, there's no telling. But one day we shall part. It's inevitable. And then how I shall hate you!" She bursts into tears. "Even now I—loathe you." She stretches out her arms uncertainly, as if about to fall; then she steadies herself on the table's edge.

JEAN, glumly: "Very well. I only wished to give you pleasure."

She looks up, as if awaking from a nightmare; the anger leaves her face, and she clutches Jean's arm.

CÉCILE, in an uncertain voice: "Ah, yes. About this evening? That's so, it's very sweet of you." She bends hastily and kisses his hand. "Thank you, darling."

Pressing her handkerchief to her lips, she walks away slowly, dejectedly; in the doorway she tries to give him a smile. Completely baffled, Jean stares at the door which has just closed behind her, then gives himself a shake, walks to the window, flings it open, and, though rain is falling, puts his head outside, like a man who has urgent need of fresh air.

Notre Dame des Victoires. 8 P.M. The church is like a mausoleum; the massed tapers dazzle but shed no light. Here nightly come, from every part of Paris, those whose courage has failed them in their need, those whose hopes were dupes but will not die, and join their prayers in shadows pungent with fumes of burning wax.

Cécile is kneeling, Jean standing; both are bowed beneath the burden of the irremediable.

Later that night, when Jean is sitting in his study, relishing his solitude, the door opens and Cécile tiptoes in, barefooted.

CÉCILE: "Aren't you coming to bed?" Shyly. "Angry with me?" She has a timid, would-be ingratiating smile, like a scolded child's. Disarmed by such guilelessness, Jean cannot help smiling in return. She is in her nightdress. Not a trace of tears remains, and with her hair let down for the night, a big black bow holding it behind, she looks no more than fifteen, the slender little girl he loved at Buis. "I couldn't bear to sleep all by myself tonight—after a day like today. I want so much to feel that all's forgotten—and forgiven." Jean is tired of words; he gently kisses the cheek that coaxingly she bends towards him. This evening, more than ever, he feels an old, old man. "You can't think how cold it is in my room. . . . But I won't keep you from your work, darling. I'll wait for you. You'll let me stay on your knee, won't you? I promise not to fidget."

She nestles against him, fondly yielding. Jean, who has his arm round her, can feel the supple warmth of her young body. Her slippers have dropped off, and he takes the small cold feet in his hands to warm them.

CÉCILE: "You see, I'm simply freezing!"

There is an almost wanton challenge in her laugh. She lets her head sink back, still laughing. Their eyes meet for a moment, and Jean notices with slight surprise a glint of smiling satisfaction between the half-closed eyelids. And then it dawns on him. Obviously. It's the ninth night. So that too was in the programme! But he is not in the least annoyed and continues holding her in his arms.

He has glimpsed the utmost depth of human folly, and he now feels incredibly remote from Cécile, a dweller on another planet. "Women are different . . . !"

III

Some pages torn from a notebook lie hidden under other papers in a drawer of

Jean's writing-desk. They are covered with notes, dashed down in rapid, incisive script:

Women: inferior beings, irremediably.

Like a worm in a fruit, sentimentality at its most virulent is lodged in them, and gnaws at their hearts, disintegrating all.

Women love mystery, with an instinctive, argument-proof adoration. The trouble is, they adore it at the lowest level.

If at night they are afraid of burglars, a night light burning at the bedside reassures them. They need religious belief to make them feel safe, and to soothe the qualms they otherwise might feel about a future state. The idea of asking for "proof" never crosses their minds.

A man should not marry until he has definitely marked out his path in life, has made some headway along it, and is sure of not swerving from it. To change its direction after marriage plays havoc with two lives, not merely one; between two people pledged to live together, it creates a gulf in which all happiness founders—beyond hope of rescue.

IV

A year later. The small drawing-room at Mme Pasquelin's house. Jean and Cécile have just arrived for a few days' stay. It is Easter Monday; the hour is noon. Abbé Joziers, who returned from Madagascar two months previously, has come to lunch.

MME PASQUELIN: "Come near the fire. What a disappointing day it's been! It looked so fine when I got up."

The sky has suddenly darkened; hail is drumming on the panes.

THE ABBÉ, standing at the window: "Oh, it's only a squall; it won't last long." He gazes at Jean. "But how my dear young friend has changed in the last five years!"

JEAN, smiling: "Well, how about yourself? You've changed almost beyond recognition. You're so much thinner, for one thing; your cheeks are yellow, and—"

THE ABBÉ, laughing: "Thanks!"

MME PASQUELIN: "Yet he's looking ever so much fitter than he did a month ago. He'd have died among his blackamoors if I hadn't got the Bishop to order him back peremptorily."

THE ABBÉ, to Jean: "Yes, my dear boy, that's so. I all but left my bones there. But then our Heavenly Father, warned no doubt by Madame Pasquelin, thought better of it. I imagine Him saying to Himself: 'We've still some work down on earth for that old servant of ours. So back he goes to France!' "

JEAN, gravely: "The first thing, sir, is to repair the damage."

THE ABBÉ: "Bless you, that's been done already. I'm sound in wind and limb." He thumps his chest. "Nothing wrong there, I think. Do you know, the day before yesterday I walked all the way to Saint-Cyr, and felt none the worse for it. Today I intend to walk to Beaumont and look up my friend the curé. So you see there's no need for me to cosset myself." He has been observing Jean as he talks. "Yes, how you have changed!"

JEAN: "So much as that?"

THE ABBÉ: "Well, there's the moustache, for one thing. And then—I can't give a name to it, but there's a great difference in your look, in the whole face, I should say."

MME PASQUELIN, in an aside to Cécile: "And what about you? How are you feeling?"

CÉCILE: "Oh, much as usual."

MME PASQUELIN: "And—there's still nothing?"

[ 51 ]

CÉCILE, with tears in her eyes: "No."
A short silence.

MME PASQUELIN, lowering her voice still more and glancing at Jean, who is talking to the priest: "And—he?"
Cécile shakes her head and sighs.

Luncheon is over.

THE ABBÉ, going to the window: "Good, it's cleared up. I'd better make a move. As I said, I'm going to Beaumont Vicarage. How about coming a bit of the way with me, Jean?"

JEAN: "With pleasure."

It is a blowy April day. The puddles left by the hailstorm are drying rapidly under a brisk west wind. On the house fronts, bathed in clean, pale light, the wooden shutters, scoured by the hail, make patches of dazzling whiteness.

JEAN: "Shall we take the short cut through the graveyard?"

THE ABBÉ: "Yes." He links his arm in Jean's. "I've much enjoyed this luncheon. Do you know, I was beginning to fear from the tone of your letters, and from what Cécile's mother left unsaid, that all was not *quite* well with you." As in the past, he stresses certain words. "But *now* I see that you are happy, *both of you,* as of course you deserve to be."

Jean gives him a smile, which the Abbé interprets as an assent to his last remark. They take some steps in silence.

JEAN, with a faintly ironical laugh: "'Happy,' you said. Well, no, I should hardly call it happiness."

The Abbé gives a slight start and halts.

THE ABBÉ: "Surely you don't mean that seriously?"

JEAN, with a wry smile: "Isn't it better to take it with a laugh? What can't be mended . . ."

THE ABBÉ, amazed and somewhat shocked: "Really, my dear Jean!"

JEAN, shrugging his shoulders: "It's too stupid for words, the story of our married life."

THE ABBÉ: "You cut me to the heart, Jean."

JEAN: "I'm sorry—but that's how it is. A deadlock."

THE ABBÉ: "A deadlock! But surely you love each other?"

JEAN, gloomily: "I wonder—"

The footpath narrows and the Abbé moves in front, without answering. As they pass the crucifix he crosses himself. They take a short cut through the graveyard, along paths overgrown with grass. A wicket-gate gives on the open country, and they step forth upon a highroad flanked on one side by telegraph poles, their black recession linked as far as eye can reach by sagging strands of wire. The limpid sunlight of a day in early spring plays on stubble-fields and sodden ploughland. Traversed by silver streaks, grassy meadows slope down towards the Oise, whose banks are still covered by recent floods. Sheltered from the wind, the broad expanse of water mirrors the cloudless pearly gray sky, and willows, submerged to the chin, lift their tousled black heads above the shining surface.

The Abbé comes beside Jean, who is gazing at the countryside. A moment later their eyes meet, the priest's troubled and dark with mute reproof.

JEAN: "Oh, I know that it's my fault. I tried to make good, when I was twenty-two, a boyish dream I had when I was sixteen. And of course it didn't work."

THE ABBÉ: "On the contrary. That affection of your boyhood—"

JEAN, cutting in bitterly: "Excuse me, I know what I'm talking about—only too well. I've had time and opportunity to observe the process working itself out."

The Abbé makes no comment and starts walking again. He is taken aback by the confidence of Jean's tone, that of a man in full maturity. And, guessing this, Jean takes a malicious pleasure in his dismay. The keen air, the sunlight, this country walk, are going to his head, and he lets his tongue run away with him.

JEAN: "A boy of sixteen, you know, has such wildly romantic ideas of love. He indulges in a splendid dream, so remote from all the possibilities of real life that there's not the least chance of his finding anything in the world to match it. So he proceeds to build up a dream figure with the materials ready to his hand; and that's easy enough. He takes any girl who comes his way and invests her with the glamour of his ideal. Of course he's careful not to try to discover what sort of person she really is. No, he enshrines her like an idol in the closed circle of his imagination, he endows her with all the qualities of a Golden Girl. Then, after prudently blindfolding himself, he kneels down before her." He laughs.

THE ABBÉ: "But, my dear Jean, I can—I can hardly believe my ears!"

JEAN: "The spell works slowly but surely. Time passes, but the veil remains over his eyes. And then, one fine day, to prove his gratitude for her embodiment of his dream girl, as they call it, he marries a young person about whom he literally knows nothing, a complete stranger." He pauses. "So, now that he has blundered into—into pledging his whole life to her . . ." He stops and looks the priest in the eyes. "I wonder do you realize what that means: to pledge one's whole life." The priest looks down. "Yes, now that he settles down to live with the girl he has chosen, and whom he intends to love—not in make-believe but in sober earnest—he discovers, too late, that he and she have nothing, *nothing,* in common. She's a stranger; maybe an enemy. And the result, as I said, is deadlock."

THE ABBÉ: "'A stranger.' Oh, come now! It's no use your talking like that. You two were brought up together."

JEAN: "Yes, and we knew less of each other than young people whose marriage has been fixed up by their parents and who have never met before. Because, in these cases, they devote the months of their engagement to feverish attempts to understand each other and straighten out their problems. That's how it always is in 'arranged' marriages. Whereas we, Cécile and I, never gave a thought to this; we supposed it had all been done in advance."

THE ABBÉ: "Still, to begin with, judging by the first letters you wrote me . . ."

JEAN: "To begin with—yes. But it didn't take me long to discover that we were very different, though I admit that didn't disturb me in the least at first."

THE ABBÉ: "Yes? And then?"

JEAN: "Ah, if you understood the rapture that possesses one in that early phase; it blinds your eyes to everything! I was so desperately keen on attaining that perfect happiness which I'd seen so many other people vainly trying to attain that I really expected my married life would be the exception that proves the rule. And, anyhow, I'd made up my mind to think it perfect.

"Then, too, in the first months of a marriage, everything runs so smoothly for the man. It's child's play for him to establish an influence over his wife. But let him make haste to establish it securely! Even the simplest of women has amazing intuition, and she very soon becomes conscious of her power. With the result that she soon regains all the territory you think you've won. Yes, those first months are quite misleading; a woman has an unconscious genius for remembering and repeating. She holds up a mirror at which—why not admit it?—you look with pleasure. Until the day when you discover that what she's showing you is a mere reflection—of yourself; and already paling, tarnished, fading out."

THE ABBÉ: "Yet, unless I'm much mistaken, you were deeply in love with her?"

JEAN: "I doubt it. I was in love with love, that's all."

THE ABBÉ: "She, anyhow, *she* truly loved you." Jean says nothing. "She loved you and she loves you still. I could see it plainly in the way she looked at you and smiled, just now at Madame Pasquelin's."

JEAN: "You were mistaken. What you saw was a piece of playacting. We were keeping up appearances." Wearily. "A truce we had agreed on for our stay here, that's all."

THE ABBÉ: "She loved you, Jean. I'm positive of that."

JEAN, shrugging his shoulders: "Yes, no doubt. In her fashion. It was a decorous little passion that for years she nursed in solitude, with the kind permission of her mother and confessor. One of those poetic loves, too ethereal to be quite human."

THE ABBÉ: "Really, Jean!"

JEAN: "Let me have my say; I'm speaking frankly. Well, I don't deny she loved me in that way, but a love like that isn't strong enough to work a miracle. And nothing short of a miracle, I assure you, would be needed to unite our lives."

THE ABBÉ: "But she was so young . . ."

JEAN, with a faint laugh: "Ah, yes, that's so. 'She was so young.'" He takes some steps, then swings excitedly round on the priest. "And that's precisely what I told myself. She's little more than a child, I thought. What I dislike in her will pass in the course of time. Fool that I was! It's quite true that Cécile had the mentality of a sixteen-year-old girl who imagines she knows everything about the world—when her whole experience of life, all she has to go on, consists of gobbets of information she's picked up on Sundays at her Bible Class."

THE ABBÉ: "Jean!"

JEAN, his voice rough with anger and hostility: "But what I did *not* foresee was that this half-baked state was as far as she ever could develop, her dead-end. So now you know how things are with us." Jean has stopped walking and assumed a combative attitude, his legs planted well apart, his breast heaving, head flung back, eyes hard as flint; his arms are level with his chest, his hands outspread, palms upward, as though he were testing the weight of some invisible object. "And how proud she was of her little stock of knowledge! Of course the sources from which she gleaned it were infallible: sermons, conversations with pious small-town worthies, or those books concocted for the use of Christian girlhood, books packed with theories none of which has the least bearing on the realities of the life before them."

The Abbé takes a step forward, places his hand on Jean's arm, and looks him in the eyes.

THE ABBÉ: "Jean, my dear Jean! You wouldn't speak that way if you hadn't changed . . . out of recognition." He lowers his voice. "Am I right in assuming that you're no longer a practicing Catholic?"

JEAN, affectionately but composedly: "Yes, you are right."

THE ABBÉ, sadly: "Ah, I now understand *everything*."

The road rises, the spire of Beaumont church comes into view. The priest quickens his steps, as though wishing to be alone. As one behind the other they reach the summit of the plateau, they are greeted by a gentle breeze coming from very far away. The telegraph wires are humming overhead. The hamlet of Beaumont consists of a few cottages dotted about the countryside. The church is some hundred yards off, guarded by the sentinel pines of the priest's garden.

Jean sits down on a heap of stones on the roadside, letting the Abbé go ahead. The sun warms his back, while the cool breeze fans his cheeks. Small dry leaves blow past his feet with a light silken rustle. In front of him stretches the plain.

The shadows are lengthening. Across the stripped crests of the elms, beyond the curtain of a row of poplars, white house fronts and blue roofs sparkle in the level light. Hardly anyone is about. Jean can hear a creak of wheels ploughing through the mud of a sunken road, but the cart itself is invisible. Etched upon the horizon, a gray horse and a bay are drawing a plough across a gently undulating expanse of stubble, the soft brown clods rising soundlessly beside the gleaming share. A belated puddle shines among the tree trunks, where, overhead, abandoned nests crouch like big black spiders in their web of leafless boughs. The ploughman has reached the end of the field; slowly he swings his horses round and starts a new furrow. The gray horse, now coming towards Jean, conceals both the plough and the bay horse, and seems to be advancing by itself.

The wind drops. The creak of cartwheels has died away. The dead leaves cease rustling. All is still.

The Abbé returns; his head is bowed. Jean gets up and walks towards him. The priest extends both hands, his eyes dim with tears. They go down the hill in silence, the Abbé with his eyes fixed on the ground before his feet.

JEAN, gently: "My dear Abbé, I'm afraid this has been very distressing to you. But sooner or later I had to let you know the truth." The Abbé makes a vague, sad gesture of assent. "I know what believers usually say in such cases: 'You have discarded religion because it prevents you from doing as you like.' But that's not true of me. I've struggled for years; you witnessed my struggles to keep my faith. But now it's over. I have squared up accounts with myself. No doubt it had to be."

The priest turns his head and gazes at Jean curiously, as if trying to discern the new man he has become.

THE ABBÉ, sorrowfully: "To think that *you*, Jean, should have come to this! You, who seemed so true a Christian, so certain to keep to the right road!"

JEAN: "Still, you shouldn't be too hard on me. In the last analysis, it's not the fact of believing or disbelieving that matters; no, what's all important is the way in which one believes or in which one disbelieves."

THE ABBÉ: "But tell me, *how* did this come about?"

JEAN: "I can't explain. There's no denying that I once was a believer, and now all that is so remote I can't even picture what it means to be one. There are currents of ideas, I suppose, that draw you with them—unescapably. And of course it depends on temperaments. Some men are more inclined than others to make do with ready-made formulas. Like the hermit crab who creeps into the first vacant shell he comes across and shapes himself to fit it. Whereas others prefer to make their own shells."

THE ABBÉ, gloomily: "It's your scientific studies that have warped your mind. That bane of scientific arrogance—ah, how many victims it has claimed! When a man directs his gaze wholly on the world of matter, he develops a sort of blindness to all else; his sense of the supernatural world becomes atrophied, and it's only a short step to disbelief."

JEAN: "I'm inclined to agree. When one practices scientific methods of research, day in, day out, and once one has ascertained time and again how apt they are for the discovery of truth—how refrain from applying them to the problems of religion?" Regretfully. "Am I to blame if religious faith won't stand up to serious critical analysis?"

THE ABBÉ: "So it's your view that the only way to understand is through the intellect? Critical analysis, *logic*? But isn't it precisely by means of logic that theologians demonstrate God's existence and the truth of revealed religion?"

JEAN, quietly: "Perhaps. Yet logic can rebut them too."

THE ABBÉ: "But when it's proved to my satisfaction that the intellect, *unaided,* would be incapable of grasping in its entirety the mystery behind the dogmas of the Church, the qualities of the soul, and the Christian solution of the problem of human destiny—well, differing from you, I see in this a convincing proof of that supramundane Authority which has *revealed* the truth to us." Jean makes no comment, and the Abbé continues, after a pause: "Then, again, can you name a single *fully established* scientific fact that is in *real* conflict with any of our dogmas? For instance, has your science proved to you that God does not exist?"

JEAN, forcing himself to answer: "Well—not quite that."

THE ABBÉ: "Ah!"

JEAN: "Science contents itself with proving that everything takes place in the universe exactly as if your personal God had no existence."

THE ABBÉ: "But, my dear Jean, your science, which is devoted *solely* to the study of the laws of nature proves—for anyone who has eyes to see—in the clearest possible way that God exists."

JEAN, sadly but resolutely: "I'm afraid it's not so simple as all that; we must not confuse the issues. It is true that I believe the universe to be governed by fixed laws, but don't jump to the conclusion that I believe in God. That's a *non sequitur* which has been greatly overworked by Christian apologists. I grant that we're in agreement as to the existence of universal law, but my opinion on the subject—a purely empirical opinion, mind you—has nothing whatever in common with the attitude of the Catholic Church, which regards God as a Supreme Being with personal attributes and exercising personal control over His creation. These are two very different standpoints. Otherwise religion and science would still be identical, as they were at the dawn of human intelligence and"—he smiles faintly—"as they certainly are not today."

THE ABBÉ, vehemently: "So when, *in good faith,* you set up your intelligence against the Christian faith—"

JEAN, breaking in: "Sorry, but I fear we could continue arguing on these lines indefinitely without ever finding common ground." He smiles again. "The truth is, I'm through with those interminable discussions; there's such a gulf between a believer and an atheist that they could wrangle a whole lifetime without ever getting any forrader. I've sometimes been tackled by expert and nimble-witted theologians, and I admit I couldn't think up any really effective answer to their case. But that didn't shake my conviction in the least. I knew that an answer *did* exist, and a mere fluke, like a chance association of ideas—or, better still, an evening's hard thinking—would have enabled me to hit on it. Arguments! One can always find an argument in defense of any theory if one applies one's mind to it." The Abbé looks so crestfallen that Jean steps beside him, smiling affectionately, and takes his arm. "I've come to be convinced, you know, that a man is never converted by any process of reasoning. He merely shores up, with logical arguments, a conviction that he entertains already; and this conviction isn't arrived at, as he fondly thinks, by way of syllogisms and dialectic, but thanks to something much more potent than these: a natural predisposition. I believe that a man is predisposed to belief or scepticism, and all the arguments in the world can do very little about it."

The Abbé makes no answer. Dusk is falling and the air is now quite cold. All that remains of the sun is a streak of orange-red low on the horizon, glowing across a violet haze. Before them stretches a field of young corn, its vivid green faintly silvered by the rising ground mist, and on its silken smoothness the fading glow of sunset mingles with the milk-white sheen of moonlight.

They quicken their pace.

With raucous cries a flurry of crows rises from a stubble-field and settles on the black boughs of an orchard just beyond.

A long silence.

THE ABBÉ: "But there's your wife to be considered. What do you propose to do about her?"

JEAN, quite composedly: "My wife? Well, the opinions you've been hearing are no new development. I've held them for fully three years, and, really, I don't see why we, Cécile and I, shouldn't continue to carry on indefinitely as we have been doing."

The priest gazes at him incredulously.


V

## The Rupture

I

A lecture room at Wenceslas College. It is eight o'clock and the students are at their desks. Jean walks in briskly and steps up on the platform.

A STUDENT, coming up to him: "Excuse me, sir, but hasn't the principal given you a notebook to return to me?"

JEAN: "No. I don't quite follow."

THE STUDENT: "Yesterday afternoon the principal asked me to let him see my notes. He said he'd give me back the book this morning."

JEAN: "What notes? The notes you take at my lectures?"

THE STUDENT: "Yes, sir."

JEAN: "No, I've not been given anything. You can go to your place."

An intermittent drone, like that of a seething vat, comes from the rows of benches. Some minutes are needed before the personalities dissociated since the previous day can coalesce again into a studious whole. Heads are raised, then lowered. Gradually order is restored, though some vagrant thoughts, gnat-like, still skim the surface. Then silence falls; a hush of expectation.

Sweeping the lecture room with his gaze, Jean sees fifty pairs of eyes intent on him, and their converging scrutiny seems to rivet him to his chair. His heart beats faster at this mute appeal, his mind grows tense, keyed up to the task before him.

JEAN: "Gentlemen, this morning I must ask you to give particular attention to what I am going to say." He takes a deep breath; there is a glint of triumph in his eyes as he gazes down at the rows of expectant faces. "A few days ago I brought to an end the set of lectures devoted to the origin of species. I am sure you all have grasped the great importance, the paramount importance, of this subject. But I cannot bring myself to close this section of our course without casting a backward glance and briefly recapitulating such points as seem to me . . ."

The door opens and the principal of the college, Abbé Miriel, enters. The priest is in his sixties, but has an easy carriage that belies his age and tendency to stoutness. He has a well-shaped if slightly fleshy face, bald above the temples, with a high-domed, freckled forehead. His upper eyelids rise and fall abruptly, and the gaze that flashes forth beneath them is shrewd, uncompromisingly lucid. A rather boyish smile plays on his lips; an affectation, perhaps, but none the less very charming.

THE PRINCIPAL, to the students, who have risen to their feet: "Sit down, my boys." He turns to Jean. "Forgive me for breaking in on you like this, Monsieur Barois, but I'd forgotten to return this notebook to one of your students." He smiles genially. "And, really, now that I am here, I'm tempted to profit by the opportunity. Will you permit me, Monsieur Barois, to listen to some portion of the lecture you are delivering today? No, no, please don't move." He notices an empty bench at the back. "I'll be quite comfortable there." He seats himself. "And please don't let my presence interfere with any of your habits."

Jean has flushed, then gone pale; the possible significance of this visit has not escaped him. For a moment he struggles with a temptation to tone down the more outspoken passages of the lecture he has prepared. Then courageously, with a tremor of defiance in his voice, he goes on speaking.

JEAN, turning to the principal: "I was about, sir, to recapitulate a series of lectures I have been giving on the origin of species." The priest nods, encouraging him to proceed. Jean turns to the students. "I explained to you the important place we must give to Lamarck and, following him, to Darwin, in the department of science that concerns origins; it owes its existence entirely to those two pioneers; to Lamarck especially. I believe I made it plain that his theory of evolution—or, to use a better term, transformism, which is a wider and less controversial solution than that of natural selection—can now be considered as a scientific truth established beyond all doubt."

He glances at the principal, who is listening, his eyes half closed, his pale hands resting on his knees, betraying no feeling of any kind.

JEAN: "We have seen, in short, that, until Lamarck, science could give no explanation of any of the phenomena of life, and the opinion prevailed that all the species known to us today were separate creations, each endowed from the start with all its present characteristics. We

can truly say that Lamarck found the Ariadne's thread to this labyrinthine universe we live in.

"I have set forth to you in detail the facts which prove to us beyond all doubt that all living things are connected with each other in a long line of descent, linking us with the primal matter of the universe. From the initial monad, hardly distinguishable from the molecules of its organic environment—the remote, amorphous ancestor of our cells, compared with which even the simplest forms of life known to us today are infinitely complex entities—from the monad up to the most complicated manifestations of the human body and mind, there has been an unbroken progress lasting over hundreds of thousands of years. And we owe it to that great thinker, Lamarck, that we now can trace and classify the various stages of that progress.

"Next—and this is a point of immediate interest in view of recent developments—I advised you not to attach overmuch importance to allegations that transformism is losing ground, in consequence of the discovery that sudden mutations occasionally take place. You will remember my telling you that, after stationary periods, a species may show abrupt variations due to the accumulation of efforts tending in the same direction over a series of generations. I also made it clear that this theory is found to be perfectly compatible with Lamarck's view, if we apply our minds to the facts impartially."

A short silence follows. Since the principal's appearance on the scene Jean has been conscious that his listeners' attention has been wandering. His words fall on an unstable surface and, in his efforts to make an impression on it, he is gradually losing his own assurance. So, abandoning the idea of summing up his previous lectures, he boldly strikes out in a new direction.

JEAN: "I thought it well to begin by this brief summary. But the main purpose of my lecture today is different."

There is now a ring of confidence in his voice, and the surface on which the words impinge seems to grow hard, resilient, like the web of a restrung racquet.

JEAN: "Above all, I wish to impress on your minds indelibly the immense importance of the theory of transformism, and its indispensability for the formation of the modern mind. I want you to understand why we must regard it as the vital core of all our biological knowledge; and how, while keeping within the limits of the most rigorous scientific precision, we find—we are bound to find—that this new manner of regarding universal life has profoundly modified the whole fabric of our present-day philosophy and remodeled most of our previous concepts of the human mind."

As it were, an electric circuit is now established between Jean and his hearers. He can feel them vibrating, thrilling, at his behest. The principal looks up. Jean meets his eyes, which are quite expressionless.

JEAN: "Once we have grasped the fact that all existing things are in a state of constant activity, we can no longer regard life as an active principle originating movement or energizing inert matter. That view was based on a serious misconception, by which we still are handicapped. Indeed, it has falsified man's observation of the phenomena of life since the dawn of human thought. Life is not a phenomenon whose beginning can be posited, since it is a phenomenon always in progress, without intermission. In other words, the universe exists, it has always existed, and cannot pass out of existence. It cannot have been created, inertia being nonexistent.

"Once we realize that an entity can never in any manner be identical with itself at any two moments of its course of existence, we automatically rule out all the arguments which, lured by the mirage of human individuality, men have built up to maintain that precarious theory of free will. In the light of our present knowledge we cannot visualize any being as in full enjoyment of free will.

"And once we also realize that our faculty of reason is no more than an inheritance transmitted through the ages from generation to generation—an heritage handed down to us with all its imperfections by the complex and capricious laws of heredity—we can no longer feel the same confidence in the metaphysics and ethics of the past.

"For transformism is of universal application and governs also the evolution of human consciousness.

"That is why Le Dantec, one of the most enlightened and independent leaders of present-day science, could write: 'For one who believes in transformism, most of the questions which naturally present themselves to the human mind change their meaning; some, indeed, cease to have any meaning.' "

Briskly, despite his bulk, the principal rises to his feet and turns his austere face, the eyes half closed, towards the platform.

THE PRINCIPAL: "Very interesting, Monsieur Barois. You show a commendable ardor in your exposition; it is highly stimulating." He smiles rather sourly. "We will have a talk about it later." He turns towards the students. His tone is genial, paternal. "The lesson, my young friends, of what we have been hearing— and no doubt I am anticipating the conclusions Monsieur Barois was about to draw at the close of his lecture—is the lesson of the perfection of the divine order of the universe. Our earthbound human intelligence can have only an inkling of those transcendent laws; but even that is enough to fill us with awe and admiration. This feeling of humility, when we are confronted by the Creator's stupendous work, is all the more incumbent on us in an age like the present, when the progress of scientific discovery tends only too often to make us forget what a paltry being man is and how relative, at best, is his knowledge." He bows frigidly to the lecturer. "Well, I must leave now. Good morning, Monsieur Barois."

No sooner has the door closed behind him than a ripple of unrest passes through the room, now that the strain of close attention is relaxed. With a quick downward glance Jean gathers to a focus, as it were, the wandering eyes, and once more the young minds strain towards him in an eager, silent communion that no official reprimand can impair.

JEAN, quietly: "I shall now continue . . ."

II

Mme Pasquelin's house at Buis. The summer vacation has begun.

Cécile is standing, half dressed, at her bedroom window. Hardly conscious of what she is doing, she draws her hand across the lower portion of her body. In her eyes is the curiously far-away gaze of all pregnant women. Her features, once vivacious, now confess languor, indifference.

It is nine in the morning. The sky is cloudless and limpid, honey-golden sunlight floods the room.

There is a knock at the door, which opens immediately.

CÉCILE, blinking her eyes: "Oh—it's you, Mother."

MME PASQUELIN: "Yes, it's I." Cécile's eyes widen apprehensively; her mother's tone implies that something is amiss. "Look at this." She holds up a leaflet and, with her lorgnette to her eyes, reads out the address on the wrapper. "Bulletin of the Free-Thought Congress.

Monsieur Barois, c/o Madame Pasquelin, Buis-la-Dame." A short silence. "Where is he?"

CÉCILE: "Jean? I don't know."

MME PASQUELIN: "Haven't you seen him yet?"

CÉCILE: "No."

MME PASQUELIN: "He's not in his room."

CÉCILE: "He must have gone out for his morning walk."

MME PASQUELIN: "So it has come to this. Not only have you separate rooms, but he doesn't come to say good morning to you before going out." Cécile sits down; she is looking tired. Mme Pasquelin drops the pamphlet on her knees. "Well, you can give him *this* when he comes back. And tell him from me, that I wish he'd arrange to have things of this sort addressed somewhere else—not to my house. And there's something else that's worrying me." She shows an open envelope, "I got a letter from Abbé Miriel this morning."

CÉCILE: "He's Jean's principal, isn't he?"

MME PASQUELIN: "Yes. He's spending the vacation with his brother, at the Bishop's Palace at Beauvais. He says he'd like to meet me there if I can manage it. He wants to have a private word with me, it seems."

CÉCILE, nervously: "Oh, dear, I wonder what it can be!"

MME PASQUELIN, gloomily: "I haven't a notion, my poor child. But I shall go there this afternoon and find out."

Abruptly she bends forward, takes her daughter's forehead between her hands, and presses her dry lips to it with a little sigh, almost like a sob. Then, frowning darkly at her thoughts, she clatters out of the bedroom.

Two hours later. Cécile is finishing dressing. Jean comes in.

JEAN: "Good morning, Cécile."

CÉCILE: "Have you seen Mother?"

JEAN: "No. I went out early."

CÉCILE, pointing to the leaflet: "Mother gave me this for you."

JEAN, his face brightening: "Ah, yes. I know. I was expecting it. Thanks."

He tears off the wrapper, sits down on the bed, and skims the pages with obvious interest. As she watches him, hostility mingles with curiosity in Cécile's gaze. Looking up, he sees the question in her eyes but he does not flinch.

JEAN: "It's the program of a Congress that's taking place in London this year. In December."

CÉCILE, on the defensive: "But—but what has that to do with you?"

JEAN: "It interests me, that's all." There is a rough edge to his voice. Cécile makes a fretful movement. "Also, someone has asked me to make a report on it, for a review."

CÉCILE: "Someone? Who?"

JEAN, curtly: "Breil-Zoeger."

CÉCILE: "I could have sworn it! That awful man!"

JEAN, coldly: "Really, Cécile!"

There is a short silence. Jean has resumed his reading.

CÉCILE, piteously: "But—no, Jean, no! I won't have you mixing yourself up with—with all that!"

Jean scowls at her and goes on reading.

JEAN: "What's that you said? You won't have me—? Now, look here!" Stowing the leaflet in his pocket, he walks up to her. "I'll ask you, my dear girl, to allow me to go my own way. This Congress, let me tell you, takes place only once every ten years. It's an international movement, with ramifications far greater than you can possibly imagine." He now is pacing the room, without looking in her direction. "What's more, the subjects down for discussion on this year's program are ones I'm particularly keen on. Zoeger asked me to take an active part in the Congress, as special correspondent of the *International Review of Ideas,* which is the organ of the movement here, in France. I all but consented." Cécile gives a slight start. "But in view of my duties at Wenceslas College, I felt I must decline. Still, I'm quite determined to attend some of the final sessions which, as it happens, take place during the Christmas vacation. And I shall publish a report of the decisions made at the Congress, for the benefit of the French Section. That much I've decided, and I shall not go back on my decision."

Cécile says nothing. He takes some more steps in silence, then at last turns his eyes towards her. She is lying on the carpet, crumpled up like a slaughtered animal; her pupils are dilated, as if she is on the point of fainting. He hurries towards her, lifts her up, and places her on the bed. And suddenly a rush of overwhelming pity comes over him.

JEAN, in a tone of gloomy resignation: "Very well, then. Have it your own way. I promise not to go."

For a moment she remains quite quiet, her eyes closed. Then she looks up at him with an almost childish smile and clasps his hand.

But Jean frees himself and walks to the window. Yes, she is the stronger of the two. Her suffering is all too real, too manifest—and thanks to it she is invincible.

Jean knows what he stands to lose by this capitulation: a unique opportunity of hearing the ideas which during the past five years have been simmering in his mind and which he has been vainly struggling to fit into a scheme for living—an opportunity of hearing these ideas discussed, combated, defended, and threshed out by men of his own stamp. He is bitterly disgusted. Yes, he can feel pity for her; but for himself no less!

JEAN, without looking round, in a low,

embittered voice: "Well, this settles it. I'm doomed to make a failure of my life. And it's not even your fault, you *can't* act otherwise. You don't understand, you'll never even have an inkling of, the ideas that mean all the world to me. You'll always regard them as mere foibles; or, worse still, as shameful, criminal aberrations. You're built like that, and you wouldn't be yourself if you thought otherwise.

"I'm slowly stifling to death in the atmosphere you compel me to breathe. All my energies, all my aspirations, are poisoned by it. The only happiness you can give me, the mild affection of which you're capable, can only do me harm and drag me down to your level. That is the truth, the hideous truth. The mere fact of your presence in my life is enough to wreck it, no matter what I do. And no matter what I do you'll always be here, in my life, year after year! You'll kill my endeavors one by one, and you won't even know what you are up to; just as you will never have the faintest notion of what you yourself are. And you'll spend your days bemoaning your little personal afflictions—being sorry for yourself!" In a burst of anger. "As for me, I'm damned and doomed. And it's your fault."

Cécile has remained quite still; her eyes express nothing but grieved surprise.

He stares at her hopelessly and gives a slight shrug; then, dry lipped, his shoulders sagging, he goes to the door.

III

Abbé Miriel
   Principal, Wenceslas College
    Paris

              August 17

Sir: I trust you will permit me to begin by expressing my surprise that you should have employed a third party for conveying your opinon of my teaching. Without dwelling further on this unusual method of approach, which (to say the least of it) lacked courtesy, I will proceed directly to your criticisms of my work. As to these, I run no risk of falling into error, since you have been at pains to state your grounds of complaint in a letter which I have been allowed to see and which ends (if I have not misread it) with an unequivocal ultimatum.

This year is the fourth in which you have assigned to me the duty of teaching natural science to seventeen- and eighteen-year-old students. I have not thought fit to confine myself to giving purely practical instruction. A teacher has a more vital duty to his students than that of merely coaching them for an examination. His duty, as I see it, is to raise their general outlook to a higher level and to inspire adolescent minds with a capacity for generous enthusiasms.

I do not wish to disclaim the tendencies to which I have given expression in my lectures. When, in some of these, I ventured beyond the frontiers normally assigned to natural science, I knew what I was doing. In my opinion, the only limit to the human intelligence should be that of its utmost reach, and the farthest flights of thought should be encouraged, not restricted.

Your animadversions have brought it home to me that a man engaged in the teaching of science cannot honestly undertake to abide by any prescribed rule in the course of his duties. For sooner or later he is led to draw independent conclusions, and, when this happens, he is bound to voice the truth that is in him. How, if he has any self-respect, could he fail to impart to his listeners the fruits of his personal experience, the conclusions he has arrived at? Whether we wish it or not, scientific research into the phenomena of life leads directly to philosophy—indeed, to my mind, this is the only philosophy that counts.

Thus, if these problems are to be

handled with the broadmindedness and thoroughness that are their due, a freedom of thought and speech is called for, which, I admit, can hardly be reconciled with the tendencies of the college over which you preside. So, I am quite ready to own that, in this respect, I have, so to say, spoken beyond my brief.

But since I cannot see my way to modifying the tone of my lectures, and since I must definitely refuse to show myself to my pupils as other than I am—a free man addressing free minds—I can see no alternative to tendering my resignation.

Very truly yours,
Jean Barois

Five o'clock. Mme Pasquelin and Cécile are out of doors, sewing in the shade of a big garden parasol. Their chairs are side by side, and they converse in undertones, their lips hardly moving.

Jean appears on the terrace, his letter in his hand. As he approaches the women he is conscious of entering a zone of mute hostility.

JEAN: "I'd like to let you know the answer I am giving to Abbé Miriel. I am resigning my post."

The women are dismayed by the firmness of his tone. However, Mme Pasquelin, the more combative of the two, begins by concealing her anxiety.

MME PASQUELIN: "Your resignation? Really, Jean, you can't be serious!"

Letting her needlework drop to her knees, Cécile looks up at him. This afternoon the high, smooth curve of her forehead has the look of a cuirass. For the last twenty-four hours she has been in a haze of utter misery, now that the principal's peremptory letter has forced her to face the cruel truth. The fact that Jean is liable to lose his post is the least of her troubles; what appals her is the menace to his immortal soul—Jean is an atheist!

JEAN: "You seem surprised. Yet I wonder what else you expected to happen—after that ultimatum."

MME PASQUELIN: "Oh, come now! Don't let's exaggerate. There never was any question of an ultimatum. Abbé Miriel was much distressed by some of the things you thought fit to say to your pupils, but he never dreamt of dismissing you. It's the last thing he's wanted to do—if only out of his personal regard for me. All he asks is for you to alter your system of teaching, and really"—she smiles—"you must admit he knows far more than you do about such matters. Don't forget he's a man of vast experience, and your principal."

Jean averts his eyes, without replying, and Mme Pasquelin hastens to take advantage of his silence. Assuming an almost genial manner, she tries to keep the discussion from turning acrimonious.

MME PASQUELIN: "Now do try to look at it sensibly, my dear Jean, like a rational being! Evidently you let your tongue—or your opinions—run away with you. But the principal's a level-headed man, he doesn't take these—these indiscretions over-seriously, and is quite ready to overlook them." Her feigned smile is almost painful to see. "So don't be pig-headed, Jean. Tear up that letter and go and write him another."

JEAN, wearily: "Please don't let's argue. My mind's made up."

MME PASQUELIN, vehemently: "But you can't, you simply *cannot* do that. Don't you agree, Cécile?"

JEAN: "It's done."

MME PASQUELIN: "No. I forbid you to send that letter."

JEAN, losing patience: "But, confound it! Suppose someone asked you—you or Cécile—to repudiate your religious convictions so as to keep a job, what would you answer?"

MME PASQUELIN, angrily: "That's absurd. It isn't the same thing."

JEAN: "Ah, yes, that was bound to

come. 'It isn't the same thing!' Well, you're mistaken; it is so much the same thing that I didn't hesitate for a moment. I should have realized long ago that my place wasn't in a college run by priests, and thrown it up of my own accord. My one regret is that I shut my eyes so long."

Mme Pasquelin is at a loss. Jean's look, his furrowed brows, the fierce line of his mouth, intimidate her. She crushes down her anger.

MME PASQUELIN: "Jean, I beg you! If you lose your post, what will you do?"

JEAN: "Oh, have no fear! I've heaps of plans, and plenty of ways of employing my energy."

MME PASQUELIN: "Plans! Fine plans too, I'll be bound! All you'll do is to go from bad to worse in your wrong-headedness."

JEAN, seizing the opportunity: "Exactly! Now that I'm a free man"—he brandishes the letter—"I shall stop making the concessions and compromises I've been forced to make hitherto—and of which I'm heartily ashamed. It was a transition period, if you like. Well, I'm through with it!"

Stung to the quick, Cécile stands up and faces him.

CÉCILE: "Now that you're a free man, you said, Jean. And—how about me?"

JEAN, taken aback: "How about you? Well . . ."

They gaze at each other; not a trace of their former love remains in either's eyes.

CÉCILE: "I was deceived—abominably! Deceived by your past, your words, your attitude. Don't forget that."

MME PASQUELIN, intervening boldly: "Yes, and do you imagine she can endure having a husband who's an atheist, an enemy of our religion? Really, it's—unthinkable that, with an upbringing like yours, you should have come to this!"

JEAN, gloomily, answering only Cécile: "What's done is done. You're distressed of course, and so am I. I can't

prevent my ideas being alive, evolving. It's not up to me to govern them; it's they that must rule my life."

CÉCILE, sternly: "No. Not so long as I'm with you."

MME PASQUELIN, taking courage from her daughter's unexpected stand: "No, she'd rather leave you. Isn't that so, Cécile?"

Cécile hesitates for a moment in an agony of indecision, then gives a quick nod. Jean, who was watching to see how she would answer, shrugs his shoulders. There is a short silence. Mme Pasquelin gazes at her daughter with a new light in her eyes. In the depths of her maternal instinct something has stirred; a formless hope that, though she is unaware of it, influences what she next says.

MME PASQUELIN: "Really it's too absurd! You insist on making our lives wretched with your ideas. Ideas! Everybody has ideas! Why can't you have sensible ones, like any normal person?" She plays her last card. "If you don't drop this mad notion of resigning your post, and if you refuse to go on with your life as in the past—well, Cécile won't go back to Paris with you."

JEAN: "Do you hear, Cécile?"

CÉCILE, committed by her nod: "Mother's right."

JEAN: "So if I resign my post, you will not return with me to Paris?"

CÉCILE: "No."

JEAN, bitterly, to his mother-in-law: "I congratulate you on your handiwork!" He brings a chair near Cécile and sits astride it. "Now, Cécile, let's have it out between us. And be assured that I'm in earnest." He takes a deep breath. "I could promise to make fresh concessions and patch up a truce between us. But I prefer to continue speaking and acting quite frankly. For your sake I've made compromise after compromise, but I've reached my limit, and it's impossible for me to continue acting thus without abandoning all my human dignity, all decency of mind. What you ask of me is to go on playing a degrading game of make-believe throughout my life and, by a non-committal attitude, by perpetual deceit, to seem to approve of a religion that I can no longer practice. I'd have you understand, once for all, that there are more important things in life than keeping up appearances. No honorable man can undertake to profess all his life long the opposite of what he thinks, even for the sake of keeping his wife's affection. You have no right to make a grievance of my moral honesty, even if it causes you to suffer." He pauses. "Now! Will you come back with me to Paris in October as we'd agreed?"

CÉCILE, with a cry of desperate resolve: "No!"

JEAN, waving away Mme Pasquelin: "Listen well to what I'm going to say, Cécile." He pauses again. "If you refuse to come with me to Paris, if you deliberately wish to break the last links that I wish to keep intact—then nothing will hold me back. I shall go to London during the winter and attend the Congress of which I told you."

MME PASQUELIN, losing all self-control: "But do you mean to kill my daughter? Considering the condition she is in . . ."

Cécile moves to her mother's side.

CÉCILE, to Jean: "I've made up my mind. I'd rather lose you than go on living with a—a heathen."

Jean rises to his feet and, gazing at the two women, is suddenly struck by their likeness to each other. They have the same rather prominent forehead, the same round black eyes, whose slight squint seems accentuated in moments of emotion, the same vacillating gaze that slips aside when challenged in discussion.

JEAN, sadly: "It was your wish, Cécile. You have chosen. But you have till this evening to think it over. If you let me go

home by myself, it means an end of all my scruples, and I shall feel free to go my own way in everything. Now I'm going to post my letter."

M. Breil-Zoeger, Editor
The International Review of Ideas
78, Boulevard Saint-Germain
Paris
August 28
My dear Breil-Zoeger: During the last few days a great change has come into my life. I have resigned my post at Wenceslas College, and I am now, in all respects, infinitely freer than I could possibly have foreseen. I can employ the coming months as I think fit, and put in a longish stay in London. So if no one else has been nominated for the front-line duties at the Congress, which you originally proposed to me, I shall be delighted to undertake them.

I shall not be staying in the country until the close of the vacation, as I said I would. I am returning to Paris this afternoon.

Could you keep a morning clear, for us to have a long talk together this week? Ever yours,

Jean Barois

IV

A bedroom in a London hotel. Evening. A powerful electric ceiling-lamp floods the room with glaring light. Heavy curtains deaden the noises of the traffic outside.

Breil-Zoeger is lying on his bed. Propped on an elbow, he gazes intently at a woman of fifty, Mme David, who is reading out her shorthand report of the day's session.

Jean is pacing the room, his arms folded, his mind obviously working at high pressure.

MME DAVID: " '. . . as Vinet, a Swiss author, wrote, as far back as 1879: "It is from revolt to revolt that human groups progress, civilization comes into its own, and justice triumphs. Freedom of the press, free trade, free education—all these freedoms, like the fecundating rain of summer, are borne to us on the wings of the tempest." ' "

JEAN, breaking in: "At this point there was some applause, especially from the Swedes, Danes, and Russians. Then the chairman rose to speak and summed up the debate." Puckering his eyebrows, Breil-Zoeger punctuates with a nod each phrase of the sentences that follow. "He explained that you had suddenly been prostrated by a sharp liver attack; then he read out your message, in which you proposed that I should speak tomorrow instead of you. This was voted unanimously."

BREIL-ZOEGER: "Did Woldsmuth give you the exact figures?"

JEAN: "Yes. And I warned Backerston that I wouldn't be attending the Reforms Committee meeting."

Breil-Zoeger nods. He is a man in his early thirties. Though he was born at Nancy, of Lorrainese parents, his face has something Japanese in its formation, which is accentuated by the yellow complexion he owes to his liver complaint; broad cheek-bones, a sparse, straggly moustache, a pointed chin. The deeply sunken eyes, whose pupils always seem dilated, flash out of pits of darkness with a keen, almost feverish intensity, which contrasts oddly with the prevailing gentleness of the face. His voice is toneless, monotonous, pleasant enough to hear, but utterly devoid of warmth.

BREIL-ZOEGER: "Madame David, will you please find the green file marked 'The Religious Problem in France'; it's among those papers at the corner of your table. Thanks."

JEAN: "Would you like me to dictate it in your presence, as I did this morning?"

BREIL-ZOEGER: "Yes, that would be best."

JEAN: "I've got the second and third parts into shape, on the lines you indicated, except that some passages are transposed. I'll explain." Breil-Zoeger lets his head sink back on the pillow, his face twisted in a wry grimace. "Are you in pain?"

BREIL-ZOEGER: "Just twinges, now and again."

Some moments' silence.

JEAN, taking some sheets of paper from his pocket: "We'd come to the second part. Heading: Causes of the General Decline of Faith. Underline, please, Madame David." He turns to Breil-Zoeger. "First cause: the vast development of scientific research during the last fifty years. Now that the field of the Unknown, from which man in earlier days derived his belief in God, is being steadily narrowed down, it follows that the hold of religion is loosening *pari passu*."

BREIL-ZOEGER: "Here you might intercalate . . ."

JEAN: "Take this down, Madame David."

BREIL-ZOEGER: ". . . some scientific truths which go to prove the incapacity of 'their' God to interfere with the inevitable processes of nature, and, therefore, the impossibility of miracles, the futility of prayer, and so forth."

JEAN: "As you wish. Second cause: historical research."

BREIL-ZOEGER: "Make that section brief."

JEAN: "No. It's a very important one. I mean to remind my hearers of the great forward step that was made when it became possible to trace the growth of the Christian legends, stage by stage, and to verify this by the original texts. I shall point out that these legends were built up from beginning to end with purely human elements that crystallized round some incident which had a perfectly normal explanation, but which simple-minded folk endowed with mystery. Leading up to this conclusion: How can anyone be a 'believer' if he studies the history of religions through the ages and observes the various brands of credulity, all equally uncompromising, that have infested the unhappy minds of men?"

BREIL-ZOEGER: "Good."

JEAN: "Then a seeming digression. Scientific progress can influence only cultivated minds. By itself, it would not have been enough to weaken a religion that has struck such deep roots in our national life. Which leads me to"—there is a knock at the door—"to the economic and social factors." He opens the door. "Who is it?"

A VOICE: "From *The Times,* sir. We want information about Monsieur Breil-Zoeger's health and the agenda of tomorrow's meeting."

JEAN: "Ah, yes. Go to Room twenty-nine, and our colleague Monsieur Woldsmuth will give you all the information you require." He returns to the bedside. "Where was I? Yes, Cause Number Three: the social and economic factors. The vast development of industry has drained our countryside of tens of thousands of young men, who have thus broken completely with the traditions of their elders—"

BREIL-ZOEGER: "Drive that point home. It's a decisive factor. We need only think of the immense number of factories operating in every civilized country—a number that will inevitably increase as time goes on, and to an extent none of us foresees today." He looks through his file and extracts a sheet. The movement, slight though it is, gives him a twinge that makes him wince. He reads the opening phrases. " 'The factory worker is almost necessarily a rationalist.

Plunged into a busy hive of industry, in which metaphysical speculations are quite out of place; and surrounded by machines whose clangorous tongues announce the triumph of human intelligence, human labor, and mathematics over nature—' Here's what I've written, make whatever use of it you like." He hands him the sheet. "Now go on."

JEAN: "It's here I want to place my description—I remember mentioning it to you—of the French nation today divided into two camps; in one the believers, in the other the unbelievers. Numerically the body of unbelievers is a strong majority, comprising as it does the proletariat, to whom I've referred already, and all the intellectuals. Then—"

BREIL-ZOEGER: "Wait! You should include among the unbelievers the half-educated, the little man who has tried to 'improve his mind,' as he calls it. It's high time for a campaign to rehabilitate him. He's too easy game, poor devil, for the ironist. But though he's never had the leisure deeply to study any subject, thanks to his sturdy common sense and the mental balance that comes of decent living, he is drawn irresistibly towards the solutions given by science—in their cruder forms, of course."

JEAN: "Yes, that's very true. As for the believers, they naturally are drawn from the two conservative communities: the peasantry and the middle class. The peasant usually lives far away from a town, in an environment which never changes and in which tradition holds its own unchecked. The middle class are systematically hostile to change; their interests are bound up with the established order, and especially with the Catholic Church, which for many centuries has held in check the cupidities of the 'have-nots.' Also, they are used to interpreting life in terms of ready-made beliefs, and their peace of mind would be endangered if they allowed doubt to rear its head. But, between the two extremes, there is a floating multitude of waverers, those who are in two minds about these matters." There is a knock at the door. Jean shouts irritably: "Come in!"

A VALET: "Here's your mail, sir."

JEAN: "Put it on the table, please." The valet leaves the letters and goes out. "Yes, the *waverers*, those who are in two minds about these matters, torn between the craving for the supernatural they have inherited and the dictates of their reason. And it is their predicament that makes the present religious crisis in France so bewildering and so—so harrowing." He stumbles over his words. His gaze has just fallen on the periodicals and letters lying on the table; among the latter is one in Mme Pasquelin's hand. "Would you excuse me?" He opens the envelope.

Buis-la-Dame,
January 14

My dear Jean: Cécile gave birth to a daughter yesterday. . . .

He stops reading. His eyes grow misted; a sudden vision of the past has risen before them.

She wants me to let you know of this and to say that if you wish to see your daughter you can come here. Need I add that, as in the past, a room is waiting for you in my house, and you can stay as long as you desire? Perhaps (as I so greatly hope) you have already learned what a terrible mistake you made, and are now prepared to make some reparation for your heartless conduct towards Cécile and myself. You will find us in the same state of mind as when you left us— quite ready to let bygones be bygones, once you have realized how mistaken you were.

M. Pasquelin

BREIL-ZOEGER: "Not bad news, I hope?"

JEAN: "No. Now I'll go on. Where were we?" His voice is unsteady; he struggles to pull himself together. "Would you please read out the last few lines, Madame David?"

MME DAVID: " ' . . . a floating multitude of waverers'—underlined—'those who are in two minds about these matters, torn between the craving for the supernatural they have inherited and the dictates of their reason. And it is their predicament that makes the present religious crisis . . .' "

But Jean, sitting on an upended valise, hears only a rumble of words, signifying nothing.

v

The railway station at Buis. Jean alights from the train; nobody has come to meet him.

He has the old omnibus with the rattling windows to himself, as it toils up the hill towards the little town. He feels an unexpected thrill as he gazes at the once-familiar streets and shops. Nothing has changed. He sees the town across the mists of childhood, which three months' absence has intensified.

There is a nip in the air, and he buttons up his double-breasted overcoat, which has kept a tang of brine from the Channel crossing.

All doors and windows of the house are closed. A maid, whose face is new to him, holds the door half open, and he slips in almost furtively.

Half-way up the stairs he pauses, tightening his grip on the handrail; the sound he has just heard—of a baby crying—has thrown his thoughts into turmoil. Then, steadying himself, he walks quickly up to the landing.

A door opens.

MME PASQUELIN: "Ah, there you are, Jean. Come in."

Cécile is in bed. A big fire blazes merrily in the fireplace. Mme Pasquelin shuts the door. Jean goes up to the bed.

JEAN: "Good morning, Cécile." Her only response is a nervous smile. He bends and kisses her on the forehead. "Is the baby—doing well?"

CÉCILE: "Yes."

JEAN: "And you?" Mme Pasquelin is standing; he can feel the impact of her steely gaze. "When exactly did it . . . ?"

CÉCILE: "Monday night."

JEAN, counting on his fingers. "Six days ago." He pauses. "I got the letter on Thursday. I couldn't be spared at once, but I left as soon as I could." Another silence. "Did you—suffer much?"

CÉCILE: "Oh, yes, indeed!"

Another silence.

MME PASQUELIN, brusquely: "Will you be dining here tonight?"

JEAN: "Well, as a matter of fact, I'd thought . . ."

MME PASQUELIN, with a touch of satisfaction: "Ah! Then you'll be staying here some days?"

JEAN: "If you'd like me to."

MME PASQUELIN: "Very good."

She goes out to make the necessary arrangements. Left to themselves, Jean and Cécile are tongue-tied, acutely embarrassed. Their eyes meet. Cécile bursts into tears. Jean bends over her again and kisses her affectionately, sadly.

JEAN, in a low voice: "I'll stay as long as you want. Until you're able to get up anyhow. Then—we'll see."

He falls silent, doubtful what to propose. Neither speaks for some moments.

CÉCILE, in a whisper, with a break in her voice: "Jean! You haven't even asked to see your daughter!"

Just then Mme Pasquelin enters with the baby in her arms.

MME PASQUELIN, to Cécile: "We're forgetting the time—what with all this to-do."

The words "all this to-do" flick Jean in the face as he goes up to Mme Pasquelin. He knows what is expected of him—to kiss his child—but cannot bring himself to do it. Partly because his mother-in-law's presence goes against the grain; partly out of a sort of physical repugnance that he cannot overcome. With feigned casualness he strokes with his forefinger the small soft cheek and the pink chin half buried in the moistened bib.

JEAN: "She's—very nice." He steps back, and a new thought waylays him. What Christian name will they give his child? It does not strike him that the official declaration has already been made. "What's her name to be?"

MME PASQUELIN, peremptorily: "Her name is Marie."

As though he were struggling to imprint a difficult name on his memory Jean echoes, "Marie." Then he glances at the tiny fingers squeezing possessively a swelling breast, whose aspect is unfamiliar to him. What eagerness to live is in this small pink lump of flesh! His gaze shifts to Cécile's face, and he is startled by the change. It is fuller, paler, younger-looking, almost her face of years ago.

When she lifts her baby there is the glint of a ring, her engagement ring. He recalls the day when he brought it from Paris, the little square box in his pocket. Cécile was by herself; he went down on his knees to slip that ring, the link, upon her finger.

And the memory rekindles the lost emotions of their youth. How sincerely, how naïvely he had dreamed of giving and receiving perfect happiness!

He is lifting a shroud, violating the sepulchre of their dead selves. Now he is a different being; she too. Irremediably different. And what of the future?

## VI

Three weeks later. Cécile's bedroom.

CÉCILE: "No! I won't hear of it!"

JEAN: "But, Cécile—"

CÉCILE: "No!"

JEAN: "Here, you are under your mother's influence. Let's get back to Paris, you and I, as soon as we can manage it; I'm convinced—"

CÉCILE: "I refuse to leave before the baptism."

JEAN: "All right. I agree."

CÉCILE: "And I insist on your attending the service."

JEAN, after a short silence: "That, as I told you, I refuse to do."

CÉCILE: "In that case you can go back by yourself."

Another silence. Cécile moves to the window, draws aside the curtain, and gazes out.

JEAN, wearily: "Now, listen! For days and days we have been wrangling—and getting not an inch forrader. Recriminations, innuendoes, hostile silences, fits of weeping—I've had my fill of them, and, well, I'm at the end of my tether. And now you want to start another futile scene!" Cécile remains at the window with her back to him. Jean studiously controls his voice as he continues: "We must try to patch things up, and I repeat that I am willing to resume our life in common, as in the past. Also, I'm ready to make a great many concessions."

CÉCILE, turning to him at last: "That's a lie. You'll never do anything to please me."

JEAN, sadly: "How bitter you are against me, Cécile!" He pauses. "On the contrary, you know quite well that I'm prepared to meet a great many of your wishes, so as to extricate us from our present impasse. Do you want proof of this? Well, were I alone and free, I'd shelter our child completely from religious influences, I'd bring her up in such a way that she'd never have those terrible searchings of conscience that I had to endure."

CÉCILE, passionately: "Oh, please stop! Don't you realize how horrible you are?"

JEAN: "I said that's what I'd do if I were a free agent. But there are the two of us; you have the same rights as I over our child, and I keep this in mind. So I shall leave you free to implant in her the faith that's yours. Only I refuse to help you in this by playing the hypocrite. That, surely, is only fair."

CÉCILE, fiercely: "No! It's all sheer nonsense, what you've just been saying. She's *my* daughter and you have no rights over her, absolutely none. If you ever had any, you have lost them; it's exactly the same as if she had a father who was shut up in an asylum!"

JEAN, in a discouraged tone: "Cécile! Are we really so utterly, so hopelessly estranged, you and I?"

CÉCILE: "Yes, there's nothing left between us now. And, oh, I'm so tired of struggling! And all our life long it will be just the same. Today it's the child's baptism; presently it'll be her confirmation; and then her First Communion—each time the same miserable struggle! In fact I shall have to defend her against you every day, every minute of the day. Against your example, your horrible way of life. Yes, I have now only one duty, and that's to save my daughter—from her father!"

JEAN: "Well? What exactly do you want?"

CÉCILE, coming towards him, her face convulsed with despair: "What do I want? Heaven knows, it's nothing so preposterous; I want an end of all this misery. I don't ask you to change back to the man you were when we were married; I doubt if you could do that—now. All I ask you is to give up parading in public those dreadful ideas that you've picked up—I can't imagine where! I ask you to be present at your daughter's baptism. And I want you to promise me—" She bursts into tears, sways forward, and collapses on her prie-dieu, burying her face in her arms. "Surely it's not asking so very much? I only want to have a husband I needn't be ashamed of. I want us to be a married couple like ordinary married couples. That's all."

JEAN: "And all I ask for myself is to have the freedom that I'm giving *you*."

CÉCILE, rising to her feet in a frenzy of revolt: "*That?* Never! Never!"

JEAN, after a short silence: "Well then?" Cécile says nothing. "I'm afraid that when you married me you expected more of life than life could give you."

CÉCILE: "No, it's you who deceived me. You can't blame me for—for what has happened. I am just as I was when you asked me to marry you."

JEAN, shrugging his shoulders: "I wonder can a man ever feel so sure of the way he will develop in after years as to risk pledging himself irrevocably in such matters?"

CÉCILE, with a cry of horrified amazement: "Apostate!"

Jean gazes at her without speaking. He is plumbing the gulf between them. After pacing to and fro for some moments, he halts, facing her, resolved to force a decision.

JEAN: "Well then?" Her hands locked over her face, Cécile remains silent. "Well then?" His tone is frigid.

CÉCILE, passionately: "Oh, go away!" A short silence.

JEAN: "Ah, Cécile, don't—don't tempt me!"

CÉCILE, sobbing: "Go away! Leave me!"

JEAN: " 'Leave me?' Do you want a divorce?" Cécile stops crying, lowers her hands from her face, and looks at him aghast. Jean puts his hands in his pockets, his lips curled in an ugly smile. "So you think you've only got to say 'Leave me!' and everything is settled? You seem unaware that before a woman can live as she chooses and keep her child, there has to be a case in court—divorce proceedings, a decree."

He goes on speaking, explaining. And suddenly, unsummoned, striking across the words that it belies, an uprush of hope thrills through him, and a fierce desire for the freedom now within his grasp, for a life at last his own.

He goes on speaking, but in the distance, straight ahead, he sees a rift in the darkness, and, try as he may, he cannot take his eyes off it.

VII

February 12

Dear Sir: I am glad to be able to inform you that, after a final interview with Mme Barois and Mme Pasquelin, and under pressure of the threat of divorce proceedings, which these ladies wish at all costs to avoid, their formal assent has been given to all the demands you asked me to formulate. It is therefore agreed that:

(1) You recover your entire independence. Mme Barois has no intention of residing in Paris and will live permanently at Buis with her mother.

(2) Mme Barois will have complete control of her daughter's education; with this single restriction, on which you insisted, that when your daughter reaches the age of eighteen she is to spend a complete year under your roof.

(3) Mme Barois agrees not to reject the allowance of 12,000 francs a year which you insist on her receiving from you. She is, however, resolved not to employ any portion of this income either for herself or on her daughter's education. It will be allowed to accumulate and be settled *in toto* on her daughter.

This last clause gave rise to much controversy, and Mme Barois consented to its inclusion in the Agreement only on my unequivocal assurance that you regarded it as a condition *sine qua non,* and to avoid recourse to a Court of Law. These ladies desired, however, to withhold their assent until I had advised you of the precise effect on your personal income of this deduction (which reduces it to approximately 5000 francs *per annum*). To prevent further delay (which, as I knew, would serve no purpose) I thought fit to inform them that I had already drawn your attention to this fact, but you had declined to go back on your project.

As requested by Mme Barois, I have given her a memorandum of the terms of agreement as set out above.

I trust that my handling of these delicate negotiations has been such as to meet with your approval, and beg to remain,

Faithfully yours,

E. Mougin

Notary, Buis-la-Dame

# PART II

## VI

## The Sower

### I

M. L. Breil-Zoeger
   Hotel des Pins
   Arcachon

Paris, May 20, 1895

My dear Breil-Zoeger: Forgive me for my delay in thanking you for the sympathy you so kindly showed me in my recent troubles. The truth is I have been exceedingly busy. Only those who have themselves been through the mill can realize what it means to have to cut those innumerable strands which link a life (even a simple one like mine) to the outside world and to its past. One fails to appreciate the toughness of these strands, their complexity and elusiveness. The task cost me two months' unremitting effort; I threw myself into it with a sort of desperate ardor, and at last I have snapped every link and can call myself *a free man.*

I doubt if you can guess the keen emotion behind this cry of triumph, this paean of Freedom, that rises to my lips; for, unlike mine, your life has always been untrammelled, fancy-free.

And this new Freedom has dawned for me in the prime of life, when my energies are at their highest, after a long hard schooling in subjection; after two years during which I never ceased longing for it secretly, unavowedly. Yes, Freedom has crashed on me at last, a gift from the gods, given without stint, and I welcome it with every sinew of my being, incorporate it in my life, and, with passionate devotion, vow myself to it forever!

I have gone to ground without giving anyone my address. For many weeks I have not seen one familiar face or heard a single voice that might remind me of the past. And now everything conspires to crown this new-found joy. Spring has come to Paris, flooding my room with light, with the fragrance of rising sap, with beauty! Never before in my life have I experienced an emotion like this.

Do not write to me, my friend; let me

drug myself with solitude until the autumn. But be assured my friendship never falters.

Always yours,
Jean Barois

II

November. An old building with a narrow doorway in the Rue Jacob, Paris.

"Monsieur Barois? Fourth floor, sir. You'll see his card on the door."

A rickety, poorly lit staircase. On the fourth-floor landing there are four doors, but only one doormat.

Harbaroux peers at each door in the dim light; finally on one of them his keen eyes decipher a dusty visiting card, the last two lines of which have been crossed out in pencil.

JEAN BAROIS, M.D.
PROFESSOR, WENCESLAS COLLEGE
80, BOULEVARD MALESHERBES

He rings.

BAROIS: "You're the first arrival, Harbaroux. Come in."

Jean Barois, now in his thirty-third year, is in the full vigor of maturity. His face has greatly changed during the last twelve months; the look of strain has gone, and it has the radiant serenity of a sky swept clear of clouds. He radiates energy and zest for life, freedom, self-assurance, a boundless confidence in the future.

The somewhat austere room is brightly lit by a gas-jet in a plain glass globe. Deal shelves piled with books line the walls. There are half a dozen cane chairs. On the mantelpiece stands a plaster cast of Michelangelo's "Slave," struggling to free his aching limbs and rebellious shoulders from their stony thrall. At the far end of the room a door gives on a bedroom; clothes can be seen hanging in a recess.

HARBAROUX: "Do you know, this is the first time I've set foot here?"

BAROIS: "Yes, I've been living like a troglodyte for the last six months."

Harbaroux glances at the chairs, which are set out in a circle, and his features twist in a brief grin. He is a wizened little man, with a hatchet face, wide at the temples and narrowing down to a sharp chin and a pointed reddish-brown beard; an ugly, ageless face, but almost diabolically intelligent, with upstanding, faun-like ears. His mouth and the deep-set eye-sockets are like holes roughed out in a wax head by a sculptor working against time. His look is keen, unwavering, ungentle. Librarian at the Arsenal, he is an indefatigable worker. His special subject was originally Medieval Law; latterly, however, he has concentrated on the history of the Revolution.

HARBAROUX: "I wanted to see you before it started. Don't you think it would be a good plan for us to settle in advance what subjects should be brought up for discussion with our friends this evening?"

BAROIS, after pondering for some moments: "No, I don't agree."

HARBAROUX, his features tightening, then relaxing, like a hairspring: "No? All the same . . ."

BAROIS: "A meeting like the one we're having tonight is bound to be preparatory. We're not out for any immediate practical result."

HARBAROUX: "Then what's the point of it?"

BAROIS: "In my opinion it will serve its purpose best if it generates, so to speak, a chain of currents between the minds of those who have been asked to attend, and as a result we find a spirit of collective enthusiasm developing from the mere fact of these minds' being brought together."

HARBAROUX: "That's desirable, I grant you—only it doesn't depend on anything we, you and I, can do."

BAROIS: "I agree. But we have a better chance of creating that atmosphere if we let everyone have his say, without keeping to a program drawn up in advance." He smiles serenely. "It'll pan out all right, you'll see."

Barois weighs his words and rounds his phrases off with the ease of a man used to platform speaking. Though he does not raise his voice, the incisiveness of his diction holds the hearer's attention.

HARBAROUX, shrugging his shoulders: "I wonder! We shall have a spate of noble sentiments. Each of us taking his hobby for a ride! Each in turn inflicting his harangue! And then, before we know where we are, two o'clock in the morning! A wasted evening!"

Barois makes a gesture implying: And what if it is? Then, without answering, he lights a cigarette with the deft precision that comes of long practice. His hard but thoughtful gaze lingers for a moment on the first puff of smoke rising in the clear air of the room.

HARBAROUX: "Hullo! So you've taken to smoking?"

BAROIS: "Yes."

A short silence.

HARBAROUX: "Have it your own way. Personally, I'd have preferred to have the work mapped out, distributed. In my opinion the launching of a review calls for—"

A ring at the bell.

BAROIS, getting up from his chair: "For method. That's what you were going to say, isn't it?" He goes to the door and opens it, while Harbaroux mumbles something with a rather sickly smile.

A HOARSE VOICE, in the hall: "My dear fellow! Would you believe it? An absolute godsend! In Lamennais, of all people! You won't find anything better, I assure you."

Cresteil d'Allize's back shows in the doorway; he is gesticulating, pouring out a stream of exclamations. He does a

brisk about-turn to enter the room and blinks when the light from the unshaded gas-jet strikes his eyes.

François Cresteil d'Allize is a tall, slim man of twenty-eight. An exceptionally thin neck emphasizes the proud carriage of his head, a small head with a skull that bulges at the back. A short, triangular face, furrowed cheeks, a wrinkled forehead, gentle yet fervent eyes, a drooping brown moustache hiding a mouth with a disdainful curve, a vacillating, disillusioned smile. He has the commanding accent and bearing of a cavalry officer, and emphasizes his remarks with wide sweeps of his arms. Torn between the conservative principles of his upbringing and a passionate desire to emancipate his mind, he resigned his commission not long ago, cutting himself off from his family and breaking with the generations-old royalist and Catholic tradition of the House of Allize. Thus he has all the rankling bitterness of a recent escapee.

With a brisk, lithe movement he goes up to Harbaroux and, bending his tall body, holds out both hands with impulsive friendliness.

CRESTEIL: "Did you hear, old chap? I found it today in that book called *Words of a Believer*." Ignoring Barois, who leaves the room in response to another ring at the bell, he thrusts a hand into his coat-tails and fishes out a rather tattered volume. Then he declaims from memory: " 'Listen, my friends, and say whence it comes, that strange rumor like the sound of many voices which we hear rising all around us . . .' "

Breil-Zoeger, Woldsmuth, Roll, and Barois enter and halt, their backs to the wall, gazing at the orator in amused surprise.

CRESTEIL, who has not noticed them, goes on speaking: " 'Lay your hands on the ground and tell me why it trembles. Something we know not is stirring in the world today. And is not every man await-ing something, each heart throbbing with expectancy? Son of man!' " He points upward, his voice vibrant with emotion. " 'Son of man, climb to the mountain-top, and declare what you behold!' "

His gaze falls on the new-comers, sweeping them off their feet with a look of rapturous ardor.

CRESTEIL: "I propose to have those lines printed in the cover of our review. They would be the perfect manifesto, concise and eloquent."

BAROIS, from the back of the room, enthusiastically: "Agreed!"

They exchange contented smiles; irony has no place here this evening. Some minutes pass in a general exchange of greetings. Barriers are down; they have come here to impart their various en-thusiasms, and this first shared emotion has warmed their hearts.

Breil-Zoeger moves to the center of the group. His oriental face looks yellower than ever. With his difficult smile and restrained, almost embarrassed gestures, the first impression he gives is one of shyness. But in the shadow of the fine-drawn eyelids, the black, restless, deeply sunken eyes have the hard glow that comes of implacable resolve.

BREIL-ZOEGER: "Suppose we sit down? Let's begin at the beginning. Is there anyone else to come?"

BAROIS: "Yes. Portal."

Smiles are exchanged.

BREIL-ZOEGER: "We won't wait for him."

He has seated himself at Barois' desk, as if he were presiding. Harbaroux, who has the intention of taking notes, draws a chair beside Breil-Zoeger's.

Cresteil remains standing, his back to the bookshelves, so as to be able to gesticulate more freely. His arms are folded, he holds his head high, and in his tight-fitting clothes he has the air of a retired colonel.

Roll is ensconced in a wicker chair. A very young man, who has just set up as a printer, he twiddles his incipient mous-tache to keep himself in countenance while he observes and listens to the older men.

Silent, his shoulders sagging, Wolds-muth hovers in the background, beside the fireplace. So small is he, one could imagine he is sitting down.

Barois hands him a chair, then plants himself in the middle of the room, sitting astride a chair.

BAROIS, opening a cigarette box on the desk: "Help yourselves. Are we ready to make the plunge?" He smiles. "Right! When you came, Harbaroux and I were having a little discussion. The question was: Should this, our first meeting, be simply a means of getting to know one another better, of exchanging views freely and amicably? Or else—" He signs to Harbaroux to speak.

HARBAROUX: "Or else devoted to real spadework, the drawing up of a concrete plan of action?"

BAROIS: "Personally, I think that our right course has been pointed out by Cresteil."

CRESTEIL: "No, by Lamennais."

BAROIS: "We don't want merely to draw up a working program; that wouldn't be enough. What we desire, above all, unless I'm much mistaken, is—how shall I put it?—to pool our temperaments and enthusiasms. And so, quite obviously, nothing cut-and-dried will meet the case." He warms to his subject. "All of us here are animated by the same aspirations, guided by the same high motives, each prepared to harness the driving force of his personal ideal to the collective effort." He hesitates for a moment. "I seem to have launched out into a regular speech, but I suppose I may as well go on. Whence did it come—the first idea of the formation of our group?"

BREIL-ZOEGER: "From you, Barois."

BAROIS, smiling: "No, it was quite as much your child as mine. But what I was going to say was this: the idea was in the air. It answers to a set of needs we, all of us, feel today. We all believe that we have something to say, a part to play in the world."

CRESTEIL, dramatically: "Yes, the hour has struck for us to give our intellectual activities a social repercussion."

No one smiles at this grandiloquence.

BAROIS: "But whenever we try to express ourselves and to bring our efforts to the notice of the public, we come up against well-established customs, caucuses of literary pundits, who have made writing and thinking their preserve; who monopolize even the humblest organs of opinion and bar the door against outsiders. Isn't that so?"

BREIL-ZOEGER: "There's only one remedy. We must create our own organ of expression."

HARBAROUX: "There you come up against the problem of ways and means —of organizing distribution and enlisting support, without frittering our time away on making approaches and arranging interviews . . ."

BAROIS: ". . . which come to nothing."

CRESTEIL: ". . . and on cultivating friendships in high places—which would degrade us."

BAROIS, quietly: "We're not youngsters of twenty. Most of us are in our thirties or thereabouts. That, to my mind, is a most important point. The fervor we shall devote, first to crystallizing, then to making good and championing our ideas, isn't the fervor of the youngster bubbling over with neophyte enthusiasm. No, it is the fine flower of our conscious selves, a well-considered standpoint towards life, that we have adopted once for all."

All signify approval.

CRESTEIL, with a sweeping gesture: "Ah, what a splendid incentive that will be, to feel we are being read, followed and discussed month by month, or week by week!"

BREIL-ZOEGER, instinctively summing up: "To play an *active* part."

HARBAROUX, with a Machiavellian smile: "Only, my friends, you'll not find it quite so easy, when you get down to brass tacks!"

BAROIS, taking up the challenge: "I don't agree. On the practical side our plan is quite feasible." He pauses. "There are funds—"

BREIL-ZOEGER: "—at our disposal; at *your* disposal, I should say."

BAROIS: "Yes, we have a capital sum available—not a big sum, I admit, but, I think, ample for our purposes—thanks to the generosity of our friend Roll." Roll murmurs a protest. "Or, if Roll prefers to put it that way, to the Collectivist Printing House of which he is managing director. What's more, we are not paying for contributions; which means that our production costs will be quite small. There will be only the paper and printing to be paid for. So we shall be able to make a flying start and keep going long enough to win a place in the public eye. After that we'll still have to put up a fight, no doubt; but by then we shall be better equipped for holding our own."

BREIL-ZOEGER: "So it's this year, at the start, that we shall need to put forth our greatest effort."

BAROIS: "Yes. The differences in our temperaments, though of course our general outlook is the same"—the doorbell rings, and he rises to his feet—"will ensure the variety so necessary for a review." He goes into the hall.

BREIL-ZOEGER, curtly, as if giving his verdict on what has gone before: "We have every chance of success."

CRESTEIL, emotionally: "Yes, we have

faith, and our faith will see us through."

HARBAROUX: "What will see us through is a steady, persevering effort."

BREIL-ZOEGER, dourly: "Faith has never worked miracles—though it may have seemed to. But will-power *has,* whenever it's been strong enough."

Shepherded by Barois, Portal at last makes his appearance. He is smoking a cigar, and beams affably on the little group in the room.

PORTAL: "Well, here I am! Begun already? No, that's impossible unless in this part of Paris you dine at six o'clock, like the people of Balzac."

Pierre Portal is a fair-haired young Alsatian, with mild, china-blue eyes, and a rather babyish face. The small flaxen moustache adds but a faint touch of virility to his smile. He has a clear, if slightly worn, complexion, and in his warm, insistent gaze there kindles, on occasion, a sudden if discreetly veiled sensuality. Women always take to him.

One detects a certain heaviness in his bearing, gestures, voice; also in his jokes. He has strong, though not violent emotions, based on solid common sense, and a shrewd awareness both of his rights and of his duties. He is secretary to an eminent Paris lawyer, Fauquet-Talon, now a leading light in politics, a man of high integrity and much energy, who has twice held ministerial posts.

BAROIS, introducing him: "Portal. Our good friend Roll."

Roll makes a rather awkward bow. Since sitting down he has kept silent, merely gazing intently at each speaker in turn. His face and bearing convey an average intelligence straining its utmost to keep abreast of the others' minds.

BAROIS, affectionately: "Well, Roll, what do you think of our project?"

Roll goes quite pale, as if he has been rebuffed, then flushes, uncrosses his legs and leans forward to speak. At first he is tongue-tied. Then, abruptly, he musters up his courage.

ROLL: "We print dozens of reviews at our works. Every year there's new ones. But none the least bit like yours."

CRESTEIL: "So much the better."

ROLL: "Reviews for connoisseurs, you know; reviews that don't tackle any problem." There is a curious inflection in his voice. "They're all dilettanti, the folks that write and read them. Aye, there's a need for a review that keeps in touch with the great movements of the day." He pauses, then thumps his knee with his fist. "That's what we need—men who've got some gumption, who understand what's coming to the world."

CRESTEIL, stepping forward, declaims ecstatically: " 'Something we know not is stirring in the world today . . .' "

BAROIS: " 'Son of man, climb to the mountain-top . . .' "

CRESTEIL, BAROIS, ROLL, together: " '. . . and declare what you behold!' "

They exchange glances, with only the faintest smiles at this rather boyish outburst, behind which lies deep-felt sincerity.

BREIL-ZOEGER, composedly, in a tone calling them to order: "We must see to it that within six months our review is recognized as the ally and mouthpiece of all the isolated groups and individuals now studying positive philosophy or sociology."

HARBAROUX, screwing up his face and blinking through his cigarette smoke: *Practical* sociology."

BAROIS: "That goes without saying."

PORTAL: "There are more lonely workers in these fields than one would imagine."

BREIL-ZOEGER: "And it's for us to bring them together."

PORTAL: "Then there are all the organizers of social leagues, ethical societies, popular universities."

CRESTEIL: "All the believers without a church."

WOLDSMUTH, timidly: "And the pacifists."

BAROIS: "In a word, all men of good will. It's they for whom our review will cater. Yes, we have a great task before us. We shall co-ordinate all the melioristic forces that too often run to waste, and give them a common direction. A splendid program indeed!"

BREIL-ZOEGER: "And one which we can realize simply by disseminating our ideas."

BAROIS: "And by setting an example of complete integrity of thought and absolute sincerity."

PORTAL, smiling: "That might be risky sometimes."

BAROIS: "I don't agree. I believe that frankness is infectious. Nothing but good can come of bringing every problem out into the open. For instance, I quite agree with our reactionaries that France is in the throes of a moral crisis. Well, I shan't hesitate to acknowledge this; I shall admit that morality has lost much of its hold. That is a fact. So far as this affects the mass of the population, I attribute it to the prevailing anemia of religious faith; as regards people like ourselves, to the disfavor and discredit that have befallen those abstract principles which our professors of metaphysics dinned into our ears, as if they were so many self-evident truths." He turns to Breil-Zoeger. "You remember what we were saying the other day?"

PORTAL: "But there's no point in making this admission unless you can suggest a remedy."

BAROIS: "That's another story. Still, even now, we can suggest some palliatives."

BREIL-ZOEGER: "Better still, we can prove that, even at the present stage, it's not impossible to visualize a code of ethics that would meet the case."

PORTAL: "Based on what?"

BREIL-ZOEGER: "For one thing, on the data of modern science; and also on the proofs we have, already well authenticated, of certain laws of life."

PORTAL: "Laws that are still extremely vague—and anyhow it's extremely difficult to see how any ethical system can derive from them."

BREIL-ZOEGER, who resents being contradicted: "No, my dear fellow, not so vague as you think. We can define and classify them. First, the instincts of self-preservation and self-improvement; second, the necessary adaptation of the individual to the social environment with which he cannot dispense."

HARBAROUX, nodding: "Two duties, in short, which every man is bound to recognize."

BREIL-ZOEGER: "Yes. He oscillates between these two poles and finds his moral balance in a give-and-take between the ego and its environment."

BAROIS: "I agree. There, certainly, we have the crux of the matter, and a basis for the ethics of tomorrow."

Cresteil steps forward, his head high, his arms uplifted in a sudden, charmingly unaffected movement of expansiveness.

CRESTEIL: "Ah, my friends, when I hear you speaking like this, I feel sure that if once we can make people realize not only what we want, but what we stand for—if once we succeed in making known the moral quality of our aspirations—we shall draw into our orbit within a very few months all the solitary seekers, all who have something"—he thumps his cavernous chest—"here."

BAROIS, whose fervor tends always to find its outlet in rhetorical exuberance: "And this we shall achieve by exalting the sense of human dignity in all our readers. By helping to restore their meaning to such fine old words as Uprightness and Probity—words that have been allowed to lose their luster in the lumber-room of romantic verbiage; and, above all, by championing man's right to freedom of thought in every field."

There is an affectionate exchange of looks and smiles, a moment of high emotional tension that gradually relaxes. Barois fills the glasses with frothing beer, whose acrid tang mingles with the cigarette smoke filling the little room.

PORTAL, cheerfully, putting down his glass: "And what's it going to be called?"

BAROIS: "That's settled. We've rallied to Cresteil's suggestion. The name's to be *The Sower.*" He smiles at Cresteil. "Of course the metaphor isn't highly original—"

CRESTEIL: "Thanks!"

BAROIS: "But it's simple and admirably expresses our intentions."

BREIL-ZOEGER: "Has Barois told you about the idea he had for the first number?"

BAROIS: "No, I haven't told him yet. It's an idea, I must confess, on which I'm particularly keen. And I hope everyone present will agree to it, as Breil-Zoeger has done. It's this: I want our first issue to be a tribute to a distinguished member of the previous generation."

SOME VOICES: "Who? Luce?"

BAROIS: "Yes, Luce."

CRESTEIL: "An excellent idea!"

BAROIS: "I've several reasons for this. For one thing, our choice of Luce would be a pointer; it would make the public understand our slant and the type of man we're backing. Then, again, it would show that wholesale destruction is no part of our program, nor are we mere utopian dreamers—since our ideal has found, as it were, an incarnation in real life; there's a man living today who admirably illustrates it."

PORTAL: "I see your point. But mightn't it give an impression that we're exploiting a prominent figure just to give our review a flying start?"

CRESTEIL, energetically: "Where a man like Luce is concerned, no one would ever—"

BAROIS, interrupting: "Listen, Portal. Surely, if those old-fashioned terms I used just now—Uprightness, Probity, and the like—have ever been applicable to any man, Luce is that man. Also, there's no question of asking him to give his blessing to our venture, or of getting a contribution from him for publicity's sake. No, we shall pay him homage spontaneously and collectively. In fact I'd suggest we don't even let him know what we are up to."

PORTAL: "Ah! That puts a different complexion on it."

BAROIS: "None of us is personally acquainted with him. All we know of him is what he has written and what he has done—his public life. What's more, he is utterly independent. As a philosopher he owns allegiance to no school; as a politician—a member of the Senate—to no party. So our homage will apply only to him personally, to the man he is. Don't let's forget how much of our moral education we all owe to him. That's why, on the eve of plunging into the arena, we cannot do less than make this public statement of our obligation. Do you agree, Cresteil?"

CRESTEIL, smiling as a memory crosses his mind: "Entirely, Barois. And I'd like to mention a little personal detail, a memory of my boyhood. Luce had been invited, at short notice, to preside at one of our school speech days. That was twelve years ago, it was my last term at school. Luce had just been given some rather important post—I forget what it was."

BAROIS: "Deputy Professor at the Collège de France, most probably."

CRESTEIL: "I can still see him there on the platform, a quite young man, hardly more than fifteen years our senior, in the midst of an array of graybeards. His face, with its look of noble fervor combined with gravity, made a deep impression on me. When addressing us, he spoke in quite ordinary terms, without raising his voice, but every word struck home with wonderful precision. Within a few minutes he had given us a concise but amazingly vivid picture of the way the universe functions, and man's place in it. The theme fitted in so aptly with the problems that engrossed my mind at the time that I really think the whole course of my life was changed by that short speech. So when, two months later, I started on philosophy, I was forearmed against the transcendentalism so dear to our official pundits."

BREIL-ZOEGER, with a harsh guffaw: "Which Coulangheon called a species of 'delusion of grandeur.'"

CRESTEIL: "Anyhow, I was spared it."

There is a short silence.

BAROIS: "Then, I take it, we agree that our first number shall begin with a 'Tribute to Marc-Élie Luce,' signed 'The Sower.'"

HARBAROUX, to Roll: "Can we get out our first number by January?"

ROLL: "In five weeks' time? It'll be a near thing. Can I count on having the copy in before the tenth?"

BAROIS: "We can do that, I think. A good deal's ready, I believe." He turns to Breil-Zoeger. "Isn't that so?"

BREIL-ZOEGER: "I haven't yet started writing my paper, but I have all my data ready."

PORTAL: "On what subject?"

Breil-Zoeger's gaze lingers on Portal; he seems reluctant to reply. Then his hard eyes survey the faces of those present, all turned towards him expectantly. At last he brings himself to speak.

BREIL-ZOEGER: "Briefly, this." His slow, monotonous voice would pass as forceless but for a curious final intonation that takes one by surprise, a crisp sound flicking the ear like a whiplash. "I think it best for our first number that our

contributions should be unequivocally tendentious and make quite clear the position we're taking up." Again he rakes the others' faces with his gaze, to make sure of their assent. "Personally, I intend to publish an article which will pave the way for those which follow. I shall confine myself to setting forth a general idea, the gist of which is this: Since, logically, any study of the human situation of today must begin with a survey of the environment in which the individual is evolving, a truly modern philosophy— the only kind that can breathe new life into the dry bones of past philosophies— is necessarily biological in trend, a philosophy which, operating on the human level, regards man primarily as part of the natural world around him. Such a philosophy has the added advantage of being amenable to new developments, since it derives spontaneously from the existing state of scientific knowledge, and, drawing its data solely from facts that can be verified, is bound to keep in step with scientific progress."

PORTAL: "That will certainly damn our review in the eyes of nine out of ten metaphysicians."

BREIL-ZOEGER, promptly: "And so much the better!"

HARBAROUX, seizing the opportunity: "I say! Wouldn't it be a good idea if each of us gave an outline of his plans, right away? Then our first issue would be more or less mapped out this evening. What do you think, Barois?"

BAROIS, after a moment's thought: "I agree."

HARBAROUX, eagerly: "I've some thirty pages ready—about the Communal movement in the twelfth century and its resemblance to the social troubles of the last fifty years. And you, Cresteil?"

Cresteil has just taken his stand with his back to the chimney-piece. His attitude seems a trifle affected, but once he begins speaking, his glowing eyes, impassioned tone, and spacious gestures carry his hearers away.

CRESTEIL: "I propose to discuss that moot question of 'Art for Art's sake.' In connection, you know, with Tolstoy's latest manifesto. I want to point out that the problem is often wrongly stated, and to claim for the artist the right—nay, the bounden duty—of giving his mind to nothing else, when the work is in gestation, than to making a thing of beauty. For only disinterested emotion is creative. However, I shall try to reconcile this view with the one set up against it, and prove that the useful is inevitably the outcome of the aesthetic quest of beauty. Thus the artist need give no conscious thought, during his creative work, to what may be its social consequences."

BREIL-ZOEGER, who has been listening attentively: "No more than does the scientist."

CRESTEIL: "Quite so. The task of the artist is to achieve beauty; of the scientist, to achieve truth—two aspects of the same purpose. And then it's for the masses to adjust themselves to these achievements, and"—loftily—"bring their petty social exigencies into line with them."

BREIL-ZOEGER: "That's very true."

BAROIS, to Cresteil: "I thought you wanted to earmark, for your contribution, an article on your quotation from Lamennais?"

CRESTEIL, smiling: "No, I leave that to you."

BAROIS, cheerfully: "Right! I'll take it on. As a matter of fact I had it in my mind while I was listening to you. I can see the makings of an excellent leading article. We could begin by explaining why we have inscribed these words in the forefront of our review, and why they so well convey the spirit of our venture."

CRESTEIL: "Yes, that's just the sort of contribution we need as a send-off for our first number."

BAROIS: "I'm glad you agree."

PORTAL: "What's this quotation you're talking about?"

HARBAROUX, ill-humoredly: "You came too late to hear it."

PORTAL: "Suppose you let us know your idea, Barois?"

BREIL-ZOEGER: "Yes, tell us how you'll handle it."

BAROIS, smiling at his thoughts as he proceeds to do so: "I'll take the passage phrase by phrase.

" 'Something we know not is stirring in the world . . .'

"What is this 'something' that is active beneath the surface? It is the increasing activity of human thought, of progress. You see how that theme could be developed. One might speak of the maturation of a gigantic task, in which each of the emotions we experience, each of our struggles, plays its part. And this movement carries in its womb all the solutions we are groping after, all those truths of tomorrow which still elude us, but which in the fullness of time will fall into our hands like ripe fruit and reveal themselves, one after the other, to the questing mind of man."

CRESTEIL: "Bravo! A hymn to progress! I see . . ."

BAROIS, encouraged to give free rein to his creative fancy: "And I'd say too that some among us have a sort of second sight, which enables them to see in advance what others fail so far to see. It is such men that Lamennais is addressing when he exclaims: 'Son of man, climb to the mountain-top, and declare what you behold!'

"Here I'd insert a brief description of our vision of the future. 'Declare what you behold!'

"I see a monstrous aggrandizement of the power of wealth, silencing, crushing under its heel, every attempt made by its victims to ventilate their grievances. But I also see a growing restlessness among

[ 81 ]

the workers, and the strident wranglings of political parties can no longer drown the voices of the malcontents.

"And I see the steady, tidal onset of a human majority, rough and brutal, dazed by illusions, hungry for security and material well-being, and up in arms against a blind minority which still retains the prestige of an established order, but whose relative stability depends, for all practical purposes, on the capitalist system. In other words, a steady, concerted drive against capitalist rule; that is to say, against the whole social fabric of the modern world—for all civilized countries are ruled in much the same way at the present time. A formidable drive, for which history has no precedent, and which can't fail to make good, since behind it is a new, vital force that is thrusting up, like sap, in the human family tree—a juvenile enthusiasm defying an old, too civilized world that has outlived its heyday."

ROLL, excitedly: "Bravo! Bravo!"

They exchange smiles. Carried away by the sound and cadence of his own voice and the knowledge that all eyes are fixed on him, Barois feels the uprush of an emotion that has been lacking in his life for many months—the emotion of the public speaker who holds his audience. His head high, his shoulders squared, his feet planted well apart, a gay challenge in his eyes, his face aglow with virile confidence, he resumes the thread of his discourse.

BAROIS: "Next, after the generalizations and in conclusion, I would cast a glance at man, the individual.

"When we look into ourselves, what do we find? Only confusion and uncertainty. The betterment of life on the material plane has pandered disastrously to our weaknesses. Never before have they had such free play or sapped our lives so deeply. An unconfessed dread of the unknown haunts the minds of the majority of cultivated men, and a civil war is raging in the heart of each, now that all that is most vital in the mind has risen in revolt, whether consciously or not, against the survival of those mythical imperatives that once ruled human life. That struggle is in progress everywhere and under many aspects, overt or disguised, and in it lies the explanation of the excessive forms taken by present-day social unrest. What makes the struggle all the graver is that it leads to an all-too-evident decline in the mental efficiency of the individual, and a hideous waste of energy." He pauses, sweeps with his gaze the rapt faces of his little audience, and smiles. "That's all!"

For yet a moment he remains keyed up; then suddenly, abruptly, as if a spring had snapped, his exaltation falls. With an embarrassed smile he sits down awkwardly. A short silence follows.

He opens a bottle of beer, fills the glasses, and drains his at a gulp. Then he turns to Portal.

BAROIS, with forced joviality: "And you, old chap? Have you thought up something for us?"

PORTAL, laughing: "Well, I must confess I haven't. Count me out for the first number. I'll give you something for the second."

CRESTEIL: "Slacker!"

PORTAL: "Oh, come now! I've hit on a subject right enough, only I haven't had time to work on it. So far it's only in my head." He smiles. "You don't believe me? Well, here's my idea. It's not exactly an article I have in mind, but some sketches—pen-pictures, you know—of people I see every day, fellows I rub shoulders with, in the courts, in society, in political circles. Average types, you know."

CRESTEIL: "Ah, *don't* I know! That incorrigibly respectable, worthy, average man!"

PORTAL: "Exactly. Fellows who are right-minded, as they say, because they haven't any minds of their own. The innumerable horde of mildly educated people, rubbed smooth by social contacts, like pebbles in a stream. Most of them have a certain rank in society, often a position of importance, but they live like so many beasts of burden." With a twinkle in his eye. "Yes, they all wear blinkers and go straight ahead like a team of docile horses. Not one has ever thought out anything for himself or had the pluck to overhaul the vague beliefs that were foisted on him along with his first knickerbockers. And when their time comes, they die, conventional and muddle-headed as they've lived, never having once been conscious of their muddlement, or having had even a glimpse of the things that rule our lives, things like instinct, love and death."

BREIL-ZOEGER, fiercely: "Show them up, Portal, don't spare them anything! They're pests, these people, and they foul the air. We'll brush them out of our way, like the noisome rubbish they are."

ROLL, grimly: "They think they're sitting pretty, like worms in rotten meat. But they're mistaken."

The bitterness of their tone contrasts with Portal's smiling irony, and he is rather startled by the hatred his almost flippant words have conjured up.

HARBAROUX: "They're doomed, anyhow. Only look at them; from father to son they're dwindling away, growing more and more spineless, shapeless, incapable of shouldering any serious task."

BAROIS, cutting into the discussion: "Yes, Harbaroux, that's how they strike you when you see them at a distance or pass them in the street. But when you've lived among them—it's a very different story. Yes, you realize then that there's lots of life yet under that shell of seeming death." He raises his fist. "And what's more, of pernicious life."

BREIL-ZOEGER, with an ugly grin: "No, Barois, they're not so dangerous as all that. We've shut them out of everything, isolated them, limited their field of action. In forest fires you cut your losses; the patch you sacrifice is allowed to go on burning while you clear the ground ahead of it to prevent the fire from spreading. That's just how it is with them."

BAROIS: "I doubt it. One needs to have lived among these people to realize their massive inertia, the powers of obstruction they still have."

CRESTEIL: "Barois is quite right—and don't I know it!"

BAROIS: "Their mausoleums may be full of cracks, but they're good to shelter many and many a generation yet before that noxious race becomes extinct. We may count ourselves lucky if they don't succeed in issuing from their stronghold once more and hoodwinking public opinion as in the past. Can one ever be sure?"

A short silence.

HARBAROUX, methodical as ever: "Wouldn't it be as well to make a written note of what we've decided on?"

There is no answer; indeed no one appears to have heard the remark. The hour is late. A vague somnolence is damping the generous ardor that fired their eloquence. Reaction has come in the form of an undefinable depression, and a stale smell of cooled-down enthusiasm seems to hover in the air.

CRESTEIL: "Our first number will be a trumpet call outside the walls of Jericho!"

But his voice has grown still hoarser and has lost its triumphant challenge. It sinks into the silence, which closes upon it like a stagnant pool.

ROLL, his eyes puffy with fatigue: "If you don't mind, I'll be going. Got to be at the works at seven, you know."

HARBAROUX: "By Jove, it's nearly two o'clock!" To Cresteil. "Good night."

CRESTEIL: "Oh, we're all leaving."

They make a gloomy exit. Barois is alone. He goes to the window and opens it; resting his elbows on the sill, he draws deep breaths of ice-cold air.

All are silent as they tramp down the wooden staircase, Portal, candle in hand, leading the way. Suddenly he looks round; used to late hours, he alone has kept his spirits.

PORTAL: "And Woldsmuth? We've forgotten all about him. What's our good friend Woldsmuth going to bestow on our first number?"

The little procession halts. All turn with smiles towards Woldsmuth, who is bringing up the rear. Torch-wise the candle is passed up from hand to hand until it reaches him.

Seen against the shadows of the upper landing, his face has a comical resemblance to a spaniel's. Amid a tangle of thick, curly hair, bushy eyebrows, and an unkempt beard, the eyes shine out, gentle yet alert, twinkling behind a pince-nez.

For some moments he is silent. Then, when he realizes the others are waiting on his words, a red stain flushes his cheeks, his eyelids flutter, droop, and then disclose, in rising, a gaze at once piteous and fervent.

WOLDSMUTH, with unlooked-for decision: "I shall simply copy out a very sad letter I've just received from Russia. Six hundred Jewish families have been expelled from a little town in the Kiev district. Why? Because a Christian child had been found dead, and the Jews were accused of killing him—a ritual murder, you know—for making their unleavened bread! Incredible, isn't it? But that's how things are over there.

"There was a pogrom, and the survivors were driven from their homes. A hundred and twenty-six new-born babes died in the exodus, because those who had little children to carry couldn't move as fast as the others and had to spend two nights in the snow.

"Yes, that's how things are over there,

and nobody in France has the slightest idea of it."

### III

A large house in the Auteuil district of Paris, giving on a garden white with hoarfrost, in which half a dozen children are scampering about. A clock strikes eight.

LUCE, stepping forth onto the terrace: "In you come, all of you! Time for lessons!"

The children race across the lawn towards him, laughing and shouting. The two eldest, a girl of thirteen and a boy of twelve, are the first to reach their goal. They are panting, and in the frosty air their breath forms white haloes round their heads. One by one the others come up, the last in the field being a little girl of six.

The dining-room stove is roaring merrily. Inkpots, blotters, and schoolbooks are set out on the big mahogany dining-table. From his study door their father watches the children getting ready. They help each other smilingly, making as little noise as possible, yet unconstrained. Then, without a word from him, silence falls on the group round the table.

Luce crosses the room and goes up the stairs to the next floor. The curtains are drawn in a child's bedroom; a woman, still young, sits at the bedside. Luce gives her a questioning glance, and she indicates by a gesture that the little girl is just dropping off to sleep.

Some moments pass. Then the mother gives a slight start. There has been a ring at the bell. The doctor?

THE MAID: "There's a gentleman to see you, sir. He says he has an appointment. Monsieur Barois."

Barois is alone in Luce's study, a sparsely furnished room, with a big writing-desk strewn with foreign periodicals, recently issued books, and correspondence. Reproductions, maps, and plans hang on two walls, the other two being lined with well-filled bookshelves. In this calm retreat each sound of the world has its echo.

Luce enters.

Marc-Élie Luce is a small man, with an enormous head out of all proportion to the body. He has bright, curiously sunken eyes, a vast forehead, a fan-shaped beard. There is much charm in the limpid pale-gray eyes. Partly owing to his baldness over the temples, the ample forehead, looming high above the remainder of the face, seems to monopolize more than its share of the skull. The auburn beard is already graying.

Luce is forty-seven. The son of a Protestant clergyman, he began by studying theology but soon desisted, feeling he could not subscribe to any dogmatic creed. All he has retained of his early studies is a keen interest in ethical problems.

When quite a young man, he published a work in five large volumes, *The Past and Future of Belief,* which brought him to the fore and secured his appointment to the Chair of Religious History at the Collège de France. He has won high esteem in Auteuil by his keen interest in the "Popular University," which he founded in that district of Paris, and in local charitable organizations. Elected to the Senate, after membership in the General Council, he is one of the youngest senators. He belongs to no party, though claimed as one of theirs in turn by all the groups seeking to make good some lofty ideal. He has published, in this order: *The Higher Levels of Socialism, The Meaning of Life,* and *The Meaning of Death.*

He goes up to Barois and shakes his hand with simple but compelling cordiality.

BAROIS: "Your letter moved us more than I can tell you, sir, and as the spokesman of our little group, I'd like—"

LUCE, cutting in with brusque informality: "Sit down. I'm delighted to make your acquaintance, Monsieur Barois." He has the thick, unctuous intonation characteristic of the part of France he hails from, the Franche-Comté. "I've read your *Sower.*" Looking Barois in the face, he smiles, without false modesty. "The praises of men younger than oneself are always dangerous, I think; one's so vulnerable to them." He pauses. He has picked up *The Sower* from his desk and is skimming the pages as he speaks. "That's a good title—*For the Cultivation of the Best in Man.*"

He is sitting with his legs wide apart, his elbows on his knees, *The Sower* open in his hands. Gazing at the massive, beetling forehead bent over their nascent venture, Barois feels a sudden thrill of pride.

Again Luce skims the pages, lingering over some notes he has pencilled in the margins. He seems to be pondering, weighing the sheets he holds. At last he looks up, meets Barois' eyes, and replaces *The Sower* on his desk.

LUCE, with quiet sincerity: "Make what use of me you like; I'm with you."

The slight provincial intonation seems to stress the gravity of this declaration of allegiance. Taken unawares and profoundly moved, Barois finds himself tongue-tied. He cannot bring himself to tender the current coin of gratitude. For some moments the two men gaze at each other, in a silent communion of thought. At last Barois breaks the silence.

BAROIS: "Ah, if only my friends could have heard what you've just said, and the way in which you said it!"

LUCE, smiling: "How old are you?"

BAROIS: "Thirty-two."

Luce observes him with the candid

smile, untouched by irony, which expresses his attitude to the world: a sort of childish wonder, an eager curiosity, which finds whatever it lights on rare and strange. The two men are silent for a while.

LUCE: "Yes, you're right. An organ like *The Sower* is badly needed. But you're taking on a gigantic task."

BAROIS: "Why?"

LUCE: "Precisely because yours will be the only periodical that makes a fair and square approach to contemporary problems. You'll be widely read—and that's a tremendous responsibility. Don't forget that every line you publish will have consequential effects that spread like ripples and will be beyond your control. More than that: oftener than not you won't even know about them.

"Ah, yes, one always writes too hastily." He seems to be talking to himself. "The sower goes forth to sow. But he must look to his seed, sort out the good from the bad, so as to make as sure as may be that he scatters only the good grain."

BAROIS, proudly: "We have weighed that responsibility—and accepted it."

LUCE, disregarding Barois' remark: "Are your friends of the same age as yourself?"

BAROIS: "About the same."

LUCE, glancing again at the review: "Who is this Breil-Zoeger? Is he related to the sculptor?"

BAROIS: "His son."

LUCE: "Really! My father knew his father; he was one of Renan's closest friends. Isn't your friend a sculptor?"

BAROIS: "No, he took his degree in philosophy. We worked together for the B. Sc."

LUCE: "His 'Prolegomena for a Positive Philosophy' reveals a highly personal outlook, but"—severely—"the outlook of a sectarian." Barois makes a slight gesture of protest. Luce looks up and gazes

at him almost affectionately. "Will you permit me to say quite frankly what I think?"

BAROIS: "Why, certainly!"

LUCE: "I'm inclined to extend that reproach to all your group"—gently—"in particular to you."

BAROIS: "Might I know why?"

LUCE: "In this your first number you've taken up an attitude that's forthright, courageous, but a shade—extremist, shall we say?"

BAROIS: "A fighting attitude."

LUCE: "I'd approve of it wholeheartedly if it were merely combative. But it's *aggressive*. Don't you agree?"

BAROIS: "We're all of us enthusiastic, convinced of the truth of our ideas and ready to fight for them. I've no compunction about showing a certain—intolerance." As Luce makes no comment he continues after a moment's pause. "I believe that any young, forceful theory of life is bound to be intolerant. A conviction which starts by admitting the possible legitimacy of convictions directly opposed to it is doomed to sterility. It has no driving force, no fixity of purpose."

LUCE, firmly: "Yet surely what we should try to cultivate in men is a spirit of mutual forbearance; each of us has the right to be as he is, without his neighbor's forbidding him to be so, on the strength of his personal principles."

BAROIS, with involuntary roughness: "Yes, universal tolerance, freedom for all—it's admirable, in theory. But consider to what the smiling skepticism of the dilettante leads. Would the Church have the power it has in the social order of today, if—"

LUCE, breaking in: "I hardly think I need tell you how heartily opposed I am to all that savors of the clerical! I was born in mid-December 1848, and it's always given me pleasure knowing that I was conceived at a time when the liberal movement was fighting its way up into the light. I detest all that the priesthood stands for, all that sails under false colors, whatever these colors may be. And yet what alienates me from all religious systems, far more than their follies, is their intolerance." He pauses before continuing, measuring his words. "No, I shall never countenance the use of evil methods to counter Evil, when all that's needed is to insist on freedom of thought for all alike—and for oneself to set an example.

"Consider the Catholic Church. It had centuries of supreme authority behind it, and yet all that was needed to shake that tremendous edifice to its foundations was that its opponents should likewise be given the right of openly declaring what they thought." Barois listens, but obviously this attentive silence goes against the grain. Luce now speaks in a conciliatory tone. "Let error have its say, by all means, but let the truth also be free to have its say. And don't let's trouble overmuch about the immediate consequences. Truth will triumph in the end. Don't you agree?"

BAROIS: "Needless to say, I know that, by all abstract standards, you are right. But a man has feelings that he can't control, feelings he simply has to voice." A brief silence. Luce seems to await an explanation. There is an undertone of bitterness in Barois' voice as he proceeds: "Oh, I know quite well that I'm intolerant; I'm through with tolerance!" He lowers his voice. "To understand, you'd need to know all I have been through. A young man of independent mind who is forced to live in an intensely pious atmosphere; who finds himself becoming daily more and more enmeshed in those supple yet fiercely tenacious nets spread by the Catholic Church; who feels religion seeping into his life and into the lives of those around him through every pore, shaping the hearts and souls of those nearest and dearest to him, leaving its imprint every-where—yes, a man who has been through all that, and he only, has the right to speak of tolerance. Not a man who has had to make occasional concessions, out of affection; but a man whose whole life was one long concession. Such a man is qualified to speak of tolerance. And then"—Barois gazes at Luce with a wry smile—"he speaks of it as one speaks of perfect virtue, or of any other ideal which is far beyond the scope of human possibilities."

LUCE, gently, after a brief silence: "You're not—living alone, then?"

Barois' face, darkened until now by memories, lights up; the anger goes out of his eyes.

BAROIS: "I *am* alone now. Free!" He smiles. "But I've enjoyed this freedom too short a time to have regained the virtue of tolerance." He pauses. "Forgive me, Monsieur Luce, for having given way to my feelings on the subject."

LUCE: "I'm to blame. Quite unintentionally of course, I reminded you of—of things you'd prefer forgotten."

They exchange friendly glances.

BAROIS, impulsively: "It's done me good. I need advice. There's more than fifteen years' difference between us. You, Monsieur Luce, have been *living* for twenty-five years. I have only just broken —after many painful struggles—all my chains. Yes, all!" His slashing gesture seems to cut his life in two: on this side, the past; on that, the future. Then he stretches forth his arms. "So, you see, I've a completely new life before me—a vista so immense that it almost makes me dizzy when I contemplate it. My first thought in launching this review was to try to get in contact with you. For I see you as the first landmark on the horizon of my new life."

LUCE, hesitantly: "I'm afraid I can only cite my own experience." He points to one of the large maps hanging on a wall. "I've always felt that life is like one of those maps of countries I have never visited; to find one's way one needs only to know how to read the map. Concentration, orderly thinking, moderation, perseverance—that's all one needs. It's quite simple, really." He again picks up the copy of *The Sower*.

"You've made an excellent start, and you've plenty of trump cards in your hand. In your team you obviously have men with active, original minds. Nothing could be better." He ponders. "If, however, I had any advice to give you, it would take this form. Don't let yourself be influenced too much by your companions. Yes, that's often the danger in groups like yours. Obviously you need community of thought, and that you have. The impulse which brought you together and started you on your venture was the same for all. But don't throw your personality into the melting-pot. 'To thine own self be true'—inexorably. And cultivate in yourself what is truly yours. Each of us has a quality peculiar to himself, a 'gift' if you like, which absolutely distinguishes him from everybody else. It's that gift one must locate within oneself, and promote it, to the exclusion of all else."

BAROIS: "But isn't that narrowing one's scope? Mayn't it sometimes be better to act quite differently, and try to get away from oneself as much as one can?"

LUCE: "No, I don't think so."

THE MAID, putting her head in at the door: "The Mistress asked me to tell you that the doctor's come."

LUCE: "Right." He turns to Barois. "My opinion is that a man should remain himself—but develop his mental stature, and try to become the most perfect specimen of the type of humanity he stands for."

BAROIS, rising: "But shouldn't he act, talk, write, put forth his utmost strength?"

LUCE: "Oh, a strong personality al- ways manages to express itself. Don't have illusions about the usefulness of mere output at all costs. Isn't a noble life as meritorious as a noble work? I too used to think that one had to keep slogging away at it. But gradually I've come to change my mind about it." He is escorting Barois to the door. As they pass the window, he points outside. "That's my garden. Well, isn't it just the same thing there? We have to see to it that the stock is good and then improve it year by year; and, if the function of the tree is to bear fruit, you'll see the crop increasing of its own accord." They are crossing the dining-room. The small heads, bent over the lesson-books, rise as they enter. "My children."

Barois nods, smiling.

LUCE, guessing what is at the back of Barois' mind: "Yes, quite a handful. And I plead guilty to having two more! There are days when I feel all those eyes fixed on me—and I'm appalled!" He shakes his head. "But life's a strict logician, and its findings will be just; of that I feel assured." He goes up to the table. "This is my eldest, quite a big girl already. And this youngster, Monsieur Barois, is a budding mathematician." He fondles the silken curls of each child as he walks by; then suddenly he turns to Barois. "Ah, life's a glorious thing, isn't it?"

## VII

# The Wind Is Rising

*I glimpse a swelling sea, a new day breaking.*
*My heart is like a world . . .*

Ibsen

### I

A June afternoon in 1896. A *brasserie* in the Boulevard Saint-Michel. The hands of the clock point to five. The ground-floor drinking-hall—a huge dark room in the Heidelberg style, with massive tables, wooden stools, and escutcheons on the walls—is thronged with a noisy crowd of students and young women.

On the mezzanine floor a low-ceilinged room is reserved one day a week for the *Sower* group. Cresteil, Harbaroux, and Breil-Zoeger are seated at a wide, semi-circular bay-window extending to floor level. It stands open, and there comes to their ears the hum of traffic in the boulevard below.

Barois comes in, a bulky attaché-case under his arm, and shakes hands with his friends. He sits down and takes some papers from the case.

BAROIS: "Portal not come yet?"

BREIL-ZOEGER: "Haven't seen him."

BAROIS: "And Woldsmuth?"

HARBAROUX: "It's rather odd. I've been going regularly to the Bibliothèque Nationale for the last few days and haven't once set eyes on him."

BAROIS: "He's sent me ten pages on the Education Act—very remarkable they are." He hands a sheaf of papers to Cresteil. "Here are your proofs. They're printed rather close, I'm afraid, but we've so much copy for this number." To Harbaroux. "And here are yours."

HARBAROUX: "Thanks. What date exactly?"

BAROIS: "Roll must have them back at the end of the week." To Breil-Zoeger. "Here are yours. By the way, I'd like to have a word with you about your paper." To the others. "Will you excuse us?" He gets up and goes with Breil-Zoeger to the far end of the room. He speaks in a low voice, affectionately. "It's about your article 'Social Determinism,' old chap. A fine piece of work, incidentally; I doubt if you've ever written anything richer in ideas or more closely reasoned. I took the liberty of reading some of it to Luce last night and he was much impressed by its forcefulness."

BREIL-ZOEGER, complacently: "Good!

Did you read out the passage relating to Pasteur?"

BAROIS: "No. And it's about that I'd like to talk to you before you correct your proofs." Seeing the sulky look that crosses his friend's face, Barois feels slightly embarrassed. "Quite frankly, I find that passage a bit too severe."

BREIL-ZOEGER, with a brisk wave of his arm: "I say nothing against the man of science; I deal with Pasteur as a metaphysician."

BAROIS: "I quite understand that. But you judge Pasteur as you'd judge one of our contemporaries, one of his pupils. Far be it from me to say that his philosophical outlook is commendable. But you seem too much inclined to forget how much our modern scientific materialism owes to that incorrigible believer in a spiritual world."

BREIL-ZOEGER, waving his arm again, as if to brush aside an obstacle: "I know as well as you do what we owe him—though this manner of speaking doesn't imply, as far as I'm concerned, any sentimental obligation." He gives a short, cackling laugh, and for a moment a streak of white flashes across the Chinese-yellow face. "Pasteur thought fit to take up, publicly mind you, a perfectly definite metaphysical standpoint, and we have every right to criticize it. Really, there are limits to one's forbearance in these matters! We've heard too much about that speech he made in answer to the address of welcome when he entered the Académie for us to need to feel any scruples regarding Pasteur."

BAROIS: "The family he sprang from and his education prevented him from drawing the philosophical conclusions that flow from his discoveries, as we of a later generation have been able to do—and thanks to him, don't forget. We can't hold it against him if he wasn't young enough to change his views when he made those great discoveries." He pauses, waiting for an answer, but Breil-Zoeger looks resolutely away. "Those opening pages of yours are unjust, old chap."

BREIL-ZOEGER: "You're under Luce's influence, I can see."

BAROIS: "I wouldn't wish to deny it."

BREIL-ZOEGER: "It's regrettable. Because of that mania he has for toleration Luce often lacks firmness, and sometimes insight too."

BAROIS: "So be it." He pauses. "We'll say no more about the matter. You're free." He smiles. "Free and responsible."

Barois goes back to the table and sits down. A waiter brings drinks.

BAROIS: "Are you sure Portal's coming?"

CRESTEIL: "He told me he'd come."

BREIL-ZOEGER: "Don't let's wait for him."

BAROIS: "The truth is that I've some good news to announce, and I'd have liked all of us to be present. Yes, on the material side our *Sower* is doing exceedingly well. I've just made up our half-yearly accounts." He holds up a ledger. "They're open to your inspection.

"We started off six months ago with thirty-eight regular subscribers. This month we have five hundred and sixty-two. Moreover, we sold last month some eight hundred copies in Paris and the provinces. Our June number, of fifteen hundred copies, is all sold out already."

CRESTEIL: "It's certain that Luce's collaboration has been a tremendous help."

BAROIS: "Obviously. Subscriptions have exactly doubled since he gave us his first contribution four month ago. We're printing two thousand copies of *The Sower* for July. I suggest to you that it should contain two hundred and twenty pages instead of one hundred and eighty as in the past."

BREIL-ZOEGER: "Why?"

BAROIS: "I'll explain. We are having more and more letters sent us relating to articles in our review. Indeed, I've had

nearly three hundred to read this month. With Harbaroux's help I have sorted them out according to the articles with which they deal, and I shall send to each of you the batch of letters relating to his contribution. You'll find that some of them are highly pertinent. In my opinion we should allot space to such correspondence when we're planning the lay-out of our subsequent issues. These letters show that our readers take a keen interest in *The Sower,* and their criticisms are often valuable. This is something to be proud of, and we should do wrong to bury these letters in our files. So I propose that we should publish every month a selection of them, followed when desirable by"— Portal enters—"by a note written by the author of the article referred to."

Portal seems lost in thought and quite unlike his usual cheerful self. After shaking hands with Cresteil and Barois he sits down.

HARBAROUX: "What's this? Won't you shake hands with me?"

PORTAL, rising: "So sorry!" With a faint smile he shakes hands with Harbaroux and sits down again.

BREIL-ZOEGER: "We'd almost given you up."

PORTAL, nervously: "Well, as a matter of fact, I'm shockingly busy just now. I've only just been able to get away from the Law Courts Library." Looking up, he sees the others' eyes intent on him. "There may be—trouble brewing, something quite unexpected."

BAROIS: "Trouble?"

PORTAL: "Yes. I've recently been having glimpses—only glimpses, mind you— of a very distressing possibility. Of a possible miscarriage of justice, to be precise. It may be rather serious, though so far nothing definite has leaked out."

Greatly puzzled, they stare at him in silence.

PORTAL, lowering his voice: "I'm alluding to that Dreyfus Affair."

CRESTEIL: "Dreyfus innocent? Well, really!"

BAROIS: "Preposterous!"

HARBAROUX: "Some mare's nest, obviously."

PORTAL: "Well, nothing tangible has come out as yet—that I admit. I can only tell you what little I know, and, so far as I can judge, no one else knows more at present. But people are feeling uneasy and inquiries are on foot. I've even been told that the General Staff is looking into it. My chief, Fauquet-Talon, is keenly interested and has asked me for a full report of the trial that took place eighteen months ago."

A short silence.

BREIL-ZOEGER, calmly, to Portal: "Obviously errors may creep into the decisions of a civil court which sits every day and may have to get through a great number of cases within a given time. But a court-martial is a very different affair. The men who sit on it are hand-picked; they're not professional purveyors of justice and, for this very reason, are on their mettle and feel bound to go very carefully into the facts before delivering their verdict."

BAROIS: "Especially in so important a case, when the charge is high treason. No, Portal, you'll find that, as Harbaroux said, it's a mare's nest."

CRESTEIL: "And I've a shrewd idea who's behind it. It's a rumor that's been set on foot by—"

WOLDSMUTH, with emotion in his voice, but unhesitatingly: "By the Jews, I suppose?"

CRESTEIL, coldly: "By the Dreyfus family."

BAROIS: "Hullo, Woldsmuth! Are you there? I didn't see you come in."

HARBAROUX: "Nor did I."

BREIL-ZOEGER: "Nor I."

They shake hands with him.

PORTAL, to Woldsmuth: "Have you too been hearing rumors on this subject?"

Slowly Woldsmuth raises his shaggy face, dark now with a vague distress, and looks at Portal. Then, lowering his red-rimmed eyelids, he gives a brief nod.

BAROIS, quickly: "But surely you agree that, in this case, a miscarriage of justice is practically unthinkable?"

Woldsmuth makes a dubious gesture, as if to say: Who knows? Anything's possible. All have a feeling of constraint, aggravated by the short silence which ensues.

BAROIS: "Here you are, Woldsmuth. I've brought your proofs."

PORTAL, to Woldsmuth: "Ever met this fellow Dreyfus?"

WOLDSMUTH, blinking his eyes even more rapidly than usual when he is spoken to: "No." He pauses. "But I was present at his dismissal from the Army. And *I saw.*"

BAROIS, irritably: "Saw what?"

Woldsmuth's eyes grow blurred with tears. Without answering, he gazes timidly at his friends, one after the other; at Barois, Cresteil, Harbaroux, Breil-Zoeger. He knows himself alone, and the forlorn smile of the vanquished molds his lips.

II

October 20, 1896

My dear Barois: It is impossible for me to come to see you, as I have had a slight accident. It's nothing serious but it compels me to stay indoors for some days. Still, I should greatly like to have a talk with you. Could you face the six stories' climb up to my rooms tomorrow, or, at the latest, the day after?

Forgive this importunity, but it's urgent.

Ever yours,
Ulric Woldsmuth

The following day. An enormous old house, more like a block of buildings, in the Rue de la Perle, in the heart of the "Marais" district of Paris. A small attic flat on the sixth floor of Staircase F, numbered 14, stands at the end of a long passage.

A young woman answers Barois' ring and asks him in. There are three rooms opening one into the other. In the first an old gray-haired woman is hanging washing on lines stretched just below the ceiling. In the second are two beds, or, rather, mattresses placed on the floor. The third door is shut. After opening it and peeping in the young woman turns to Barois.

JULIA: "Oh, he's asleep. If you're not in a great hurry . . ."

BAROIS, promptly: "No, please don't wake him. I can wait."

JULIA: "Sleep does him so much good."

Barois, who had no idea that Woldsmuth was married, studies her with interest. There is no mistaking Julia Woldsmuth's oriental origin. Her age is twenty-five. At a first glance she strikes one as very tall and thin. Actually her torso—uncorseted under a black blouse—is thick and short. But her limbs, her arms especially, are extraordinarily long. Her face tapers forward like a knife-blade, and the mass of frizzy jet-black hair bunched on her neck increases its prow-like effect. A pointed nose prolongs the slope of the rather receding forehead. The slotted, half-closed eyes draw upwards towards the temples. The oddly shaped upper lip, which always seems arrested on the brink of a smile, juts out above the lower without touching it.

Briskly she motions Barois to the only chair in the room, and she herself without the least embarrassment squats down on one of the unmade beds.

BAROIS, tentatively: "Might I know

how this—this accident happened, Madame?"

JULIA: "No. Mademoiselle."

BAROIS, smiling: "Sorry!"

JULIA, taking no notice of the remark: "We didn't know at the time. It was after midnight and we'd gone to bed, Mother and I." She points to Woldsmuth's room. "We heard a slight explosion, but that didn't alarm us. In fact I was glad to think my uncle had started work again and was beginning to think less about that case. Next morning he called to us; his face had some nasty cuts—from the splinters of glass, you know—and was burned as well."

BAROIS, much puzzled: "An explosion, you said. Of what?"

JULIA, curtly: "A retort over the Bunsen burner blew up."

Only now does Barois remember that Woldsmuth was once a laboratory assistant. There is a short silence.

BAROIS: "Please don't let me keep you from your work."

Julia is sitting on the tumbled sheets, her legs crossed, her elbows propped on her knees, and is frankly studying Barois' face. Her gaze is friendly and quite un-self-conscious.

JULIA: "You're not disturbing me. I'm glad you called today. I've heard so much about you and I've read all your articles and comments in *The Sower*." After a brief pause she adds with a bluntness that seems curiously impersonal: "Ah, what a splendid life you lead!"

She has Woldsmuth's guttural voice, but her free-and-easy manner makes a striking contrast to his shyness. A queer creature! Barois muses, gazing at her.

BAROIS: "I didn't know that Woldsmuth was still interested in chemistry—in a practical way, I mean."

Julia averts her eyes; a sudden glint of fervor has kindled in their moist pupils.

JULIA: "He never tells anything because he is aiming at a great discovery. 'When I've made it, I'll speak out—but not before'—that's how he feels." Barois says nothing but his look conveys his interest. "Still, he has no reason to make a mystery of it with you, Monsieur Barois. You're a biologist." She warms to her subject. "My uncle believes that some day it will be possible to create life by bringing together certain elements under suitable conditions—I'm sorry I can't express it better." She gives him an almost childish smile.

BAROIS: "To create life?"

JULIA: "Don't you think it possible?"

BAROIS: "Well, I know that, theoretically, it's not ruled out. All the same—"

JULIA, quickly: "Uncle's positive it can be done."

BAROIS: "It's a fine ambition in any case. And really there's no reason why it shouldn't be realized some day." He thinks aloud. "We know that at a certain period of the remote past the temperature of the earth was too high to allow of the vital synthesis. So there was a moment when life did not exist; and then a moment when life existed."

JULIA: "Exactly. And the thing to do is to reproduce the conditions of the moment when life began."

BAROIS, puckering his brows: "Wait a bit! I didn't put it quite that way—'the moment when life began.' I'd be more inclined to say, 'the moment when under certain conditions the vital synthesis took place, a synthesis of elements already existing—from all eternity.'"

JULIA, keenly interested: "Why do you draw that distinction?"

BAROIS, somewhat disconcerted by the technical turn the conversation is taking: "Well, to tell the truth, I think that when one uses the expression 'life began,' it's an unfortunate way of putting it. It panders to that all-too-common tendency to insist on a beginning."

JULIA, still squatting on the bed, an elbow on each knee, and cupping her chin with her hand: "But surely the mere fact of knowing that living matter exists obliges us to assume that it came into existence?"

BAROIS, impulsively: "Certainly not! Personally, I simply cannot stomach that notion of a beginning. But I find it quite easy to accept the notion of a substance that exists, that is always undergoing transformation, and will continue to evolve eternally."

JULIA: "The whole universe being included in the process."

BAROIS: "Yes, and forming a single cosmic substance which can transmit life to all that emanates from it." He pauses. "No doubt you help your uncle in his work?"

JULIA: "A bit."

BAROIS: "And you're experimenting with the rays emitted by radium, I presume?"

JULIA: "Yes."

BAROIS, pensively: "One thing's certain: recent discoveries in chemistry have gone far to bridge the gulf that separated life from death in the past."

For some moments neither speaks.

JULIA, pointing to the typewriter: "You'll excuse me if I go on with my work? Anyhow, I hope you won't have to wait much longer."

She sits down at the table; the tick-tack of the typewriter echoes in the room. Her face shows in dark outline against the whiteness of the window; light ripples on her busy hands, which are paler underneath and seem endowed with almost simian agility. The fingers taper off into very long, ivory-yellow nails. Five minutes go by thus.

WOLDSMUTH'S VOICE: "Julia!"

JULIA: "Ah, you're awake, Uncle! Monsieur Barois has just this minute come."

She opens the door and stands aside to let Barois pass. It is a very narrow doorway, and he cannot help brushing against her, but she seems hardly to notice, and there is nothing feminine in her slight movement of recoil. Indeed, she thrusts her head forward, so close that he feels her breath fan his cheek.

JULIA, under her breath: "Don't say I made you wait."

He reassures her with a glance.

Woldsmuth's bedroom has a glassed-in fore-part, formerly a photographer's studio and now used as a laboratory. In the back of the room is an alcove containing Woldsmuth's bed. The body under the sheets might be a child's; indeed, so small is it that the big head swathed in bandages seems hardly to belong to it.

BAROIS: "Dreadfully sorry, old chap, to see you like this. Are you in pain?"

WOLDSMUTH: "No." He still clasps Barois' hand. "Julia will bring you a chair." Barois forestalls her and draws a chair up to the bedside. Julia goes out. Speaking with a proud affection that tries to sound paternal, Woldsmuth adds: "She's my niece."

The tone of voice is the same, but Woldsmuth himself is unrecognizable. Layers of dressing cover his hair, nose, and beard; the only signs of life are a dim smile and the soft brown eyes under the bushy eyebrows.

WOLDSMUTH: "Thank you very much for coming, Barois."

BAROIS: "But, my dear Woldsmuth, that was only natural. What's the trouble?"

WOLDSMUTH, in a changed tone: "Oh, Barois, it's high time that all people of good will should know what's happening. He's exiled over there, he'll die of his privations—and he's innocent!"

BAROIS, smiling at this obsession, due he thinks to illness: "Still harping on that fellow Dreyfus?"

WOLDSMUTH, propping himself on his elbows, excitedly: "I beg you, Barois, I beseech you in the name of all that's just and decent in the world, to clear your mind of prejudice. Forget all you read in the newspapers two years ago and all the stories that you've heard. I entreat you, Barois, to listen to me." He sinks back upon the pillows. "Oh, I know we're always talking about our duty to the cause of human happiness. Yes, it's easy to take an interest in humanity at large, in mankind in the mass, in people whose sufferings will never come under our eyes." He gives a nervous laugh. "But that's nothing, *nothing!* The love one feels for one's real, *literal* neighbor, for those whose sufferings are visible at our door—that's love indeed, the only love that matters." He sits up in bed. "So, Barois, I beg you to forget all you've learned about this business and hear me out."

All the life of the man, a shapeless lump of bandages, seems concentrated in the restless, ardent eyes, full of mute appeal.

BAROIS: "I'm listening. And please don't overexcite yourself."

Woldsmuth ponders for some moments, then takes from underneath the sheets a sheaf of typewritten pages and runs his eyes over them. But in the alcove where he lies darkness is closing in.

WOLDSMUTH, raising his voice: "Julia! Bring a lamp, please."

The typewriter stops clicking. Julia enters with a small hand-lamp that she places on the bedside table.

WOLDSMUTH: "Thanks." She gives him a frigid smile. The brown eyes, glowing between the bandages, follow affectionately her receding form. Then he turns to Barois. "Let's go right back to the begin-

ning, as if you knew nothing at all about it. The bare facts to start with.

"Well then, a discovery is made at the War Ministry that there has been a leakage of official documents. Next, the head of the Bureau of Statistics, so-called—meaning, of course, the French Intelligence—hands the Minister a letter said to have been found among other papers filched from the German Embassy. The letter, written by hand, is what they call the *bordereau* and consists of a list of documents which the writer of the letter is making over to his addressee.

"So much for the initial facts.

"Efforts are made to trace the traitor. Of five documents listed in the *bordereau* three relate to the Artillery. So the inquiry centers on the artillery officers of the General Staff. Owing to a certain resemblance in the handwriting suspicion falls on Dreyfus. He is a Jew, and unpopular. But at the preliminary investigation nothing against him is discovered."

BAROIS: "So you say."

WOLDSMUTH: "What I say is borne out by the fact that the indictment sets forth nothing suspicious either in Dreyfus's private life or in his contacts with outsiders. Nothing, that is to say, but mere guess work."

BAROIS: "Have you read the bill of indictment?"

WOLDSMUTH, holding up a sheet: "I have a copy here, which I'll let you have." A short silence. "The next step is to call in two handwriting experts. One of them does not think that the incriminating letter is in Dreyfus's hand. The other thinks it may be, but his report begins with a very important reservation." He looks through his papers. "This is how it reads: 'If we ignore the possibility that this may be a very carefully executed forgery . . .' Meaning, I think .you will agree, that the writing has much in common with that of Dreyfus, but it's

impossible definitely to say if it is his or the work of a forger.

"Do you follow, Barois?"

BAROIS, very coldly: "Yes, I follow."

WOLDSMUTH: "On the strength of these two conflicting opinions his arrest is ordered. Yes—without any further investigation, without even keeping the movements of the suspect under surveillance. Everyone is morally convinced that he is guilty—and that suffices. He is arrested.

"Here comes a dramatic incident which I'll describe in detail.

"Dreyfus is summoned one morning to the War Office for a 'general inspection.' He is instructed to attend in civilian clothes—which is contrary to all military precedent. That's the first remarkable feature of these proceedings. Note that, were he guilty, this would have roused his suspicion and he'd have had time to make his escape. He does nothing of the kind. He duly arrives at the appointed hour and finds none of the brother-officers present who would normally have been summoned to attend a meeting of this sort. Another surprise.

"He is promptly ushered into the Chief of Staff's office. The General is not there, but a small group of men in mufti whom he does not know are standing in a corner of the room, all watching him intently. Then, without a word about the inspection, a Major says to him, 'I've hurt my hand. Would you kindly write a letter for me?'

"The moment seems an odd one for asking of a junior officer a friendly service of this kind. There is, in fact, an atmosphere of mystery about the whole proceedings—in the attitude of those present no less than in the things they say.

"Much puzzled, Dreyfus sits down at the desk.

"Then the Major starts dictating to

him a letter so phrased as to include some passages from the famous *bordereau*. Naturally they mean nothing to Dreyfus, but the hostility of his superior officer's voice, coupled with the tension in the air of which he has been conscious since entering the room, affects his nerves and, as a result, his handwriting. The Major looks over his shoulder and exclaims, 'Ah, your hand is trembling!' Dreyfus, who has failed to grasp the reason for this remark, which sounds like a reprimand, apologizes. 'My fingers are a bit cold, I'm afraid.'

"The dictation continues. Dreyfus tries to write more steadily. The Major breaks in irritably, 'Take care! It's serious.' Then suddenly, 'I arrest you, in the name of the law!' "

BAROIS, greatly impressed: "But from where did you get this story of yours? The *Éclair* version of what happened was quite different." Rising, he takes some steps in the dimly lighted room. "What reasons have you for assuming that your version is the true one?"

WOLDSMUTH: "I know the source from which the newspaper got its information. The published description of the incident is a travesty of the facts." He lowers his voice. "Barois, I've had in my hands a photograph of the dictated letter. Yes, I've seen it with my own eyes. Well, the traces of emotion in the writing are very slight and easily explicable. I cannot believe that a traitor who has been found out and is ordered to write the very words he used when betraying a secret to a foreign power could conceivably show such imperturbability. It's unthinkable!" Barois says nothing. "And there's something else I've discovered. The warrant of arrest was signed a day before the dictation took place; in fact his arrest had been so effectively decided on—whatever might take place that morning—that the prison cell had been got ready on the previous evening."

Barois still keeps silent. He sits at the bedside, his arms folded, holding himself very straight, his head thrown back a little, his eyebrows lifted, his chin thrust pugnaciously forward.

There is a short silence while Woldsmuth peers at his notes. Then, raising his eyes, he leans towards Barois.

WOLDSMUTH: "So Dreyfus is thrown into prison. Though the mental torture would have been enough to drive many a man crazy, for a whole fortnight he was not allowed even to know why he had been arrested, nor was he informed of the charge against him.

"Meanwhile inquiries were being pushed forward in various quarters. He was repeatedly interrogated—without result. Searches were made at his home. His wife was questioned under the most brutal conditions; she was not allowed to know where her husband was, and was even told she'd be signing his death-warrant if she told anyone whomsoever about his disappearance.

"At last, on the fifteenth day, Dreyfus was shown the *bordereau*. With the energy of despair he protested that he knew nothing about it. But all to no avail; the preliminary inquiry ran its course.

"The Court-Martial Board took cognizance of the case, and a second inquiry was set on foot. Dreyfus was interrogated again, plied with new questions, witnesses were examined, accomplices sought—but still to no effect. No solid evidence against him was forthcoming.

"Then, Barois, for the first time the Minister of War publicly entered the lists; in a press interview he declared that the guilt of the accused man was proved to the hilt, but he could make no further statement on the subject.

"Some weeks later Dreyfus was tried *in camera*, found guilty, and sentenced to transportation for life."

BAROIS: "Well, my dear fellow, doesn't

his conviction shake your confidence that the man was innocent? If no serious charge had been established against Dreyfus, can you possibly imagine that a board of officers—"

WOLDSMUTH, excitedly: "Yes, I tell you, I *assure* you, that in a four days' trial it was proved beyond all doubt that Dreyfus had never engaged in any treasonable practices, that his alleged journeys abroad, his straitened circumstances, his love affairs, and all the anti-Semitic press had published to rouse popular opinion against him—all these things were so much idle talk, without the least foundation in fact."

BAROIS, shrugging his shoulders: "None the less, two colonels, two majors, and two captains were prepared to . . . Really, my dear fellow, it's preposterous, what you've been saying."

A glint of satisfaction flickers in the sick man's eyes; he is glad that Barois is not yet convinced. The more resistance he puts up now, the stronger will be his conviction, the fiercer his indignation in the end.

WOLDSMUTH, holding up the typewritten pages: "The whole truth is here."

BAROIS: "What exactly have you there?"

WOLDSMUTH: "A report, Barois; a verbatim report of all that happened. Compiled by a man who's practically unknown, a man who has a heart of gold and, with it, a lucid, admirably logical mind."

BAROIS: "And what's your paragon's name?"

WOLDSMUTH: "Bernard Lazare." Barois makes a gesture implying: Never heard of him. "Now you must hear me out. For there's more to tell, much more. I asked you to come to see me so that you should know what's happened. But for another reason too." In a tone whose authoritativeness is as unlooked-for as it is compelling, he goes on: "Barois, we

must defeat this conspiracy of lies, of reticences and foul insinuations, which is crushing out the truth. We must see to it that a voice respected by all secures a hearing; that a man whose honesty none dares to question learns the true facts, obeys the dictates of his conscience, and boldly denounces, on behalf of all of us, the wrong that has been done." Shoring himself up on his arms, he is watching his friend's face to see if he has grasped what is expected of him. But Barois' face is hard, impassive. A note of pleading enters Woldsmuth's voice as he makes himself explicit. "In a word, what's wanted is that Luce should give an interview to Bernard Lazare." Barois makes a fretful gesture. "Luce must be induced to listen to him, without prejudice, with all the impartiality of the upright man he is." He waves the typewritten sheets. "A hundred thousand copies of this pamphlet must be printed. This is a crusade in the cause of justice in which neither you nor I nor Luce can fail to take up arms."

Barois begins to rise from his chair.

WOLDSMUTH: "Wait, Barois. Do, please, suspend judgment a little longer. And please, oh, please, don't say anything—yet." In a tone of entreaty. "All I ask is for you to judge for yourself, and not to let your mind be biased by what you may have heard from others. I shall now read out some fragments of Lazare's pamphlet, and you cannot fail, I think, to be impressed by its fervor in the cause of justice—simple, human justice." Feverishly. "Where shall I begin? Yes. Listen to this first.

" 'Captain Dreyfus was arrested after two experts had given *contradictory* opinions.

" 'The inquiry was conducted in a most high-handed fashion. Yet all it revealed was the utter absurdity of the rumors current about Dreyfus, and the falsehood of the police reports, which were flatly contradicted by the witnesses, and on which the prosecution dared not insist.

" 'Thus the whole case for the prosecution rested on a sheet of thin notepaper, a schedule of documents written in a peculiar hand and style, which had been torn in four pieces and carefully stuck together again.

" 'Where did this incriminating document come from? According to Besson d'Ormescheville's report, General Joux, when handing it to the police officer conducting the inquiry, told him that this *bordereau* had originally been addressed to a foreign Power, and had reached its destination. However, under orders from the War Minister, he could not divulge the channel by which the *bordereau* had come to him.

" 'Thus the prosecution has no idea how this unsigned, undated piece of writing was sent by the accused man to its destination; while the defense is kept in ignorance of the channels through which it made its way from the Embassy to the War Office; to whom it was originally addressed; and who it was who purloined it or by some other means procured it.' " Woldsmuth looks up from the page he has just read aloud.

"I should mention that in an earlier page he makes clear the unconvincingness of the document in itself. Just a moment, please. Ah, yes, here it is. I'll read out the passage.

" 'Is the document itself authentic? No.

" 'Let us first consider its origin; or, rather, the origin attributed to it. According to M. Montville, writing in *Le Journal* of September 16, 1894, it was found at the German Embassy by an office-boy who had the habit of making over to the French Intelligence Service the contents of the wastepaper baskets. Was there ever any employee at the Embassy who indulged in these practices? Yes. Was the

Embassy staff unaware of this? No. When did it come to the knowledge of the Embassy? A year before the Dreyfus case. Under what circumstances?' " Woldsmuth looks up again.

"I have a report of the trial of Mme Millescamps in the Court of Summary Jurisdiction. You can peruse it later. Meanwhile I'll go straight on with Lazare's summary.

" 'Thus, a year before the Dreyfus trial, the staff of the German Embassy was well aware that the contents of wastepaper baskets were being transmitted by some unknown person to the French Intelligence Service. At the time of the trial it was not known whether the person in question was or was not still in the Embassy's employ. Thus they were constantly on the alert and took every possible precaution.

" 'This being so, can it be believed that a member of the staff would merely tear into four pieces and drop into a wastepaper basket a document so compromising for a highly valuable agent, a man whose services they wanted at all costs to retain—when they knew full well that these scraps of paper would find their way to the French Intelligence Service?

" 'Thus the origin we are asked to attribute to this document lacks all plausibility; unless'—this is important—'it was deliberately concocted by a forger working hand in glove with one of the German Embassy servants, thanks to whose assistance this forged *bordereau*—giving a list of documents which actually have never been delivered to the German Embassy—was dropped into a wastepaper basket, from which it was taken and transmitted to the War Ministry through the usual channels.

" 'Now let us examine the verisimilitude of the *bordereau* itself. Can we see any plausible reason why a man who makes a business of malpractices of this kind should attach a superfluous and compromising invoice to the documents he is sending? Normally a spy or traitor takes care not to leave any traces behind him. If he is transmitting documents, he commits them to a chain of intermediaries whose task it is to see they reach their destination. *But never will he put anything down in writing.* Here we should note that the prosecution finds much difficulty in explaining how a document of this kind could have been transmitted. To send it by ordinary post would be the height of folly. Was it then delivered by hand? If so, what was the point of giving a list, what need was there for writing one, instead of handing over the secret documents direct to their recipient?

" 'Indeed, the absurdity of both hypotheses was so patent that the prosecution did not even venture to put them forward.'

"Do you follow me, Barois?"

Barois nods emphatically. He is no longer feigning aloofness. Leaning forward, his elbows on his knees, his chin between his hands, his eyes intently, almost sternly, fixed on the inexpressive bandage-swathed head, none of whose movements escapes him, his nostrils fluttering, his heart thudding, lips parted in tense absorption, he is waiting for what is yet to come, hoping still that what he has just heard is a mere piece of special pleading.

WOLDSMUTH, after a long, silent scrutiny of his friend's face: "Now I'll continue reading.

" 'During the investigation, which lasted two months, was it discovered that Captain Dreyfus had associated with any suspicious characters? No. Yet in that curious missive we find the words: "Unless I hear from you that you wish to see me . . ." Had he then been seeing his mysterious correspondent? His life has been ransacked, all his movements and doings have been scrutinized minutely,

yet not a single compromising contact has been alleged against him.

" 'At no stage of the case has the prosecution been able to produce a single fact or make a single allegation suggesting that Captain Dreyfus had any dealings whatsoever with any foreign agent, even in the service of the French High Command.

" 'Then, again, what motives could have prompted Captain Dreyfus to the crime with which he has been charged? Was he short of money? No, he was a rich man. Had he any expensive liaisons or vices? None. Was he a miser? No, he lived up to his considerable means and did not increase his wealth. Is he a neurotic type, liable to sudden, irrational impulses? No, he is an eminently levelheaded man, lacking neither competence nor courage. What motive, then, could this happy man have had for imperilling his happiness? None.

" 'So here we have an Army officer with a spotless character, with no bad habits or tendencies, whom the persons themselves who conducted the inquiry found to be honest, industrious, conscientious, and a reliable officer—and suddenly he is shown a piece of notepaper, whose origin is as obscure as its wording is equivocal, and told: "This was written by you! Three experts affirm it, and two deny it!" With the energy inspired by a clear conscience this man denies the odious charge brought against him and protests his innocence. While admitting the blamelessness of his past life, but basing its judgment on the evidence of the handwriting experts, contradictory though this is, the Court sentences him to military degradation and imprisonment for life.' "

There is a long silence.

WOLDSMUTH: "Now I'll read you what Lazare has to say about the 'secret dossier.'

" 'The "evidence" so far produced was

obviously inadequate, and General Mercier, the Minister of War, was informed that the Court, having nothing else to go on, leaned towards an acquittal.

" 'And now, despite a definite promise given to the Minister for Foreign Affairs to the contrary, General Mercier thought fit to communicate to the Court *in secret* —even the counsel for the accused man was not permitted to be present—a document he had been keeping in reserve for such an emergency, should it arise. What was this crucial piece of evidence?

" 'It related, according to *L'Éclair*, to the activities of spies in Paris, and contained the phrase, "Definitely that rascal Dreyfus is beginning to expect too much."

" 'Did any such letter exist? Yes. Was it shown confidentially to the judges? Yes.

" 'Was the phrase quoted by *L'Éclair* in that letter? I say it was *not*.

" 'I affirm that the man who handed over to the newspaper in question this highly confidential document—whose divulgence, owing to the diplomatic complications that might ensue, was so much feared that it was produced only in a secret session of the Court—I affirm that this man did not shrink from yet another infamous deed, that of falsifying this highly important document, whose publication was intended to assure the world at large of the guilt of that unhappy victim of injustice who for two years has been undergoing hell on earth.

" 'For the letter shown the Court did not contain the name of Dreyfus, but only an initial *D*.

" 'In its issue of November 10, 1894, *L'Éclair* does not contest my statement; but on this subject I have more to say.

" 'This letter, made public for the first time by *L'Éclair*—despite the veil of secrecy which the authorities had sought to impose—was transmitted to the Ministry of War by the Minister for Foreign Affairs *about eight months before the Dreyfus case.*

" 'So true is it that the letter did not contain Dreyfus's name that for several weeks an employee in the Ministry of War was shadowed and kept under close surveillance because he was unlucky enough to have a name beginning with *D*. Then this trail was abandoned, as were some others subsequently followed, and finally the letter was pigeon-holed and forgotten. No suspicions fell on Dreyfus, and no further thought was given to this letter until the *bordereau* was intercepted and attributed to Dreyfus.

" 'Thus the account given in *L'Éclair* of September 15, 1894, was inaccurate.

" 'We may now consider the plausibility of this letter on internal grounds. Let us suppose that a foreign Power has been fortunate enough to secure the complicity of a staff officer and this officer supplies it with documents of a highly confidential nature. That Power will set a very high value on his services, will do its utmost to safeguard his co-operation, and will take, in consultation with him, all possible precautions to prevent his coming under suspicion. Moreover, obeying the dictates of the most elementary prudence, this foreign Power will be at pains not to compromise by any indiscretion the career of a man so useful to itself; still less will it risk mentioning in a letter, which may go astray or be intercepted, the name of the officer in question.

" 'From which it follows that, unless and until the Government formally denies this, the conviction of Dreyfus, unjustified by any adequate evidence, was secured by the eleventh-hour production of a letter, inspection of which was persistently refused to the accused man and to his counsel. In the course of the trial the letter was not put in evidence; thus there was no opportunity of discussing it, questioning its authenticity or the justification for assuming that the initial *D* should be taken to refer to a man against whom there was no other evidence of any value.

" 'Can we tolerate a man's being thus convicted out of hand, without allowing him access to anything that might serve him to defend his cause? Is it not scandalous that pressure should have been brought to bear, outside the Court, on the minds of the judges, so as to influence their decision? Is it legal for any person whomsoever to enter a courtroom where a case is under trial and to say to the President of the Court, "Forget all you may have heard in favor of the man you are trying. We have documents in our hands which, *for reasons of State* and for the avoidance of diplomatic complications, we have kept secret from him and which we ask you, too, to keep secret. We can vouch for their authenticity and reliability." Yet it was on such grounds as these that the Court delivered judgment! Not one of its members rose and said: "You are asking us to act against the most elementary principles of equity; we cannot do as you wish."

" 'And so effectively had public opinion been misled and the accused man held up to the nation as the most despicable of criminals, unworthy of any pity, that no one even thought of protesting against the *manner* in which the "traitor" had been tried and sentenced. Even those whose patriotism is normally outraged whenever proceedings are taken against an Army officer chose to overlook the irregularities of procedure in this trial; so convinced were they that, in the interests of the country, this man, no matter what the means employed, must pay the penalty of his crime.

" 'Had this feeling not prevailed, many a voice would have been heard—and perhaps ere long, once the cloud of prejudice has lifted, such voices *will* be

heard—protesting in the cause of justice. We seem to hear them saying: "If such abuse of authority and such high-handed methods be connived at, the freedom of every Frenchman is imperilled, placed at the mercy of officialdom. No French citizen, facing a criminal charge, can feel assured of being permitted to exercise even the elementary rights of self-defense to which every man on trial is entitled." ' "

Barois is bending forward, his hands pressed to his forehead. His look conveys compassion and profound distress. He is staring fixedly, desperately, at the bare floor, his gaze focused on a split tile welded together by dust. Woldsmuth's deep voice, hoarse with fatigue and the stress of his emotion, comes to him again across the shadows.

WOLDSMUTH, still reading the typescript: " 'There still is time to make amends. We must not allow it to be said that because a Jew was on trial, a French court made light of justice. It is in the cause of justice that I protest; in the cause of the justice that these men flouted. For Captain Dreyfus is an innocent man; his conviction was procured by illegal methods, and the case must be reviewed.

" 'And the new trial must not take place *in camera,* the whole French public must have access to the courtroom.

" 'I therefore lodge an appeal against the judgment of the Court-Martial. New facts have been elicited; therefore, on legal grounds, the judgment should be quashed and a retrial ordered. But there are things at stake on a higher level than that of legal quibbles. What is at stake is a man's right to preserve his freedom and to defend his innocence when a false charge has been made against him.' "

Completely exhausted, Woldsmuth sinks back heavily on the pillows. His eyes are closed, and all life seems to have receded from the bandaged head, monstrous as that of the grotesque puppets paraded at *mi-carême*. Only the small hands resting on the sheets and quivering spasmodically seem alive.

Barois rises and takes some heavy steps across the room; then goes up to the bed and halts, his legs planted well apart, his breast heaving, his hands spread open, level with his chest. Before speaking he draws a deep breath.

BAROIS: "Anyhow, we must make inquiries and get at the truth of the matter. This feeling of doubt is unbearable. And I promise that Luce shall see your friend, not later than tomorrow."

October 22, 1896
My dear Barois: Monsieur Bernard Lazare has just left, after spending the afternoon with me. You know what was my state of mind yesterday evening; I am unable to change so quickly, but I must admit I was greatly impressed by what he said to me.

This whole business seems to me of such gravity and so beset with dangers that I feel it would be disastrous to take up a position hastily or decide on any line of conduct without very serious reflection. I therefore refused, for the moment, to lend my name to any project that may be now on foot, but I assured M. Lazare of my good will, which indeed is not only sincere but wholehearted. One soon realizes that he is one of those men for whom the whole array of the powers-that-be—the State, officialdom, the intellectual, and even the moral arbiters of our present-day world—weighs less than a feather in the balance against the dictates of his conscience. Moreover, he has a lucid, logical mind, and his arguments were most disturbing.

Yes, it is impossible not to be horrified at the thought that so flagrant a travesty of justice may have been enacted under our eyes. And I should find a life, haunted by such an apprehension, quite intolerable.

Therefore I wish to know the truth. I want to be reassured. I am still convinced that there is something behind all this which we do not know, and which will put an end to our anxiety. So I have decided to make thorough and conscientious inquiries on my own account, and of course I shall keep you posted as to their results.

Meanwhile, my dear Barois, please do not speak to me of this most distressing matter; let me retain all the lucidity and detachment I would wish to bring to so difficult a problem. I attach great importance to this request. And, if I may give you a word of advice, avoid this subject likewise when talking to your friends. Opinions are already overheated, and all this stirring up of passions can lead to no good result.

My eldest boy has quite recovered. But now we are worried again by the health of our dear little Antoinette; I greatly fear we shall have to risk the operation. It is a terrible anxiety for me, my dear Barois, and for my poor wife. But, with a large family, peace of mind is always round the corner.

All my good wishes—and meanwhile, I beg you, not a word about that subject.
Yours,
Marc-Élie Luce

III

Luce's study. It is mid-July 1897, and the morning sun is shining gaily, the air shimmering with heat outside the open windows. Beyond the white cambric curtains lies an expanse of vividly green foliage, and the garden is loud with twittering sparrows and the happy cries of children.

Barois is sitting, silent and attentive, facing Luce, who is at his desk, holding himself straight in his chair, but with his head slightly bowed, as though the weight of the big skull were dragging it down. Shaded by the brows, his vision-haunted eyes are fixed on Barois.

LUCE, in a carefully controlled voice: "You understand, Barois, that I would not make these statements without being quite positive about the facts. When you came here eight months ago and arranged for my meeting with Bernard Lazare, I realized at once the risks involved. I had read the *Éclair* article and knew about that story of a 'secret document.'" Bitterly. "But I'd refused to believe it. Then the details given by Lazare shook my confidence; I wanted to *know.*" Sadly. "And now I know!" He pauses, then, in a louder voice: "Eight months ago I didn't dare to suspect that the military judges, fully aware of their responsibilities, would have allowed the Minister of War personally to intervene in the trial; still less, that they'd have let him put in evidence secret documents, which neither the accused nor his counsel was permitted to see.

"Since then, alas, I've learned far more. I've discovered not only that a secret dossier was produced and deliberately concealed from the accused man by his officer-judges, but also that this file did not even contain any evidence of such an overwhelming nature—though this could not excuse the irregular procedure of the Court—that it might at least have set our minds at rest as to the verdict. No, none of the documents in it seriously implicated Dreyfus; they merely raised presumptions which could as easily be interpreted in his favor as against him." He taps the table with his fingers, to emphasize each point. "That, I can assure you, is the truth of the matter."

Barois keeps quite still. His legs splayed out, his hands resting on his knees, he listens. His darkly glowing eyes and set features betray no surprise, only a keen interest in what he now is hearing.

LUCE, placing his hand on a sheaf of documents tied up with tape: "I'll spare you the details, and only tell you that I've spent eight solid months on this investigation, putting all my other work aside." A brief smile lights up his face. "You'll have noticed that I've not been able regularly to supply *The Sower* with the weekly article I promised. Thanks to my seat in the Senate, and with the help of some old friends, I have been enabled to tap the sources and verify all the information given me. Lazare supplied me with photographs of all the essential documents. So I have been able to con them here in my study, at leisure. I've also had them examined by the best handwriting experts in Europe." He lays his hand on a file. "It's all recorded there. I now know all that can be known about the case, and"—he weighs his words—"I no longer have any doubts—not the shadow of a doubt."

BAROIS, rising to his feet: "The world must hear of this! We must make these facts known—to the Ministry of War, to start with."

Luce says nothing for a moment; then he fixes his eyes on Barois. A faint, sad smile flickers over his lips and seems to vanish into his beard. Then, in an impulse of expansiveness, he leans forward.

LUCE: "Let me tell you of a curious experience I've had. Only last Monday—at exactly this hour of the morning, to be precise—I was closeted in one of the offices of the Ministry of War with an old friend of mine, a cavalryman, who now holds a very high post on the staff.

"I hadn't seen him for two years. He welcomed me with many demonstrations of friendship. But no sooner did I mention the name of Dreyfus than he sprang to his feet in a tearing rage! He wouldn't let me put a word in, shouted me down, and behaved exactly as if I'd come there just to pick a quarrel with him! All this gave me a most disagreeable impression, as you may imagine. But I'd made up my mind to see it through and stood my ground. Finally I was able to tell him what I'd come to tell; I set out the facts I'd patiently collected and verified and for whose truth I could vouch. Folding his arms, he fell to pacing his office—with such heavy strides that I could hear his jack-boots creak—but not a word came from his lips. No doubt the medicine I'd been giving him had proved too strong! After a while he returned to his chair and, with all the calmness he could muster, asked me some questions about the feeling on the subject in the Senate, and in the world of university professors, scientists, and others with whom I came in contact. I had an impression that he wanted to size up the potential opposition before deciding what line to adopt. I gripped his hand and begged him on the strength of our long friendship, in the cause of justice, to take action. 'There still is time,' I said. 'A scandal's liable to break at any moment, but so far it's only latent. By acting promptly you may still avert it. Let the Army make the first move and the situation will be saved. The best of men may blunder on occasion, and then the only decent thing to do is to own up to one's mistake and make amends.' But I came up against an obviously uneasy, but none the less obstinate silence. Then brusquely he rose, had a third party come into the office, and showed me out politely—without a word as to his intentions, without a word of encouragement."

Luce's emotion shows in his face; he is silent for some moments.

LUCE: "Then, Barois, I came back slowly, on foot, along the Seine." In a broken voice. "And for quite a while—incredible as this may sound—I wondered if it weren't he who was in the right." Barois gives a slight start. Luce raises his arm, then lets it fall despondently. "I saw so clearly what the result would be once we made public our doubts of Dreyfus's guilt."

BAROIS: "The chief result would be his rehabilitation."

LUCE: "Granted. But don't let's hoodwink ourselves. There would be other consequences, more far-reaching ones. It would mean a bitter conflict between the claims of strict justice and the whole structure of the nation. A war to the knife and perhaps, viewed from one angle, an unholy war."

BAROIS, vehemently: "Really, Luce! How can you—?"

LUCE, breaking in: "Hear me out. If Dreyfus is innocent, as is certain, or practically certain—on whom will the blame fall? Who will take his place in the dock? The General Staff of the French Army."

BAROIS: "What of it?"

LUCE: "And behind the General Staff is the present government of the French Republic, that established order to which we have owed our national life for a quarter of a century." Barois says nothing; Luce pauses before continuing: "Never shall I forget that long slow walk along the river-bank! I was faced by the most horrible dilemma. That of knowing the truth and shutting one's eyes to it; of bowing to an unjust decision because it was made in the due course of law by the Army and by the Government and—this we must admit—with the whole-hearted approval of public opinion. *Or,* of choosing the other alternative: impugning, evidence in hand, a judicial error, stirring up a world-wide scandal and deliberately, like a red revolutionary, launching a direct attack on the established order of our country, the Constitution to which we owe allegiance."

Barois ponders for some moments; then, abruptly, squares his shoulders.

BAROIS: "No hesitation is possible."

LUCE, tranquilly: "Yet I *did* hesitate. I couldn't bring myself to shatter without compunction the relative peace and good esteem which our young republic has been enjoying for a number of years." He gazes intently at Barois. "I quite understand your indignation, your fervor in the cause of the right, of doing justice though the skies fall! But I hope you'll let me say, Barois, that our respective attitudes cannot be quite the same in this respect. Into your ardor to take sides there enters—how shall I put it?—a personal element. Let me know if I'm mistaken. You feel, as it were, a private satisfaction in all this; to put it bluntly, a sense of having your revenge."

BAROIS, smiling: "That's so; you've sized me up accurately enough. Yes, I rather enjoy taking up a position on what 'right-minded' people call the wrong side of the barricade." Earnestly. "For there's no denying it, our adversaries today are the same as those I took up arms against in my youth: routine, despotism, indifference to all that's noble and sincere. And, when you come to think of it, our faith, whether it's founded on truth or on illusion—ah, what an infinitely finer thing it is than theirs!"

LUCE: "I appreciate your feelings. But don't blame me if I hesitate at a moment when we may be called on to lay bare our rottenness to the eyes of all the world." Barois makes no reply, but his smile and the look in his eyes convey: I admire you with all my heart; how can you speak of my "blaming" you? "This whole last week has been a terrible ordeal to me; I've been torn among a host of conflicting motives." Sadly. "I have even caught myself listening to the voice of self-interest. Yes, my dear Barois, I've counted the cost of what I would be risking as a private person if I spoke out, if I elected to cut a figure in this ugly business. And, to my disgust, I felt a qualm of fear."

BAROIS: "You're exaggerating the risk, surely?"

LUCE: "No. There's every chance, given the prevailing mood of the public, that I'd be sunk, irremediably sunk, within a couple of months. And don't forget, my friend, I have nine children." Barois nods. "You see, you know I'm right about the risks. Nevertheless"—a new warmth enters his voice—"such is our predicament today that I cannot 'slink out of the race' without playing false to the whole trend of my life. I have always made truth my ideal and, with it, justice—which is truth put into practice. I've always had a firm conviction—and events have borne it out time and again —that a man's most obvious duty, the one form of satisfaction that never lets him down, lies in the pursuit of truth with all the strength that is in him and in his refusal to allow any consideration whatever to deflect him from that end. And sooner or later, appearances notwithstanding, he discovers that in choosing this path he chose best.

"Each of us must bow to his life principle; mine forbids me to hold my peace today. Indeed, never have I so clearly realized that, while the work of all enables some of us to lead the meditative life, and these solitary efforts are needful since, joined end to end, they further progress—in return this privileged position of the thinker imposes on him duties that he may not, *cannot*, shirk. He must recognize them as such whenever they present themselves; and this is one of those occasions."

Barois nods quietly. Luce rises to his feet.

LUCE: "I've no intention of setting up as a knight-errant. All I want is for my cry of warning to reach the ears of the authorities, and to swing public opinion round towards a saner outlook. Once this is done I intend to hand over the results of my investigations—as a working plan—to whomever it may concern. You follow?" With a look of profound distress. "If only to shake off this incubus of doubt that's stifling me . . .

"If Dreyfus is guilty—and with all my heart I still hope that he is!—let it be proved in open court. But, at all costs, let's have done with this hideous uncertainty!"

He walks heavily to the window and steeps his gaze in the cool green shadows of the garden. Some moments pass. Then, as if suddenly remembering why he had asked Barois to come, he swings round and places both hands on his friend's shoulders.

LUCE: "Barois, if I'm to voice my appeal to all that's decent in France today, I shall need a springboard." Hesitantly. "Would you consent to flinging your *Sower* into the fray?" So revealing is the glow of pride that lights up Barois' face that he makes haste to continue: "No, no, my friend; hear me first and think it over carefully. For two years you've been throwing yourself wholeheartedly into this review and it's making splendid headway. Well, if it becomes my mouthpiece, everything's imperilled and, likely as not, your fine endeavor will fall to pieces."

Barois has squared his shoulders, but he is too much carried away by his feelings to answer. A rush of joy, of fanatic pride, traverses him as he gazes at his friend. Luce understands. The tension in the air increases, and impulsively, their hearts throbbing in the silence of unspoken thoughts, the two men stretch out their arms and embrace each other.

It is the beginning of a phase of supreme, tumultuous emotions.

A week later. The courtyard of the old house in the Rue Jacob, where Barois lives. Inside an open lean-to Woldsmuth and some helpers are sitting at a table, while Breil-Zoeger, Harbaroux, Cresteil, and Portal move to and fro. Behind them, stacked in neat piles, are eighty

thousand copies of *The Sower;* a smell of fresh printer's ink hovers in the air.

Other copies, in bundles tied with string, are ready for dispatch to the provinces. Like the line outside a soup-kitchen a hundred down-and-outs are drawn up in single file. At three o'clock the distribution begins. While Barois jots down figures in a ledger, copies of the review, in packets of three hundred, disappear under the arms of the ragged vendors, who promptly start padding down the street in soft-soled slippers.

Soon the first away are outside the zone within which silence is enjoined; only when they have fanned out into the Boulevard Saint-Germain, the Rue des Saints-Pères, and the streets adjoining the Seine, may they give tongue—with a raucous stridence like the sound of a pack in full cry.

"*The Sower.* Extra Special Number. Revelations on the Dreyfus Case. 'Conscience, an Open Letter to the French Public,' by Senator Luce. *The Sower.* Extra Special . . ."

Passers-by stop and turn, shop-doors fly open, children run up, the vendors of *The Sower* ply a busy trade, and the copies disperse like leaves before an autumn gale. Within two hours they have reached the outlying suburbs, coming to rest on dining-tables, on market-stalls, in pockets.

Presently the vendors troop back, empty-handed, thirsty, and, as the courtyard fills, wine flows freely. The last reserves are broached, carried away, exhausted. Again the noisy pack sallies out, shattering the languor of a hot summer afternoon.

There is a stirring in the Paris crowd, a ferment on the boulevards. The eve of battle.

Already in a thousand homes, throughout the great city, French hearts are beating faster, roused to a generous enthusiasm, and thought clashes against thought. Passions are unleashed, clamorous in the warm darkness, like a gathering storm.

## VIII

## Storm

### I

The new *Sower* office in the Rue de l'Université. Bolted to uprights outside the first-floor windows are two long metal strips, painted white and inscribed in black capitals: *THE SOWER*. The *Sower's* new home is a small first-floor flat. The first two rooms, on entering, are occupied by the clerical staff and other employees, and are devoted to business activities. The third, a larger room, serves as the editorial room. The next, which overlooks a courtyard, is Barois' office, and adjoining it is a recess where a stenographer works.

It is 5 P.M. on January 17, 1898. An animated conversation is in progress in the editorial room, in the center of which is a big table strewn with inkpots and blotting pads. Pinned to the wall is an unfurled copy of a newspaper, *L'Aurore* of January 13, containing Zola's famous letter *"J'accuse."* Beside it are two posters, printed by Roll, reproducing in thick type the closing passages of the letter.

Barois, Harbaroux, Cresteil, Breil-Zoeger, Portal, and other members of the *Sower* staff are eagerly confabulating. "Cavaignac maintained that Dreyfus made a confession on the day he was cashiered." "Which was a downright lie, needless to say." "Still, I'm convinced Cavaignac spoke in good faith." "Somebody must have told him a document existed to that effect." "Anyhow, he doesn't claim to have seen the document."

BAROIS: "It's grotesque! Can they seriously expect us to believe that as far back as 1896 a piece of wholly conclusive evidence was available—a document whose publication would have promptly put a stop to all the agitation—and yet for all this time no one ever has had the idea of producing it?"

CRESTEIL: "That's self-evident."

BAROIS: "Here are the true facts of that incident." Promptly silence falls on the room. "I have them from Luce, who has been at great pains to ensure their accuracy. Really it's all quite simple, as you'll see.

"On the morning of his dismissal from the Army Dreyfus spent a full hour in the company of an officer of the Republican Guard, Captain Lebrun-Renault. He protested with the utmost vigor that he was innocent. Moreover, he declared that he would see to it that this declaration of his innocence reached the public ear—to such effect that Lebrun-Renault took alarm and, fearing there might be a scandal, felt it his duty to report this to his Colonel.

"Then Dreyfus described a new 'test' to which he had been subjected, somewhat similar to the dictation 'test' of a few days previously.

"The Minister of War, who hadn't lost hope of securing some piece of evidence which would set his mind completely at rest, sent Major du Paty du Clam to the prisoner's cell with instructions to ask Dreyfus if, when offering certain documents to Germany, he was not acting from a patriotic motive, with the object of securing more valuable documents in exchange. This, the Major was to point out, might be deemed by the Court an extenuating circumstance and ensure a lighter sentence. Naturally enough, Lebrun-Renault knew nothing of this maneuver. Dreyfus was expecting his ordeal to begin at any moment, and, as may well be imagined, his nerves were badly rattled. He kept talking to Lebrun-Renault with feverish volubility, and sometimes incoherently. We can easily see how what he then said may have been misunderstood and garbled in transmission from one mouth to another. This explains how the story got afloat that Dreyfus proposed an 'exchange' of documents with a foreign Power.

"Lebrun-Renault himself never spoke of a confession at the time. That very morning when, after sentence had been passed, General Darras asked him 'if nothing special had transpired,' his answer was, 'Nothing, sir,' and the General reported to the Ministry to this effect. Likewise the written report that Lebrun-Renault sent to the Commanding Officer of the Paris Garrison, after he had carried out the task assigned to him—a document that Luce has seen with his own eyes—has an entry: 'Nothing special to report.'

"Can we suppose that if Dreyfus had really made an incriminating statement to him, even if not a formal confession, he would not have hastened to report it to his superior officers? And when the vague rumors, circulated next day by the press, came to the notice of the Minister of War, wouldn't he, had there been the least foundation to them, have taken action? Would he not have promptly ordered a further inquiry, so as to secure this conlusive piece of evidence? Would he not have brought pressure to bear on Dreyfus himself, so as to glean more explicit information and to ascertain—a matter of vital importance for our national security—what exactly were the documents he made over to a foreign Power?

"No, really the more one thinks about it, the more incredible it seems, this story of a confession."

CRESTEIL: "You should publish an interview with Luce on the subject."

BAROIS: "He considers the time not yet ripe. He's waiting for Casimir-Périer to give his evidence at the Zola trial."

JULIA WOLDSMUTH, entering: "You are wanted at the telephone, Monsieur Barois."

Barois rises and walks out.

BREIL-ZOEGER: "All things considered, I regard Cavaignac's latest move as definitely helpful."

PORTAL: "Helpful? I don't follow."

BREIL-ZOEGER: "Surely it's obvious. Here we have an ex-Minister of War who gets on his legs in the Chamber of Deputies and formally announces that there exists a document establishing the guilt of Dreyfus beyond all possible doubt. Well, on the day it's proved for all to know that no such document exists, or that if it exists it was deliberately trumped up as an afterthought, and antedated, so as to fill out gaps in the evidence—well, that day public opinion will have a nasty jolt. I'll see to that myself, if needs be! Or, if there's no reaction, it will mean that it's abominably changed, the France we knew."

CRESTEIL, sadly: "Changed abominably! Alas, you've never spoken a truer word."

PORTAL: "All this will be threshed out, anyhow, at the Zola trial."

Barois returns.

BAROIS, a troubled look on his face: "It was Woldsmuth who rang me up. He's just learned that they're talking of limiting the scope of the proceedings against Zola. The idea is to restrict the charges to his allegations as regards the 1894 Court-Martial, and ignore the rest. I wonder what the idea is."

PORTAL, rising: "It's a very serious matter."

CRESTEIL: "But they've no right to do that."

PORTAL: "I'm afraid they have."

CRESTEIL: "Anyhow, what difference would it make?"

BAROIS: "Let Portal tell us what he means."

PORTAL: "It would be serious for this

reason: the Government's trying by every possible means to narrow down the field of this trial and keep off dangerous ground. Now there's a Section of the Criminal Procedure Code which expressly forbids the accused person's offering evidence other than that relating to the facts specified on the charge sheet. In other words, by limiting the range of evidence that can be called, they can limit at their will the points raised at the trial."

CRESTEIL: "And thus whittle down Zola's defense to practically nil."

PORTAL: "Exactly."

BAROIS: "It's scandalous. It means that they can smother up the whole proceedings if they feel like it."

CRESTEIL, indignantly: "It's just one of those damned legal quibbles dear to Government attorneys."

PORTAL, curtly: "Hardly that, Cresteil. It's the law."

General dismay.

BREIL-ZOEGER, quietly: "Personally, I cannot believe they'll take that line. The allegations made were too outrageous to be disregarded. They are simply bound to prosecute the man who dared to write things like this." He goes up to the placard on which Zola's letter is printed in thick type, and reads:

" 'I accuse Lieutenant-Colonel du Paty du Clam of having been the fiendish organizer of this miscarriage of justice.

" 'I accuse General Mercier of having abetted this. . . .

" 'I accuse General Billot of having had in his hands decisive proof of Dreyfus's innocence and of having suppressed it. . . .

" 'I accuse General de Boisdeffre. . . .

" 'I accuse General de Pellieux . . . of having made a scandalously biased preliminary inquiry. . . .

" 'I accuse the Ministry of War of having conducted a foul campaign in the press, with the object of misleading public opinion and covering up its misdeeds.' "

CRESTEIL: "And then that challenge with which the letter ends:

" 'In making these charges I am well aware that I expose myself to proceedings under Sections 30 and 31 of the Code. . . .

" 'I have but one desire, a passionate desire for the light of truth, and I speak in the cause of suffering humanity that has a right to happiness. This burning protest is but my heart-felt cry. May they be bold enough to arraign me, and may the trial take place in the full light of day!

" 'I am ready!' "

BAROIS: "And you think a Government can swallow taunts like that without reacting!"

PORTAL: "In any case, Barois, it would be as well, before the charge sheet is drawn up, to direct public attention to this piece of knavery."

BREIL-ZOEGER: "Yes, and your article must hit Paris like a bombshell, first thing tomorrow morning."

BAROIS: "I'll start on it at once. Portal, would you supply me with the exact wording of that Section of the Code you mentioned?"

PORTAL: "Can I telephone the Law Courts Library?"

BAROIS, opening the door: "Mademoiselle Julia!"

PORTAL: "It's for me, Mademoiselle. Would you call eight-eight-nine-two-one?"

BAROIS, going to his private office: "I'll leave you now. Will you all be at the café this evening?"

SEVERAL VOICES: "Yes."

BAROIS: "Good. I'll show you my article before taking it to Roll, and we'll run over it together. Good-bye for the present."

An hour later. The editorial room is empty. All the staff have gone to their homes and an office-boy is sweeping the floors. Barois is at work in his back-room office.

Suddenly the door is flung open by Julia. She is pale as a ghost, obviously terrified, and with her there enters through the open door a curious buzzing sound.

JULIA: "Monsieur Barois, there's a—a demonstration. Don't you hear?"

Much surprised, Barois goes to the rooms giving on the street, and, opening a window, leans out into the darkness. The yellow flame of a street-lamp dazzles him at first. As his eyes get used to the darkness he sees that the street below is empty as yet, but in the distance, between cliffs of shadow, a black, heaving mass is creeping forward like some sluggish monster. And the confused hubbub of voices and footsteps is steadily growing louder.

Barois' first impulse is to hurry down the stairs to see what is happening. But now there is a sudden increase in the volume of sound outside. Some are singing, some shouting.

"Dreyfus!"

A small isolated group, the vanguard, is now only some fifty yards away. Barois can see faces craning up, arms brandished towards the *Sower* windows.

"To hell with Barois!" "Down with *The Sower!*"

He draws back hastily.

BAROIS: "The shutters! Quick!"

He helps the office-boy, who is half paralyzed with terror, to bolt the shutters. Just as they are securing the last window, a walking stick hurtles through the panes, covering Barois and the boy with splintered glass.

The crowd is now immediately below, only four or five yards away; he even can distinguish the different tones of voice.

"Down with *The Sower!*" "Traitors!" "Lynch the bastards!"

Stones and sticks break through the windows and rattle against the wooden shutters. Listening intently, Barois stays in the middle of the room.

"Down with Zola!" "Down with Dreyfus!" "Death to the traitors!"

In the dim light he can just make out the form of Julia beside him. He pushes her towards his office.

BAROIS: "Call up the police station."

Evidently the crowd has run out of projectiles. But the shouts are louder and timed to the rhythm of stamping feet.

"Death to Luce!" "Lynch the traitors!" "Death to Barois!"

BAROIS, very pale, to the office-boy: "Bolt the door and stay in the hall." He goes to his office, unlocks a drawer, and takes out a revolver. Then he goes and stands beside the trembling boy. "If anyone comes in I'll shoot him like a dog." The telephone rings, and he goes to his office again. "Hullo? Is this the Superintendent of Police? . . . Right. I'm the editor of *The Sower*. There's a riot taking place just under my windows, in the Rue de l'Université. . . . What? Already? Thank you, I'm much obliged. . . . I couldn't say. A thousand. Fifteen hundred perhaps."

The noise outside is now continuous: a rhythmic stamping of feet on the roadway, like an army marking time, accompanied by a long, low, feral growling, above which rise shrill cries.

"Death to Dreyfus!" "Down with Zola!" "Lynch the bastards!"

Suddenly the tumult diminishes, there are sounds of scuffling. Evidently the police have arrived on the scene. A few shouts can still be heard, but less distinctly. The noise of footsteps recedes, and within a few minutes dies away altogether. The rioters have been dispersed.

Switching on the light, Barois sees

Julia beside him, her hand resting on the table. Emotion has played such havoc with her face that he has to stare for some moments before recognizing her. Her features are convulsed, her skin is ashen-gray, her face has curiously coarsened and is now like that of a much older woman. Its expression is frankly bestial, instinct has come to the surface, and there is something repellent in its blatant sensuality.

That, he thinks, is how she must look in the act of love. And the glance he throws her now is brutal, violent as rape, and she accepts it, like a woman yielding to her ravisher.

Suddenly her nerves give way and, bursting into tears, she sinks into a chair. He leaves the room without a word; his own nerves are on edge and he can feel the fever of his blood. He opens the shutters.

The street is quiet now, little more animated than usual at this hour except for some people standing on their balconies or watching from windows.

Policemen are patrolling the street, under the broken street-lamps, whose gas-flames twist and flicker in the night wind.

THE OFFICE-BOY: "Please, sir, the Police Inspector's come to take your statement."

II

February 17, 1898. The Assize Court on the tenth day of the Zola case.

There has been a short adjournment. The courtroom is filled with a seething, chattering, gesticulating crowd, among which one notices a sprinkling of uniforms, gold epaulettes, smartly dressed women. People are eagerly pointing out to each other well-known figures—staff officers, popular journalists, leading lights of the stage and the political world. A black phalanx of gowned lawyers sepa-

rates the spectators from the still-empty Bench, over which hangs Bonnat's melodramatic "Christ."

Sudden and violent as electric discharges, waves of sympathy or hatred traverse the thick, over-charged air of the courtroom. In the front row is a small, compact group, talking in undertones: Harbaroux, Barois, Breil-Zoeger, Cresteil, Woldsmuth, and among the men one woman—the dark, enigmatic form of Julia Woldsmuth.

A clock strikes three and the crowd heaves, as if rocked by a ground-swell, while a flood of new-comers seeps into the smallest crannies of the all-but-solid mass. Students in berets, lawyers in their gowns, clamber over the high barrier separating the public from the Bench and Bar and perch themselves on window-sills and ledges.

Patiently Luce worms his way through the crowd, which mutters his name and scowls at him. At last he succeeds in reaching the place that Barois has been keeping for him in the *Sower* group.

LUCE, in a low tone to Barois: "I've just been 'over there.' It's going to be a rough crossing. Most of the jury are in favor of acquitting Zola. The military know this and they're shaking in their shoes. They'll certainly try to bring off some big coup today or, anyhow, to-morrow."

An abrupt, short-lived silence falls as the Court enters. The red-robed judges take their seats; two by two, with the self-conscious gravity of a Town Council parading in their Sunday best at some civic function, the jury file to their places.

Émile Zola takes his seat in the dock beside the manager of *L'Aurore;* behind them are their counsel, Maîtres Labori and Albert and Georges Clemenceau, with their clerks.

A low sound, like the rumble of a

nearing storm, jars the air; then abruptly a whistle shrills across it. Zola and Labori glance to the right, whence the whistle came. Zola's hands are locked on the knob of his walking stick, his legs are crossed. There is an anxious look on the deeply furrowed, bearded face, which at some angles reminds one of a hedgehog's. Whenever he moves his head the pince-nez flashes, intensifying the scalpel keen-ness of the eyes. Slowly his gaze roves the concourse of his ill-wishers, then lingers for a moment on the *Sower* group.

A man in uniform comes up the central aisle, accompanied by whispers. "Pellieux. That's Pellieux." The General walks firmly up to the witness-box, then halts with military precision.

BAROIS, to Luce: "Ah, so it's Pellieux they're throwing into the breach."

Feelings are running high and the public making such a din that the General swings round and gazes sternly at the culprits. And promptly—such is the soldierly dignity of his bearing, the sense of high authority that emanates from this distinguished officer—they are reduced to silence, if only momentarily.

The Presiding Judge, a burly, moon-faced man whose shaven lips are like a narrow horizontal line drawn between the bushy side-whiskers, scowls darkly and raises his arm in protest against the noise that has broken out again; but to no immediate effect. After some minutes, however, snatches of what the General is saying in his precise, military tones can be heard through the subsiding din. ". . . in a perfectly legal manner . . . the Dreyfus trial . . . I ask the Court to hear me."

VOICES: "Ssh! Ssh!"

GENERAL DE PELLIEUX: "I will repeat that characteristic remark of Colonel Henry's. 'You want light on the matter, do you? Well, you shall have it!' " Steely, challenging, his voice rings through the crowded courtroom, which now at last has quieted down. "When Castelin put his question in the House, something had just occurred which I wish to bring to the notice of this Court. At the Ministry of War—I ask you here to bear in mind that I am *not* speaking of the original Dreyfus trial—conclusive proof had been obtained of Dreyfus's guilt, and when I say 'conclusive,' I know what I am talk-ing about. For I have seen this evidence with my own eyes." He sweeps the jury, then the counsel for the defense, then the public, with his gaze, and the rugged face lights up with the smile of the skilled fencer taking his opponent's measure. "Just before this question was put in the Chamber a document, whose authenticity is indubitable, was handed in at the Ministry. This is its exact wording: 'A question is going to be put in the Chamber of Deputies about the Dreyfus case. Be careful not to mention the dealings we had with that Jew.' That document, mind you, is signed. Not by a known name, it is true, but one that is vouched for by a visiting card, on the back of which is inscribed a trivial invitation signed with an alias, the same alias as that with which the document is signed. And the visiting card bears the real name of the person in question."

There is a short silence. A flutter of excitement runs through the public; faces turn eagerly towards the Bench, the wit-ness, and Zola, who has been unable to conceal his indignation; lastly, towards the jury, whose rather commonplace fea-tures now wear a look of satisfaction, as if a load had been lifted from their minds.

GENERAL DE PELLIEUX, in ringing tones: "That is all I wish to say. Let those persons who have been agitating for a revision of the trial bear in mind the fact that I have just brought to their notice, a fact to which I can testify on my honor. Moreover, I now ask General de Boisdeffre to confirm what I have told the Court."

There is a buzz of voices, through which breaks a thunder of applause. Luce keeps his arms closely folded on his breast; his face is pale and drawn as he gazes sadly up at the Bench. His friends exchange fiercely indignant glances, but none the less they have been rudely shaken by this bolt from the blue.

BREIL-ZOEGER, in an undertone: "It's a forgery, of course."

BAROIS, with a shake of his shoulders: "That's obvious." He points to a group of officers, very spruce in their uniforms, raising white-gloved hands and clapping frantically. "But just try to get those fellows to admit it!"

Labori has sprung to his feet, squaring up pugnaciously. Indeed, he looks less like the skillful lawyer he is than a veteran boxer entering the ring. But even he cannot make himself heard; his voice beats vainly on a solid wall of sound. Opening his mouth to its widest, he rams home his words with whirling gestures, turning towards the Judge, who seems to wish to interrupt him.

At last, in a lull, the Judge's voice becomes audible, shrill with vexation.

THE JUDGE: "But, Maître Labori—"

LABORI, angrily: "Really, Your Honor, I must protest—"

THE JUDGE, stiffly: "The witness has given his evidence. Have you any questions to put?"

LABORI: "Permit me to point out, before proceeding further—"

Like a rapier, the steely voice of General de Pellieux cuts through the altercation.

GENERAL DE PELLIEUX: "I ask the Court to call General de Boisdeffre to the witness-box."

LABORI, so peremptorily that at last silence is imposed: "I request Your Honor—and what has just transpired in this Court carries such serious implications that the defense cannot fail to press the point—I request Your Honor to hear me for a moment, not only with a view to answering the General's statement—though a bare assertion does not call for an answer—but also with a view to pointing out, before things go any further, the effect the statement we have just heard from General de Pellieux must necessarily have on these proceedings. I ask Your Honor's permission to put in a few words."

THE JUDGE, dryly: "A few words, Maître Labori, no more."

LABORI: "As Your Honor wishes."

THE JUDGE: "Unless you have a question to put in cross-examination."

LABORI, vehemently: "How could I have questions to put with reference to an entirely new piece of evidence that has just been sprung on us? Still, I have one question, and shall now proceed to put it."

GENERAL DE PELLIEUX: "It was you who sprang on the Court a new piece of evidence when you read out a charge framed by Major d'Ormescheville, a charge that figured in proceedings heard *in camera*."

LABORI, triumphantly: "Ah, we're making progress, we're making progress!"

GENERAL GONSE: "I ask to be heard by the Court."

THE JUDGE: "Presently, General."

LABORI: "All I have to say is this. An incident of quite exceptional gravity has just taken place in this Court; that is a point on which we are all in accord. General de Pellieux did not speak about the Dreyfus trial; he spoke of something that happened subsequently to the trial. It is impossible that this happening should not be discussed here—or elsewhere, before another Court. It is clear that after such an incident there can no longer be any question of narrowing down or circumscribing these proceedings. Will General de Pellieux permit me, with all due respect, to point out that no document whatsoever can have evidential value or be treated as proof of any fact in issue, until it has been put in evidence and admitted or traversed by the parties? And will he permit me to add that in this trial—which, whatever we may do and whatever we may wish, is assuming the proportions of an affair of State—we are concerned with two documents or dossiers, equally unsatisfactory, indeed irrelevant, because they are kept secret? One of them, the *bordereau*, served to procure the condemnation of Dreyfus in 1894, without discussion, without hearing the other side, without the accused man's speaking in his defense. And now we have a second document, which, by reason of its secrecy, has served for weeks to prevent anything being given the Court but bare affirmations." He pauses. "Great as is my respect for the statement made by General de Pellieux on his honor as an officer of the French Army, I cannot attach the slightest importance to this document." A furious din breaks out in the courtroom; howls of derision greet the lawyer's last remark. Intrepidly he faces the storm he has invoked and goes on speaking in a tone of contained violence, emphasizing every word.

"So long as this document is withheld, so long as we are debarred from discussing it, and so long as it has not been made public, it can have no bearing on these proceedings. And it is in the name of immemorial justice, of principles that every race has venerated since the youth of the world and the dawn of civilization, that I speak thus." The public is obviously impressed. Opinions are divided, and there are some approving cries of "Hear! Hear!" Labori continues in a quieter tone.

"This leads me to an aspect of the case which has now emerged so clearly that my mind is easier in many respects. One

consideration dominates all others in this trial, as I now see it. I refer to its persistent obscurity and the anxiety that is growing among the public as the fog enveloping the issues is thickened day by day, I will not say by deliberate lies, but I *will* say by subterfuges.

"No doubt the question whether Dreyfus is innocent or guilty, and whether Esterhazy is innocent or guilty, is one of the utmost gravity. Each of us—General de Pellieux, the Minister of War, General Gonse, and I myself—has, obviously, his personal opinion on the matter, and we may well persist indefinitely in our opinions unless and until this atmosphere of mystery is dissipated and no shadow of doubt remains.

"But the one thing to be strenuously guarded against is any increase or prolongation of the nation-wide anxiety to which this case has given rise. Well, we have here and now a way of getting light, anyhow partial light, on the matter, without giving any loophole for imposing the ban necessitated by proceedings *in camera*, or anticipating any subsequent decision of a competent court. For, come what may, a revision of the Dreyfus trial must and will take place."

There are violent protests. Cries of "No! No! Our country first!" Labori squares his shoulders, then swings round furiously on the demonstrators and rakes them with a gaze of withering scorn. His fist crashes down on the open files in front of him.

"These demonstrators only serve to show that some of you are still blind to the gravity of the issues in this case—from the point of view of civilization and even common decency."

Again there is a din of voices, through which rises some discreet but persistent applause. Labori turns towards the Bench and, folding his arms, waits for order to be restored.

LABORI: "If Dreyfus is guilty and if the

allegations of these generals, whom I believe to be speaking in good faith—and this it is that most perturbs me—if their allegations are well founded, sound in fact and sound in law, they will have an opportunity of proving this in open court. If, however, they are mistaken, the other party will prove his case.

"And when once the truth has come to light and the shadows have been lifted, perhaps one or two men will be revealed as those responsible for everything, as criminals and traitors. On whatever side they may be, we shall know them for what they are and hold them up to obloquy. And then we shall settle down, our minds at rest, each to his respective duties, whether those of peace or those of war." He turns to General de Pellieux. "For as to war, General—I think you will agree—it is not when generals who are worthy to speak in the name of the Army they command are standing in the witness-box, it is not at such a moment that anyone need fear war; nor is it by the threat of a war that is not for tomorrow, whatever some people may say, that these gentlemen of the jury will be intimidated.

"I shall end with a question. Your Honor will observe that I have been leading up to something quite definite—and I will take this opportunity of thanking Your Honor for having allowed me to speak at some length. May I say how much I appreciate the consideration shown me by the Court and its awareness of the importance of the issues here at stake?

"The question, sir, is this: Will General de Pellieux state quite frankly all he knows, and will the document he refers to be produced in Court?"

There is tension in the air; the jury stir uneasily, their eyes fixed on the General. For some moments there is complete silence in the courtroom.

THE JUDGE: "General Gonse, what have you to say?"

General Gonse rises from his seat and approaches General de Pellieux, who steps down from the box to make place for him. General Gonse betrays some nervousness, and his voice seems curiously flat after those of General de Pellieux and Maître Labori.

GENERAL GONSE: "Your Honor, I corroborate in every detail the statement which General de Pellieux has made. He took the initiative and he acted rightly; in his place I should have done the same, so as to clear up any possible misunderstanding. The Army has no fear of the fullest light being thrown on the proceedings; nor does it fear, when its honor is at stake, to say where the truth lies." Labori makes a gesture indicating approbation of these words. There is a ripple of applause. The General continues, weighing his words: "Nevertheless, prudence is called for, and I have grave doubts about the wisdom of producing documents of this nature at a public hearing, though they exist and are no less authentic than conclusive."

Coming as an anticlimax after the General's opening phrases, these reservations cause some murmurs of dissatisfaction among the public. The majority, however, keep an open mind.

Composedly Maître Clemenceau rises to his feet.

CLEMENCEAU: "Your Honor, may I make an observation at this stage?"

Before he can continue, General de Pellieux walks quickly to the witness-box and, gripping its rail with both hands, addresses the Court in a loud, commanding voice.

GENERAL DE PELLIEUX: "I ask permission to add some words to my statement."

With a wave of the hand the Presiding Judge invites the General to speak. Maître Clemenceau resumes his seat.

GENERAL DE PELLIEUX: "Maître Labori spoke just now of proceedings in revision, with special reference to the document that was produced before the military court. I would point out that no evidence of the production of this document has been tendered."

This statement is so incongruous with the facts—after the dramatic hearing of Maître Salle, whom the Judge had to cut short abruptly when about to divulge what he knew on the subject, and after the explicit statement made by Maître Demange—that the public no longer dares to make any demonstration and listens in uneasy silence to the noisy protests of Dreyfus's friends. Taken aback by this reception, General de Pellieux hesitates.

GENERAL DE PELLIEUX: "I do not know—" He is interrupted by some loud guffaws. Swinging round, he confronts his hecklers with the candor of his soldierly face, the frankness of his deep-set eyes, and an intrepid gaze used to ampler horizons. Spoken in the authoritative tone of an experienced officer who can quell an incipient mutiny with a brief command, his words slash the grinning faces like a whip. "Stop that clownish nonsense!" For some moments he remains quite still, mastering the crowd with his gaze. Then, unhurrying, he turns towards the Bench. "I do not know if due attention was given to the statement made by Colonel Henry some days ago. Colonel Henry stated that Colonel Sandherr had handed over to him an envelope marked 'Secret'; that this envelope had been sealed before the Court-Martial took place, and that it had never been opened. Gentlemen of the Jury, I direct your attention to this point. Next, as to the proposed revision of the Dreyfus verdict on the strength of this document—"

THE JUDGE: "We are not concerned with a revision; that lies outside the jurisdiction of this Court."

GENERAL DE PELLIEUX: "But it is being constantly referred to."

THE JUDGE: "I am aware of that; but, as you well know, an Assize Court is not competent in the matter."

GENERAL DE PELLIEUX: "Very well, I bow to your decision. I have nothing more to say."

THE JUDGE, to General Gonse: "Have you anything to add?"

GENERAL GONSE: "No, Your Honor."

GENERAL DE PELLIEUX: "I ask that General de Boisdeffre be called to corroborate my statement."

THE JUDGE: "Then will you arrange for him to come tomorrow?"

Without answering, the General turns his head and, in the peremptory tone of a man who is used to being obeyed without demur, flings an order over his shoulder to his orderly officer, who is standing in the background among the public.

GENERAL DE PELLIEUX: "Major Ducasse, will you go and bring General de Boisdeffre here—immediately."

He is the Army incarnate. His attitude of high disdain impresses all alike—the judges, jury, even his opponents. And the crowd, tamed to submission, fawns on its master, like a whipped dog.

CLEMENCEAU, rising again to his feet: "Your Honor, I wish to make some observations on what we have just heard from General de Pellieux."

Again the General interrupts him, and Clemenceau stops speaking. Then, still standing, squarely planted on his robust limbs, an ironic twinkle in the bright eyes lighting up the rather flat, Levantine-seeming face, he listens to a brief duel of words between Labori and General de Pellieux, relating to the publication of the 1894 indictment.

With his gown billowing round him and his shirt-sleeves visible up to the elbow when he raises his arms, Labori seems to be hurling anathemas at his adversary.

LABORI: "General de Pellieux has sent for General de Boisdeffre; that is very

wise of him! But let me warn the Court
—and within twenty-four hours you will
find I am no false prophet—that nothing
General de Pellieux has said, and nothing
that General de Boisdeffre may say, will
avail to bring the proceedings to an end.
For it is not mere oral evidence, however
eminent the witnesses, that can replace
the secret documents themselves. That is
why I say to General de Pellieux: Either
produce the documents, or else stop talking about them."

CLEMENCEAU, raising his arm quietly,
to the Presiding Judge: "Your Honor, I
ask your permission briefly to address the
Court." In contrast to his colleague's
vehemence his calm assurance makes all
the more effect. "General de Pellieux has
told us that just before Monsieur Castelin
put his question in the Chamber of
Deputies, *conclusive* proof of Dreyfus's
guilt had been secured. Are we then to
assume that until then only *inconclusive*
proof had been forthcoming?"

There is a short silence. A faintly
mocking smile narrows Clemenceau's
slotted eyes. His hands still clasped on
his walking stick, Zola turns his head and
gives the lawyer an approving glance.

LUCE, to Barois, in a whisper: "Of
course he knows the document to be a
forgery."

CLEMENCEAU, in the same flat, unemotional voice: "May I ask General de
Pellieux: How is it—and this is what a
great many people in all walks of life are
beginning to ask themselves today—how
is it that so important a fact has been
divulged for the first time in a Court of
Common Law? How is it that when the
question was put in the Chamber, General Billot never said a word about these
secret documents or warned Members of
the danger of war, and that it was only at
a hearing in this Court that the startling
allegation we heard today was made, and
the existence of these documents first
disclosed?"

GENERAL DE PELLIEUX, irritably: "All
this is mere quibbling. I never said the
country was in danger of war. As to why
General Billot chose not to mention this
document or the others—for, as General
de Boisdeffre will inform you, there *are*
others—when the question was put in the
Chamber—that is none of my business.
General Billot is free to do as he thinks
fit." He turns to the jury. "One thing,
anyhow, is certain. General Billot assured the Chamber, not once or twice but
several times, that Dreyfus was justly and
legally convicted."

LABORI, aggressively: "Here I really
must protest. One, anyhow, of those two
words is patently false, and that is
'legally.' "

GENERAL DE PELLIEUX, challengingly:
"Prove it!"

LABORI, coldly: "It *has* been proved—
to the hilt!"

CLEMENCEAU, in a more conciliatory
tone: "We have made persistent efforts to
prove this fact but have always been prevented from so doing. If General de
Pellieux wishes me to make my meaning
clearer, I ask for nothing better."

THE JUDGE, curtly: "Unnecessary,
Maître Clemenceau."

LABORI, losing all self-control: "It has
been proved by Maître Salle! It has been
proved by Maître Demange! It has been
proved again and again by statements in
the newspapers which have never been
officially denied. It was proved by General Mercier, who did not dare, when I
confronted him with the facts, to say the
contrary. On the previous day I had
issued a challenge through the newspapers, and his only response was to
draw a pettifogging distinction, which in
itself sufficed to prove the point beyond
all doubt. When I said, 'General Mercier
handed in a certain document to the
Court-Martial and then went around
boasting of having done so,' General
Mercier's answer was, 'That is not

true'—thus fogging the issue again, I will not say deliberately; more likely he spoke without thinking. So I followed up with the question, '*What* was untrue? that you tendered a certain document or that you went around boasting of having done so?' To which General Mercier replied, 'That I went around boasting of having done so.'

"I maintain that, for anyone whose mind is free from prejudice, my point is proved. Its proof is that, in spite of the feelings the Dreyfus case has aroused throughout the country, no one has come forward to say what General de Pellieux has not dared to say—and what I defy him to say!" He pauses, then smiles. "So I make bold to say my point is proved."

GENERAL DE PELLIEUX, haughtily: "How do you expect me to say what happened at the Dreyfus trial? I wasn't present at it."

Labori gazes first at the jury, then at the judges, then at the public, as though inviting them to take note of this evasive answer. After this, he bows politely to the General, with a smile of triumph.

LABORI: "Very good. Thank you, General."

CLEMENCEAU, intervening: "Your Honor, we have a witness now in Court who has it from the mouth of one of the members of the Court-Martial that a secret document was handed to the President of the Court. But we have not been allowed to put him in the box."

LABORI: "I have two letters to the same effect in my brief. And I also have a letter emanating from a friend of the President of the Republic. He declines to give evidence, as he has been warned that, were he to depose to the true facts, other witnesses would be called to controvert him."

CLEMENCEAU: "And why did General Billot say nothing on this point to Monsieur Scheurer-Kestner when he came to ask him about it? Had he done so, the whole matter would have been cleared up by now."

THE JUDGE, fretfully: "All that can wait, Maître Labori, until we have finished with the evidence and you are addressing the Court."

GENERAL GONSE, coming forward again: "I have something to say regarding the deposition made earlier in the proceedings, in which certain notes were referred to. I informed the Court that those notes were of a secret nature. Such documents *always* are secret. All correspondence between the various departments of the Ministry of War is conducted by way of 'minutes,' and these are invariably marked 'Secret.' So when we speak of a memorandum on this or that point, its secrecy is taken for granted.

"Next, when you were told that Dreyfus did not know what took place in the office of the General Staff in September 1893, this, too, was incorrect. For one thing, Dreyfus began by spending six months—"

THE JUDGE, brusquely intervening: "The Court is not concerned with the original Dreyfus case." To Generals de Pellieux and Gonse. "You can return to your seats, both of you." The Judge takes advantage of the amazed silence that follows these words to give a peremptory order to the Clerk of the Court. "Call the next witness."

The Clerk hesitates. Labori has risen to his feet and stretched his arms wide, almost as though he were setting up a physical barrier against the continuation of the hearing.

LABORI: "Your Honor, it is absolutely impossible after what has just transpired—"

THE JUDGE, resolutely: "The hearing will proceed."

LABORI, indignantly: "But, Your Honor, that's impossible. You are well aware that when an incident of this kind has taken place the trial cannot proceed unless and until the matter has been threshed out. Therefore we are obliged to hear the evidence of General de Boisdeffre."

THE JUDGE: "We shall hear it in good time." To the Clerk. "Call the next witness."

LABORI, tenaciously: "Your Honor will permit me to point out—"

THE JUDGE, peremptorily to the Clerk: "Go and call the next witness."

The Clerk goes out.

LABORI: "With all due deference, I submit that the hearing should be suspended at this point."

Major Esterhazy enters the courtroom, escorted by the Clerk of the Court.

THE JUDGE, to Labori: "I will give my ruling on your application when the witnesses have been heard."

Esterhazy walks to the witness-box; he has a pronounced stoop, a sallow complexion with red patches over the cheekbones, and restless, feverish eyes. Very thin, he has all the appearances of a consumptive. He is loudly applauded by the public as he enters.

The Judge is about to address him when Labori intervenes for the last time, boiling with indignation.

LABORI: "But I have asked the Court that the hearing of other witnesses should be stayed until General de Boisdeffre has given his evidence. The Court cannot postpone its ruling on my petition until after the witnesses have been examined."

Uncertain how to act, the Presiding Judge glares at him in silence. To keep himself in countenance, Esterhazy folds his arms and waits, obviously embarrassed and puzzled by what is happening. Labori has resumed his seat and is busy writing his petition.

THE JUDGE, harshly, almost truculently: "Will it take you long, drawing up your petition?"

LABORI, surlily, without looking up: "Ten minutes."

The hearing is suspended. The Judge signs to the Clerk to escort Esterhazy back to the witnesses' waiting-room. Nerves are on edge, and the public goes on cheering Esterhazy until he has left. Without seeming to notice the noise in the courtroom, the judges rise and, unhurrying, vacate the Bench, followed by the jury, the defendants, and their counsel.

The growing exasperation of the public, so far kept partially at bay by the presence of the judges, at last has free vent. Shouts, excited comments on the evidence, angry retorts, fill the overheated air, now tainted with the smell of packed humanity. The noise is deafening.

The *Sower* staff gather round Luce. Portal, who is in his gown, joins them. His blunt, candid face, now showing signs of his vast disappointment, seems chubbier, more pink-and-white than ever under his lawyer's cap.

PORTAL, sinking wearily into a chair: "Another secret document!"

BAROIS: "What exactly is it, do you know?"

BREIL-ZOEGER, in his iciest, most cutting tone: "This is the first time it's been heard of, to the best of my knowledge."

LUCE: "No, I knew of its existence. But I didn't think they'd ever dare to use it."

BREIL-ZOEGER: "Who's it written by?"

LUCE: "It purports to have been written by the Italian Military Attaché, and it's said to have been intercepted in the German Attaché's mail."

BAROIS: "Anyhow, it stinks of forgery!"

LUCE: "Naturally. It's a palpable fake. For one thing, it reached the Ministry— by what channel, I have no idea—at a strangely convenient moment, the very day before the Minister was due to answer that awkward question in the Chamber. And, also, just at the time when the General Staff was beginning to grow anxious about the turn the Affair was taking."

BREIL-ZOEGER: "And then the way it was worded."

JULIA: "We don't really know what was in it. The General was quoting from memory."

LUCE: "Still, he assured us that the name of Dreyfus was there in black and white. That in itself casts doubt on its authenticity. It's straining credulity too far to ask us to believe that, at a time when the press was beginning to take an active interest in the case, these two attachés would have spoken openly of Dreyfus in their correspondence. Even assuming that they actually had dealings with him, they'd never have made such a blunder as to mention him by name, especially after the formal denials made by their respective governments."

BAROIS: "That's obvious."

PORTAL: "But who the devil can be forging documents of that sort?"

BREIL-ZOEGER, with a ferocious guffaw: "Why, the Army Staff! Who else should it be?"

HARBAROUX: "Yes, our Ministry of War has a team of expert forgers on its pay-roll, that's certain."

LUCE, quietly: "No. There I can't follow you."

The frankness and assurance of his tone carry conviction. Only Breil-Zoeger lifts his shoulders incredulously.

BREIL-ZOEGER: "Still, surely, the facts point—"

LUCE, firmly to all the group: "No, my friends, you're wrong. Don't let yourselves be carried away. The General Staff's no more a gang of forgers than we are, as some people think, a gang of traitors. Never will you make me believe that men like General de Boisdeffre, General Gonse, General Billot, and the others would conspire to fabricate false evidence."

Cresteil d'Allize has been listening to the dispute with a wry smile, fretfully tugging at his long moustache.

CRESTEIL: "I quite agree with Luce. I used to know General de Pellieux; he's the soul of honesty."

LUCE: "Indeed, you need only see and hear him to feel sure he believes what he says. There's a ring of complete sincerity in his voice. And until the contrary is proved, I'll hold this true of the other generals as well."

CRESTEIL: "They were easy game, and they've been hoodwinked."

BREIL-ZOEGER, with a tart smile: "You attribute to them a gullibility that's hardly credible."

CRESTEIL, promptly: "Quite credible, I assure you. Take my word for it, old chap, if you'd had as much to do with Army officers as I have. Wait! Turn your head a moment. See that group behind us? Now, study them without prejudice, and what do you see? A look of stolid self-assurance, I grant you; it comes of always being obeyed and the officer's prerogative of being infallible vis-à-vis his men. But they're honest faces, fundamentally honest."

LUCE: "Yes, look round the courtroom, Zoeger. Most revealing, isn't it? The truth is that men of the officer class aren't used to predicaments which call for subtle thinking. So they're at a loss when someone springs a dilemma of this kind on them. If there's a guilty man about, who is he? Are they to look for him in the Government or in the Army, among those staff officers who have affirmed on their honor that Dreyfus was justly sentenced? Or is the criminal that obscure Jew, a mere nonentity, who was convicted by a tribunal of seven brother-officers, and at whom so much mud has been slung during the last three years that some of it inevitably has stuck?"

BREIL-ZOEGER, superiorly: "Surely it's obvious even to the meanest intelligence that whenever the military authorities were asked for definite proof of Dreyfus's guilt they balked at producing it? Everyone, even an officer, has brains enough to draw his conclusions from that."

JULIA: "And then what weight can those precious 'words of honor' they're so fond of have as against solid arguments like Lazare's book, or Duclaux's pamphlets, or your letter, Monsieur Luce?"

BREIL-ZOEGER: "Or even Zola's letter, over-emotional though it is?"

BAROIS: "Patience, my friends! We're getting near our goal." To Luce. "Today we've made a great step forward."

Luce does not reply.

PORTAL: "'A great step forward!' You're easily satisfied, Barois."

BAROIS: "Surely you see my point? General de Boisdeffre will be here any moment; they've sent to fetch him. With his first words Labori will put the General's back to the wall, and he'll be *obliged* to produce that secret document in court. Once that's done, it will be open to inspection, and it won't stand up long under any serious examination, that's a certainty. So the military authorities will be convicted of having tendered a forgery in evidence, there'll be a prompt swing-round of public opinion, and within three months a retrial."

He makes his points with slashing gestures, his eyes blazing with exultation. His whole bearing radiates strength and optimism.

LUCE, carried away by his friend's enthusiasm: "After all, who knows? Perhaps you're right."

BAROIS, with a boisterous laugh: "There's no 'perhaps' about it! This time, I'm certain, we have them at our mercy!"

BREIL-ZOEGER, tartly: "And suppose General de Boisdeffre finds a way of wriggling out of it? It wouldn't be the first time."

WOLDSMUTH, who slipped out when the adjournment was announced, has re-turned to his seat: "Here's the latest! General de Boisdeffre's just arrived in a carriage. The hearing's going to proceed."

BAROIS: "Did you see him?"

WOLDSMUTH: "Yes. I recognized him at once. He's in mufti. One of the officers of the Court was waiting for him on the steps. He went straight to the witnesses' room."

JULIA, to Barois, clapping her hands: "You see!"

BAROIS, exultantly: "This time, my friends, they've no loophole left. It's an open fight—and we're going to win it!"

The lawyers and members of the public who had left the courtroom bustle back to their places. In the midst of the confusion the judges and jury resume their seats. The defendants are brought in.

Labori steps briskly to his place, remains standing for a moment, his clenched fist resting on his hip, then bends towards Zola, who whispers to him, smiling.

Silence falls, unbidden. All nerves are strained to breaking point. There is a general feeling that at last decisive battle is about to be joined. The Presiding Judge rises to his feet.

THE JUDGE: "The hearing will continue." Quickly, without sitting down again. "In the absence of General de Boisdeffre the hearing is adjourned till tomorrow." A short pause. "The Court will now rise for the day."

At first nobody seems to take in this announcement, and in the amazed silence which ensues the judges make a dignified exeunt. The jury have remained at their places. Taken by surprise, Zola turns to Labori, who continues standing with his back to his chair, in an attitude of defiance that now serves no purpose.

At last the meaning of what has happened sinks in: the battle is postponed, it will not take place today. And now cries of disappointment fill the air, merging into a confused din. The crowd is out of hand; everyone is standing, stamping his feet, emitting catcalls, whistles, objurgations. No sooner is the Bench empty than there is a general rush to the exits. Within a few moments these are blocked by the surging mass; women faint, faces stream with sweat, all self-control is cast to the winds in a blind, insensate stampede.

The *Sower* group remain at their places, appalled by what has happened.

JULIA: "The cowards!"

BREIL-ZOEGER: "Humpf! They prefer to wait for orders."

LUCE, sadly to Barois: "You see! They've the whip hand."

BAROIS, boiling with rage: "Ah, but this time they won't get away with it without a scandal, unscrupulous dogs that they are! I'll see to that in my article of tomorrow. Whom do they expect to fool? When Parliament takes the matter up and forces the authorities concerned to show their hand, they get the answer: 'This isn't the place. Go to the Law Courts and everything will be cleared up.' Then, when the case comes on, whenever any attempt is made to get to the bottom of the matter, whenever the truth seems to be on the point of emerging—slowly, laboriously—at long last, it's kicked back into the mud and trampled underfoot. 'The point cannot be raised'—and so forth. No, all that has got to stop, the country must realize the damnable way in which its wishes are being flouted."

Shouting is heard outside the doors.

WOLDSMUTH: "Listen! Something's happening. Let's go and see."

CRESTEIL: "Easier said than done! We'll never get through."

BAROIS: "Try for that gangway." To Julia. "Follow me."

BREIL-ZOEGER, starting to climb over the benches: "No, this is the quickest way."

BAROIS, shouting: "Same rendezvous as yesterday! At Zola's side!"

They hurry pell-mell out of the courtroom.

Wild cries are echoing in the vaulted corridors of the Law Courts; it is as if another Revolution had broken out in Paris. A cordon of Republican Guards, elbow to elbow, tries to contain the onrush, but without success. Yelling groups charge through the barrage, clash and mingle in the dimly lit passages. The air is loud with cries. "Traitors!" "The swine!" "Three cheers for Pellieux!" "Bravo, the Army!" "Down with the Jews!"

Just as Barois and Luce are joining the small, compact group of Zola's friends, a sudden eddy of the crowd, breaking through the line of police officers, pins them against the wall. Barois tries to shield Julia. Portal, who knows his way about the building, hastily opens the door of a cloak-room; Zola and his companions pour in precipitately.

Zola leans against a pilaster, bareheaded, very pale, the lids of his shortsighted, ferrety eyes half closed. Apparently he has lost his prince-nez in the scuffle. His lips are set in a hard line, and his gaze shifts uneasily from side to side. Catching sight of Luce and Barois, he shakes hands with them hastily, without a word.

At last the police succeed in clearing a passage. The Chief of Police has appeared on the scene and personally directs operations. The small, faithful band starts off again, joined now by Breil-Zoeger, Harbaroux, Woldsmuth, and Cresteil.

A dense crowd fills the courtyard and adjoining streets; the demonstrators are in occupation of the whole district round the Law Courts, up to the walls of the great hospital, the Hôtel Dieu. They form a gray, heaving mass, dappled here

[ 122 ]

and there with blurs of yellow light from the gas-lamps, which have just been lit, as a wintery dusk falls on the city. Now and again strident police whistles cut through the yells, catcalls, and concerted volleys of abuse. Across the din comes a persistent, rhythmic call, a leitmotiv. "Death to the traitors! Death!"

At the top of the flight of steps Zola pauses and bends towards his friends, his face convulsed with horror and disgust. "The cannibals!"

Then, with a sinking heart but at an even pace, he walks down the steps, leaning on a friend's arm, to where his carriage is waiting, surrounded by an escort of mounted police, who keep the crowd at bay.

When he turns to shake hands with some of his group, the yelling swells to a roar. "Chuck him into the Seine!" "Death to the traitor!"

The Chief of Police, fearing the worst, orders the coachman to drive off at once. As the carriage rumbles away at trotting pace a volley of missiles splinters the windows. Like a pack of hounds in full cry, the crowd surges forward, shrieking at the top of their voices, in pursuit of the receding carriage, which disappears into the dusk.

LUCE, in a broken voice to Barois: "If a drop of blood were shed just now, there would be a shambles."

Major Esterhazy comes down the steps, followed by a general; they are cheered all the way to their carriage. The police cordon is broken again. Barois tries to extricate Luce and Julia, but the crowd is too dense.

Zola's friends are recognized and loudly hissed. "Reinach! Luce! Barois! Death to the traitors! Long live the Army!" Strings of young fellows holding hands, students and well-dressed youngsters from the fashionable districts, wind their way snake-wise through the gaping crowd. Each of them has a paper badge, like the numbered labels worn by conscripts when reporting for military training, fastened to his hat, a badge that has been distributed by the thousands in the streets, inscribed: *"What every Frenchman says to Zola:* TO HELL WITH YOU!"

Officers in uniform thread their way through the mob, acclaimed by bursts of cheering.

Some individuals with Jewish noses are rounded up and roughly handled by boisterous youths, who do a war dance round them, brandishing torches made of rolled-up copies of *L'Aurore.* In the gathering darkness the effect is eerie, like some savage witch dance.

At the corner of a street, on the Seine bank, Luce and Julia halt to wait for the others. Suddenly a smartly dressed woman rushes towards them. Supposing she is being pursued, they make room for her, to offer their protection. But she heads straight for Luce and, gripping the lapel of his coat, tears off his Legion of Honor rosette. And, as she runs away, she flings contemptuously over her shoulder, "You rotter!"

Luce watches her receding form with a smile of infinite sadness.

An hour later. Luce, Barois, Julia, Breil-Zoeger, and Cresteil are walking slowly along the railings of the "Infanta's Garden." Night has fallen and a slight drizzle wets their shoulders. Barois links his arm affectionately in Luce's but Luce says nothing.

BAROIS: "Oh, come now! Why feel so discouraged? Nothing's lost, and the fight goes on." He laughs.

Luce turns and studies his friend's face under a street-lamp. With his virile zest for action, vast reserves of dynamism and confidence, Barois makes him think of an accumulator charged with vital energy.

LUCE, to Breil-Zoeger and Julia: "Look at him! You can almost see the sparks flying out of him!" Wearily. "Ah, how I envy you, Barois! Personally, I'm at the end of my tether, I've lost hope. France today is a drunk woman who can't see straight or walk straight; she can't distinguish false from true, she's ceased to know what justice means. No, really she's sunk too low—and it's heartbreaking."

BAROIS, with a vivacity that whips up their drooping spirits: "You're wrong, Luce, utterly wrong. You heard those shouts, didn't you? You saw those excited crowds? Well, a nation that still can work itself up to such a pitch of excitement over ideas—ideas, mind you!—is very far from being down-and-out."

CRESTEIL: "Good old Barois! He's hit the nail on the head as usual."

BREIL-ZOEGER: "That's obvious. Granted things have taken a nasty turn—but why should that surprise us? It may well be the first time in our history that morality has taken a hand in politics, so there are bound to be ructions."

BAROIS: "Really, it's a sort of *coup d'état*, what's happening."

LUCE: "Yes, from the very start I've had the impression that we were witnessing a revolution."

BREIL-ZOEGER: "Not 'witnessing'—making one."

BAROIS, exultantly: "And like all revolutions it's being launched by an enlightened few, a little group that pulls it off, unaided, by dint of passion, will-power, perseverance. Ah, what a damned fine thing it is, a fight like the one we're putting up!"

Luce shakes his head evasively.

Impulsively Julia comes up to Barois and clings to his arm; but he does not seem to notice her.

BAROIS, with a boisterous, almost boyish laugh: "Yes, I admit that, just at present, the situation is as ugly, as bes-

tial, as imbecile, as it well can be. But what matter? It's from this vile substratum that truth and beauty will flash forth one day." To Luce. "You've always told me that sooner or later lies find their punishment in the mere course of things. Well, I too believe in the inevitable triumph of truth, and though this afternoon we seem to have lost again, that's no reason for despair. Perhaps we'll win on the next round."

### III

August 31, 1898. Paris is comatose, half empty. The *Sower* group has met on the first floor of the café in the Boulevard Saint-Michel. It is nine in the evening.

The windows stand open on the hot darkness, and immediately beneath them the canvas awning over the café terrace glows softly, lit up from below. On all sides stretches the Latin Quarter, silent and abandoned by its gay fraternity of youth during the vacation. Empty streetcars, all their lights on, clang and clatter up the rise towards the Luxembourg Gardens.

Barois has tipped out the contents of his big attaché-case onto the table. Seated round him, the others are delving in the pile, running their eyes over pamphlets and newspapers.

PORTAL, to Cresteil: "Any news of Luce?" Portal has just returned from a holiday in his home town in Lorraine.

CRESTEIL: "Yes, I saw him last Sunday. Really I was most distressed. He has aged terribly in the last three months."

BAROIS: "I suppose you know that he's been asked—oh, very tactfully, needless to say—to discontinue his lectures at the Collège de France as of the beginning of next term? They'd been creating too much of a stir, towards the end of June, for the taste of the authorities. In fact everyone's cold-shouldering him these days. At the last session of the Senate hardly a dozen of his colleagues deigned to shake hands with him."

PORTAL: "It's unbelievable, the stupidity of the public at large!"

HARBAROUX, scowling darkly: "It's that damned nationalist press that's responsible for everything. Those people won't give the public a moment's breathing space to come to its senses."

BAROIS: "On the contrary, they're wantonly crushing out all the generous emotions that are normal to our people; all those fine qualities which placed France—at her risk and peril but to her glory!—in the vanguard of civilization. And in acting thus they profess to be combating anarchy and anti-militarism, which they have the impertinence and dishonesty to identify with the most elementary instincts of justice and human decency. And the masses are only too ready to be fooled."

WOLDSMUTH, shaking his fuzzy head: "Ah, yes indeed! You can always do what you like with a nation if you set them on to Jew-baiting."

CRESTEIL: "What makes the success these people have with the general public so amazing to me is that their arguments are really quite beneath contempt. A moment's reflection is enough to show their hollowness—when they tell us, for instance, that the Dreyfus case is a huge conspiracy engineered by the Jews."

BAROIS: "As though a complicated operation of this sort could have been thought out in advance and every step foreseen!"

CRESTEIL: "And even when you ask, 'But what if Esterhazy were the writer of that precious *bordereau?*' they take it in their stride. 'That only shows,' they reply, 'that the Jews bought him over, and got him to copy Dreyfus's handwriting so perfectly that you couldn't tell the difference.' Really it's too childishly absurd!"

BREIL-ZOEGER: "The trouble comes from the endless complications that have been dragged into the case. A spate of investigations, of inquiries into side issues, has completely hidden its true significance, submerged the basic facts. All sorts of hares have been started, and off they've gone in every conceivable direction, along the most preposterous bypaths. What's needed now is some dramatic incident that will swing public opinion right around, and get people to take a saner view of the case as a whole."

CRESTEIL: "Yes, a dramatic incident —I agree."

BAROIS: "And perhaps we're on the way to one, thanks to this talk about the High Court's taking action." He produces a letter from his pocket. "Here's something I got in this morning's mail." He smiles. "An anonymous letter full of kind intentions."

HARBAROUX, who has taken the letter from Barois, reads it out: " 'I have it on good authority that the Minister of War has submitted to the Government a proposal to indict before the High Court all the leaders of the party seeking a review of the Dreyfus case. Your name, with that of M. Luce, figures on the list.' "

BAROIS: "A flattering propinquity!"

HARBAROUX, reading on: " 'Their arrest is to take place on September 2 at an early hour. So you still have time to make your escape. A Friend.' "

BAROIS, laughing heartily: "Priceless, isn't it! A nice little billet-doux to get first thing in the morning!"

BREIL-ZOEGER: "It's that article of yours on Saturday that moved your 'friend' to action."

PORTAL: "I didn't read it." To Cresteil. "What was it about?"

CRESTEIL: "About that famous sitting of the Chamber when, in his innocence, the Minister of War thought fit to produce from his pocket five 'highly important documents'—and in reality produced five forgeries. Barois proved convincingly that these documents are false."

The manager of the café comes in.

THE MANAGER: "Monsieur Barois, there's a gentleman waiting to see you below."

Barois follows him out. At the foot of the stairs he sees Luce.

BAROIS: "Hullo? What brings you here at this hour of the night?"

LUCE: "I've news for you."

BAROIS: "About the High Court?"

LUCE: "No. Who's upstairs?"

BAROIS: "Only our *Sower* friends."

LUCE: "Right. Let's go up."

On seeing Luce, all show signs of surprise and some anxiety. In silence he shakes their hands, then sinks wearily into a chair. With his face so drawn and wasted, the massiveness of the forehead is even more impressive.

LUCE: "I've just heard some news of grave importance." They gather round him. "Either yesterday or the day before there was a startling development at the Ministry of War. Colonel Henry fell under suspicion of having forged the documents produced at the trial." All gaze at him in stupefaction. "Henry was promptly called and questioned by the Minister. Did he confess? That I don't know; but I *do* know that for the last twenty-four hours he's been under arrest at Mont-Valérien."

BAROIS: "Henry arrested! But that means—!"

Such is their excitement that they can hardly think coherently for some moments; only utter stifled exclamations of delight.

BREIL-ZOEGER, in a voice hoarse with emotion: "That means the whole case will be reopened."

BAROIS: "It means revision obviously."

HARBAROUX, meticulous as usual: "But what documents exactly did he forge?"

LUCE: "The letter to the Italian Military Attaché which contained the name of Dreyfus written in full."

BAROIS: "What? That precious letter General de Pellieux made so much of?"

BREIL-ZOEGER: "The letter the Minister read out six weeks ago to the Chamber of Deputies!"

LUCE: "Yes, it's a complete forgery, except for the heading and the signature, which were got, it seems, from a letter on some routine matter."

BAROIS: "It's almost too good to be true!"

WOLDSMUTH, like an echo: "Too good to be true—yes. I don't feel easy about it."

LUCE: "But it's only a start. Once the inquiry takes this turn, a number of other questions will need answering. For instance: Who invented the tale that Dreyfus had confessed? Why wasn't a word breathed about it until 1896—two years after he had been cashiered? Then, again, who erased the original address and wrote in Esterhazy's on that incriminating letter, the *"petit bleu,"* so as to raise the presumption that Colonel Picquart was trying to shield Dreyfus and inculpate Esterhazy by means of a document he'd tampered with?"

WOLDSMUTH, his eyes full of tears, repeats: "It's too good to be true. I don't feel easy about it."

LUCE: "In any case, this arrest has already had important consequences. Boisdeffre, Pellieux, and Zurlinden are leaving their posts. And I hear that the Minister too is tendering his resignation —which I can well understand. After having read out to the Chamber—albeit in good faith—a forgery, he can hardly do less."

BAROIS, laughing: "But it's *they* who should be arraigned before the High Court, not we!"

LUCE: "What's more, Brisson has swung round completely."

PORTAL: "At last!"

BAROIS: "That confirms what I have always said. Once an old-school republican like Brisson has his eyes opened, he'll move heaven and earth to have the case reviewed."

WOLDSMUTH: "I should say he must be feeling pretty sick at the thought of those million copies of Henry's forgery he had printed and posted up all over France."

HARBAROUX, with a loud guffaw: "Good Lord, yes! I wouldn't care to be in Brisson's shoes. That famous piece of evidence is on show in every town hall; it's fresh in every mind, and our patriotic papers gloat over it in every issue. And now, all of a sudden, it turns out to be a fake. Well, well!"

PORTAL: "The game is up, and they know it."

WOLDSMUTH, gloomily: "I wouldn't be too sure. I don't feel easy in the least."

BAROIS, laughing: "Oh, come, Woldsmuth! Really you're carrying your pessimism too far this time. The Government thought twice before ordering Henry's arrest, you may be sure. It means they couldn't see their way to hushing the matter up; they knew the truth would out, and there was no stopping it."

WOLDSMUTH, gently: "But Henry isn't even in the military prison."

BAROIS: "But surely—?"

CRESTEIL, breaking in with a sudden look of discouragement: "Yes, Woldsmuth's right, confound it! The fellow's only under open arrest, at the Mont-Valérien fort—which isn't the same thing."

They gaze at each other in consternation; the reaction is all the more pronounced because their hopes had run so high.

LUCE, dejectedly: "Perhaps they only wanted to gain time, so as to devise some way of getting out of the difficulty."

CRESTEIL: "And treat the forgery as a mere breach of military discipline? That's possible, I fear."

WOLDSMUTH, mournfully: "No, I haven't much confidence."

BAROIS, angrily: "That's enough of it,

Woldsmuth! This is no time for pessimism." Firmly. "Our duty's plain. We've got to stir up such a rumpus about what's happened that they won't be able to hush it up."

LUCE: "Ah, if only Henry had confessed in the presence of witnesses!"

Shouts echo up the boulevard, newsboys are crying the day's "Late Specials." Though there is little traffic, the confused din of voices makes it almost impossible to distinguish what they are shouting.

PORTAL: "Ssh! That sounded like 'Colonel Henry.' "

LUCE: "What? Have they learned of it already?"

Impulsively all have moved to the open windows and are hanging out, craning their necks, trying to catch what the boys are saying.

BREIL-ZOEGER, running to the door: "Waiter! The evening papers! Quickly!"

But already Woldsmuth has dashed down the stairs and out into the street. The shouts are growing fainter; the boys have turned off into side streets. Some minutes pass.

At last, breathless, his hair in disorder, his eyes sparkling, Woldsmuth appears at the head of the stairs brandishing a newspaper with headlines in large type:

"SUICIDE OF COLONEL HENRY AT

FORT MONT-VALÉRIEN"

BAROIS, with a shout of triumph: "There we have it—our confession!"

He turns to Luce, and in a rush of emotion the two men embrace each other silently. Portal, Breil-Zoeger, and Cresteil try to snatch the newspaper from Woldsmuth, but he quietly hands it to Luce, who, jerkily adjusting his pince-nez, his face very pale, reads in a voice shaken by emotion.

LUCE: " 'Last night, at a meeting at the Ministry of War, it was ascertained that Lieutenant-Colonel Henry was the author of the letter in which the name of Dreyfus appears in full. The Minister gave orders for Lieutenant-Colonel Henry's arrest, and he was removed to Fort Mont-Valérien.

" 'This evening, on entering the cell at 6 P.M., the orderly assigned to the Lieutenant-Colonel found him lying on the bed in a pool of blood, his throat cut in two places, a razor in his hand. Death had taken place some two hours previously.

" 'The forger had paid the penalty of his crime.' "

The paper drops from his fingers. The others snatch it up, and it passes from hand to hand; each wishes to see the great news with his own eyes. And then a long, fierce cry of exultation, shrill with an almost insensate glee, breaks from their lips.

LUCE, in a choking voice: "Now that Henry's dead, it's over; there are some aspects of the Affair that will never come to light."

But his words are lost in the general excitement. Only Breil-Zoeger has heard and sadly nods his head. Woldsmuth has moved, unnoticed, to the window and, leaning out into the darkness, is shedding tears of joy.

IV

A year later, August 6, 1899, the eve of the Rennes trial. The *Sower* office, a Sunday afternoon. Barois, who is in his shirt-sleeves, paces his office, his hands in his pockets, thinking out an article. His mind is at its most alert; the strong features that twitch now and again, the faint smile of satisfaction on his lips, vouch for his confident assurance of success. The bad days are over.

BAROIS: "Come in. Ah, it's you, Woldsmuth. Good." Woldsmuth looks even tinier than usual in a light dustcoat. He has a satchel slung over his shoulder and a big attaché-case under his arm. "We haven't met for several days. What have you been up to?"

WOLDSMUTH, settling into the nearest chair: "I've just come back from Germany."

BAROIS, without surprise: "From Germany?" After a moment's silence. "Anyhow, I knew you'd turn up today, to take over the management, as we'd agreed."

WOLDSMUTH: "Are you all leaving by the night express?"

BAROIS: "No, the others reached Rennes this morning. Luce had things to do there, and they went with him. I shall take the night train."

WOLDSMUTH: "When is Luce giving his evidence?"

BAROIS: "Not until the fifth or sixth day's hearing. I stayed behind so as to hand over to you, and also to write a final article which will appear tomorrow."

WOLDSMUTH, eagerly: "Ah? So there's a number coming out tomorrow?"

Barois, who takes Woldsmuth's interest for curiosity, gathers up some loose sheets on the desk.

BAROIS: "Oh, something quite short; just a few lines by way of prelude to the trial. Look here! I'll read out what I've written:

" 'Our goal is well in sight at last; the long-protracted nightmare is drawing to a close. We are no longer interested in the last act, the verdict which is a foregone conclusion, inevitable as the triumph of justice.

" 'All that remains to us today is the memory of having lived through an historic drama, unique of its kind, a drama in which thousands of characters played their parts and whose stage was the whole world. For its issues were at once so poignant and so universal in their appeal that first the entire nation and then all civilized mankind followed it with breathless interest. For what is assuredly the last time, humanity, divided into two unequal groups, joined vital issue; on one side was organized author-

ity, which always turns a deaf ear to the voice of reason, and, on the other, the spirit of honest inquiry, which proudly disdains all social considerations.

" 'Generations to come will speak of "the Affair" as we today speak of "the Revolution," and will welcome as the happiest of coincidences that the dawn of a new century is also the dawn of a new era. And how glorious is the promise of a century ushered in by such a victory!'

"As you see, my dear Woldsmuth, a mere ebullition, a trumpet call!"

Woldsmuth gazes at him in stupefaction, then timidly draws his chair nearer.

WOLDSMUTH: "Tell me, Barois. Are you really so confident as that?"

BAROIS, smiling: "Why, of course!"

WOLDSMUTH, putting more energy into his voice: "Well, personally, I'm not. I don't feel confident at all."

Barois, who now is pacing the room with a look of almost gloating triumph, stops abruptly, then shrugs his shoulders.

BAROIS: "I seem to have heard that before! What a wet blanket you are, old chap!"

WOLDSMUTH, quickly: "So far facts have proved me right, I fear."

BAROIS: "But the conditions are very different today. There's been a change of government and our new government is convinced of Dreyfus's innocence and determined to clear the matter up. This time the trial will take place in public; there'll be no scope for hole-and-corner work. Why, really, to feel any doubt about the verdict is tantamount to assuming Dreyfus's guilt." He ends with a hearty laugh, a boisterous affirmation of common sense and certitude.

Woldsmuth gazes at him silently. The small, stubborn eyes glow darkly in the hairy, dust-stained face.

WOLDSMUTH, affectionately: "Do sit down, Barois. I want to talk to you seriously. I see a great many people, you know." Half closing his eyes, he goes on

speaking in a muffled, toneless voice. "And I pick up lots of information."

BAROIS, sharply: "So do I."

WOLDSMUTH, in a conciliatory tone: "Then no doubt you've noticed. Well, consider the nationalist press. All the forgeries have been shown up, all the illegalities of the trial revealed, and yet their newspapers aren't climbing down. They've been forced to give ground on the facts, but they are having their revenge. They're slinging mud at all their enemies, indiscriminately. That report by Ballot-Beaupré—a completely honest summing up of the Affair—do you think any of their papers published it? Not they! They described it as the report of a man who'd been corrupted by Jewish gold—as were Duclaux, Anatole France, and Zola."

BAROIS: "What of it? Do you suppose their readers are so gullible as that?"

By way of retort Woldsmuth produces a sheaf of nationalist papers from his pocket and flings them on the table.

BAROIS, growing irritated: "That proves nothing. My answer is that during the last two months three thousand new subscriptions to *The Sower* have come in; you know it as well as I. The truth is that a great wave of enthusiasm—for public honesty and fair-dealing—is sweeping France today."

WOLDSMUTH, morosely: "It may be. But it hasn't yet reached our Ministry of War."

BAROIS, after reflection: "That's so. I admit that the judges, decent men, perhaps, but military-minded, are all against the agitation for revision of the case. But don't forget that the eyes of Europe, indeed of the whole civilized world, are fixed on Rennes today—and the military judges know this." He rises to his feet. "Well, there are some situations that compel, and these worthy officers will be forced to recognize that all those early allegations won't bear a moment's serious inspection, and"—he laughs—"there aren't any new ones."

WOLDSMUTH: "That depends."

Thrusting his hands in his pockets, Barois shrugs his shoulders again and once more starts pacing up and down the room. But the firmness of Woldsmuth's voice has taken effect, and presently he comes to a halt, facing him.

BAROIS: "Depends on what?"

WOLDSMUTH, with a wry smile: "Do sit down, Barois. You make me think of a caged lion." Frowning, Barois goes back to his seat behind the desk. "You remember that story about some tremendously secret documents?" Barois' look invites him to explain. "No? Then let me tell you. This is the story that's being circulated now. That a whole series of letters between Dreyfus and the Kaiser were somehow stolen." He smiles. "Grotesque, isn't it? But let that pass.

"According to this legend, the real *bordereau* formed part of this correspondence. It was written by Dreyfus on ordinary notepaper, and the German Emperor made some notes in the margin in his own hand. When Wilhelm II learned of the theft he insisted on the return of the stolen letters, threatening to declare war if they were not restored. So as to have documentary evidence of Dreyfus's guilt, the Ministry had a tracing made of the *bordereau* on thin paper, before complying with the Kaiser's request. The marginal comments in his handwriting were, of course, omitted. Thus the whole affair was built up on this tracing of the original—a counterfeit in one sense, but a faithful reproduction of the incriminating original."

BAROIS: "A grotesque story! So grotesque, in fact, that never to my knowledge has it been formulated officially or even semi-officially."

WOLDSMUTH: "I know. But all the same it's going round, passed from mouth to mouth in gatherings attended by officers, magistrates, lawyers, and society people. None claims first-hand knowledge of course. What's said is: 'A well-informed friend gave me to understand . . .' and so forth, to the accompaniment of knowing winks and smiles. And gradually it has taken effect and paved the way. So tomorrow when the case starts at Rennes and the defense tries to force the staff officers to show their hand, they'll play their little parts. All they'll need to do is to make a show of embarrassment at certain points, to pause and stammer—you see the tactics? And everyone will take this to mean: 'Draw your own conclusions. Anyhow, we'd rather be accused of forgery than bring about a European war.' "

BAROIS: "A war! But at this hour of the day there can't be any question of a danger of that sort. Considering all that's been said and written about the foreign military attachés, about German espionage and counter-espionage, who can be such a simpleton as to think that any 'dangerous' diplomatic documents still remain to be made public? Did any such document exist, it's obvious that the General Staff would have produced it long ago, just to put an end to all the trouble."

WOLDSMUTH, gloomily: "It's not quite so simple as all that, I fear. All along I've been worried about the 'diplomatic' issue—it's the thread that runs through the Affair from end to end, and though it's kept invisible, everything, every incident, links up with it. That's where the danger lies, a very real danger." About to speak, Barois thinks better of it; his look betrays his deep concern. "But, happily, there's still time to forestall their machinations. I've been compiling a kind of 'brief,' containing nothing but facts for whose veracity I can vouch. During my recent visit to Germany I have verified those about which I felt the slightest doubt."

BAROIS: "Ah, that's why—"

WOLDSMUTH: "Yes." He opens his attaché-case. "I've material here that will blow their 'State Secret' arguments sky high. But there's no time to lose. Here is my 'brief.' Publish it tomorrow."

BAROIS, after pondering for some moments: "Thanks, Woldsmuth. But I think the publication of evidence of that kind today would be most unwise." Woldsmuth makes a discouraged gesture. "It would draw attention to a feature of the case which, whatever you may think, has been deliberately relegated to obscurity. They might feel moved to fall back on it, by way of a reprisal, and that would have a bad effect on public opinion.

"No, publication would be a tactical blunder as things stand. For there is bound to be an acquittal. Let's have our triumph in beauty, without raking up old animosities." His shoulders drooping, Woldsmuth begins to close his attaché-case. "No, leave your notes with me."

WOLDSMUTH: "What's the good? If they're to serve any purpose they must be used at once, preventively."

BAROIS: "I'll take them with me to Rennes and show them to Luce. If he thinks as you do, I promise—"

WOLDSMUTH, with a gleam of hope: "Yes, do show them to Luce, and please repeat exactly what I've told you." He thinks for a moment. "But you can't possibly take them as they stand. They're in such a muddle. I shall have to go through them carefully. You see, I'd hoped we could do the job together for tomorrow's issue."

BAROIS: "Your niece is here. If you dictate to her, it shouldn't take long."

WOLDSMUTH, his face lighting up: "Oh, Julia's here?"

Barois gets up and opens the door.

BAROIS: "Julia!"

JULIA, from the next room, without moving: "Yes? What is it?"

The familiarity of her tone is so noticeable that Barois flushes and glances hastily at Woldsmuth, who, poring over his papers, has betrayed no surprise.

BAROIS, controlling his voice: "Would you come here for a moment, to take down some notes?"

Julia enters. On noticing Woldsmuth, her eyelids flutter slightly—no more than that. Her rebellious air seems a reminder to her uncle: "I'm my own mistress anyhow!"

JULIA, curtly: "Good afternoon, Uncle Ulric. How was your trip?"

Woldsmuth raises his head but does not look at her. And now she notices the twisted, disconcerting smile, the strained look on his face. She guesses something she had never even suspected until now. When at last Woldsmuth looks towards her, it is she who lowers her eyes.

WOLDSMUTH: "So you're here, Julia. All's well with you, I hope. And with your mother."

JULIA, with an effort: "Yes, we're both quite fit."

WOLDSMUTH: "Then would you . . . ? I've some notes to be taken down . . . for Barois."

BAROIS, who has noticed nothing: "Go to her office, Woldsmuth, you'll be more comfortable there. And meanwhile I'll finish my article."

Rennes,
August 13, 1899

My dear Woldsmuth: I assume you have read the shorthand reports for yesterday and the day before. How right you were, my friend! Yet who could have suspected it at the time?

All these last days our enemies have been eagerly awaiting the "conclusive" evidence against Dreyfus that they have so often been promised. The generals had their say; disappointment all along the line! Then, as public opinion obstinately refused to admit that no such conclusive argument existed, they interpreted the reticences of the General Staff exactly as you foresaw. Which was what the General Staff intended. A rumor has actually being going round that at the last moment Germany forced this heroic silence on our officers!

I am sending herewith the notes you dictated to Julia before I left; they are, alas, of vital importance as things stand today. Breil-Zoeger, who is going back to Paris to take over from you, will hand them to you this evening with this letter.

Get in touch with Roll at once and see that your article appears tomorrow on the front page. Also, before leaving Paris, please arrange for a wide distribution of this issue. Bring two thousand copies to Rennes; that will be enough.

Sadly and sincerely yours,

J.B.

Next day, on the front page of *The Sower:*

WILHELM II AND THE DREYFUS CASE

"During the last few weeks we have been surprised to observe that an ingenious legend, which, to the minds of simple persons, seems to solve the mysteries of the Affair, has made its reappearance. It is the story that a French agent purloined from the Kaiser's desk a *bordereau* on stout paper annotated by the Kaiser himself. Under the threat of war the French authorities were compelled hastily to restore the original document, and the *bordereau* we know (on thin, transparent paper) is a tracing of the original, which was made at the Ministry of War in view of the 1894 trial.

"We need not trouble to point out the glaring improbabilities of this romantic tale, and shall limit ourselves to asking three questions.

"(1) If the *bordereau* is a tracing of words written by Dreyfus, how is it that the handwriting is little if at all like that of Dreyfus, but identical with Esterhazy's?

"(2) If Henry's forgeries can be accounted for by the necessity of substituting diplomatically harmless documents for those in which the German Emperor's handwriting appeared and which therefore could not be made use of, how was it that Henry, when questioned by the Minister of War just before his arrest, did not clear himself by explaining that his forgeries were reproductions of authentic documents? Several generals were present when he was questioned, and General Roget took the statements down in shorthand. Henry did not attempt to justify his forgeries by any allegation of the kind.

"(3) If the story of the annotated *bordereau* is true, how was it that when Brisson, greatly shocked by Henry's suicide, manifested intentions of making a public confession of his mistake and securing a revision of the Dreyfus verdict —how was it that the Minister of War, who took such pains to argue Brisson out of this resolve, did not simply inform him of the German Emperor's intervention, and thus bring the swing-round of opinion, which was causing the anti-revisionists such dismay, to an immediate stop?

"After asking these pertinent questions we shall confine ourselves to setting forth in chronological order certain facts whose significance seems so obvious that no comment is called for.

"(1) On November 1, 1894, the name of Dreyfus appeared for the first time in the newspapers, with the allegation that he was a spy in the service of Germany or Italy. The German and Italian Military Attachés were amazed; the name was wholly unfamiliar to them both. This is proved by the fact that on June 5, 1899, the Italian Ambassador forwarded to the Minister for Foreign Affairs, for transmission to the Court of Appeal, a code communication dated 1894 from the Italian Attaché (who was working hand in glove with the German Attaché) in which he secretly informed his Government that neither of them had ever had any dealings with the Dreyfus in question. At the same time the General Staffs of Germany, Italy, and Austria had inquiries made in their respective secret services and failed to elicit information regarding anyone by the name of Dreyfus.

"(2) On November 9, 1894, the German Attaché was implicated by name in a French paper. After another inquiry the German Embassy issued a formal *dementi* in the form of a press communiqué. It should be noted that this denial cannot have been made without due care and caution, since Germany would not have run the risk of making a statement, under such conditions, which might thereafter be proved false in the course of a public trial. Moreover, at the same time the Imperial Chancellor instructed the German Ambassador in Paris to make an official declaration, *suo motu,* to this effect to the French Minister for Foreign Affairs.

"(3) On November 28 the interview with General Mercier was published in *Figaro.* Five days before the conclusion of the inquiry, which was to lead to the indictment of Dreyfus before a military court, the Minister stated that there was 'conclusive proof' of the guilt of the accused man, and that Dreyfus had offered his documents *neither to Italy nor to Austria.* The inference that Germany was implicated was obvious, and a new and strongly worded protest was made by Germany through diplomatic channels.

"When the French press failed to take this into account, the Kaiser, the German General Staff, and the German press were greatly incensed at finding that the veracity of their formal declaration was being questioned. Accordingly, on De-

cember 4, on the Kaiser's orders, another interview took place between the Ambassador and our Minister for Foreign Affairs. An official communiqué was issued, vigorously protesting against all allegations tending to implicate the German Embassy in the Dreyfus Affair.

"(4) The trial took place. As regards the 'secret dossier' shown the trial judges, without inspection of it being granted to the accused man or his counsel, we are in a position to state that there was nothing in this dossier bearing out the tale of a *bordereau* annotated by the German Emperor. This can be verified by questioning the members of the 1894 Council of War, now present at Rennes, on this point.

"(5) At the close of December 1894, after the verdict, the press openly accused Germany of having insisted on a trial *in camera,* because Germany was directly involved in the circumstances of Dreyfus's guilt. This also was tantamount to giving the lie to the Ambassador's statement. On December 25, immediately after the sentence, the Ambassador made a further official statement to the press. But the newspapers continued their campaign, talking about a document returned to Germany so as to avoid the risk of war.

"(6) On January 5, 1895, the day on which Dreyfus was formally 'degraded,' the German Ambassador received a very important dispatch from the Imperial Chancellor. In the absence of our Minister for Foreign Affairs he took it directly to our Premier. This dispatch, now published for the first time, ran as follows:

" 'H.H. the Emperor, who feels the utmost confidence in the good faith of the President and Government of the French Republic, requests Your Excellency to inform M. Casimir-Périer that, if it is proved that the German Embassy was never implicated in any way in the Dreyfus Affair, His Majesty hopes that the Government of the Republic will not hesitate to make this publicly known.

" 'Without a formal declaration to this effect, the rumors that the press continues to circulate regarding Germany will persist, and compromise the position of the Emperor's representative in Paris —Von Hohenlohe.'

"Thus the Kaiser, at the end of his patience, made a direct appeal to the French President himself.

"The Ambassador was received by the President at his official residence, and we have it on unimpeachable authority that M. Casimir-Périer chose to regard the incident as of a private rather than a diplomatic order, since the German Emperor was asking him to intervene personally. In fact, as he himself subsequently stated, 'an appeal was made to his good will in his private capacity.'

"In this connection we may refer to the evidence given by M. Casimir-Périer before the Supreme Court of Appeal and Revision. He began by stating explicitly that he had no secrets of any kind to conceal. 'I have observed,' he went on to say, 'that my silence (at the Zola trial) seemed to countenance the notion that I—and perhaps only I—had knowledge of incidents, of facts, or of documents which might influence the course of justice. I feel it my duty, in view of the present unhappy state of dissension and unrest prevailing in France, to place myself at the disposal of the Supreme Court *unreservedly* . . .'

"This puts an end to any suspicion whatsoever that (as some have alleged) the President was bound by a pledge of secrecy. A declaration of this sort coming from a man of his high integrity is conclusive. He went on to describe the diplomatic conversation that ensued, leading to an official communiqué through the Havas Agency, which definitely exonerated all foreign embassies in Paris. And on the next day but one the Kaiser expressed his satisfaction.

"Nor must we overlook the statement made by M. Hanotaux, the Minister for Foreign Affairs at the time of the 1894 trial. To the question, 'Have you any knowledge of certain letters from a foreign ruler, which were written at the time of the Dreyfus trial and tended to prove the guilt of the accused man?' he gave a perfectly definite answer: 'I have never seen any such letter, nor have I ever heard of one. Nobody ever offered me anything of the kind. I have never been consulted as to the existence or the value of any such documents. In short, the whole story is completely mythical; moreover, it has been denied in communiqués to the newspapers.'

"Let us cite, in conclusion, the evidence given before the Appeal Court by M. Paléologue, who was liaison officer between the Ministry of War and the Ministry for Foreign Affairs at the time of the Dreyfus trial.

" 'Neither before nor after the Dreyfus trial did I hear anything about the existence of a letter from the German Emperor, or of letters from Dreyfus to that monarch. The allegations to which the Presiding Judge has alluded seem to me completely unfounded. The nature of my then duties authorizes me to say that, had documents of this kind existed, I would certainly have known of their existence.'

"(7) On November 17, 1897, the German Ambassador informed our Minister for Foreign Affairs that the German Military Attaché, Colonel von Schwartzkoppen, affirmed on his honor that he had never had any dealings, direct or indirect, with Dreyfus.

"(8) In 1898, just before the Zola trial, the Emperor was extremely anxious to make a decisive, *personal* intervention, but his advisers discouraged him from doing so. They knew how high feelings were running in France and feared some personal insult might be levelled at the Kaiser, leading to grave complications. However, he insisted that an official statement should be made publicly, at a sitting of the Reichstag.

"This is the statement made accordingly, by the German Foreign Secretary, at the session of January 24, 1898:

" 'You will understand that I must approach this subject with extreme prudence. Any indiscreet approach might be regarded as an unwarrantable intervention on our part in matters concerning France. I deem it all the more incumbent on me to maintain a wise reserve on this subject since we may anticipate that the trials being held in France will throw the fullest light on the Affair.

" 'Therefore I will confine myself to affirming, in the most formal and categorical manner, that no relations or contacts of any kind whatsoever have ever existed between ex-Captain Dreyfus, now undergoing penal servitude on Devil's Island, and any German agent whatsoever.'

"(9) Five days later the Emperor himself called on our Ambassador in Berlin, gave him his personal declaration on the subject, and asked him to communicate it officially to our Government.

"(10) Finally, at the present moment, the state of mind prevailing in the Emperor's entourage is the same. The Kaiser himself is fervently desirous of making a personal 'gesture.' But his advisers dissuade him from it, and will continue to dissuade him, so as to avert a serious danger—that, by reaffirming Dreyfus's guilt, France might once again give the Kaiser the lie direct, and thus create an intolerable position which would lead to the breaking off of diplomatic relations. However, the German authorities are prepared to confirm, through the usual channels, all the declarations already made.

"If we are prepared to believe that the Kaiser was really compromised in an affair of espionage, we may, at a pinch, assume that, for political considerations, he might feel called on to deny the truth in an official statement. But is it credible that, once this diplomatically necessary lie had been told and put on record, he would have voiced his protest again and again on every possible occasion, with such deliberate emphasis and such extreme insistence?

"Even if we leave out of account the temperament of the German Emperor and his well-known touchiness regarding points of personal honor, is it to be believed that a monarch would dare to make such vehement and plain-spoken declarations if there were the slightest risk of his being one day, as a result of the discovery of some conclusive piece of evidence, shown up to the world as having lied?

"Who can fail to see in the Kaiser's attitude anything other than a very simple, heart-felt sense of duty? He knows, better than anyone, that Dreyfus is innocent, and he does his best to proclaim this knowledge as emphatically and frequently as is possible without exposing his country to the risk of diplomatic complications.

"None are so deaf as they who will not hear!"

M. Marc-Élie Luce
 Auteuil
   Rennes, September 5, 1899
My dear Luce: We are utterly despondent. To all intents and purposes ours is a lost cause. The past fortnight has put the seal on the Affair. The judges have made up their minds and they know well that the majority think as they do.

Woldsmuth blames me for having published his article belatedly. I too blame myself, though I doubt if earlier publication would have made much difference. How combat a myth which no one has ever clearly formulated? Anyhow, there would have been no way of coming to grips with it, since all agree that those alleged marginal comments in the Kaiser's hand cannot be verified. Under such conditions anyone's word is as good as another's, and in this war against mere phantoms we were helpless, doomed from the start.

Had a swing-round of public opinion been feasible, it would have been brought about on the day after you left Rennes by the attitude of Casimir-Périer, the man in France best qualified to know whether or not the Kaiser was involved in the Affair. I saw this man, whose character is spotless, facing the Presiding Judge, and his voice rang true when he made his statement. This is what he said:

"You ask me to tell the whole truth and nothing but the truth. I have sworn to do this, and I shall speak out without withholding anything. Despite what I have reiterated in the past, some people persist in believing, or in saying—which, alas, is not always the same thing—that I alone know of certain incidents or facts which might throw light on the case, and that I have not yet revealed all that, in the interests of justice, should be known. That is false. I do not wish to leave these precincts until I feel satisfied that everyone present is convinced, unshakably convinced, that I know nothing as to which I am bound to silence, and that I have frankly and completely stated all I know."

I don't question the good faith of the military judges. I believe them to be as impartial as they can be. But they are soldiers. The newspapers they read have seen to it that they, like the whole Army, are kept in complete ignorance of the inside history of the Affair. These worthy officers have been confronted by an outrageously simplified pair of alternatives, a most damnable dilemma: "You have to choose between finding Dreyfus guilty and blackening the Army's good name."

There might be some hope, if they were kept apart from outside influences and left to themselves to judge the facts, according to the promptings of their consciences. But unfortunately every evening, when the hearing ends, they still frequent circles in which the accused man's betrayal of his country is a foregone conclusion.

I wouldn't say they are determined to find Dreyfus guilty, but I feel quite sure they will bring in a verdict to that effect. How indeed could these men, whose natural dispositions have been vitiated year after year by the exigencies of their profession, act otherwise? They have been, as it were, crusted over by twenty-five years of wearing uniforms, a quarter of a century during which, day in and day out, they have had the virtues of military discipline, the sense of Army hierarchy, drubbed into them. And in the high officers who appear before them they see living symbols of the Army to which they have dedicated their lives. How could they decide in favor of a Jew, against the General Staff? Even if, in their heart of hearts, they have an uneasy feeling that they should act thus, it is *physically impossible* for them to do so.

Moreover, I am bound to admit that the figure Dreyfus cuts in Court has nothing to counterbalance the fine presence of the men in uniform opposing him. Yes, the majority even of his friends are disappointed in him. Wrongly, to my mind. For four years we have been fighting for ideas, and have made Dreyfus, so to speak, their figurehead. All of us had conjured up in our imagination a picture, none the less precise for its capriciousness, of the stranger we were championing. He returns to France and, as might have been expected, the reality doesn't conform to our expectation. And a good many of us have not yet forgiven him for our disillusionment.

Dreyfus is a simple man, all of whose energies are of the introversive order. He is also an invalid; long confinement and the ordeal he has been through have sapped his vigor. A few pints of milk are all he can digest; you can see him shivering with fever. How could he rise effectively to the occasion, when confronted by an excited mob of people three-quarters of whom regard him as the blackest of traitors, and the remaining quarter venerate him as a symbol? Surely, under such conditions, no one could play the heroic part we asked of poor Dreyfus! He no longer has strength enough to proclaim his innocence in the proud, defiant tone he used at the first trial. What little energy is left him he husbands, using it not against his accusers but against himself, to prevent himself from breaking down, and to put up a show of courage.

The true nobility and tragic grandeur of this attitude are completely lost on the average man. He might perhaps have won over the crowd by striking a more theatrical pose; but the self-control which he strains every effort to maintain is regarded as mere apathy, and the men who have been fighting in his cause for the past four years hold this up against him.

Personally, I confess that when I saw him at the first hearing—I had never set eyes on him before—in spite of my friends' enthusiasm and the high hopes I had voiced so proudly that very morning in *The Sower*, my heart sank, and I had a foreboding of defeat. I hid my feeling then even from you. But I can now see that I realized, with a conviction as absolute as it was abruptly come by, that we were fighting in a lost cause—lost, moreover, in an ugly way. Nothing would

remain in hearts once fired with generous emotion but a residue of sordid memories. And now this odious thought is always present at the back of my mind.

You did well to leave Rennes; your place was not here, in this maelstrom of absurdity.

We are at the end of our tether. Don't forget that for many of us this is the second sweltering summer we have to live through in an atmosphere oppressive as a nightmare. Picture to yourself our days of long-drawn-out suspense in the stifling atmosphere of that courtroom, listening to evidence that reeks of prejudice and hatred. And picture, too, those evenings, even worse than the days, when, to escape our suffocating hotel bedrooms where sleep is out of the question, we forgather in streets or cafés and reckon up for the $n$th time our chances of victory or defeat! If we have managed to see it through so far, it is because the conviction that justice would prevail steeled our endurance. But, though we are nearing the conclusion of yet another phase, the end still seems as far off as ever. And how long the road before us yet—there is no knowing.

It is sad indeed to see our admirable country sunk so low, both intellectually and morally. To think that at this moment there is a truly world-wide stirring of the human conscience, a movement of revolt, and for the first time in centuries France lags behind!

Please tell Breil-Zoeger that if he wishes to return to Rennes, Harbaroux can go to Paris to take over at the office.

*Au revoir*, my dear friend, and ever yours,

Jean Barois

P.S. I have just learnt that Labori intends to make a personal appeal to the Kaiser, with a view to obtaining, before the close of the trial, yet another declaration from the Emperor of Dreyfus's innocence.

What's the use? Considering how things are, it's bound to be too late.

Telegram to:
   Barois, 103 Lycée, Rennes.
       Paris, September 8, 11:30 A.M.
Have just received telegram reporting new protest by German Government in this morning's *Imperial Monitor,* in response Labori's appeal:

"We are authorized to renew declarations made by His Majesty's Government to safeguard personal dignity and obey dictates of common humanity. On Emperor's instructions, Ambassador, January 1894 and January 1895 handed to Hanotaux, Minister Foreign Affairs, to Premier Dupuy and President Casimir-Périer, repeated declarations that German Embassy in France never entertained relations direct or indirect with Dreyfus.

"On January 24, 1898, Secretary of State von Bülow stated before Reichstag commission: 'I declare in the most solemn manner that no dealings or intercourse of any kind took place between ex-Captain Dreyfus and any German organizations whatsoever.'

"Minister Foreign Affairs has undertaken officially to transmit this protest to the judges before verdict rendered."

Still have hopes. Spread the news through all local newspapers.
                                        Luce.

Telegram to:
   Luce, Auteuil.
       Rennes, September 9, 6 P.M.
Guilty of treason with extenuating circumstances. Ten years' imprisonment. A nonsensical self-contradictory verdict. But we're not beaten yet. On with the fight for justice!
                                        Barois.

                    v

September 9, 1899. The evening of the verdict. At Rennes station three succes-sive trains have been boarded at a rush. A fourth, composed of ramshackle cars collected from various sidings, gets laboriously under way amid the seething turmoil on the platforms. Barois, Cresteil, and Woldsmuth have squeezed into an ancient third-class car divided into compartments by partitions reaching half-way up to the roof. Two oil lamps do duty for the whole car.

There is not a breath of wind. The open windows give glimpses of the night-bound countryside. The engine crawls along, trailing through the sultry darkness a din of voices like that of an election meeting. Heated comments flash back and forth through the foul air of the compartment in which are Barois and his friends.

"Of course those damned Jesuits were behind it!"

"That's no thing to say. What about the honor of the Army?"

"Anyhow, it's a death-blow to the trade-union movement, I should say."

"They were quite right. The safety of the country would be endangered if an officer who's been sentenced by seven brother-officers and declared guilty by the High Command were to be reinstated. It would be infinitely worse than a miscarriage of justice."

"You're right. And I'd go further. Suppose I'd been one of the judges and suppose I *knew* that Dreyfus was innocent. Well, sir, for the safety of our country, for the maintenance of order, I'd have sent him to the firing-squad without a moment's hesitation."

CRESTEIL, springing up impulsively and making his raucous voice heard through the din: "There's a French scientist, Duclaux, who has answered that argument about the safety of the country. This is what he said, more or less: 'No reason of State can hinder a Court of Justice from doing justice.'" Cries of "Traitor!" "Blackguard!" "Dirty Jew!"

Cresteil strikes an attitude of challenge. "Gentlemen, I am ready to meet you wherever you may desire." There is another volley of abuse. Cresteil remains standing.

BAROIS: "Oh, let them be, Cresteil!"

Gradually, as a result of the stifling heat, the murky light, the jolts and lurches of the decrepit car, everyone grows drowsy. The noise becomes localized, diminishes. Huddled together in their corner, Barois, Cresteil, and Woldsmuth converse in undertones.

WOLDSMUTH: "The saddest thing is that this quite laudable idea of serving the country's best interests has been, I'm positive, behind much of the opposition we came up against."

CRESTEIL: "You're wrong there. You're much too fond, my dear Woldsmuth, of giving people credit for noble sentiments. Oftener than not they're guided by self-interest, consciously or unconsciously, or by mere blind deference to convention."

BAROIS: "Talking of convention, I was greatly struck by a little scene I witnessed at the second or third hearing. I came a bit late and entered by the press corridor just as the officer-judges were arriving. At the same moment four witnesses, four generals in full uniform, came up, a little behind them. Well, the seven judges stopped dead, lined up along the wall and stood to attention. And the generals, mere witnesses, walked past them, as if they were on parade, and the judges automatically saluted."

CRESTEIL, impulsively: "That has its beauty!"

BAROIS: "No, old chap. That was the military college cadet you once were speaking, not the Cresteil of today."

CRESTEIL, sadly: "I suppose so. Still, really it's excusable when you come to think of it. To make a man of action, proud of his vocation, discipline asks so much at every moment of the day that

you can't lose the habit of valuing it at the price it costs."

BAROIS, following up his train of thought: "The verdict we heard given, you see, fits in with that little scene in the passage. On the face of it, the conviction of a traitor 'with extenuating circumstances' seems sheer idiocy. But consider the facts: the conviction was a military necessity—to save the Army's face—and their sense of discipline obliged them, though they were unaware of this, to vote for it. The 'extenuating circumstances' meant that, after all, as decent private individuals, they couldn't altogether square their consciences."

The train reaches Paris at daybreak. A gloomy silence fills the cars, which disgorge their draggled, shivering denizens upon the platform. Luce is there, waiting, his gentle eyes searching for his friends among the crowd. Breil-Zoeger, too, has come. Silently they all shake hands, their hearts filled with a vast affection, a vast sadness. Weeping, Woldsmuth kisses Luce's hand.

BAROIS, after a brief hesitation: "Julia isn't with you?"

BREIL-ZOEGER, looking up quickly: "No."

They move away, in a compact group, without speaking.

BAROIS, with a shade of nervousness, to Luce: "Any news?" He is troubled by Luce's silence. "Any talk of an appeal?"

LUCE: "No, it seems that, on technical grounds, there's no possibility of an appeal."

BAROIS: "So—what then?"

LUCE, after some moments' silence: "Perhaps a pardon."

CRESTEIL and BAROIS, together: "He'll refuse it."

LUCE, firmly: "No."

It is the last, the knock-out blow. They halt on the pavement, stunned, unseeing, their shoulders sagging.

WOLDSMUTH: "Try to put yourselves in his place. Should he go back to that island and endure that hell on earth again? And to what purpose?"

CRESTEIL, dramatically: "To remain a symbol."

WOLDSMUTH, doggedly: "It would kill him. What would be the good?"

LUCE, with deep compassion in his voice: "Woldsmuth's right. At least we shall rehabilitate a living man."

The evening of the same day. Barois has left the *Sower* office early and walks blindly ahead, gripping in his pocket the note from Julia which he found on his desk.

You are coming back from Rennes and you will be surprised at not finding me in the office.

I don't want to deceive you. I gave myself freely; I take back my freedom on the same terms. So long as I loved you, I belonged to you without reserve. But now that I love someone else, I must tell you quite frankly that you have ceased to count in my life. I make no secret of this change, it is my way of proving the respect I have for you, to the end.

By the time you read this note, I shall have regained the liberty to dispose of my life as I think fit. You're brave enough and intelligent enough to understand me, and not to waste your energies on vain regrets.

But I shall always remain your friend.

Julia

Once back in his room in the Rue Jacob, he stretches himself fully dressed on the bed. A morbid, personal, and poignant grief has been grafted onto the grief he felt before, the bleak discouragement that had already sapped his energy. His head is burning, heavy as lead. And suddenly, in the darkness of the bedroom, memory rekindles past emotion,

and he feels a sudden uprush of sensual desire, a longing to recapture, cost what it may, certain unforgettable thrills he has experienced in this very room. He springs up, biting his lips, wringing his hands, his features working convulsively; then, as abruptly, he lets himself fall back, sobbing, upon the bed.

For yet some moments he struggles, like a drowning man caught in the undertow. Then he founders into dark, dreamless sleep.

A ring at the bell awakes him and plunges him headlong into his despair. The sun is high; a clock strikes ten. Opening the door, he sees Woldsmuth on the threshold.

WOLDSMUTH, startled by Barois' haggard, disheveled appearance: "Sorry! I'm disturbing you."

BAROIS, irritably: "No. Come in. Come in."

WOLDSMUTH, refraining from looking at him: "I tried to find you at the *Sower* office—about that information you wanted." He raises his eyes. "I managed to see Reinach." Awkwardly. "I'm very—I mean, I wanted . . ."

He cannot get the words out. The two men gaze at each other, and Barois realizes that Woldsmuth knows all. Somehow he feels relieved. He holds out both hands to his friend.

WOLDSMUTH, shyly: "Yes. And to think that Zoeger, a friend . . ."

BAROIS, who has gone quite pale, in a choking voice: "What? Breil-Zoeger?"

WOLDSMUTH, taken aback: "Well, I don't know for sure. I thought . . ." Barois is seated, his fists clenched, his head thrust forward, his mind void of thoughts—like a figure hewn in stone. Woldsmuth is alarmed by his silence. "I'm dreadfully sorry. I'm meddling in something that's none of my business. But I thought I'd come round. I'd like to—to help you to feel less badly about it."

Without answering or looking at him, Barois thrusts his hand into his coat-pocket and hands him Julia's letter. Woldsmuth reads it with a sort of forlorn eagerness, and his lips begin to tremble weakly; his breath comes in short, wheezy gasps. Then, folding the sheet of notepaper, he seats himself at Barois' side and clumsily puts his short stumpy arm round his friend's shoulders.

WOLDSMUTH: "Ah, that girl Julia! I know. It hurts, hurts horribly, one feels like killing." With a wistful smile. "And then it dies down."

Suddenly, without moving, he begins to sob quietly, persistently, letting the tears flow down his cheeks unchecked, as one weeps for a personal distress. As Barois watches, noting his tone, his words, his tears, he knows what so far he has but dimly surmised. And suddenly, before pity comes, he feels a morose satisfaction; he is less alone, another shares the blow. But then a wave of sentimental compassion brings tears to his eyes. How cruel life can be!

BAROIS, humbly, as if words could erase the past: "Ah, Woldsmuth, my poor friend, how I must have made you suffer!"

VI

May 30, 1900. At the Paris Exposition. In one of the lath-and-plaster restaurants, beflagged and lavishly beflowered, that have been run up for the occasion on the banks of the Seine, some thirty young men are seated round a dinner-table.

Waiters have just lit the candelabra; bathed in a soft yellow glow, wine-glasses and drooping flowers glimmer in the gathering dusk. The banquet is ending on a mood of languid, reminiscent calm.

Luce, who is presiding, rises. Overshadowed by the massive forehead, his limpid gaze, serene yet searching, lingers for a moment on the group around the table. He smiles, as though in humorous excuse of the written sheets he produces from his pocket.

The slight provincial burr adds color to his diction and imparts a note of geniality, at once simple and compelling.

LUCE: "My friends, exactly a year ago we had great occasion for rejoicing. Monsieur Ballot-Beaupré had just read his report at a public meeting, and we had seen the whole Affair come to life under our eyes in his admirable summing-up. It had a clean-cut precision of detail and an eloquence which made it a model for all time of what such a résumé should be. The approving silence which greeted his speech was proof of the great change of heart of that very same public which, only a year before, was hurling abuse at Zola. And, now that the incubus which had been weighing on us for three years was lifted—by official hands—we felt a limitless confidence as to the future.

"Ever and again there rose to our lips those words pregnant with hope with which Monsieur Mornard concluded his address to the Court: 'I await your verdict as the dawn of a new day that will flood this land of France with the light of truth and amity.'

"It is to commemorate those glorious hours—which, I think you will agree, were the last unsullied hours of the Affair —that we have gathered here tonight. I will not dwell on the painful memories of last summer. Already the details are growing blurred for most of us. The generous desire shown by the Government to nullify the half-hearted verdict of the military judges justifies us in awaiting, with a patience that is new to us, the moment when, by the sheer force of things, truth will sweep away the last traces of injustice. For truth is invincible and always ends by bending events to its will.

"The worst, we may be sure, is over. As one of our friends wrote recently:

'Mass violence is like the storm-winds of spring; like them it swells and blusters, then calms down and dies away, leaving the growing seeds to thrust their way up to the light.'

"This is a difficult time, I know, for all those who for several years have been living in a ferment of activity. Panting like hounds at the end of the day's run, they have to halt, once the arduous pursuit is over and their work is done. But now a new anxiety begins to haunt them, when they survey the havoc and the victims strewing the battlefield. Am I not right in saying that this anxiety is shared by us all? For how could it be otherwise when we see the plight of France today, a land rent by dissension, a house divided against itself?

"In the thick of the fight we gave little thought to its aftermath. That was what our enemies reproached us with. We did not burke the issue, but retorted that national honor must rank before public order and that an act of flagrant illegality, even if its pretext be the national security, spells infinitely worse evils than a transient period of unrest. It imperils the one achievement for which a certain pride is justified on our part; those noble ideals of freedom with which French blood has enriched the world at large. Nay, I would go further: it jeopardizes justice and fair-dealing throughout the whole civilized world."

There is a ripple of applause.

"Nevertheless, now that we have gained the day, we can but recognize the predicament into which the obstinacy of public opinion plunged the country; we are living on the morrow of a revolution.

"In the chaotic period that immediately preceded the climax, and under cover of our final onslaught, a whole horde of partisans, men we had never heard of, attached themselves to the group of militants and intellectuals that we had constituted hitherto. They snatched from our hands our humble but unvanquished flag and brandished it in our stead, for all to see. They swarmed over the terrain we had opened up in our task of social scavenging. And now that the battle's won, it is they who hold the field as conquerors. May I here draw a verbal distinction—a matter of jargon, if you will; yet one on which I set much store? *We* were a handful of 'Dreyfusites'; they are an army of 'Dreyfusards.'

"What kind of men are they? I have no idea. They exploit certain false identifications, which we rigorously forbade ourselves; thus they identify militarism and the Army, nationalism and France. What is their program and what are they capable of building on the ruins we left behind our advance? Of that too I have no idea. Will that splendid future whose promise lit our dreams dawn at their bidding, as they profess? I wonder!

"No, I greatly fear that in some respects they are no better than the men whom we defeated. Still, it's a consolation to think they cannot be worse.

"As for us, our task is ended; the achievement of what we so passionately longed for is in the hands of others. Deliberately we initiated a vast upheaval, and most of us are paying the price of this today—in the loss of peace of mind and personal happiness.

"It's hard, my dear friends, very hard —I know it as well as you. I have lost my hearers at the Collège de France, and, though I have been re-elected to the Senate, I have no illusions. No committee invites me to sit on it, and I play no active part in national affairs.

"Those who are deriving the most obvious benefits from our crusade are, for the most part, cold-shouldering us, and they view us with the greatest suspicion. They are wrong. Their conduct almost suggests that, now they know the danger we present to anyone who has not—shall I say?—clean hands, they feel slightly nervous in our company." He smiles.

"Less to be pitied are the younger men, those who have time ahead of them for reshaping their lives. That baptism of fire, on the threshold of a life of high endeavor, has, I feel convinced, done them a world of good. It has burned away the overgrowth of false sentiments and make-believe from their personalities, leaving only the essential substance— solid rock! How salutary for them was the necessity of choosing once for all their course in life, their loyalties! Yes, I know many such younger men who will have come out of this ordeal the better for it." Smiling, he raises his eyes for a moment from the sheet he is holding and turns towards Barois, who is sitting next him. "Our friend Barois, for instance, whose generous enthusiasm and fine courage never faltered, and who was a pillar of strength when things were at their worst." He goes on reading.

"Yes, Barois is the guardian of our vestal flame, *The Sower,* his creation, and, come what may, we must stand by him. Only consider the great work he has done and still is doing, and let his example be our inspiration and our safeguard. For many years he has devoted himself whole-heartedly to *The Sower,* scattering abroad all his ideas and projects without stint, without the sordid fear that someone might filch them from him and put them into execution first, and obeying no dictates but those of his own conscience. At his side there will always be work for men of good will. After enjoying a sensational circulation—which will go down in journalistic history—*The Sower* has settled down to a more normal one, better fitted to its aims, for it's addressed to a minority, and that intellectual minority will never fail in its allegiance. Let us support it, gentlemen, in every way we can; let us bring to it

those fruits of experience to which even the youngest of us can lay claim today— for those crowded years have taught them as much as a whole ordinary lifetime. And let Barois continue to centralize our efforts and give them the widespread influence that at once encourages and justifies them.

"But, above all, my friends, let us steel ourselves against that sterile defeatism which is already making insidious progress. Oh, I know as well as you how often one is tempted to despair!" He speaks very earnestly. "Who of us has not been appalled by the difficulties in which our unhappy country has entangled itself? Who has not felt a sense of personal responsibility weighing on his mind? How, indeed, could it be otherwise? When one considers the ordeal we have lived through, is it surprising that a certain pessimism has left its mark on us, indelibly? For inevitably our path has been strewn with lost illusions." He raises his head.

"But we must not let feelings of this sort, however poignant, darken counsel. We know our sacrifice was in a noble cause, and this should suffice us. What we did, my friends, we *had* to do; nor would we hesitate to do it again if the need arose. Let us remind ourselves of this in our moments of perplexity and doubt.

"France today is a land divided against itself—a grave predicament, but not beyond redress. The worst that can befall our country is a material and momentary setback. But, as against this, we have kept France loyal to her ideal, to that sense of national honor without which no people can survive.

"Let us remember, too, that fifty years hence the Dreyfus Affair will be no more than one of many minor battles in the long conflict between human reason and the passions which blind it; a moment, no more than that, in the slow but glorious progress of humanity towards a better world.

"Our present conceptions of truth and justice will be superseded in times to come; of that we may be sure. But, far from damping our ardor, this certainty should be a spur to our activity today. It is the duty of each successive generation to advance along the path of truth to the farthest limit of its capacity and strain its eyes towards the vision far ahead—aspiring, vainly, no doubt, but resolutely, to the ultimate light of Absolute Truth. That, in fact, is the *sine qua non* of human progress.

"The value of a generation consists in the effort it puts forth, an effort paving the way to higher and still higher achievement. Well, my friends, our generation has made its effort—worthily.

"May peace be with us all."

Luce sits down. A long silence follows, vibrant with emotion.

## IX

## Calm

I

Several years later. An entire five-floor building in the Rue de l'Université is now occupied by *The Sower*. The entrance hall is stacked with bales of paper; the ground and first floors house the printing press; in the upper floors are the editorial offices of *The Sower* and the premises of Sower Publications.

A clerk enters one of the offices on the fourth floor.

THE CLERK: "A gentleman wants you on the phone, sir. 'Harry' was the name he gave."

THE SUB-EDITOR: " 'Harry'? Don't know him."

THE CLERK: "He's on the *New York Herald*."

THE SUB-EDITOR: "Ah, Harris you mean. Put him through." He picks up the receiver. "Yes, that's quite all right. I mentioned it to Monsieur Barois and he agrees. But no writing up, please; no boosting. Just the bare facts. . . . Certainly. What do you want to know? . . . Since the Dreyfus Affair?" He laughs. "Why not since 1870, while you're about it? . . . Yes, what he's doing at present, that would be better. . . .

"With pleasure. . . . Well, he has lecture courses in the evenings at three townhalls; in the Belville, Vaugirard, and Panthéon districts. They're largely attended by the working class. At the Panthéon Hall, mostly students, as might be expected. . . . Yes, stress that. It's something he's very keen on, raising the mental level of the masses and directing them towards freedom of thought. . . .

"Twice a week he lectures at the Institute of Social Studies. . . . This year? The title is 'The World-Wide Crisis of Religion.' It works out to a book a year.

"Then, of course, there's *The Sower*. That's his biggest chore. Two hundred pages every fortnight. . . . I wouldn't know. At least fifteen articles of his own a year, at a rough guess. And there's a 'Notes and Comments' section in each issue—all the ideas that have come to him during the fortnight. . . .

"No, the *Sower Conversations*, that's something quite different. I'll explain. Every week we have a meeting here, articles are handed in and plans made for the next issue. Monsieur Barois had the idea of getting these conversations taken down in shorthand and publishing under the title 'Memoranda' any passages that seemed of general interest. Then our subscribers began to take a hand in it; they wrote proposing topics for discussion. An excellent development—it keeps us in touch with the public and we learn what subjects are of immediate interest. Then the 'Memoranda' blossomed out into *The*

*Sower Conversations,* which appears in book form every three months or so.

"Gladly. . . . But you could have found the list anywhere. Firstly, his books on the Affair: *For Truth's Sake,* First, Second, and Third Series, not to mention a host of pamphlets. Next, his public speeches, a collection of which is published at the end of each year. There have been six volumes so far, under the title *Fighting Speeches.* The seventh is on press. Then there are four volumes of his lectures at the Institute. Want to know their names? . . . Right. *The Progress of Popular Education, Free Thought Abroad, A Study of Determinism, The Divisibility of Matter*—Wait! It would be a good idea to say that the lecture he's giving next Sunday at the Trocadéro is something quite exceptional. It's not his habit to address large audiences of this kind; in fact Barois has never done anything of the sort before. Stress that, please. . . .

"No, I couldn't tell you. About three thousand seats, I think. Half of them, it seems, are booked already. . . . Yes, the name's a draw, and so's the subject: 'The Future of Unbelief.'

"Thanks. . . . Always ready to help. . . . Good-bye."

## II

The afternoon of the following Sunday, at the Trocadéro. There is a large crowd; cabs and carriages arriving in a steady stream disgorge their occupants at the foot of the steps leading up to the huge building. The police have turned out in force to keep order.

Suddenly a ripple of excitement traverses the group of young people gathered at the entrance giving access to the platform of the great hall. Barois and Luce alight from their carriage. Many bystanders take off their hats. The two men walk briskly into the building, accompanied by some friends.

At three o'clock the auditorium is packed, the exits blocked by people who have failed to get seats. Slowly the curtains are drawn aside, disclosing an empty platform. Almost immediately Barois makes his appearance; he is greeted by a vast clamor of applause, which rises, falls, and rises massively again, with a buzz like that of a swarm of bees about to take wing, then abruptly gives place to dead silence.

Unhurrying, Barois climbs the steps leading to the raised platform. The spacious proscenium dwarfs him, and his features can hardly be distinguished, but the manner of his entrance, the dignity of his bow to the assembly, the calmness of the gaze with which he slowly sweeps the thousands of faces aligned concentrically below and around him, testify to the assurance of a man who knows the tide is running in his favor. His eyes still fixed on the audience, he sits down.

BAROIS: "Ladies and Gentlemen . . ."

He has a brief access of nervousness, a tightening of the heart. But then the silence of the crowded auditorium and the look of friendly expectation on all those rows and rows of faces turned towards him break the tension. Yielding to a sudden inspiration and abandoning the opening he has prepared, he lets fall his notes and, smilingly, drops into a tone of friendly conversation.

"My dear friends, I see you have turned out in force today. You have not hesitated to give up your normal program for a Sunday afternoon, so as to come and hear a talk on 'The Future of Unbelief.' Obviously its title was enough to draw you here. I find this deeply moving and significant of the age we're living in.

"All civilized nations are undergoing today the same religious crisis. In every land where culture or intelligence has taken root, the same questions are stirring in men's minds; rationalism and unbelief are undermining the authority of the fables taught by the priests; the same drive towards emancipation of the mind is shattering the tyrannous prestige of all the gods that be.

"Thanks to her innate love of freedom, her sense of logic, and her demand for positive proof, France has for two centuries led the way in the world-wide movement towards free thought. It was France, indeed, that set that movement on foot. All the Latin countries in which Roman Catholicism once reigned supreme—Italy, Spain, and South America—have followed France's lead. A similar change of heart is taking place in the Protestant countries—North America, England, and South Africa. So general is this movement that the more enlightened elements of Islam and Buddhism are being affected by it, and the same applies to the civilized parts of India and Africa, and the whole of Japan. Throughout the world the Churches have been forced to give up the temporal power they had exercised for many a century, and which was skillfully directed to shoring up their spiritual authority. They have seen their privileges withdrawn one by one, and have found themselves forbidden to meddle in nonreligious matters. In fact, to all intents and purposes, State religions have ceased to exist. Everywhere the State is nonsectarian and observes a strict neutrality towards the various faiths whose practices it tolerates.

"This concerted drive against the embattled forces of religion covers too wide a field for me to deal with it in detail in my talk today. I shall confine myself to pointing out again that it is *world-wide;* for I would not have you think, as you may have been inclined to think, that the irreligious evolution of our country is a local development and goes no farther than our frontiers. On the contrary, it is bound up with an awakening of the critical spirit in all the nations of the world."

He pauses. Before, he had a miscellaneous concourse of men, women, and young people; this now is welded together into an audience, synthesis has been achieved. His eyes, voice, and mind are now in direct contact with a uniform mass, a single entity pregnant with thoughts from which his own thought is distinct no longer, but of which it forms the nucleus, the dynamic core.

"The Catholic Church, which claims to be above all man-made laws, put up a stubborn fight against being subjected to the law of the land. However, it has had to capitulate and to transfer what influence it still possesses to the field of spiritual things. That is its last stronghold, and even there the rising tide, whatever some may think, is steadily, ineluctably, sapping the foundations. For the modern mind is ever less and less satisfied with dogma—and this aversion is growing prodigiously with each new generation. Every advance of science adds yet another argument against religious dogmatism, which, moreover, has long ceased to gain any support, however flimsy, from contemporary research.

"In its struggle against the implacable advance of knowledge, I can see only one potential hope for the Church, if it is to survive at all—and that is to evolve and bring its tenets into line with modern thought. For the Church this is a matter of life and death. If it refuses to adapt itself, we may feel certain that, within the space of a few generations, there will be no believers left.

"But at this point I wish to make it clear to you that it's literally impossible for the dogmas of Catholicism to be modified, even to the most trifling extent. Thus nothing can save it from extinction; not only can we count on this as a foregone conclusion, but we can almost fix the date of its decease!

"A philosophical doctrine can develop; its texture is the stuff of human thought disposed in a manner which is necessarily tentative and therefore capable of revision. But a revealed religion starts with tenets which cannot be amended, since, by definition, they were divinely inspired when first enounced. Thus a religion of this kind can change only at the price of self-destruction. For any alteration would be tantamount to an admission that its earlier form fell short of perfection; that it did not come directly from God, and no 'revelation' ushered it into the world. This, indeed, is so obvious that the Catholic Church has never ceased pointing to its immutability as a proof of its divine origin. Quite recently the 1870 Vatican Council did not hesitate to affirm that 'the doctrine of the true faith revealed by God was not bestowed as a philosophical instrument for the betterment of the human intellect, but has been committed to us as a *divine endowment*.'

"Thus Catholicism is irrevocably committed; change is ruled out by its first principles.

"But we may go still further. Even were it possible for the Church to modify its tenets without contradicting itself, this would give it only a brief reprieve, for the following reasons.

"Even the most cursory study of the origins of the various religions shows us that all were born of the curiosity primitive man felt when confronted by the universe. You will find that all begin with a set of myths which embody the childish theories concocted to explain natural phenomena. So true is this that, strictly speaking, there has never been a primitive religion, in our sense of the term. From the dawn of human life up to our times there has been only one persistent train of thought: the train of *scientific* thought, which began as a jumble of nature myths. Thus what we call 'religion' is really one of the early stages of scientific progress, when the deist expla-

nation was accepted, for want of a better one. And, absurdly enough, this early phase in the long history of research has left after-effects persisting to our times, owing to man's dread of the supernatural. In a word, man has never been able to discard that legacy of mystical hypotheses which were invented in those early days to 'explain' the mysteries of nature. This fortuitous crystallization, as we may call it, held up the advance of science for many centuries. And thereafter the paths of science and religion diverged irrevocably.

"I will now revert to what I was saying a moment ago. Religion is simply a relict of an extinct type of science, a dead husk that has taken on the form of dogma. It is no more than the shell of a scientific hypothesis which has long since been superseded and in this process of drying up has lost whatever life it may once have had. Thus, if religion were to try to change itself and to catch up with scientific progress—which stands for what it would have been had not its development been arrested—well, it would be bound to fail. It has contrived to last out so many centuries only because it comforted man's troubled heart with lies; allayed his dread of death with specious promises; and dulled his speculative instinct with assertions both unfounded and impossible to check. Were the Church one day to renounce all that flummery which puts it on a level with a Christmas pantomime, not an iota would survive of that substructure which, for some, gives it a semblance of vitality. For the religious instinct in man, on which the Church could reckon in earlier days, has no place in the truly modern mind. It would be quite wrong to regard man's natural craving to understand and investigate as a residue of the mystical beliefs of our ancestors. Actually, it existed long before religious emotion was known to man, and it has found full and ample satisfaction in the triumphs of contemporary science.

"Thus, as you see, we can have little doubt that a dogmatic religion like Catholicism is irrevocably doomed. The absolute rigidity of its tenets makes it less and less credible to modern minds, which are too well aware of the relativity of their knowledge to accept a doctrine purporting to be unchangeable and infallible.

"Moreover, the forces undermining it do not all come from without; Catholicism is languishing internally as well, attacked by a creeping paralysis which unfits it for the contemporary world.

"In fact the tide is flowing strongly towards a godless society and towards a purely scientific conception of the universe."

No sooner has he uttered this last phrase than he realizes it has given a fillip to his hearers' interest. Their gaze grows more intent, he feels the impact of a collective will urging him in a certain direction. And he understands. After following his destructive arguments to the end, they are now eager for some vision of the coming world; like children, they are waiting for their fairy-tale. He has no notes on this subject, but he obeys. His eyes grow luminous, a visionary smile plays on his lips.

"What form will it take, this irreligion of the future? Who of us can answer this question with any confidence? But one thing's certain, it will not be, in any sense whatever, a 'deification of science.' We are often, too often, told that our scientists are the high priests of a new cult and are replacing one faith by another. It may be that, in the confusion of a transitional age, some men of science transfer a remnant of the religious emotions they have inherited and for which they have no ready-made outlet, to the science which they serve. But that's a mere aberration. Actually there's no scope for new

idols, and anyhow science cannot possibly be set up as one. For intelligence is negative; this is a truth to which even the most idealistic temperaments have sadly to resign themselves.

"My personal belief is that the union of men's intellects and hearts—and the latter are still groping for their way—will come relatively soon, and that it will find fruition by way of social solidarity on the one hand and scientific knowledge on the other. I foresee the possibility of moral laws based on a searching analysis of the individual and his relations with his environment. This will bring satisfaction to the heart of man, since the new order will give free play to his altruistic instinct. Faced by the crushing indifference of nature, men are bound to feel the need to get together, and from this need ethical compulsions will naturally ensue. It seems to me more than likely that these duties, inspired as they will be by the mutual affection that draws men into fellowship, will establish, anyhow for a time, a reign of social peace.

"Of course these are mere flights of fancy. I know how dangerous it is to play the prophet." He smiles. "And, as we know, a prophet is 'without honor' in our midst.

"Anyhow, one thing's certain; there will be nothing metaphysical in the principles on which the new social order is founded. The day has come when nothing but factual demonstration can satisfy our minds. Those religions which claimed to solve the riddle of the universe will be replaced, I feel certain, by a philosophy as positive as it is strictly unemotional, a philosophy nourished continually by scientific discoveries; variable and transient, shaped to the changing trends of thought. Thus we can be pretty sure that it will never cease enlarging its frontiers—far beyond the narrow conceptions which limit our field of vision today. Only think how incomplete and paltry it now seems, the so-called scientific materialism of fifty years ago! Our age, more truly scientific, is already tending to rise above the outlook of the world that satisfied our fathers; the next generation will carry the process a stage farther. The mind of man today is blazing trails through the unknown, and the new methods of research we now employ are highly promising. But as yet we cannot even guess at the new aspects of reality our progressive discoveries will open up to us."

A short pause. His look changes. His eyes regain their wonted hardness, and his voice its characteristic "edge." Looking down, he fingers the loose sheets lying on the table.

"But enough of visions of the future, tempting as these may be! Time is passing, and there is a second point I'd like to dwell on in this talk, before I leave you.

"What steps can each of us take towards the more or less rapid attainment of our hopes?

"A vast field of activity lies open to us all. Thankless as it may sometimes seem, man's task today, by contrast with the future I have just been picturing, this task is of capital importance and on no account must we neglect it.

"Ours is one of those generations to whom has fallen the duty of actively furthering scientific evolution. We are living in one of those tragic periods of world history when an outworn age is in its death throes.

"Ah, my friends, when once we realize what hideous moral torture is the lot of a generation such as ours, an epoch in which men's consciences are, as it were, stretched on a rack, torn between an age that is dying and an age that is coming to birth; and when we remember that the energy with which we make and proclaim our choice may determine the

duration of the agony these suffering sensibilities endure—how grave is the responsibility that falls on each and all of us!

"Briefly speaking, we have two means of taking action: by our personal attitude, and by the education of our children. Suppose we now, as the Church would put it, 'examine our consciences' in this respect?

"How many of us, whose convictions are definitely hostile to any kind of religious faith—how many of us, none the less, allow religion to preside at the most important occasions of our lives, from the marriage rite to the death-bed!" Sadly. "Oh, yes, I know, I know as well as you—better than some of you, perhaps—all the excuses we can make for these concessions. I know the cruel self-humiliation of the free man who deems it his duty to submit himself to these ritual observances. Only too well I know those inner conflicts, the cruel ordeal of a conscience that is torn between the desire to keep faith with itself and all the forces sapping its integrity: family ties, affection, respect for others' feelings. But we must not throw dust in our own eyes. To give in on such occasions is an act of flagrant immorality that nothing can condone. In the age of moral crisis we are living through nothing is more momentous than a public declaration of faith; not only as regards the man who makes it, but also because of its possible effect on others whose minds are not yet made up. Honesty towards ourselves and towards those whose eyes are on us—that, as things are, should be our guiding principle, the most inflexible of moral laws. Those who palter with their personal integrity, or by a non-committal attitude impede, in their environment, the progress of evolution, are committing a crime against society, a crime infinitely more serious than all the sentimental

[ 149 ]

grievances their families might feel, did they choose the harder path—of honesty!

"More unpardonable still is their offense as regards the education of their children. The child's mind is uncritical. The notion of doubt comes only after long experience of the everyday world; it implies acquaintance with the possibility of error, mistrust not only of oneself and one's own sensations, but of other people too, and their advice. Like all primitives, the child is credulous, he has no sense of probabilities, a miracle would not surprise him.

"If you confide this wax tablet, a young mind, to a priest, he will easily make an indelible imprint on it. He will begin by inspiring the child with an irrational fear of God; then he will impart to him the mysteries of his cult as so many revealed truths, which surpass, and always *must* surpass, the human understanding. The priest is ever ready with assertions; never with proofs. The child is readier to believe than to apply his intellect. So they get on well together. Reasoning is the opposite of faith; a mind that faith has formed remains for a long while, perhaps always, incapable of drawing rational conclusions.

"Can you, then, expose a personality as innocent and defenseless as a child's to religious influences?"

He has risen to his feet, carried away by the violence of his indignation, vibrant with memories of his own childhood. The man of action is awake in Barois; the polemics of his daily life have made him conscious of his power, he feels the zest of battle. So impetuous is his onrush that he sometimes overthrows an obstacle on his path before it even meets his eye; his is a blind force sweeping all before it.

"Only think! The Church inveighs against us, it launches its anathemas at all that constitutes the most vital part of our being, and yet, fools that we are, we hand our children over to the priest! How account for such obtuseness? Is it that we nurse a secret hope that they will rid themselves of superstition as they grow up? If so, what name is bad enough for such hypocrisy?

"And what, indeed, could be more fatuous than the belief that the mind, as it matures, will necessarily dispel those fumes of pious poison? Do you not realize how tenacious a child's faith can be? No, we must face the facts. A man on whom religion has set its mark in childhood cannot discard it with a mere shake of his shoulders, like a garment that has worn out or become too small for him. In the child, religion finds a soil made ready for it by eighteen centuries of voluntary servitude. It twines itself inextricably round all the other elements of his mental and moral growth. The process of disentangling himself, if it be possible at all, is tedious, laborious, often inconclusive, and always painful. And how many people living under present-day conditions have either leisure or energy enough to set about this reshaping of their whole personality?

"Moreover, I have so far limited the issue; I have spoken of the dangers of religious education only in so far as it affects the individual. But it also directly threatens the social fabric as a whole. At a time like ours, when religious beliefs are tottering everywhere, there is a very real peril in letting the moral law be linked up with religious dogma in the minds of the younger generation. For once they have got it into their heads that the rules of social morality have a divine origin, and once the day comes, as come it must, when they begin to feel unsure of God's existence, their whole moral structure will promptly collapse, and they will be like ships without a rudder.

"There, briefly, you have the dangers we run when we act as shortsighted or time-serving parents. And what are the would-be noble principles with which we disguise our spinelessness?

"I can hear your answer: 'We take the broad-minded view; we declare our neutrality.'

"Oh, I know it's hard to see where one's duty lies. But don't let's be deceived by words. That vaunted neutrality—our opponents do wrong in accusing us of often violating it; for can any sort of teaching be absolutely neutral?—yes, it's we alone who are hampered by that declaration of neutrality! In fact neutrality today means simply deference to the propaganda, the tireless propaganda, of the Church.

"Well, this one-sided compromise has lasted far too long. Let us openly take up our position in a conflict that is now inevitable, the greatest conflict of our age. And instead of conducting it surreptitiously, let us fight in the open, in the light, and on equal terms. By all means leave the priests free to open schools and teach our youngsters that the world was created out of nothing in six days; that Jesus Christ was the Son of God the Father and a Virgin; that his body came forth, unaided, from the tomb three days after his burial, and ascended into heaven, where he has been seated ever since on God's right hand.

"But, my friends, let us, too, be free to open schools in which we have the right to prove, with science and common sense as our allies, how preposterous are the superstitions on which Catholicism is founded. Give truth and lies a fair field, and it's not the lies that will win! Freedom, yes, but not only for the priest and his catechism; freedom for the intellect, freedom for the child!"

He walks to the front of the platform, his arms outspread, his eyes aflame with enthusiasm.

"Yes, my friends, I would like to conclude with that appeal: Freedom for the child! I want to feel that I have

quickened your consciences, and to see in your eyes a light of new, unshakable resolve. Let us remember all that we have gone through to cast out of ourselves the 'old' man. Let us remember those fires of anguish that laid waste our souls. Let us remember our night fears, our tremulous revolts, our agonized confessions. Let us remember our prayers and tears and terrors.

"And have pity on our sons!"

### III

The same year, some months later. The Place de la Madeleine. Barois steps into a cab.

BAROIS: "The *Sower* office, Rue de l'Université." He slams the door. The cab does not move; the driver flicks the horse with his whip. The horse tosses his head, but refuses to start. "Get a move on, cabby! I'm in a hurry."

The cabman lays on vigorously with his whip. The horse, a young, restive animal, hesitates, rears, jerks up its head, then starts off like an arrow. The vehicle whisks down the Rue Royale, crosses the Place de la Concorde hell-for-leather, swerves left along the Boulevard Saint-Germain.

It is four in the afternoon, and the traffic is at its thickest. Leaning well back, the cabby tries vainly to hold in his horse; the utmost he can do is to direct its course to some extent.

A broken-down streetcar bars the way; to avoid it, the driver swings round to the left where the road is momentarily empty, but he has failed to see another streetcar bearing down on him in the opposite direction. It is impossible to slow down; equally impossible to pass between the two streetcars.

Pale with terror, Barois huddles back against the cushions. A sense of utter helplessness, shut up as he is in the swaying, box-like cab, and the certainty of disaster flash like lightning through the chaos of his thoughts.

He utters a low cry. "Hail, Mary, full of grace . . ."

A crash of shattered glass, a violent shock. Then all the world goes black.

In Barois' apartment, some days later. Shadows are gathering in the room. Sitting quite still at the window, Woldsmuth is reading. Barois lies on the bed, his legs in plaster up to the waist. He regained full consciousness only a few hours ago; for the tenth time he is mentally recapitulating his experience.

There'd have been room, he thinks, if that damned car on the right hadn't put on speed. . . . Had I time to realize death's nearness? Can't remember. All I know is that I was in a panic. And then that hideous screech of brakes!

He smiles to himself; the joy of life regained sweeps through him. A close shave—but I brought it off! Curious how scared one is of dying. Why dread the extinction of all thought, all pain, all sensation? Why this horror of mere not-being?

Perhaps it's just one's fear of the unknown. That business of dying is obviously the only sensation utterly unknown to us. No one has anything to tell about what it really feels like.

And yet anyone with a scientific training, given a few seconds to think it out, should manage to resign himself to death without much ado. He knows quite well that life's no more than a series of transformations, so why be frightened of *that* one? It's not the first and, presumably, not the last incident in the *processus* of becoming.

Then, again, when one has led a useful life, put up a good fight, and has something to leave behind one—why repine? Personally, I feel sure I shall say good-bye to life quite calmly.

Suddenly a look of dismay settles on his face. All his confidence is dashed. It has come back to him, that dramatic moment just before the crash, and he has recalled the cry that sprang instinctively to his lips: "Hail, Mary . . . !"

An hour goes by. Without moving, Woldsmuth turns the pages of his book.

Pascal brings a lamp, closes the shutters, and comes to his master's bedside. The flat, Swiss face, with its close-cropped hair and big blue eyes, is comfortably reassuring. But Barois does not see it; he is gazing straight in front of him, his brain working at a prodigious speed. And his thoughts are fantastically clear, pellucid as mountain air after a thunderstorm. After a while his features, tense with the mental effort he is putting forth, slowly relax.

BAROIS: "Woldsmuth!"

WOLDSMUTH, jumping up hastily: "Are you in pain?"

BAROIS, curtly: "No. Now listen. Bring your chair up."

WOLDSMUTH, holding his wrist: "You've a touch of fever. Keep quite still and don't tire yourself speaking."

BAROIS, freeing his arm: "Sit down and listen, I tell you!" Angrily. "No, I insist on speaking. I didn't remember all. I was forgetting the last bit! Listen, Woldsmuth! When I saw a smash was inevitable, what do you think I did? Well, I prayed to the Virgin Mary! Grotesque!"

WOLDSMUTH, soothingly: "Don't think about it any more. You've got to rest. The doctor—"

BAROIS: "No, my wits aren't wandering. I know very well what I'm saying and I want you to hear me out. I shan't be able to rest until I've done what I have now to do." Woldsmuth sits down. Barois' cheeks are flushed, his eyes unnaturally bright. "At that moment I, Jean Barois, had only one idea, a crazy hope. I put up a prayer—a heart-felt prayer, mind you!—to the Holy Virgin, beseeching her to perform a miracle." He guffaws. "A miracle, I tell you! Well, my dear fellow, you can imagine how little confident one feels in one's mental equipment after an experience like that." He sits up in bed. "So, as you'll understand, I'm haunted by the thought that this may quite well happen again—this evening, tonight, at any moment—there's no knowing. I want to get something down in writing and forestall that possibility. And I shan't feel quiet till I've done it."

WOLDSMUTH: "Yes, we'll see to it tomorrow, I promise you. You shall dictate to me, and—"

BAROIS, with a vehemence that sweeps all before it: "At once, Woldsmuth, *at once.* I insist. I shall write it all out in my own hand, this evening. Otherwise I couldn't sleep." He taps his forehead. "It's all in here, all ready, and writing it down won't tire me in the least. The hardest part is done."

Woldsmuth yields and, after propping Barois up on two pillows, hands him his fountain-pen and some sheets of paper. Then he remains standing at the bedside.

Barois writes steadily, without raising his eyes, in a firm, clear hand.

*This is my Last Will and Testament. What I write today, in my early forties, in the full mental vigor of my prime, should obviously outweigh anything I may say or think or write at the close of my existence, when my intellect and judgment may well be impaired by the infirmities of old age. I know nothing more harrowing than to see an old man, whose whole life has been devoted to the furtherance of some noble idea, go back in his declining years on the principles that inspired his life's work and play traitor to his past.*

*When I reflect that conceivably this may be my fate, and my life's work end with a betrayal of this nature, and when I picture the use to which those whose lies*

*and malpractices I have combated with so much ardor will not fail to put this final, miserable lapse of mine, my whole being is up in arms, and I protest in advance, with all the energy of the man I now am, the* living *man I shall have been, against the groundless repudiations —even, perhaps, the prayers in extremis!—of the dotard I may then have become.*

*I deserve to die, combatant and defiant, as I have lived, without capitulating, without whoring after idle hopes, without fearing my return to the primal matter that nourishes the slow processes of evolution.*

*I do not believe in an immortal, independently existing soul.*

*I do not believe that mind and matter are mutually exclusive entities. The "soul" is a complex of psychic phenomena, and the body is a complex of organic phenomena. Consciousness is a by-product of life, an attribute of living matter. I see no reason why that universal energy which produces motion, heat, and light should not also produce thought. Physiological functions and psychological functions interlock; like all other activities of the nervous system, thought is a manifestation of organic life. I have never found thought existing apart from matter and a living body; and I am aware of one universal substance only, living substance. Whether we regard it as "life" or "matter," I believe it to be eternal. Life had no beginning, and it will go on producing life forever. But I know that my personality is but an agglomeration of particles of matter, whose disintegration will end it absolutely.*

*I believe in universal determinism; that we are conditioned by circumstances in all respects. Everything evolves, everything reacts; men and stones alike. There is no such thing as inert matter. Thus I have no reason to attribute more indi-*

*vidual liberty to my acts than I attribute to the slower transformations of a crystal.*

*My life is thus the product of an endless struggle between my organism and my environment. Because at every moment I act in accordance with my personal reflexes—in other words, for reasons applicable to myself alone—a spectator has the illusion that I am free to behave as I like. In reality none of my actions is free in that sense; none of my responses could be other than what it is. Free will would imply the power of performing miracles, of tampering with the relations between causes and effects. It is one of those metaphysical notions which only prove the ignorance, under which we labored for so long (and indeed still labor), of the laws which govern our existence.*

*Thus I deny that a man can exercise the slightest influence on his destiny.*

*Good and Evil are mere arbitrary distinctions. I admit, however, that these distinctions will retain their practical utility so long as that illusion of the mind, the idea of personal responsibility, is needful for the maintenance of our social structure.*

*I believe that though all the phenomena of life have not yet been analyzed, they will be analyzed one day. As for the first causes of these phenomena, I believe they lie outside our range, and no research, however thorough, can elucidate them. Owing to his limited place in the universe, man is by nature a relative and finite being, incapable of forming conceptions of the Absolute and the Infinite. He has invented names for what transcends himself, but these have not got him any further; he is a victim of his terminology, for those words and names do not, so far as human understanding is concerned, correspond to any cognizable reality. He is a mere element of the whole and, naturally enough, that whole lies beyond his apprehension.*

*To revolt against these limitations is to revolt against the planetary conditions of the world we live in.*

*Thus I consider it a waste of mental energy to try to explain the unknowable by mere hypotheses which have no empirical backing. It is high time for us to cure ourselves of our metaphysical moon-madness and to cease troubling about those unanswerable* Whys *which our* mystic-ridden *heredity leads us to propound.*

*Man is confronted by a practically limitless field of observation. Gradually science will thrust back the frontiers of the unknown so far that, if man applies himself to understanding fully all the real world within his compass, he will have no time left for mourning over all that lies ineluctably beyond his mental reach. And I am certain that by teaching men to accept their ignorance of the unknowable, science will give them a peace of mind such as no religion has ever been able to provide.*

*Jean Barois*

His hand is heavy on the pen as he slowly writes his signature. Then abruptly the tension of his will breaks like a snapped violin string. His flushed face suddenly grows deathly pale and he sinks back, exhausted, into Woldsmuth's arms.

Sheets of manuscript flutter across the counterpane.

Alarmed by this sudden collapse, Woldsmuth has called to Pascal. But already Barois is opening his eyes and smiling up at the two men.

Some moments later his steady breathing shows that he has sunk into deep, tranquil sleep.

# THE LIFE AND WORKS OF
# ROGER MARTIN DU GARD

## By ANDRÉ BERNE-JOFFROY

ROGER MARTIN DU GARD was born at Neuilly-sur-Seine on March 23, 1881. His father was a lawyer and the son of a lawyer, and his maternal grandfather was a stockbroker. Born "with a handle to his name," he was careful to explain that it was neither aristocratic nor geographic. His forebears did not come from the department of the Gard, but from the old Bourbonnais province where for generations they were farmers. Toward the middle of the eighteenth century, to make it easier to distinguish between the different branches of the family, various Martins of the same stock decided to add to their name, in accordance with a custom of the time, that of the farm allotted to them. So Martin du Gard and his family were commoners and proud of it. On both sides of the family there were a number of lawyers, but no military men, businessmen, or artists.

At the age of eleven, Martin du Gard went to the Ecole Fénelon, a day school run by independent priests. He grew close to one of them, Abbé Marcel Hébert, and chose him as his confessor. Later he would dedicate *Jean Barois,* his first novel, to him. The pupils at the Ecole Fénelon attended courses at the Lycée Condorcet, where, by a happy coincidence, Martin du Gard had Gaston Gallimard as a fellow pupil. Both were keenly interested in literature and a firm friendship began between the future writer and his future publisher.

Martin du Gard was not a very brilliant student. After a particularly weak performance in the third form, his father sent him to study further with a teacher at the Lycée Janson de Sailly. The few months he spent in this school, a world altogether different from the one he had been accustomed to, were decisive for his future. Hitherto inclined to despise the academic world, he now saw it with fresh respect: "Until then," he confessed, "I had scarcely been aware that there were any views other than those held by my own social circle, that there were other ways—just as legitimate and mentally satisfying, if not more so—of living, of thinking, of judging people and things." The mental attitudes of his own circle, the middle class, were henceforth intolerable to him. Nevertheless, he remained attached throughout his life to the practical virtues in which—for all its fettered outlook—the middle class was founded.

In school, du Gard learned well the techniques of analysis and reflection. He was never asked to produce a full-length essay, but only a carefully constructed summary. Every morning a new subject was set, and every evening du Gard submitted an outline. "In this way I learned," said Martin du Gard, "to cover any subject by selecting the essentials and dividing them into principal, secondary, and accessory." From then on, he began to write by making a plan. He did not write a line of *Les Thibault,* his greatest masterpiece, until he had accumulated masses of notes, index cards, and diagrams concerning his characters and their backgrounds, roughed out the main scenes on loose sheets of paper, and had arranged all this preliminary material in a room into which he had crammed every table in the house.

He studied for his baccalaureate at the Lycée Janson and had no trouble passing. He failed, however, in his first examination for a degree in literature, and it was then that he had the idea of entering the Ecole des Chartes (School of Paleography) in Paris. From 1900 to 1901 he studied at the Sorbonne, and had fairly frequent contacts with Emile Faguet, who encouraged him to write. In 1902 he did his military service in Rouen, where he met Marcel de Coppet. From 1903 to 1905 he was enrolled at the School of Paleography, where he wrote a thesis on the ruins of the Abbey of Jumièges and graduated with the degree of archivist-paleographer. His studies in paleography greatly influenced his later working methods. He modeled himself on "those historians who would not allow themselves to make the slightest pronouncement without a meticulous examination of the evidence." Later on, when he was preparing *Jean Barois, Les Thibault,* and *Les Souvenirs du Colonel de Maumort* (the memoirs of Colonel de Maumort), he spent an enormous amount of time studying documentation of the events of the period.

In February, 1906, a few weeks after finishing his studies, Martin du Gard married Hélène Foucault. Their only

daughter, Christiane, was born the following year. During his honeymoon in North Africa, he began writing a novel entitled *Une Vie de Saint* (A Saint's Life). He worked on it conscientiously for more than six months, then, after reading the manuscript to a friend, decided to shelve it. Somewhat discouraged, he spent the year 1908 picking up the rudiments of psychiatry, frequenting various laboratories and clinics. It was probably at that time that he learned Bleuler's distinction between syntonic and schizoid personalities. "Those who accept life and those who reject it." Being stockily built, Martin du Gard was obviously the syntonic type, i.e., one who accepted. Henceforth he would be consciously so. Fleeting as it was, there can be no doubt that his contact with medical circles influenced his intellectual approach, giving him a resolutely positivist turn of mind. Antoine Thibault —among his heroes, the one to whom he felt most akin—was a surgeon and said, "When it comes to men of ability, I have known hardly any apart from doctors."

Thus began Martin du Gard's long association with Positivism, which he repressed with a frankness that sometimes confused his readers, who may have wondered whether the author of *Jean Barois,* for example, was not really a frightful reactionary secretly scoffing at the appallingly rigid scientific approach he described. Far from it—once he had adopted the Positivist point of view, Martin du Gard was not the sort of man to temper it with polite concessions. Gide noted in his *Journal* from March 1, 1927: "Long conversation with Martin du Gard—ensconced in his materialism like a wild boar in its lair."

What he prized above all was not positivism itself but the clarity of vision from which science derives so much; anything unclear was suspect to him. He did not reject or ignore the obscure, but he held that the obscure must be illuminated and that this can only be done in the light of what is already clear. His whole work is imbued with this idea. His aim was to reveal what things meant, not to speak in riddles: "No poetry!" Thus he deprived himself of a great deal. Being of an uncompromising nature, he was determined to make his work conform to his convictions and confident in his own ability, he felt he could deprive himself without any risk of starving.

In the spring of 1908, Martin du Gard began another novel. Quickly written, it was published by Ollendorf in the autumn of 1908 at the author's own expense. *Devenir!* (Becoming!) bristled with a feeling for the picturesque and a gift for description. The way in which it reflects the author's psychological problems is even more striking. Martin du Gard was worried about being a failure and, as he explained in *Souvenirs* (Memoirs): "I had an urge to write about a presumptuous young author with no talent, full of illusions about his gifts, whose life would be a long succession of barren impulses and frustrations. I felt that if I could manage to portray such a failure convincingly, it would prove that I was not threatened with the same unhappy fate as my hero."

It was as a novelist that Martin du Gard wished to succeed in life. The age of Balzac, Stendhal, Flaubert, Tolstoy, and Dostoevsky had only just ended, and the novel was the major literary genre. Martin du Gard claimed Tolstoy as his model, but it has often been observed that in fact their novels have very little in common. Skeptical, organized, and coolly methodical, Martin du Gard could hardly produce the same impression of charm and mystical fervor as Tolstoy with his magnificent disorder. What Martin du Gard sought to emulate, perhaps, was Tolstoy's lack of affectation and his simplicity. Tolstoy's example also

taught him not to be afraid of the commonplace, and was an enormous asset to a modern writer. But there was something more. Martin du Gard has explained that what he most envied in Tolstoy was the verisimilitude of his characters: "The characters he offers us are, by and large, those that life offers us; but he has the gift of showing in the least of them those secret depths that lurk below the surface and that we should not have seen without him. By dint of living with him in the universe he has created, our faculty for observation is developed and refined, our perception is sharpened, and the mystery of others becomes less impenetrable to us."

Immediately after *Devenir!*, Martin du Gard embarked on a new novel: *Marise.* Dissatisfied, he scrapped most of it, retaining only a section entitled *L'une de nous* (One of Us) (1909), which formed a short novel in itself and was published by Grasset—again at the author's own expense, though Grasset promised to cover the costs of his next book. It was then that Martin du Gard started *Jean Barois.* The subject had haunted him for many years, and the book took three years to write. His aim was, among other things, to analyze the broad moral implications of two famous scandals that had seared the souls of his elders: the Dreyfus affair and the "Modernism" affair. The Dreyfus affair had meant very little to Martin du Gard at the time of its occurrence. He took an interest in it only afterward, when he realized what a turning point it had been for so many people. After making a thorough study of it, he dealt with it at length in *Jean Barois.* The affair was by then regarded as ancient history without any contemporary relevance, dwarfed to insignificance by later, more world-shaking events, and *Jean Barois* was accordingly considered to be somewhat lacking in interest. But subsequent events were to show that the affair had lost none of its topicality. The actual form chosen by Martin du Gard for *Jean Barois* was highly unconventional: the long stretches of dialogue, mingled with short descriptive passages and the copious quotations, sometimes seemed to make undue demands on the reader's patience. Grasset—soon to be so enthusiastic about Marcel Proust's *Swann's Way*—was disappointed and showed it.

Then Martin du Gard had an almost miraculous stroke of luck. He happened to run into his old school friend Gallimard, who belonged to "the Gide gang," a literary group that was already making a name for itself, and who had been entrusted with the publication of the newly founded periodical, *Nouvelle Revue Française (N.R.F.)*. He asked to see Martin du Gard's manuscript, and a few days later Gide read *Jean Barois* and telegraphed, "Should be published at once!" A letter followed, containing the famous sentence: "The man who wrote it may not be an artist, but he certainly is a character!" Martin du Gard was thus launched on his career. Rushed into print, *Jean Barois* was highly praised, and from then on, things took care of themselves. As an *N.R.F.* author, it was natural that Martin du Gard should become friendly with Copeau, Rivière, Schlumberger, and Gide, though he was rather dumbfounded by Gide's appearance and behavior at their first meeting and they did not become close friends until 1920.

The first of the group with whom he struck up an acquaintance was Jacques Copeau, who had just handed the running of the magazine over to Rivière and was about to found the Vieux-Colombier Theater. Martin du Gard was extremely keen on the theater, and there can be little doubt that he was tempted to make his career as a dramatist. At any rate, in August 1913, even before *Jean Barois*

had appeared, he had written a rural farce, *Le Testament du Père Leleu* (Old Leleu's Will). This play was put on at the Vieux-Colombier in February 1914, and it has been a popular success ever since.

Then came World War I. After the Armistice of 1918, Martin du Gard and his wife, as close friends of Copeau's, were active in getting the Vieux-Colombier Theater on its feet again. At the same time, du Gard dreamed of establishing a sort of fairground theater: La Comédie des Tréteaux. However he seems to have found this idea incompatible with life's realities, for he gave it up and instead launched into a sequence of novels.

In the spring of 1920, Martin du Gard withdrew to his parents' country estate, Le Verger de Augy, in the Nièvre. Ten years earlier he had started *Jean Barois* there; now, he began to plan *Les Thibault*. The first volume of *Les Thibault* appeared in April 1922, and was rapidly followed by the second in May 1922. These opening volumes, short and easy to read, clearly showed that Martin du Gard had no intention to embarking on another risky experiment like *Jean Barois*. He had not forgotten Grasset's reaction. The author of *Les Thibault* had not the slightest desire to wind up as a failure. He had to be a success both materially and socially, and this meant being widely read. He was backed by the enormous prestige of the *N.R.F.*, which had given him a free hand. Unlike some of his friends, he had no particular liking for unpopular literature. He set out to win readers over by the most tried and tested methods, employing the infallible formula of the misunderstood, ill-treated, unhappy child.

From 1923 to 1926 appeared three more volumes of *Les Thibault*. In the meantime, Martin du Gard's parents had died, and he had bought the Château du Tertre, near Bellême, from his father-in-law. He spent a great deal of time and money on alterations and improvements on the estate.

In 1928, he published another volume of *Les Thibault*. Soon afterward, his daughter became the wife of Marcel de Coppet, who had been his best friend since 1902. This unexpected marriage was a great emotional shock to him. He started work on *L'Appareillage*, the next volume of *Les Thibault*. Then, on January 1, 1931, he and his wife were badly injured in a motor accident while driving back to Le Tertre. During his convalescence in a nursing home at Le Mans, he pondered deeply over *Les Thibault*, thought up a different ending, and scrapped *L'Appareillage*. *Les Thibault* was temporarily interrupted.

It was at this point that he published a rather daring short novel *La Confidence africaine* (African Secret, 1931), and returned to the theater with *Un Taciturne* (The Silent One, 1931). This play was put on in the autumn of 1931 and starred Louis Jouvet, who was sent a letter by Claudel protesting against this "foul" piece by an "abominable" author.

Two years later he had got back to work on *Les Thibault*. He published the three volumes of *L'Été 1914* (*Summer 1914*), the culminating books of *Les Thibault*, at one fell swoop in 1936. *Epilogue*, the final volume, did not appear until January 1940.

*Summer 1914* was a daring venture. No other part of *Les Thibault* demands so much patience on the part of the reader. It is longer even than *Jean Barois*. The agitation that prevailed on the eve of World War I, particularly among those who had founded their hopes on the Socialist International, is evoked by means of interminable dialogues in which the pros and cons are weighed indefinitely but no clearcut conclusion is reached. No real risk was involved, however; Martin du Gard's earlier books had won him a faithful public, and the war was a subject that still aroused enormous interest. Moreover, since Malraux's *La Condition Humaine* (*Man's Fate*, 1933), another book that was none too easy to read, there had been a vogue for political novels. The book created a great stir, and the following year, 1937, Roger Martin du Gard was awarded the Nobel Prize for Literature.

These were turbulent years and again war was on the horizon. Martin du Gard's pacifism was so extreme that at the time of the Spanish Civil War he wrote to Marcel Lallemand: "Anything *rather than war!* Anything, anything! Even Fascism in Spain! And don't goad me or I shall say: yes . . . and even Fascism in France! . . . One would need to have forgotten what war means for a people, the supreme evil, suffering to the nth degree. Nothing, no trial, no bondage, can be compared with war." This type of pacifism is very different from Romain Rolland's, but then the period was different. Martin du Gard was convinced that it was wishful thinking to believe that the Socialist parties could, through strikes and international action prevent a war from breaking out. He considered, like Plekhanov and Liebknecht, that in such a situation the most Socialist country would be at the mercy of the least. And he was especially aware of the fact that many Socialists are naturally aggressive and secretly chauvinistic, and that it would never be possible to stop a militant from pouncing on his rifle as soon as he thought the enemy had crossed the frontier. Believing that the human race was irremediably mediocre and could be appealed to only through its basest instincts, Martin du Gard based his pacifist hopes not on any development of idealism but on a realization of the material advantages of peace.

Saddened by the general baseness of humanity, Martin du Gard depicted it coldly, almost mathematically, in a little book that analyzes, one by one, the inhabitants of an imaginary, yet typical, French village: "A collection of ugly faces, of frigid, covetous, and cruel hearts." He wrote this book with great verve and ease in less than two months, giving it the provocative title *Vieille France* (literally "Old France"—the English version is entitled *The Postman*, 1933). The aptness of its detail, the restraint of each little episode, and its skillful handling are the work of a virtuoso, but of one who keeps his virtuosity well concealed. Each scrap of narrative is beautifully written, forming an essential and significant part of a flawless whole. All this goes with a perfect evenness of tone, a biting sarcasm carefully hidden behind an innocent façade. Maupassant himself could not have done it better. It is interesting that Martin du Gard, having demonstrated his gift for satire in *The Postman*, never wrote another work of this kind. Perhaps the type of literature, in which he could have excelled, struck him as not worth the slightest effort.

During the German occupation of France in World War II, Martin du Gard, then living in Nice, began making notes for a new book: *Les Souvenirs du Colonel de Maumort* (The Memoirs of Colonel de Maumort). This was planned as yet another work on the grand scale. His intention was to interweave, in diary form, a chronicle of the events of 1940 and the Colonel's memories, putting into it all he still felt he had to say, making full use of the mountain of documentation he had accumulated on every conceivable subject. In his earlier *Souvenirs*, he related how he got bogged down in all this work, piling up notes and plans about the life of the old soldier and his various cronies. At one point he decided to give up the diary idea, and he hesitated between a sequence of linked short stories and a correspondence between Maumort and a friend. He was never able to make up his mind, although he wrote away feverishly sometimes in one form and sometimes in the other. Finally, snowed under by drafts, plans, notes, and completed fragments, he decided to give it all up and to let his friend Pierre Herbart arrange the whole thing as best he could after his death. It could then be published as a posthumous work, unfinished but rewarding, with the effect of density that he had so often aimed at but had never managed to achieve because of his mania for order.

Knowing that he had never succeeded in what he wanted without a great deal of preliminary fumbling, he resigned himself to fumbling indefinitely with Maumort's story. Having all the fame and glory he needed, he allowed himself to do only what he really enjoyed doing: compiling files as befitted an archivist and a lawyer's son. And, with some relief, he relinquished the task he enjoyed least: knocking a book into shape. In the last years of his life he laid down all sorts of stringent and complicated conditions for the posthumous publication of his *Correspondence* and his *Journal*, to which he obviously attached a great deal of importance.

He died at Le Tertre on August 22, 1958, from a myocardial infarction. Knowing that the last days of the author of *Jean Barois* would arouse a certain amount of curiosity, he was eager that they should be shrouded in secrecy. His circle accordingly saw to it that this was so. But it seems clear that, for Martin du Gard, Jean Barois's problems had long ago been surmounted and left far behind. Antoine Thibault observed toward the end of his life: "I should consent *at a pinch*, if it would give pleasure to somebody. But for whom would I play at a Christian death?" Madame Martin du Gard had died nine years previously;

moreover, as Martin du Gard told various friends with some insistence, he had been reassured once and for all by Gide's serenity as he lay dying in 1951.

This fits in with one of his last recorded sayings:

"I am gradually being overcome by indifference . . . even about my death."

---

André Berne-Joffroy is a French literary critic.
Translated by Helga Harrison.

# THE 1937 PRIZE

## By KJELL STRÖMBERG

WHEN the Nobel Prize for Literature was awarded to Roger Martin du Gard in 1937 "for the artistic vigor and truthfulness with which he has pictured human contrasts as well as some fundamental aspects of contemporary life in the series of novels entitled *Les Thibault*," he became the sixth Frenchman to win the Prize. Martin du Gard was the first winner selected from among the new generation whose work reached the public after the First World War.

Thirty-six candidates were in the field, among them Paul Valéry, Georges Duhamel, Jean Giono (whose candidacy was supported by several thousands of Franco-American admirers) and, for the first time, Paul Claudel. Although not questioning Martin du Gard's merits, the Scandinavian press insistently beat the drum for the Finnish novelist Frans Eemil Sillanpää, who was to win two years later.

Martin du Gard won without much of a struggle. He had been a strong "perennial" since 1934, and his final victory resulted, to a great extent, from the fact that the year before he had published what was expected to be the final volume of his *magnum opus, Les Thibault,* after many years of silence. The first six volumes, published in the twenties and translated into dozens of languages, had already been the subject

of highly favorable reports drawn up for the Nobel Committee. The Committee seemed only to be awaiting the final volume before taking action. The book, *Summer 1914,* was as long as all the previous volumes put together and quite as rich in content. It convinced the Nobel Committee members that the remarkable creative powers of the author were in no way reduced.

The choice was greeted throughout the world as a happy event honoring both the novelist and the jury. One of the latter, Anders Österling, wrote in the *Stockholms-Tidningen* that "For the first time the Swedish Academy is paying tribute, in the person of Roger Martin du Gard, to that school of French realism whose influence on world literature has been and still is today so vital." The new laureate, on receiving the news in Nice, proved a great disappointment to the reporters who besieged his home for the customary interrogations on his past, his present activity, and his future projects. His door stayed firmly shut. All during his life the hermit of Bellême (he rarely left his estate in the Orne region, and then only for brief trips to Nice or Paris) had carefully avoided all personal publicity, shunning the entire social side of literary life. Suddenly famous, he succeeded in maintaining his silence until he arrived in Stockholm; there, overnight, his attitude changed. During the two weeks of his visit he became as cordial and outgoing as anyone could ask, even with reporters.

Martin du Gard went to Stockholm with his wife and their old friend Lucien Maury, director of the Swedish College at the Cité Universitaire of Paris. The novelist was so delighted that he stayed an extra two weeks after completing his skillful, smiling performance of all the gestures and speeches expected from the winner of the Nobel Prize for Literature. His press conference became an eloquent plea for the writer's sacred right to have a private life and to keep it intact in order to devote himself completely to his work, "because it is only in his privacy that even the most secret of writers takes off his mask and, in spite of himself, gives up his secrets."

When Martin du Gard took his place on the flower-decked platform at the Concert Palace before the royal family, he had already won the public with a declaration of love for Sweden issued through the press. Per Hallström, permanent secretary of the Swedish Academy and president of the Nobel Committee, praised the novelist's work highly. Then, in a blizzard, the laureate went on to the Stockholm Town Hall where, before five hundred people, he gave the first speech he had ever given in public. It was a brilliant, searching address, which in a way was basically a heartfelt tribute to Tolstoy.

A few days later the laureate gave a second address in the eighteenth-century hall of the Swedish Academy, in which he discussed his novel, *Jean Barois.* Characterizing it as simply the novel of a

young man, the drama of a human consciousness, nothing more, with no dialectical intentions, he concluded with a quotation from Montaigne, who he said was ever-present in his mind, a quotation that he would like to use as epigraph for all his books: *"Je n'enseigne pas, je raconte"* (I do not teach, I simply narrate).

In a letter to a friend, Martin du Gard gave a frank account of his long stay in the Swedish capital. It was published in the *Nouvelle Revue Française* in a special issue honoring Martin du Gard, dated December 1, 1958, shortly after the writer had died. He wrote:

The trip, first to Paris, then on to Stockholm, was something I cannot describe. For a month I inhabited the skin of a movie star. At least I took advantage of this brief notoriety to say and publish a number of things that I set store by and which, considering the circumstances, had a certain repercussion. But I am terribly tired, physically and spiritually, and I have a greater need than ever of silence and solitude in which to absorb this incredible adventure. My wife has held up very well, but she is plagued by this polar weather, which has given her bronchitis. Don't worry about me—everything that is happening to me is heavy, heavy, but I am determined not to let it change anything. I have done everything I was supposed to do, everything that was expected of me. I think my stay in Sweden has had a certain effect, and of the kind I should have wished for. But right now it's a bit like being convalescent.

Translated by Dale McAdoo.

# Gabriela Mistral

## 1945

---

"For her lyric poetry, which, inspired

by powerful emotions, has made her name

a symbol of the idealistic aspirations of the

entire Latin-American world"

---

*Illustrated by MARIANE CLOUZOT*

# PRESENTATION ADDRESS

## By HJALMAR GULLBERG

MEMBER OF THE SWEDISH ACADEMY

---

O̲NE DAY a mother's tears caused a whole language, disdained at that time in good society, to rediscover its nobility and gain glory through the power of its poetry. It is said that when Frédéric Mistral, the first of the two poets bearing the name of the Mediterranean wind, had written his first verses in French as a young student, his mother began to shed inexhaustible tears. An ignorant country woman from Languedoc, she did not understand this distinguished language. Mistral then wrote *Mirèio,* recounting the love of the pretty little peasant for the poor artisan, an epic that exudes the perfume of the flowering land and ends in cruel death. Thus the old language of the troubadours became again the language of poetry. The Nobel Prize of 1904 drew the world's attention to this event. Ten years later the poet of *Mirèio* died.

In that same year, 1914, the year in which the First World War broke out, a new Mistral appeared at the other end of the world. At the Floral Games of Santiago de Chile, Gabriela Mistral won the prize with some poems dedicated to a dead man.

Her story is so well known to the people of South America that, passed on from country to country, it has become almost a legend. And now that she has at last come to us, over the crests of the Cordilleran Andes and across the immensities of the Atlantic, we may retell it once again.

In a small village in the Elquis valley, several decades ago, was born a future schoolteacher named Lucila Godoy y Alcayaga. Godoy was her father's name, Alcayaga her mother's; both were of Basque origin. Her father, who had been a schoolteacher, improvised verses with ease. His talent seems to have been mixed with the anxiety and the instability common to poets. He left his family when his daughter, for whom he had made a small garden, was still a child. Her beautiful mother, who was to live a long time, has said that sometimes she discovered her lonely little daughter engaged in intimate conversations with the birds and the flowers of the garden. According to one version of the legend, she was expelled from school. Apparently she was considered too stupid for teaching hours to be wasted on her. Yet she taught herself by her own methods, educating herself to the extent that she became a teacher in the small village school of Cantera. There her destiny was fulfilled at the age of twenty, when a passionate love arose between her and a railroad employee.

We know little of their story. We know only that he betrayed her. One day in November, 1909, he fatally shot himself in the head. The young girl was seized with boundless despair. Like Job, she lifted her cry to the Heaven that had allowed this. From the lost valley in the barren, scorched mountains of Chile a voice arose, and far around men heard it. A banal tragedy of everyday life lost its private character and entered into universal literature. Lucila Godoy y Alcayaga became Gabriela Mistral. The little provincial schoolteacher, the young colleague of Selma Lagerlöf of Maarbacka, was to become the spiritual queen of Latin America.

When the poems written in memory of the dead man had made known the name of the new poet, the somber and passionate poems of Gabriela Mistral began to spread over all South America. It was not until 1922, however, that she had her large collection of poems, *Desolación* (*Despair*), printed in New York. A mother's tears burst forth in the middle of the book, in the fifteenth poem, tears shed for the son of the dead man, a son who would never be born.

Gabriela Mistral transferred her natural love to the children she taught. For them she wrote the collections of simple songs and rounds, collected in Madrid in 1924 under the title *Ternura* (*Tenderness*). In her honor, four thousand Mexican children at one time sang these rounds. Gabriela Mistral became the poet of motherhood by adoption.

In 1938 her third large collection, *Tala* (a title which can be translated as "ravage" but which is also the name of a children's game), appeared in Buenos Aires for the benefit of the infant victims of the

Spanish Civil War. Contrasting with the pathos of *Desolación, Tala* expresses the cosmic calm which envelopes the South American land whose fragrance comes all the way to us. We are again in the garden of her childhood; I listen again to the intimate dialogues with nature and common things. There is a curious mixture of sacred hymn and naive song for children; the poems on bread and wine, salt, corn, and water— water that can be offered to thirsty men—celebrate the primordial foods of human life!

From her maternal hand this poet gives us a drink which tastes of the earth and which appeases the thirst of the heart. It is drawn from the spring which ran for Sappho on a Greek island and for Gabriela Mistral in the valley of Elquis, the spring of poetry that will never dry up.

Madame Gabriela Mistral— You have indeed made a long voyage to be received by so short a speech. In the space of a few minutes I have described to the compatriots of Selma Lagerlöf your remarkable pilgrimage from the chair of a schoolmistress to the throne of poetry. In rendering homage to the rich Latin American literature, we address ourselves today quite specially to its queen, the poet of *Desolación,* who has become the great singer of sorrow and of motherhood.

I ask you now to receive from the hands of His Majesty the King the Nobel Prize for Literature, which the Swedish Academy has awarded you.

# ACCEPTANCE SPEECH

## By GABRIELA MISTRAL

---

Today Sweden turns toward a distant Latin American country to honor it in the person of one of the many exponents of its culture. It would have pleased the cosmopolitan spirit of Alfred Nobel to extend the scope of his protectorate of civilization by including within its radius the southern hemisphere of the American continent. As a daughter of Chilean democracy, I am moved to have before me a representative of the Swedish democratic tradition, a tradition whose originality consists in perpetually renewing itself within the framework of the most valuable creations of society. The admirable work of freeing a tradition from deadwood while conserving intact the core of the old virtues, the acceptance of the present and the anticipation of the future, these are what we call Sweden, and these achievements are an honor to Europe and an inspiring example for the American continent.

The daughter of a new people, I salute the spiritual pioneers of Sweden, by whom I have been helped more than once. I recall its men of science who have enriched its national body and mind. I remember the legion of professors and teachers who show the foreigner unquestionably exemplary schools, and I look with trusting love to those other members of the Swedish people: farmers, craftsmen, and workers.

At this moment, by an undeserved stroke of fortune, I am the direct voice of the poets of my race and the indirect voice for the noble Spanish and Portuguese tongues. Both rejoice to have been invited to this festival of Nordic life with its tradition of centuries of folklore and poetry.

May God preserve this exemplary nation, its heritage and its creations, its efforts to conserve the imponderables of the past and to cross the present with the confidence of maritime people who overcome every challenge.

My homeland, represented here today by our learned Minister Gajardo, respects and loves Sweden, and it has sent me here to accept the special honor you have awarded to it. Chile will treasure your generosity among her purest memories.

# POEMS

## By GABRIELA MISTRAL

*Translated by* Langston Hughes

---

### CRADLE SONGS

#### CLOSE TO ME

Tiny fleece of my own flesh
woven deep within me,
tiny fleece so hating cold,
sleep close to me!

The partridge sleeps in the clover
alert to the barking dogs:
but my breathing does not disturb you.
Sleep close to me!

Trembling little blade of grass
frightened at life,
do not turn loose my breasts:
sleep close to me!

I who have lost everything
shiver at the thought of sleep.
Do not slip from my arms:
sleep close to me!

## I AM NOT LONELY

The night is left lonely
from the hills to the sea.
But I, who cradle you,
I am not lonely!

The sky is left lonely
should the moon fall in the sea.
But I, who cling to you,
I am not lonely!

The world is left lonely
and all know misery.
But I, who hug you close,
I am not lonely!

## CRADLE SONG

The sea cradles
its millions of stars divine.
Listening to the seas in love,
I cradle the one who is mine.

The errant wind in the night
cradles the wheat.
Listening to the winds in love,
I cradle my sweet.

God Our Father cradles
His thousands of worlds without sound.
Feeling His hand in the darkness,
I cradle the babe I have found.

POEMS

## NIGHT

Because you sleep, my little one,
the sunset will no longer glow:
Now nothing brighter than the dew
nor whiter than my face you know.

Because you sleep, my little one,
nothing on the highroad do we see,
nothing sighs except the river,
nothing is except me.

The plain is turning into mist,
the sky's blue breath is still.
Like a hand upon the world
silence works its will.

Not only do I rock to sleep
my baby with my singing,
but the whole world goes to sleep
to the sway of my cradle swinging.

## YOU HAVE ME

Sleep, my little one,
sleep and smile,
for the night-watch of stars
rocks you awhile.

Drink in the light,
and happy be.
All good you have
in having me.

Sleep, my little one,
sleep and smile,
for the earth in love
rocks you awhile.

Look at the bright rose,
red as can be.
Reach out to the world
as you reach out to me.

Sleep, my little one,
sleep and smile,
For God in the shade
rocks you awhile.

CHARM

This child is as charming
as the sweetest winds that blow:
if he suckles me while I'm sleeping
he drinks, and I do not know.

This child is sweeter than the river
that circles the hill with its crook.
This son of mine is more beautiful
than the world on which he steals a look.

This child has greater riches
than to heaven or earth belong—
on my breast he has ermine,
and velvet in my song.

His little body is so small
it seems a tiny seed so fine:
weighing less than dreams weigh,
no one sees him, yet he's mine.

## SAD MOTHER

Sleep, sleep, master mine,
without worry, without fear,
even though my soul sleeps not,
even though I do not rest.

Sleep, sleep, and in the night
may you a lesser murmur be
than a blade of grass
or the silk of fleece.

In you let my flesh sleep,
my worry and my fear.
In you let my eyes close.
May my heart sleep in you.

## GENTILITIES

When I am singing to you,
on Earth wrongdoing ceases:
all is sweetness at your temples:
the gulley and the patch of brambles.

When I am singing to you
evil is erased from all:
gentle as your eyelids
become the lion and the jackal.

BITTER SONG

Little one, let's play at
being king and queen.

This green field is yours.
To whom else could it belong?
The waving fields of grain
for you are growing strong.

This whole valley is yours.
To whom else could it belong?
So that we might enjoy them,
orchards give us honey.

(No, it's not true that you shiver
like the Child of Bethlehem,
and that the breasts of your mother
are going dry through wrong!)

The sheep is growing wooly
with the fleece I'll weave so strong.
And the flocks all are yours.
To whom else could they belong?

The milk flowing sweet from udders
in stables at evensong,
and the gathering of the harvests
to whom else could they belong?

(No, it's not true that you shiver
like the Child of Bethlehem,
and that the breasts of your mother
are going dry through wrong!)

Yes, little one, let's play
at being king and queen.

## F E A R

I do not want them to turn
my child into a swallow;
she might fly away into the sky
and never come down again to my doormat;
or nest in the eaves where my hands
could not comb her hair.
I do not want them to turn
my child into a swallow.

I do not want them to make
my child into a princess.
In tiny golden slippers how could
she play in the field?
And when night came, no longer
would she lie by my side.
I do not want them to make
my child into a princess.

And I would like even less
that one day they crown her queen.
They would raise her to a throne
where my feet could not climb.
I could not rock her to sleep
when nighttime came.
I do not want them to make
my child into a queen.

## L I T T L E   L A M B

Little lamb of mine
with such softness blest,
your grotto of velvet moss
is my breast.

Flesh as white
as a moonray is white,
all else I forget
to be your cradle tonight.

I forget about the world
and want only to make
greater my breasts
for your hunger's sake.

For your fiesta, son of mine,
other fiestas end—
I only know that you
on me depend.


DEW

This was a rose
kissed by the dew:
this was my breast
my son knew.

Little leaves meet,
soft not to harm him,
and the wind makes a detour
not to alarm him.

He came down one night
from the great sky;
for him she holds her breath
so he won't cry.

Happily quiet,
not a sound ever:
rose among roses
more marvelous never.

This was a rose
kissed by the dew:
this was my breast
my son knew.

## DISCOVERY

I found this child
when I went to the country:
asleep I discovered him
among the sprigs of grain  .  .  .

Or maybe it was while
cutting through the vineyard:
searching in its branches
I struck his cheek  .  .  .

Because of this, I fear
when I am asleep,
he might melt as frost does
on the grapevines  .  .  .

## MY SONG

The song that I have sung
for sad children,
out of pity
sing to me.

The song that I have crooned
suffering children,
now that I am hurt,
sing to me.

The cruel light stabs my eyes
and any sound upsets me.
The song to which I rocked him,
sing to me.

When I was knitting them
soft as the softness of ermine,
I did not know that my poor soul
was like a child.

The song that I have sung
for sad children,
out of pity
sing to me.


# POEMS FOR MOTHERS


### POET'S NOTE

*One afternoon, walking through a poor street in Temuco, I saw a quite ordinary woman sitting in the doorway of her hut. She was approaching childbirth, and her face was heavy with pain. A man came by and flung at her an ugly phrase that made her blush. At that moment I felt toward her all the solidarity of our sex, the infinite pity of one woman for another, and I passed on thinking, "One of us must proclaim (since men have not done so) the sacredness of this painful yet divine condition. If the mission of art is to beautify all in an immensity of pity, why have we not, in the eyes of the impure, purified this?" So I wrote these poems with an almost religious meaning.*

*Some women who, because of high social standing, feel it necessary to close their eyes to cruel but inevitable realities, have made of these poems a vile commentary—which saddened me for their sakes. They even went so far as to insinuate that they should be dropped from my book. . . . No! Here they remain, dedicated to those women capable of seeing that the sacredness of life begins with maternity which is, in itself, holy. They will understand the deep tenderness with which this woman who cares for the children of others, looks upon the mothers of all the children in the world.*

### HE KISSED ME

He kissed me and now I am someone else; someone
else in the pulse that repeats the pulse of my
own veins and in the breath that mingles with my
breath. Now my belly is as noble as my heart.

And even on my breath is found the breath of
flowers; all because of the one who rests gently
in my being, like dew on the grass!

### WHAT WILL IT BE LIKE?

What will it be like? For a long time I looked at
the petals of a rose. I touched them with delight;
I would like their softness for his cheeks. And I
played in a tangle of brambles, because I would like his
hair dark and tangled that way. But if it is brownish,
with the rich color of the red clays that potters love,
I won't care, either, or if his stringy hair is as plain
as was my life.

I watch the hollows in the mountains when they are filling
with mist, and from the mist I make the shape of a little
girl, a very sweet little girl: that mine could well be.

But, more than anything else, I want its look to have the
sweetness that he has in his look, and may the light timbre
of its voice be like his when he speaks to me, for in the
one that is coming, I want to love the one who kissed me.

## WISDOM

Now I know why I have had twenty summers of sunshine on my
head and it was given me to gather flowers in the fields.
Why, I once asked myself on the most beautiful of days,
this wonderful gift of warm sun and cool grass?

Like the blue cluster, I took in light for the sweetness
I am to give forth. That which is deep within me comes
into being, drop by drop, from the wine of my veins.

For this I prayed, to receive in the name of God the
clay with which he would be made. And when with trembling
pulse I read a poem for him, its beauty burns me like a
live coal so that he catches from my own flesh fire
that can never be extinguished.

## SWEETNESS

Because of the sleeping child I carry, my footsteps
have grown silent. And my whole heart is reverent since
it bears the mystery.

My voice is soft like a mute of love, for I am afraid
to awaken it.

With my eyes in passing faces now, I seek this pain of
mine in other entrails, hoping that seeing me, others
understand why my cheek is pale.

I stir the grasses where quail nestle, tenderly afraid.
And through the countryside I go quietly, cautiously:
I believe that trees and things have sleeping children
over whom they hover watching.

## SISTER

Today I saw a woman plowing a furrow. Her hips are broad,
like mine, for love, and she goes about her work bent over
the earth.

I caressed her waist; I brought her home with me. She will
drink rich milk from my own glass and bask in the shade of
my arbors growing pregnant with the pregnancy of love.
And if my own breasts be not generous, my son will put his
lips to hers, that are rich.

## PRAYER

Oh, no! How could God let the bud of my breasts go dry when
He himself so swelled my girth? I feel my breasts growing,
rising like water in a wide pool, noiselessly. And their
great sponginess casts a shadow like a promise across my belly.

Who in all the valley could be poorer than I if my breasts
never grew moist?

Like those jars that women put out to catch the dew of night,
I place my breasts before God. I give Him a new name, I call
Him the Filler, and I beg of him the abundant liquid of life.
Thirstily looking for it, will come my son.

## SENSITIVE

I no longer play in the meadows and I am afraid now to
swing back and forth with the girls. I am like a branch
full of fruit.

I am weak, so weak that the scent of roses made me faint
at siesta time when I went down into the garden. And the
simple singing of the wind or that drop of blood in the
sky when the afternoon gives its last gasp, troubles me,
floods me with sadness. Just from the look of my master,
if it is a harsh look tonight, I could die.


## ETERNAL GRIEF

If he suffers within me I grow pale; grief overtakes me
at his hidden pressure, and I could die from a single
motion of this one I can not see.

But do not think that only while I carry him, will he be
entangled within me. When he shall roam free on the
highways, even though he is far away from me, the wind that
lashes him will tear at my flesh, and his cry will be in my
throat, too. My grief and my smile begin in your face, my
son.


## FOR HIM

For his sake, for him now lulled to sleep like a
thread of water in the grass, do not hurt me, do not
give me work to do. Forgive me everything: my irritation
at the way the table is set and my hatred of noise.

You may tell me about the problems of the house,
its worries and its tasks, after I have tucked him away
in his covers.

On my forehead, on my breast, wherever you touch me,
he is, and he would moan if you hurt me.

## QUIETNESS

Now I cannot go into the streets: I sense the blush of my
great girdle and the deep dark circles under my eyes. But
bring to me here, put right here beside me a pot full of
flowers, and slowly play soft strings: for his sake I want
to be flooded with beauty.

I put roses on my body, and over him who sleeps I say ageless
verses. In the arbor hour after hour I gather the acid of
the sun. I want to distill within me honey as the fruit does.
I feel in my face the wind from the pine groves.

Let the light and the winds color and cleanse my blood.
To rinse it, I will no longer hate, no longer gossip—only
love!

Because in this stillness, in this quietude, I am knitting
a body, a miraculous body with veins, and face, and eyes,
and heart quite clean.

## LITTLE WHITE GARMENTS

I knit tiny socks of wool, cut soft diapers: I want to make
everything with my own hands. He will come out of my own
body, he will be a part of my own perfume.

Soft fleece of a sheep: this summer they shear it for him.
For eight months its wool grew sponge-like and the January
moon bleached it. Now there are no little needles of thistle
or thorns or bramble in it. Equally soft is the fleece of my
flesh where he has slept.

Such little white garments! He looks at them through my eyes
and he laughs, guessing how very, very soft they will be . . .

## IMAGE OF THE EARTH

I had never before seen the true image of the Earth. The
Earth looks like a woman with a child in her arms (with
her creatures in her wide arms).

Now I know the maternal feeling of things. The mountain
that looks down at me is a mother, too, and in the afternoons
the mist plays like a child around her shoulders and about
her knees.

Now I remember a cleft in the valley. In its deep bed a
stream went singing, hidden by a tangle of crags and brambles.
I am like that cleft; I feel singing deep within me this little
brook, and I have given it my flesh for a cover of crags and
brambles until it comes up toward the light.

## TO MY HUSBAND

Husband, do not embrace me. You caused it to rise from the
depths of me like a water lily. Let me be like still water.

Love me, love me now a little more! I, so small, will
duplicate you on all the highways. I, so poor, will give
you other eyes, other lips, through which you may enjoy the
world; I, so frail, will split myself asunder for love's
sake like a broken jar, that the wine of life might flow.

Forgive me! I walk so clumsily, so clumsily serve your
glass; but you filled me like this and gave me this strangeness
with which I move among things.

Treat me more than ever kindly. Do not roughly stir my
blood; do not disturb my breathing.

Now I am nothing but a veil; all my body is a veil beneath
which a child sleeps.

## MOTHER

My mother came to see me; she sat right here beside me,
and, for the first time in our lives, we were two sisters
who talked about a great event to come.

She felt the trembling of my belly and she gently uncovered
my bosom. At the touch of her hands to me it seemed as if
all within me half-opened softly like leaves, and up into
my breasts shot the spurt of milk.

Blushing, full of confusion, I talked with her about my
worries and the fear in my body. I fell on her breasts,
and all over again I became a little girl sobbing in her
arms at the terror of life.

## TELL ME, MOTHER

Mother, tell me all you have learned from your own
pain. Tell me how he is born and how from within me
all entangled comes a little body.

Tell me if he will seek my breast alone, or if I
should offer it to him, coaxing.

Now teach me the science of love, mother. Show me
new caresses, gentle ones, gentler than those of a
husband.

How, in days to come, shall I wash his little head?
And how shall I swaddle him so as not to hurt him?

Teach me that lullaby, mother, you sang to rock me
to sleep. It will make him sleep better than any
other songs.

## DAWN

All night I suffered, all night my body trembled
to deliver its offering. There is the sweat of
death on my temples; but it is not death, it is
life!

And I call you now Infinite Sweetness, God, that
you release it gently.

Let it be born! And let my cry of pain rise in
the dawn, braided into the singing of birds!

## HOLY LAW

They say that life has flown from my body, that my
veins have spouted like wine presses: but I feel only
the relief a breast knows after a long sigh.

"Who am I," I say to myself, "to have a son on my knee?"
And I myself answer, "A woman who loved, and whose love,
when he kissed me, asked for eternity."

Let the Earth observe me with my son in my arms, and
bless me, because now I am fruitful like the palm trees
and furrows in the earth.

# FOR THE SADDEST OF MOTHERS

## THROWN OUT

My father said he would get rid of me, yelled at my mother
that he would throw me out this very night.

The night is mild; by the light of the stars, I might find
my way to the nearest village; but suppose he is born at such
a time as this? My sobs perhaps have aroused him; perhaps he
wants to come out now to see my face covered with tears.
But he might shiver in the naked air, although I would cover him.

## WHY DID YOU COME?

Why did you come? Nobody will love you although you are
beautiful, son of mine. Though you smile so cutely
like the other children, like the smallest of my little
brothers, nobody will kiss you but me, son of mine. And
though your little hands flutter about looking for toys, you will
have for your toys only my breasts and the beads of my
tears, son of mine.

Why did you come, since the one who created you hated you
when he felt you in my belly?

But no! For me you came; for me who was alone, alone until he
held me in his arms, son of mine!

## GRAIN DIVINE

### PRAYER

Lord, you know with what frenzy fine
Your help for strangers I have often sought.
Now I come to plead for one who was mine,
honeycomb of my mouth, spring of my drought.

Lime of my bones, sweet reason to be,
birdsong at my ear, a belt my waist to trim.
I have sought help for others who meant nothing to me.
Do not turn Your head now when I plead for him.

I tell You he was good, and I say
his heart like a flower in his breast did sing,
gentle of nature, frank as the light of day,
bursting with miracles as is the Spring.

Unworthy of my pleas is he, You sternly say,
since no sign of prayer crossed his fevered face
and one day, with no nod from You, he went away,
shattering his temples like a fragile vase.

But I tell you, Lord, I once caressed
his gentle and tormented heart—
as a lily might his brow have pressed—
and found it silky as a bud when petals part.

You say he was cruel? You forget I loved him ever.
He knew my wounded flesh was his to shatter.
Now the waters of my gladness he disturbs forever?
I loved him! You know, I loved him—so that does not matter.

To love (as You well understand) is a bitter task—
eyelids wet with tears may be,
kisses in prickly tresses may bask,
beneath them guarding eyes of ecstasy.

To welcome the chill of iron one may choose
when loving flesh its thrust encloses.
And the Cross (You recall, Oh, King of the Jews)
may be gently borne like a sheaf of roses.

So here I am, Lord, my head in the dust,
pleading with You through a dusk unending,
through all the dusks that bear I must
if You should prove unbending.

I shall wear down your ears with prayers and with cries,
licking the hem of your garment like a dog full of fears—
never to avoid me anymore Your eyes,
or your feet escape the hot rain of my tears.

Grant him forgiveness at last! Then all winds will blow
rich with a hundred vials of perfume,
all waters will sparkle, all cobblestones glow,
and the wilderness burst into bloom.

From the eyes of wild beasts gentle tears will flow,
and the mountains You forged of stone will understand
and weep through their white eyelids of snow:
the whole earth will learn of forgiveness at Your hand.

POEM OF THE SON

I

A son, a son, a son! I wanted a son of yours
and mine, in those distant days of burning bliss
when my bones would tremble at your least murmur
and my brow would glow with a radiant mist.

I said *a son,* as a tree in spring
lifts its branches yearning toward the skies,
a son with innocent mien and anxious mouth,
and wondering, wide and Christ-like eyes.

His arms like a garland entwine around my neck,
the fertile river of my life is within him pent,
and from the depths of my being over all the hills
a sweet perfume spreads its gentle scent.

We look as we pass at a mother big with child,
whose lips are trembling and whose eyes are a prayer.
When deep in love we walk through the crowd,
the wonder of a babe's sweet eyes makes us stare.

Through sleepless nights full of joy and dreams
no fiery lust invaded my bed.
For him who would be born swaddled in song,
I hollowed my breasts to pillow his head.

The sun never seemed too warm to bathe him;
but my lap I hated as too rough a place.
My heart beat wildly at so wonderful a gift,
and tears of humility streamed down my face.

Of death's vile destruction I had no fear,
for the child's eyes would free your eyes from such doom,
and I would not mind walking beneath death's dark stare
in the brilliance of morning or at evening's gloom.


II


Now I am thirty years old, and my brow is streaked
with the precocious ashes of death. And slow tears
like eternal rain at the poles,
salty, bitter, and cold, water my years.

While the pine burns with a gentle flame,
musing, I think it would have been meet
that my son be born with my own weary mouth,
my bitter heart and my voice of defeat.

With your heart like a poisonous fruit,
and me whom your lips would again betray,
for forty moons he might not have slept on my breast;
and because he was yours, he might have gone away.

In what flowering orchards, beside what running waters
in what springtime might he have cleansed his blood of my sorrow,
though I wandered afar in gentler climes,
while it coursed through his veins in some mystical tomorrow?

The fear that some day from his mouth hot with hate
he might say to me, as I to my father did protest,
"Why was your weeping flesh so fertile
as to fill with nectar a mother's breast?"

I find bitter joy in that you sleep now
deep in a bed of earth, and I cradle no child,
for I sleep, too, with no cares, no remorse,
beneath my tangle of brambles wild.

Since I may no longer close my eyes
like a crazy woman I hear voices from outer space,
and with twisted mouth on torn knees I would kneel
if I saw him pass with my pain in his face.

To me God's respite never would be given:
through his innocent flesh the wicked wound me now:
for through all eternity my blood will cry aloud
in my son ecstatic of eye and brow.

Blessed be my breast in which kin is lost
and blessed be my belly in which they die!
The face of my mother will no longer cross the world
nor her voice in the wind change to sorrow's cry.

Forests decayed to ashes will rise a hundred times
to fall again a hundred times by axe or nature's blight.
But in the month of harvest I will fall to rise no more:
me and mine shall disappear in endless night.

As though I were paying the debt of a whole race,
like cells in a beehive, my breast fills with pain.

Each passing hour to me seems a lifetime,
a bitter river flowing seaward is each vein.

I am blind to the sun and blind to the wind
for which my poor dead ones so anxiously long.
And my lips are weary of fervent prayers that,
before I grow mute, my mouth pours into song.

I did not plant for my own granary, nor teach in hope
of loving arms' support when death I might meet
and my broken body sustain me no longer,
and my hand grope for the winding sheet.

I taught the children of others, trusting only in You
to fill my granary with grain divine.
Our Father Who art in heaven, lift up this beggar.
Should I die tonight, let me be Thine.

## FOR CHILDREN

Many years from now, when I am a little mound of silent dust, play with me, with the earth of my heart and my bones. Should a mason gather me up, he would make me into a brick, and I would be stuck forever in a wall, and I hate quiet corners. If they put me in the wall of a prison, I would blush with shame at hearing a man sob. Or if I became the wall of a school, I would suffer from not being able to sing with you in the mornings.

I had rather be dust that you play with on the country roads. Pound me, because I have been yours. Scatter me, as I did you. Stomp me because I never gave you truth entire and beauty whole. O, I mean, sing and run above me that I might kiss your precious footprints.

Say a pretty verse when you have me in your hands, and I will run with pleasure through your fingers. Uplifted at the sight of you, in your eyes I will look for the curly heads of those I taught.

And when you have made of me some sort of statue, shatter it each time, as each time before children shattered me in tenderness and sorrow.

## CHILDREN'S HAIR

Soft hair, hair that has all the softness in the world, how could I be happy dressed in silk, if I did not have you in my lap? Each passing day is sweet and nourishing only because of those hours when it runs through my hands.

Put it close to my cheek; rest it in my lap like flowers; braid it into me to ease my sorrows; strengthen the dying light with it.

When I am in heaven, may God give me no angel's wings to soothe the hurt in my heart; spread instead across the sky the hair of the children I loved, and let their hair sweep forever in the wind across my face.

## COUNTRY WITH NO NAME

### COUNTRY THAT IS MISSING

Country that is missing,
strange country,
lighter than angel
and nebulous password,
color of dead algae,
color of mist,
ageless as time
lacking ageless bliss.

No pomegranates spring
or jasmines blow,
it has neither skies
nor seas of indigo.
Your name is a name
never heard called have I,
and in country with no name
I am going to die.

Neither bridge nor boat
brought me hither.
Nobody told me
it was island or shore.
I did not seek
or discover it either.

It seems like a fable now
that I've learned it,
dreaming to stay
and dreaming to fly.
But it is my country
where I live and I die.

I was born of things
that are no country:
of lands upon lands
I had and I lost;
of children I have watched die;
and things mine no longer
to which once I said *my*.

I lost mountain ranges
where once I slept;
orchards of gold I lost
sweet with life;
islands I lost
of cane and indigo,

and I watched their shadows
close in on me
and crowds and lovers
become country.

Manes of mist
with no napes and no backs
I watched the sleeping
winds make fly
and through errant years
turn into a country,
and in country with no name
I am going to die.


STRANGER

"She speaks in a slight accent about her wild seas
with God knows what seaweeds and God knows what sands;
so old it's as if she herself were dying,
she prays to a god with no volume and no weight.
She has sown cactus and claw-like grasses
in gardens of ours that she makes strange.
She draws her breath from the panting of the desert
and loves with a passion all that it whitens,
all that never says anything and if it should
it would be like the map of another planet.
Were she to live in our midst for eighty years
it would be always as though she had just come,
speaking in a language that pants and moans
and that is understood only by beasts.
And some night when her suffering is greatest
from a death both silent and strange,
she is going to die right here among us
with nothing but her fate for a pillow."

## THINGS

**1.**

I love the things I never had
along with those I have no more.

I touch still water
standing in chilly pastures
where not a single wind shivers
in the orchard that was my orchard.

I stare at it as it stared;
it starts me thinking strangely,
and I play with this water listlessly
as with fish or with mystery.

**2.**

I think of a threshold where I left
gay steps no longer with me,
and on the threshold I see a wound
covered with moss and silence.

**3.**

I search for a rhyme they said to me
when I was seven but now have lost.
She was a woman baking bread
and I look at her saintly mouth.

**4.**

An aroma ripped to threads arises;
I am very lucky if I sense it;
so thin that it has no aroma,
being but trace of almond trees.

My senses turn into a child;
I search for a name but can not guess it.
I smell the wind and all its spaces
seeking almond trees I do not find . . .

5.

Ever near a river dreams.
Forty years now that I feel it,
a humming in my blood or rather
a rhythm that they gave me.

O, River Elqui of my childhood
in which I wade upstream,
never shall I lose you; side by side
like two children, we have each other.

6.

As the Cordillera dreams,
I walk through gorges,
and keep hearing with no relief
a hissing that is almost curse.

7.

I see at the edge of the Pacific
my livid archipelago,
and left over for me from an island
is the sour scent of passion dead.

8.

A back, a back solemn and sweet,
ends the dream I dream.
It is the terminus of my road,
and when I reach it, I rest.

This indistinct and ashen back
is a dead tree trunk or is my father.
I ask no questions, nor disturb it.
Together, I keep still and sleep.

9.

I love the stone that I draw to me
from Oaxaca or Guatemala,
flushed and firm as is my face
and from whose fissure comes a breathing.

When I go to sleep, it is naked.
Why I turn it over, I do not know.
Perhaps I never had it
and what I see is my tomb.

## ABSENCE

My body leaves you drop by drop,
my face leaves in a silence of the oil of death;
my hands leave in live mercury;
my feet leave in two puffs of dust.

All leaves you, all leaves us!

My voice leaves that you make a bell,
silent when we are not ourselves.
Expression leaves, dizzily entangled
in knots and bows before your eyes.
And the glance that I gave you leaves
as I look at you, juniper and elm.

I go from you with your own breath:
as the vapor from your body evaporates.
I go from you in sleeplessness and in sleep,
and from your remembrance I am erased.
And in your memory I become like those
born neither in plains nor in thickets.

I will be blood, and you will find me in the palms
of your hands and the wine of your mouth.
Your entrails I become, and I will be burned
in your footsteps I hear no more
and in your pain that pounds in the night
like the madness of seas that are lonely.

All leaves us, all leaves us!

## TWO ANGELS

I have not only one angel
with flapping wings:
the angel that gives joy
and the one who gives pain
rock me like the sea
rocked by two shores,
the one of fluttering wings
and the one whose wings are still.

I know at dawn
which one will rule my day,
the one the color of flame
or the one the color of ashes,
and I give myself to them contrite
like seaweed to the wave.

Only once did they fly
all with wings together:
on the day of love
and on Epiphany.

Then they joined
their warring wings as one
and tied the knot
of life and death.

## THE FLOWER OF THE AIR

I found her standing in my path
half way across the meadow,
mistress of all who passed her way
or spoke or looked upon her.

She said to me, "Go up the mountain—
I never leave the meadow—
and gather me flowers white as snow,
sturdy and tender."

I went up the bitter mountain
seeking flowers where they whiten
half asleep and half awake
among the crags.

When I came down with my burden,
in the middle of the meadow I found her,
and frantically covered her
with a shower of white lilies.

But without looking at the whiteness
she said to me, "This time bring back
only flowers that are red.
I cannot go beyond the meadow."

I scaled the rocks with deer
and sought the flowers of madness,
those that grew so red they seemed
to live and die of redness.

When I descended happily trembling,
I gave them as my offering,
and she became as water
that from a wounded deer turns bloody.

But, like a sleepwalker, looking at me,
she said, "Go up and bring back now
golden ones, the golden ones.
I never leave the meadow."

Up the mountain straight I climbed
to search for the thickest flowers,
those the color of sun and saffron,
just born but yet eternal.

When I found her as usual
in the middle of the meadow,
I covered her once more with flowers
and left her as in a garden.

Still, crazy with gold,
she said, "Slave of mine, climb up
and gather flowers without color,
neither saffron nor of crimson—

"Those that I love in memory
of Leonara and Ligeia,
the color of sleep and the color of dreams.
I am the Mother of the Meadow."

Climbing I went up the mountain
dark now as Medea,
like a vague but certain grotto
with no tiles high gleaming.

There grew no flowers on any branches,
none bloomed among the crags,
so from the air I gathered blossoms,
cutting them lightly.

I picked them as if I were
a picker who was blind,
cutting here and there from air
and taking air as garden.

When I descended from the mountain
and went looking for the queen,
no longer pale or wild-eyed
she was strolling now:

Like a sleepwalker,
she started from the meadow,
and I followed, followed, followed
through the pasture, through the grove.

Quite loaded down with flowers,
shoulders and hands aerial,
she went on plucking them from air
and the wind became her harvest.

On she goes now with no face,
on she goes and leaves no footprints,
bearing flowers without color,
neither white nor crimson.

Still I follow, follow after
through the branches of the mist,
until she leads me to the brink
where Time dissolves . . .


OLD LION

"Your hair
 is white now, too;
 fear, rough voice,
 mouth, *amen*.

Too late you sought,
 too late you saw
 eyes without brilliance,
 temples deaf.

So much you suffered
 to learn
 the quiet hearth,
 the rancid honey.

Much love and grief
 it took to know
 my lion gray-haired,
 and such old feet!"

[ 206 ]

## SONG

A woman is singing in the valley. The shadows falling blot her out, but her song spreads over the fields.

Her heart is broken, like the jar she dropped this afternoon among the pebbles in the brook. As she sings, the hidden wound sharpens on the thread of her song, and becomes thin and hard. Her voice in modulation dampens with blood.

In the fields the other voices die with the dying day, and a moment ago the song of the last slow-poke bird stopped. But her deathless heart, alive with grief, gathers all the silent voices into her voice, sharp now, yet very sweet.

Does she sing for a husband who looks at her silently in the dusk, or for a child whom her song caresses? Or does she sing for her own heart, more helpless than a babe at nightfall.

Night grows maternal before this song that goes to meet it; the stars, with a sweetness that is human, are beginning to come out; the sky full of stars becomes human and understands the sorrows of this world.

Her song, as pure as water filled with light, cleanses the plain and rinses the mean air of day in which men hate. From the throat of the woman who keeps on singing, day rises nobly evaporating toward the stars.

# THE LIFE AND WORKS OF

# GABRIELA MISTRAL

## By *JORGE EDWARDS*

THE Elqui River Valley in northern Chile is one of those small connecting valleys between the Andes and the Pacific Ocean. It enjoys a mild climate, something like California's, an abundant tropical fruit production, and it is surrounded by barren plains rich in minerals.

In a magazine article, Gabriela Mistral has described the particular character of the men of the region: adventurous, given to gambling, they are incapable of working steadily at any job because of the teasing illusion of immediate riches to be gained by prospecting. In describing the northern Chilean, Gabriela was possibly thinking of her father, except that he was not a miner, but a schoolteacher by profession. Jerónimo Godoy, in the opinion of all who knew him, was a light-hearted type, something of a poet, somewhat taken in by the vagabond life, and he loved fiestas. Toward the end of the nineteenth century, Godoy married a widow, Doña Petronila Alcayaga, who had a daughter who was also a teacher. The family lived in the village of Montegrande in the Elqui Valley until 1889. That year they moved to the nearby town of Vicuña when Doña Petronila Alcayaga learned she was pregnant.

Even today the town of Vicuña, capital of the department of Elqui, has fewer than 2000 inhabitants. There, on April 7, 1889, Doña Petronila Alcayaga gave birth to Lucila Godoy, who was to become famous in South American literature as Gabriela Mistral. Her father, out of work at the time, wrote a poem celebrating her birth and at the same time lamenting the fate of the new arrival. Three years later Jerónimo Godoy left home and soon disappeared from the region.

In Gabriela Mistral's writing, the family nucleus made up of mother and child, is the theme of many poems. The father is a distant figure, rarely mentioned. A few verses are sufficient to give us an idea of what her mother was like:

*Mi madre era pequeñita*
*como la menta o la hierba;*
*apenas echaba sombra*
*sobre las cosas, apenas,*
*y la Tierra la quería*
*por sentírsela ligera*
*y porque le sonreía*
*en la dicha y en la pena.*

My mother was tiny,
like mint or grass;
she barely cast a shadow
over things, barely,

and the Earth loved her
for her lightness
and because she smiled
in good fortune and in sorrow.

Although the mother was nearly illiterate, she was a woman of great courage and tenacity. When her husband left her, she took up the burden of supporting her family with no sign of bitterness. She was helped by her older daughter, a schoolteacher, who also had an important influence on her younger sister.

Gabriela's poetry gives us a clear picture of her early years, apparently the only joyful years of her life. She is the rural poet *par excellence*. She once wrote of her poems *Recados* (Messages), "These *Recados* have my most characteristic note: I am a peasant, and as a peasant I shall live and die." In another note explaining her reasons for daring to publish certain passages which she considered imperfect, she wrote, "I face up to ridicule with the smile of the country woman when her berry patch doesn't produce or when her jam burns." Sometimes the memory of her childhood is so pungent that she prefers to imagine that those years were not real. In one of her poems on her mother's death she says:

*Tan lejanos se encuentran los años*
*de los panes de harina candeal*
*disfrutados en mesa de pino,*
*que negamos, mejor, su verdad,*
*y decimos que siempre estuvieron*
*nuestras vidas lo mismo que estan,*
*y vendemos la blanca memoria*
*que dejamos tendida al umbral.*

So far gone are those years
of white-flour bread
enjoyed on a pine table
that we deny the truth of them
and say that our lives
have always been the same,
and we sell the white memory
which we keep hanging at the door.

The earliest bitter experience of her life happened in Vicuña, when she was still a child. Gabriela was in the care of the directress of the local school, a blind woman. The little girl served her as helper and guide, and among other duties she had the task of passing out the school supplies. When she was distributing these, the other pupils would snatch them from her, and she could not defend herself very energetically. In this way the supplies for a whole month were exhausted ahead of time. She was accused, and since she could not give a satisfactory explanation she was censured by the directress before the whole class. Some of the pupils ambushed her after school and pelted her with stones.

When Gabriela visited Vicuña many years later she came across the tomb of the blind woman without being aware of what it was. When told who was buried there and asked if she remembered her, she replied, "I never forget."

By vocation, by family influence, and because there was no other career open to a girl in her particular circumstances, Gabriela began to teach school while still very young. She was already a country schoolteacher at the age of fifteen. From 1905 to 1907 she taught in two small villages of the Elqui Valley near La Serena, the provincial capital.

By this time she was already publishing poems and articles in the local newspapers. Her chief influence at the time was the Colombian poet Vargas Vila, the rebel romantic whose writings galvanized the youth of the day. Also during those years she was introduced to the Bible, and while the echo of Vargas Vila's writings later disappeared from Gabriela's poetry, the Biblical influence remained strong throughout her life. This direct experience of the Bible separated Gabriela from the old Spanish form of Catholicism (in which the reading of the Bible was practically forbidden), and gave her an admiration for the Jews that stayed with her all her life. In *Tala* (1938) she wrote:

*Yo nací de una carne tajada*
*en el seco riñón de Israel . . .*

I was born of flesh slashed
from the dry kidney of Israel . . .

In 1906 at La Serena she met a young railway worker named Romelio Ureta, and thus began that dramatic love affair which was to dominate her entire youth. It has been said that Gabriela saw Romelio Ureta only a few times in her life, and that the love story told in the poems of *Desolación* (*Despair,* 1922) is imaginary. Almost certainly there was more to it than that. She once gave her version of the story to a Chilean writer in these words:

We were truly in love. One sad day we broke it off. At that time I was of an irascible temperament, and we shouted so loud in the room where we were that my mother sent him away. As time passed, my family thought that I was peaceful. Five years passed during which we avoided each other. We hated each other, and we were almost living in the same house. He lived in a room near the top of the building, and my room was immediately below. He knew that I left for school at nine o'clock. He left a half-hour earlier. He was a vulgar fellow— a fine head, but with a face that was almost ugly. During those five years we met only once, while riding. On our return, he suggested that we go back together again. I refused.

In his last years he gave himself up to a life of dissipation and women. He threw away a lot of money on this. His fiancée was very elegant. Her family were spendthrifts, and they exploited him pitilessly. In this way he spent more than he earned and was forced to steal.

One day we met in a lonely street after so long a time of avoiding each other. He came up to me and we started to talk. "When are you getting married?" I asked. "Did you think I could marry that woman?" he asked in reply. "Never," I said. And indeed, not even in my dreams could I imagine him married to her, never! "But your life?" I asked. "My life! My life is loathsome to me now. Don't bother about my life, it could only make you angry." Two weeks later he shot himself. In the inner pocket of his coat they found one of the two postcards I had sent him.

Some of the most passionate poems ever written in Spanish were inspired by this experience.

Meanwhile, Gabriela continued her career as a teacher, and not without hardships. She had been accepted for the Normal School at La Serena and then rejected with no explanation. The reasons behind this rejection were clear; it suffices to imagine the situation of an unmarried woman, without influence, who writes poetry which is considered "advanced" in a provincial Chilean town in the early years of this century.

In spite of all obstacles, however, and by taking cram courses, she managed to get the needed diplomas. She held appointments in the *liceos* of various towns, and at the same time she continued publishing poems and articles in Chilean and foreign publications. About 1913 the pseudonym Gabriela Mistral first appeared. Under this name she took part in the "floral games" organized in 1914 by the city of Santiago. She submitted three sonnets under the general title *Sometos de la muerte* (Sonnets of Death, 1914). The poems told with extraordinary intensity the story of a love and a suicide. The awards ceremony had a festival queen and speeches were made in praise of the winners. Gabriela was awarded the first prize, but her timidity kept her from going forward to accept it, and she watched the ceremony concealed in the audience.

The Prize brought certain advantages, and newspapers and magazines throughout South America began to invite her to write for them. Her poems were attacked by the more conservative critics, but influential admirers came forth and supported her in her career. Prizes of this type are usually quickly forgotten; but, in this case the prize had gone to a true poet, and the award marked the beginning of her literary consecration.

The publication of her first great collection of poems, *Despair*, in 1921, consolidated her fame in South America. In 1922, José Vasconcellos, the politician, critic, and Minister of Education in Mexico, sent her an official invitation to visit his country and to take part in a program of educational reform. The trip also gave a wider circulation to *Despair*.

This trip to Mexico, coming as it did at a time when the revolution was still a vital movement, especially in the educational and artistic field, was of decisive importance in Gabriela Mistral's career. The Mexican revolution proclaimed the end of Mexico's cultural vassalage to Spain and the birth of a new, original, authentically Latin American culture and art.

The poet could sympathize with these aims. Her own disdain of everything Spanish and her insistence on being taken as a native were not far removed from the ideology of this revolution. Gabriela rejected the cosmopolitan mentality, and she declined to follow those Latin Americans who seek, for the most part in vain, integration into European life. Throughout her tireless travels

to many countries, she remained constantly faithful to her land and to the peasants of the Elqui Valley. Here were the surest sources of her inspiration, together with love and motherhood.

The germ of these attitudes already existed in Gabriela, as many early poems show; but it took root and developed in contact with a revolution which had, as one of its principal goals, land reform in America—a revolution whose artists (Diego Rivera, Orozco, Siqueiros, Mariano Azuela) condemned Latin American leanings toward the styles and influences of Europe as symptoms of cultural colonialism.

From Mexico she went to Europe in 1924, returned briefly to Chile, then left again for Europe in 1926 as an official emissary of her government. In 1932 she entered the Chilean diplomatic service, and a few years later by decree of the Chilean government became a career consul. It was then that she began the life of a wanderer, interspersed with only occasional visits to Chile. She lived in Spain, Italy, Portugal, the United States, Brazil, Mexico, Central America, the Antilles, and Puerto Rico. An insatiable nostalgia seemed to drive her to move continuously, and she often speaks of her lack of roots in her poems:

> *País de la ausencia,*
> *extraño país,*
> *mas ligero que ángel*
> *y seña sutil,*
> *color de alga muerta,*
> *color de neblí,*
> *con edad de siempre,*
> *sin edad feliz.*

> Land of absence,
> foreign shore,
> lighter than an angel,
> subtle sign,
> color of dead algae,
> color of mist

as old as forever,
with never an age of joy.

Gabriela Mistral was in Petropolis, Brazil, when she received the news of the Nobel award. According to all witnesses, this honor, going to a Latin American writer for the first time, did not change her habits in any way. Indeed her simplicity was at times disconcerting. Praise could not change her, as the Chileans were to find out when she returned to her country in 1954, toward the end of her life. It was a visit which took on the character of a national apotheosis.

She died in New York on January 11, 1957, after a long illness. As she had requested, she was buried in the cemetery of the village of Montegrande, in the Elqui Valley, where she had lived as a child.

The various versions of her poems as they were published in magazines show Gabriela's practice of tireless revision. She was never fully satisfied with the results of her work. Rarely she might decide that a poem had attained its definitive form. Consequently, although she published a great deal in newspapers and magazines, she stubbornly resisted collecting her poems into a book. It was only on the initiative of a group of New York admirers, who had been introduced to her work by Professor Federico de Onís of Columbia University, that *Despair* was published in 1922.

Gabriela's literary taste in that period explains her style in *Despair*—rough, strong, often exaggerated. A Chilean critic has remarked, "The Hellenic example of France leaves her indifferent. She prefers the Russian novel, chaotic and great; she loves the pantheistic vagueness of Tagore, and she does not have what is called impeccable taste." She herself has listed her favorite books and authors of that period in *Mis Libros* (My Books): the Bible, Dante, St.

Francis of Assisi, the Mexican Amado Nervo: there are no Spanish authors in her list. Someone has quoted her as speaking of "our father, Dante," and denying that term to Cervantes. This indifference to the tradition of the language explains, at least in part, the roughness of style in *Despair*, a roughness almost always redeemed by her originality and expressive power.

The authors listed in "My Books" coincide perfectly with the principle themes of *Despair*: amorous passion, the obsession with death and eternity, God, nature, and peasant life. The most important part of the book is the section entitled *"Dolor"* (Grief), which describes all the steps of her youthful passion, from the first meeting to the forgetfulness after the despair caused by the suicide of her beloved. In love, as in all things, Gabriela Mistral sought the absolute, the eternal. She could not find satisfaction in actual love, with its limitations, and thus the first meeting was stamped with tragedy:

*Llevaba un canto ligero*
*en la boca descuidada,*
*y al mirarme se la ha vuelto*
*grave el canto que entonaba.*
*Miré la senda, la hallé*
*extraña y como soñada.*
*y en el alba de diamante*
*tuve mi cara con lagrimas!*

A blithesome song
came from his carefree lips;
but when he saw me,
his song darkened.
I looked down at the path
and found it strange as in a dream.
And in the diamond dawn
my face was wet with tears!

The awareness of eventual tragedy appears insistently in "Grief," and indeed it is a trait that characterizes all her later poems. In "Extasis" (Ecstasy), describing a conversation with her lover, she says:

*Le hablé de su destino y mi destino,*
*amasi jo fatal de sangre y de lagrimas.*

I spoke to him of his future and of mine,
a fatal paste of blood and tears.

Her poetry is dominated by religious feeling. Through love and the contemplation of nature she is seeking an unchanging essence beyond the material world. Physical love is never an end in itself. After her lover's suicide, her despair was mixed with a strange gladness at possessing him free of all rivals, beyond life. In the first of her "Sonnets of Death" she tells how she will take him from his crypt and lower him into the earth, far from mankind. This she will do, she says, with "a mother's gentleness as she takes her sleeping child." Then she will cover him with earth. The last lines of her poem *"Intima"* (Intimacy) are:

*Me alejaré cantando mis venganzas*
*hermosas,*
*¡porque a ese hondor recóndito la man-*
*onde ningúna*
*bajará a disputarme tú puñado de huesos!*

I shall go then, singing my sweet revenge,
for no woman's hand shall ever reach
that secret depth to dispute your clutch
of bones!

Her later poetry is less intense, less subjective, and she embraces a broader world, a world where nature, people, and history, all have their place. She begins by turning her affection to children: as a schoolteacher she was close to children, and it was they who finally permitted her to free herself from anguish. This theme is already present in *Despair,* but undeveloped and less important than later.

The volume entitled *Ternura* (Tenderness) was published in Madrid in 1924. It includes poems already printed in *Despair,* as well as some new, unpublished ones. The second edition published in Buenos Aires in 1945, included several new poems. Some do not consider it a separate book from *Despair* because several of the poems are the same. In fact, these verses are ones that went unnoticed in the earlier volume, in which *"Dolor"* distracted attention from the rest. Now, published together with new poems, they reveal a clear unity of style.

The language of the poems in *Tenderness* is marked by an originality of tone far removed from that Latin American *fin-de-siècle* rhetoric which still lingered in the love poetry of *Despair,* though *Despair* was much closer to the spoken language of South America. Gabriela Mistral was always highly conscious of the problems of the Latin American writer who must work with a language and a tradition that he only half possesses. In the Argentinian edition of *Tenderness,* the poet appended a "postscript by way of an excuse,": "Once again I am aware of being weighted down by verbal *mestizaje* ('halfbreedism,' so to speak). I belong to that unfortunate group of peoples born without antiquity or Middle Ages, who have innards, faces and expressions in which the anguish resulting from the grafting is evident. I count myself among the children of that twisted thing which is called a 'racial experience,' which might better be called a 'racial violation.' "

In spite of the difference in style, the poetry of *Tenderness* stems directly from that of *Despair.* Frustrated passion leads the poet to desire motherhood; a desire that is also inescapably frustrated, but one of such force that it is capable of creating an imaginary son, who on contact with reality dissolves.

The tenderness she feels toward childhood saves her from the anguish that otherwise would have destroyed her poetic inspiration, a tenderness toward children and, in general, toward all that is purest in existence. She ends up by emerging from the abyss of despair thanks to her love of nature and of others, following by a different path the same evolution as that other great Chilean poet, Pablo Neruda. Both began with romantic, subjective poems of despair and with maturity, both change into poets who write of nature and the history of Latin America, both feeling the obligation to describe the world to their fellowman.

Although Gabriela never interrupted her literary labors, her third book, *Tala*, was not published until 1938 in Buenos Aires; and *Lagar* (*Wine Press*) her fourth and final book, sixteen years later in Santiago del Chile in 1954.

Between *Despair* and the two books of her maturity, her poetry underwent a profound transformation. The intensity and the despair of the love poems disappeared, and in its place there was a new theme which had already appeared in *Tenderness*, the theme of Latin America and its indigenous tradition.

Her style lost its flavor of Spanish-American modern, the heritage from Amado Nervo, Rubén Darío, and Vargas Vila. Now it became obscure, at times hermetic. It did not succeed completely in escaping from the overwhelming, contagious influence of Neruda. Moreover, the rural, archaic character of the language was accentuated. "Not only in the writing," according to one of the notes prefacing *Tala*, "but also in my speech, I use many archaic expressions, the only condition being that they be alive and plain."

The entire first part of *Tala* is devoted to the death of Gabriela's mother, which occurred in 1929. "She made for me a spacious, shaded abode," the poet tells

us; "For me she created a land where I lived for six or seven years, a country beloved because of her death, hateful because of the upheaval of my soul in a deep religious crisis."

There is nothing left in her heart but a great dryness, and she craves absolute annihilation in contrast with her earlier yearning for survival beyond death.

In *"Nocturno de los Tejedores Viejos"* (Nocturne of the Old Weavers) we find a poignantly nostalgic tone. The evocation of her rural childhood when her mother was alive sends her into such a state of melancholy that she prefers to deny the past, to leave her memory "hanging in the doorway." As in the love lyrics of *Despair*, the last of the poems in the group dedicated to the death of her mother is one of both resignation and hope.

In *Wine Press*, the very title suggests a program of rustic verse, we also find many poems on nature, but here the inspiration is leaner, purer, free of the folklore which continually appears in *Tala*. This stylistic cleansing results in a greater subtlety and less of the passion which is the most constant trait of Gabriela's work.

We must bear in mind the message of *"La Otra"* (The Other), the first poem of the book:

> *Una en mi maté:*
> *ya no la amaba.*

> I killed someone within me:
> I had ceased to love her.

This "someone" was the passionate, grieving woman whom she had been and no longer wanted to be. In *"Ultimo Árbol"* (The Last Tree), the epilogue of *Wine Press* and, indeed, of all her work, she looks forward to death and expresses the illusion of having crossed over beyond life and suggests that perhaps she has already begun her second life, where she will find the *"árbol de paradero,"* the tree of rest:

> *Pero tal vez su follaje*
> *ya va arropando mi sueño*
> *y estoy, de muerta, cantando*
> *debajo de él, sin saberlo.*

Sometimes, however, its leaves disturb my sleep, and in my death I sing beneath it, unaware.

Love, the earth, meditation on death, these are the themes that give unity to the poetry of Gabriela Mistral, the only things which endure.

---

Jorge Edwards is in the Chilean foreign service.
Translated by Dale McAdoo.

# THE 1945 PRIZE

## By KJELL STRÖMBERG

THE YEAR 1945 could have been—and should have been—the one in which the name of Paul Valéry was inscribed on the roll of honor of the Nobel Prizes. His candidacy had been put forward at least ten times since 1930, as often by other countries as by the French. In 1933 he was recommended for the award in the most laudatory terms by no less than eighteen of his fellow members of the Académie Française, and by as many professors of literature, representing all the universities of France. Five years before, Henri Bergson had been honored as the result of a similar manifestation, amid worldwide applause. In 1936 an impressive number of Academicians from Belgium and the Netherlands joined the French in once again drawing the attention of their Swedish colleagues to the candidacy of Paul Valéry.

Why did the Academicians always turn a deaf ear? Because the experts they consulted emphasized the exclusive and somewhat hermetic character of Valéry's poetry.

During the war years, the demise of several illustrious members of advanced age had enabled the Swedish Academy to introduce some younger men into its ranks. In 1940 the aging Per Hallström relinquished the post of permanent secretary to a colleague who was then in his prime, the poet and critic Anders Öster-

ling, who at the same time became head of the Nobel Committee of the Prize for Literature. With the help of other influential members of this Committee, including the novelist Sigfrid Siwertz and Professor Fredrik Böök, the *doyen* of literary critics, Österling managed to overcome lingering doubts and unite the votes practically unanimously in favor of Paul Valéry for the 1945 Nobel Prize.

But death snatched away the already chosen laureate before the final scrutiny, and the question arose as to whether to make a posthumous award, as had already been done in 1931 in the case of the great Swedish poet Erik Axel Karlfeldt. In face of the bitter criticism aroused by this proposal, and although this would not have transgressed any of the Nobel Foundation's statutes, the Swedish Academy decided not to make a precedent of it.

In this way, the path was opened to Gabriela Mistral, the Chilean poetess. She had been proposed as a candidate in 1940 by professors and governments of almost all the Latin American countries. Gabriela Mistral was recommended by her Chilean compatriots in strong terms: "Her forceful and high-minded personality makes her the most important moral and intellectual power in ᴛatin America today, and without any possible doubt the greatest woman poet who has ever existed, in other words the greatest po-etess of all time." In December 1945, Gabriela Mistral arrived in Stockholm by boat to receive the insignia of the Nobel Prize from the hands of King Gustavus V. That year, for the first time since 1938, the Prize giving took place with all the traditional ceremony. No less than thir-teen laureates, representing the years 1943, 1944, and 1945, were present at the ceremony. In the name of the Swedish Academy, the excellent poet Hjalmar Gullberg paid tribute to "the little country schoolteacher, this young col-league of Miss Lagerlöf of Maarbacka, who is about to become the spiritual queen of the whole of Latin America."

Gabriela Mistral replied with a re-sounding tribute to Sweden, where she enjoyed herself so much that she stayed for a whole month. She took advantage of this long visit to make her own pilgri-mage to Maarbacka, to Selma Lagerlöf's old house and to put flowers on her grave

in the little cemetery of Emtervik nearby. It was not until nine years later, in 1954, that Gabriela Mistral returned to Chile, which she had left sixteen years before. Meanwhile she was feted in Paris, Rome and New York, and when she arrived at Valparaiso, the principal Chilean seaport, she found the presidential train waiting to take her to Santiago. At every station she was greeted like a queen by the local authorities and in the capital, hung with flags in her honor, people went wild with joy. The poetess was covered with flowers and gold medals: while passing through, she was made an honorary citizen of the town and given the honorary doctorate degree of Santiago University. It was expected that she would be appointed an ambassador somewhere, but she was quite content to be sent as consul general to Los Angeles, where she had just ac-quired a small seaside property. Here she built a villa for her old age with the money from her Nobel Prize.

# Boris Pasternak

## 1958

---

"For his important achievement both in
contemporary lyrical poetry and in the field
of the great Russian epic tradition"

---

*Illustrated by ROYAT*

# ANNOUNCEMENT

## By ANDERS ÖSTERLING

PERMANENT SECRETARY
OF THE SWEDISH ACADEMY

---

THIS year's Nobel Prize for Literature has been awarded by the Swedish Academy to the Soviet Russian writer Boris Pasternak for his notable achievement in both contemporary poetry and the field of the great Russian narrative tradition.

As is well known, Pasternak has sent word that he does not wish to accept the distinction. This refusal, of course, in no way alters the validity of the award. There remains only for the Academy, however, to announce with regret that the presentation of the Prize cannot take place.

On October 25, 1958, two days after the official communication from the Swedish Academy that he had been selected as the Nobel Prize winner in literature, the Russian writer sent the following telegram to the Swedish Academy: "Immensely thankful, touched, proud, astonished, abashed." This telegram was followed, on October 29, by another one with this content: "Considering the meaning this award has been given in the society to which I belong, I must reject this undeserved Prize which has been presented to me. Please do not receive my voluntary rejection with displeasure."

# FIFTY POEMS

## By BORIS PASTERNAK

*Translated by* Lydia Pasternak Slater

---

### FEBRUARY

Black spring! Pick up your pen, and
    weeping,
Of February, in sobs and ink,
Write poems, while the slush in thunder
Is burning in the black of spring.

Through clanking wheels, through
    church bells ringing
A hired cab will take you where
The town has ended, where the showers
Are louder still than ink and tears. ·

Where rooks, like charred pears, from
    the branches
In thousands break away, and sweep
Into the melting snow, instilling
Dry sadness into eyes that weep.

Beneath—the earth is black in puddles,
The wind with croaking screeches throbs,
And—the more randomly, the surer
Poems are forming out of sobs.

---

Why *black* spring? Dirty, thundering slush of the melting snow, black rooks, black ink, black earth in the puddles on the outskirts of the town, 'where the showers are blacker still than ink and tears,' says a different version. Many of the lines have been changed many times in the original. The work of the sun used to be helped in Moscow by giant black cauldrons (like those used for heating asphalt), in which the dirty snow was melted down over bonfires in the streets.

### VENICE

A click of window glass had roused me
Out of my sleep at early dawn.
Beneath me Venice swam in water,
A sodden pretzel made of stone.

It was all quiet now; however,
While still asleep, I heard a cry—
And like a sign that had been silenced
It still disturbed the morning sky.

It hung—a trident of the Scorpion—
Above the sleeping mandolins
And had been uttered by an angry
Insulted woman's voice, maybe.

Now it was silent. To the handle
Its fork was stuck in morning haze.
The Grand Canal, obliquely grinning
Kept looking back—a runaway.

Reality was born of dream-shreds
Far off, among the hired boats.
Like a Venetian woman, Venice
Dived from the bank to glide afloat.

---

Pasternak mentions this poem in his 'Essay in Autobiography' as follows: 'for instance, I was writing the poem "Venice" and the poem "The Railway-station." The town on the water stood before me and the circles and figures-of-eight of its reflections swam and multiplied, swelling like a rusk, dipped in tea. . . . I wanted nothing from myself, from my reader, from the theory of art. I wanted that one poem should contain the town of Venice, and the other—the Brest railway-station.'

[ 223 ]

## SPRING

(fragment 3)

Is it only dirt you notice?
Does the thaw not catch your glance?
As a dapple-gray fine stallion
Does it not through ditches dance?

Is it only birds that chatter
In the blueness of the skies,
Sipping through the straws of sunrays
Lemon liturgies on ice?

Only look, and you will see it:
From the rooftops to the ground
Moscow, all day long, like Kitezh
Lies, in light-blue water drowned.

Why are all the roofs transparent
And the colors crystal-bright?
Bricks like rushes gently swaying,
Mornings rush into the night.

Like a bog the town is swampy
And the scabs of snow are rare.
February, like saturated
Cottonwool in spirits, flares.

This white flame wears out the garrets,
And the air, in the oblique
Interlace of twigs and birds, is
Naked, weightless and unique.

In such days the crowds of people
Knock you down; you are unknown,
Nameless; and your girl is with them,
But you, too, are not alone.

———

Kitezh—a legendary town, sunk in a lake.

## THE SWIFTS

The swifts have no strength any more to
    retain,
To check the light-blue evening coolness.
It bursts from their breasts, from their
    throats, under strain

And flows out of hand in its fullness.

There is not a thing that could stop them,
    up there,
From shrilly, exultedly crying,
Exclaiming: The earth has made off to
    nowhere,
O look! It has vanished—O triumph!

As cauldrons of water are ended in
    steam
When quarrelsome bubbles are rising—
Look—there is no room for the earth
    —from the seam
Of the gorge to the drawn-out horizon!

## THREE VARIANTS

I

When in front of you hangs the day with
    its
Smallest detail—fine or crude—
The intensely hot cracking squirrel-
    sounds
Do not cease in the resinous wood.

The high line of pine-trees stands asleep,
Drinking in and storing strength,
And the wood is peeling and drip by
    drip
Is shedding freckled sweat.

II

From miles of calm the garden sickens,
The stupor of the angered glen
Is more alarming than an evil
Wild storm, a frightful hurricane.

The garden's mouth is dry, and smells
    of
Decay, of nettles, roofing, fear . . .
The cattle's bellowing is closing
Its ranks. A thunderstorm is near.

III

On the bushes grow the tatters
Of disrupted clouds; the garden

Has its mouth full of damp nettles:
Such—the smell of storms and treasures.

Tired shrubs are sick of sighing.
Patches in the sky increase. The
Barefoot blueness has the gait of
Cautious herons in the marshes.

And they gleam, like lips that glisten,
When the hand forgets to wipe them:
Supple willow-switches, oak-leaves,
And the hoofprints by the horsepond.

## ON THE STEAMER

The stir of leaves, the chilly morning air
Were like delirium; half awake
Jaws clamped; the dawn beyond the
    Kama glared
Blue, as the plumage of a drake.

There was a clattering of crockery,
A yawning steward taking stock,
And in the depth, as high as candlesticks,
Within the river, glow-worms flocked.

They hung from streets along the water-
    front,
A scintillating string; it chimed
Three times; the steward with a napkin
    tried
To scratch away some candle grime.

Like a gray rumor, crawling from the
    past,
A mighty epic of the reeds,
With ripples in the beads of street lamps,
    fast
Towards Perm the Kama ran upon a
    breeze.

Choking on waves, and almost drowning,
    but
Still swimming on beyond the boat
A star kept diving and resurfacing
An icon's shining light afloat.

A smell of paint mixed with the galley
    smells,
And on the Kama all along,
The twilight drifted, secrets gathering,
With not a splash it drifted on . . .

A glass in hand, your pupils narrowing
You watched the slips of tongue perform
A whirling play on words, at suppertime,
But were not drawn into their swarm.

You called your partner to old happen-
    ings,
To waves of days before your day,
To plunge in them, a final residue
Of the last drop, and fade away.

The stir of leaves in chilly morning air
Was like delirium; half awake
One yawned; the east beyond the Kama
    glared
Blue, as the plumage of a drake.

And, like a bloodbath now the morning
    came,
A flaming flood of oil—to drown
The steamer's gaslights in the stateroom
    and
The waning street lamps of the town.

## TO THE MEMORY OF DEMON

Used to come in the blue
Of the glacier, at night, from Tamara.
With his wingtips he drew
Where the nightmares should boom,
    where to bar them.

Did not sob, nor entwine
The denuded, the wounded, the ailing . . .
A stone slab has survived
By the Georgian church, at the railings.

Hunchback shadows, distressed,
Did not dance by the fence of the temple.
Soft, about the princess

[ 225 ]

The zurná did not question the lamplight,

But the sparks in his hair
Were aglitter and bursting phosphórus,
And the giant did not hear
The dark Caucasus graying for sorrow.

From the window a step,
'Sleep, beloved,' he swore by the burning
Icy peaks (stroking strands of his wrap),
'As a snowslip I will be returning.'

———

'Demon,' one of Lermontov's great poems:
the Demon, a banished angel, having experienced everything there is on earth, sick
of pleasures and wisdom, of evil and power,
glides sad and lonely over the Caucasian
mountains. He sees a young Georgian
princess, about to be married; falling desperately in love with her, he kills the bride-
groom, and appears to Tamara in her
dreams; unable to resist him, torn by love
and conscience, she flees to a nunnery, but
there, too, the Demon pursues her relentlessly with his sincere and dramatic wooing;
at last she gives in, and dies from the blaze
of his kiss. As he flies away with her soul in
his arms, an angel snatches her from him
and takes her to Heaven, while the Demon
is once again alone. There is a wonderful
line in Lermontov's poem about the stone,
into which a deep hole had been burnt by a
tear, a tear not of human origin. Pasternak
loved Lermontov's poetry and dedicated *My
Sister, Life* to him. 'To the memory of Demon' is a difficult poem, full of vague al-
lusions and unfinished sentences, leaving it
to the reader's imagination to fill in the gaps.
(Occasionally this has led to rather comic
interpretations.) My line 'The denuded, the
wounded, the ailing' reproduces correctly the
vagueness of the Russian sentence, where,
too, the subject is missing: the Demon's
naked arms are meant here, of course. Zurna
is a kind of lute. I apologize for my impossible 'phosphórus,' but I think it is in keeping with the kind of word-somersaults my
brother occasionally performed in his early
poems. For the 'snowslip' I owe yet another
apology; but both the newest Russian Dictionary of Prof Smirnitsky and the Concise
Oxford Dictionary give the word as a legitimate alternative for 'avalanche' (which in its
English corruption of the French word
sounds terrible to me, and quite out of place
in the last line of a lyric poem).

## ABOUT THESE POEMS

On winter pavements I will pound
Them down with glistening glass and
sun,
Will let the ceiling hear their sound,
Damp corners—read them, one by one.

The attic will repeat my themes
And bow to winter with my lines,
And send leapfrogging to the beams
Bad luck and oddities and signs.

Snow will not monthly sweep and fall
And cover up beginnings, ends.
One day I'll suddenly recall:
The sun exists! Will see new trends,

Will see—the world is not the same;
Then, Christmas jackdaw-like will blink
And with a frosty day explain
What we, my love and I, should think.

The window-halves I'll throw apart,
In muffler from the cold to hide,
And call to children in the yard
'What century is it outside?

Who trod a trail towards the door,
The hole blocked up with sleet and snow,
The while I smoked with Byron or
Was having drinks with Edgar Poe?

While known in Darial or hell
Or armory, as friend, I dipped
Like Lermontov's deep thrill, as well
My life in vermouth as my lips.'

———

Darial—a gorge in the Caucasian Mountains, pierced by the river Terek between
vertical walls of rock.

## THE GIRL

From the swing, from the garden, helter-
skelter,
A twig runs up to the glass.

Enormous, close, with a drop of emerald
At the tip of the cluster cast.

The garden is clouded, lost in confusion,
In staggering, teeming fuss.
The dear one, as big as the garden, a
    sister
By nature—a second glass!

But then this twig is brought in a tumbler
And put by the looking-glass;
Which wonders:—Who is it that blurs
    my vision,
From the dull, from the prison-class?

--------

A pier glass is meant. The idea is that
while the branch is still in the garden, and is
part of a tree, it is huge, throbbing and alive;
but, detached from it, it becomes artificial,
dull and hardly noticeable.

Neckline and knuckles and rowlocks— O
    wait,
This could have happened to anyone,
    listen!

This could be used in a song, to beguile.
This then would mean—the ashes of
    lilac,
Richness of dew-drenched and crushed
    camomile,
Bartering lips for a star after twilight.

This    is—embracing    the    firmament;
    strong
Hercules holding it, clasping still fonder.
This then would mean—whole centuries
    long
Fortunes for nightingales' singing to
    squander.

## WET PAINT

'Look out! Wet paint.' My soul was blind,
I have to pay the price,
All marked with stains of calves and
    cheeks
And hands and lips and eyes.

I loved you more than luck or grief
Because with you in sight
The old and yellowed world became
As white as painters' white.

I swear my friend, my gloom—it will
One day still whiter gleam,
Than lampshades, than a bandaged brow,
Than a delirious dream.

## WITH OARS AT REST

A boat is beating in the breast of the
    lake.
Willows hang over, tickling and kissing

## IMITATORS

A boat came in; the cliff was baked;
The noisy boat-chain fell and clanked
    on
The sand—an iron rattle-snake,
A rattling rust among the plankton.

And two got out; and from the cliff
I felt like calling down, 'Forgive me,
But would you kindly throw your-
    selves
Apart or else into the river?

Your miming is without a fault—
Of course the seeker finds the fancied—
But stop this playing with the boat!
Your model on the cliff resents it.'

--------

This poem is a sequel to a love poem
called 'The Model,' but it appears even more
connected with the preceding poem 'With
oars at rest': the lonely poet on the cliff resents the two lovers' imitations of his and his
beloved's past happiness in a boat and on the
shore.

## THUNDERSTORM, INSTANTANEOUS FOREVER

After this the halt and summer
Parted company; and taking
Off his cap at night the thunder
Took a hundred blinding stills.

Lilac clusters faded; plucking
Off an armful of new lightnings,
From the field he tried to throw them
At the mansion in the hills.

And when waves of evil laughter
Rolled along the iron roofing
And, like charcoal on a drawing,
Showers thundered on the fence,

Then the crumbling mind began to
Blink; it seemed it would be floodlit
Even in those distant corners
Where the light is now intense.

———

Halt = railway-halt. The last two lines of
the poem seem illogical, not only in my
translation; or does Pasternak mean that not
only the dark corners, but also those which
already are as light as day would then get
brighter still? I have already commented in
my Introduction on the interesting rhyme
patterns of this poem in the original.

## STARS WERE RACING

Stars were racing; waves were washing
  headlands.
Salt went blind, and tears were slowly
  drying.
Darkened were the bedrooms; thoughts
  were racing,
And the Sphinx was listening to the desert.

Candles swam. It seemed that the
  Colossus'
Blood grew cold; upon his lips was
  spreading

The blue shadow smile of the Sahara.
With the turning tide the night was
  waning.

Sea-breeze from Morocco touched the
  water.
Simooms blew. In snowdrifts snored
  Archangel.
Candles swam; the rough draft of 'The
  Prophet'
Slowly dried, and dawn broke on the
  Ganges.

———

This is one of a series of poems on Pushkin. My brother was fascinated by the fact
that the greatest Russian poet was of African
descent, and Africa, the desert, the Sphinx,
and the foaming sea play a great part in my
brother's imagery. This particular poem
deals with a night in which Pushkin writes
his poem 'The Prophet.' The laconic sentences, giving glimpses of this night in
various parts of the earth, are very effective
in creating an atmosphere of awe and
solemnity, and in implying that Pushkin's
inspiration is a thing of the same order as a
snowstorm, a simoom or the birth of a new
day.

## THE PATIENT'S SWEATER

A life of its own and a long one is led
By this penguin, with nothing to do with
  the breast—
The wingless pullover, the patient's old
  vest;
Now pass it some warmth, move the
  lamp to the bed.

It dreams of the skiing; in darkness it
  poured
From shaftbows, from harness, from
  bodies; it seemed
That Christmas itself also sweated and
  snored;
The walking, the riding—all squeaked
  and all steamed.

A homestead, and horror and bareness
  beside,

Cut-glass in the sideboards, and carpets
   and chests;
The house was inflamed; this attracted
   the fence;
The lights swam in pleurisy, seen from
   outside.

Consumed by the sky, bloated shrubs on
   the way
Were white as a scare and had ice in
   their looks.
The blaze from the kitchen laid down by
   the sleigh
On the snow the enormous hands of the
   cooks.

## YOU ARE DISAPPOINTED?
(from 'The Break,' section 6)

You are disappointed? You thought that
   in peace we
Would part to the sound of a requiem, a
   swan-song?
You counted on grief, with your pupils
   dilated,
Their invincibility trying in tears on?

At the mass from the vaults then the
   murals had crumbled,
By the play on the lips of Sebastian
   shaken. . . .
But tonight to my hatred all seems drawn-
   out dawdling,
What a pity there is not a whip for my
   hatred!

In darkness, collecting its wits instan-
   taneously,
It knew without thinking: it would
   plough it over—
That it's time; that a suicide would be
   superfluous;
That this too would have been of a
   tortoise-like slowness.

## HERE A RIDDLE . . .

Here a riddle has drawn a strange nail-
   mark. To sleep now!
I'll reread, understand with the light of
   the sun,
But until I am wakened, to touch the
   beloved
As I do has been given to none.

How I touched you! So touched were
   you even by the copper
Of my lips, as an audience is touched by
   a play,
And the kiss was like summer; it lingered
   and lingered,
Only later the thunderstorm came.

And I drank in long draughts, like the
   birds, half-unconscious.
The stars trickle slowly through the
   throat to the crop,
While the nightingales roll up their eyes
   in a shudder
From the firmament draining the night
   drop by drop.

## THE ZOO

The zoo lies in the parkland thickets.
We enter and hold out our tickets
To park attendants who surround
The entrance-arch; and look around.

Here through the gates in grotto fashion
We now encounter in succession
Huge limestone mouldings, and beyond—
The wind-swept silver-surfaced pond,
Throughout peculiarly aquiver,
Seized with an abstract fever-shiver.

Now mixing with haphazard sounds,
The puma's distant roar resounds

All through the park; this far-off roaring
Rolls on like thunder skyward soaring,
Exciting, menacing, and loud—
But there is not a single cloud!

With a good-neighborly appearance
The children chat with brown-bear
    parents;
The ringing slabs are damped, one feels,
By thumping bear-cubs' naked heels.

Here, after their exhaustive sunning,
Into their swimming-pool are running
Child, father, mother polar-bear,
In nothing but their underwear.
This trio splashes, roars and pants,
But does not lose the beltless pants,
And no amount of washing betters
The soiled and shaggy trouser-tatters.

Prior to dirtying, the vixen
Will look askance and sniff, then fix on
The chosen spot. Avid and lanky,
Their bark like padlocks sharp and
    clanky,
The wolves are famished in their greed;
Their eyes are full of dried-up heat.
The snapping mother-wolf is stung
By children laughing at her young.

A lioness, the people facing,
Relentlessly the floorboards pacing
And turning on her only track
First there, then back, then there, then
    back,
Is driven by her very raging
When brushing at the iron caging;
The barrier pattern stark and black,
Is moving with her there and back.

The self same iron pattern sends a
Bewildered panther into frenzy.

The same recurring bars again
Will chase a cheetah on a chain.

More lady-like than any lady
The llama looks when promenading;
She curtsies, spits into your face,
And leaps away with haughty grace.

The desert ship observes with sadness
This shallow act of sudden madness.
The camel's reasoning is wise:
'One does not spit in grown-ups' eyes!'
All round him human waves are surging,
And out of them he is emerging
With his steep rounded camel's breast—
A rowing boat upon a crest.

The garb of guinea-fowl and pheasants
Is brightest Sunday-best of peasants
Here tinsel, steel and silver thread
Are glittering as they are shed.

The peacock: seeing is believing.
A shot-silk shawl of blue-black weaving
He wears, a hot and sooty sight.
He walks, mysterious as night,
Extinguished now behind a turning,
Now once again in splendor burning,
Emerging from behind a fence,
His tail like skies at night immense,
With falling stars defying counting,
Of falling stars a playing fountain.

The parrots push away their trough,
They've had a snack and had enough;
They peck one grain and feel they must
Rub clean their beaks in sheer disgust.
Perhaps because of jokes they crack,
Their tongues like coffee-beans are black.
Some of their family have feathers
Like Persian lilac; some, one gathers,
In error classed as birds, instead
Should blossom on a flower bed.

The scarlet-bottomed great attraction,
The gray baboon is seen in action.
The public seem to like him best.
By quiet lunacy possessed
He either lingers, grinning, baring
His teeth, or suddenly, a daring

Gymnast, into the air he flings
And from the lofty branches swings,
Intent on making an impression.
Or on all fours in poodle fashion
He runs around; or in a twist
Scratches his cheekbone with a fist;
Or else again, as monkeys should,
He pesters you and begs for food.

In a thick-sided tub, decaying,
Lie pickled guts—the notice saying
That this is mud with a reptile:
A young Egyptian crocodile.
He does not look at all aggressive;
When grown he may be more impressive.

By-passing on our way some cages,
Stopping at others, thus in stages
We follow notices which lead
Us 'To The Elephants': Indeed
Here is the drowsy mass, ascending
Up to the beams, a cartload standing
Within a warehouse, and a flock
Of hay is whirling on the block.
The monster turns around thereafter,
Dislodging block and hay and rafter,
And sweeping up a cloud of husks
Towards the ceiling and the tusks.
His trunk is knitting lofty stitches
Or shuffles over tiles and twitches;
A hoop has made his ankle sore,
He drags a chain along the floor
And something in this dryness hackles:
Perhaps it is the straw that crackles,
Perhaps his ears, patched up and drab,
Like two old aprons of a cab.

Time to return now to the city,
It's getting late, but what a pity!
There still are wonders by the score:
We've seen a third perhaps, no more.

For the last time the tramlines' rumbling
Is mingling with an eagle's grumbling,
And street-noise drowns the lions' roar
Just once again and then—no more.

## THE ROUNDABOUTS

Maple leaves were rustling softly
And the East grew rosy-red;
On a perfect summer morning
No-one wants to stay in bed.

Up, we pack in joyful hurry
Apples, sandwiches and buns.
When we name our destination
The full tram takes off at once.

At the terminus another
Tram is waiting for the crowds.
In the distance, whitely gleaming,
We can see the roundabouts.

Waist-deep now in fragrant carpets
Of convolvulus we roll
Down the steep ravine, and scramble
Up the fair-bank one and all.

Swings are there, and games for children,
Flags are flying from a mast,
Wooden horses gallop gaily
Round and round, and raise no dust.

Black their manes and long their horse-
      tails.
Tail and forelock, fringe and mane
Now are lifted up and floating,
Lowered gently then again,

Lower with each round, and slower,
Slower, slower, slower, stop.
Whirlwinds hide within the roofwork,
Spinning on a center prop.

Spreading out a spoky circle
The machine is bent with weight;
Strained and burdened the tarpaulin
Tries in vain to fly away.

As if fresh out of a workshop,
Sounding smarter than the click

Of two croquet-balls, the horses
Sharply snap as children kick.

Crowds are milling in the clearing,
Munching, nibbling this and that.
Look—a funny organ-grinder,
Bells adorn his Punch's hat.

Swiftly, deftly, as if sprinkling
Water round him with a mop,
He is shaking all his trinkets,
Lame, he moves without a stop.

And the bells all shake with laughter,
Burst in rapture as they jump,
When the hurdy-gurdy grinder
Drums and knocks and jerks his stump.

Like a trace-horse, neck and body
In an arc he steeply bends,
Shifts about and turns the handle,
Rattles on, and claps his hands.

While submerging manes and fringes,
Lace and ribbon and festoon,
Swings and roundabouts are drowning
In the depth of summer noon.

To the roundabouts to meet them,
Rush and lift them in their flight,
Giddy, spinning, joy-infected,
Lime-grove left and duck-pond right.

Steep the turning from the cross-roads
To the horse-rides. In delight
Children gallop, whirling, greeting
Lime-grove left and duck-pond right.

Vanished now, again returning,
Past they rush and back in sight,
And they keep and keep recurring:
Lime-grove left and duck-pond right.

Whirlwinds fill the roof-umbrella
Spinning on a center-prop;
Slower circles the propeller,
Slower, slower, slower, stop.

## TO A FRIEND

Do I not know that groping in the dim-
    ness
The darkness would have never found
    the sun?
Do I, a freak, feel happiness of millions
No closer than the happiness of some?

Does not the Five-Year Plan assess and
    score us,
And do I with it, too, not rise and fall?
But what am I to do about my thorax,
And that which is the sluggishest of all?

How pointless in the days of the Great-
    Soviet,
Where strongest passions are assigned a
    place,
To have a vacancy left over for the
    poet:
It's dangerous if not an empty space.

## HERE WILL BE ECHOES . . .
### (from 'Waves,' fragment 4)

Here will be echoes in the mountains,
The distant landslides' rumbling boom,
The rocks, the dwellings in the village,
The sorry little inn, the gloom

Of something black beyond the Terek,
Clouds moving heavily. Up there
The day was breaking very slowly;
It dawned, but light was nowhere near.

One sensed the heaviness of darkness
For miles ahead around Kazbek
Wound on the heights: though some
    were trying
To throw the halter from their neck.

As if cemented in an oven,
In the strange substance of a dream,

[ 232 ]

A pot of poisoned food, the region
Of Daghestan there slowly steamed.

Its towering peaks towards us rolling,
All black from top to foot, it strained
To meet our car, if not with clashing
Of daggers, then with pouring rain.

The mountains were preparing trouble.
The handsome giants, fierce and black,
Each one more evil than the other
Were closing down upon our track.

---

In my translation the first line of the
second stanza is not identical with that of
the original: my brother's 'Vladikavkaz' is
such an unwieldy word in English that I
have replaced it with 'Terek,' the name of
the river in that region, not mentioned in
the original. However, this does not change
the meaning of the stanza and is geographi-
cally correct; the same applies to the next
stanza, where I mention the mountain Kas-
bek by name, contrary to the original, where
it is only implied; I think this, too, was
legitimate.

## O HAD I KNOWN . . .

O had I known that thus it happens,
When first I started, that at will
Your lines with blood in them destroy
    you,
Roll up into your throat and kill,

My answer to this kind of joking
Had been a most decisive 'no.'
So distant was the start, so timid
The first approach—what could one
    know?

But older age is Rome, demanding
From actors not a gaudy blend
Of props and reading, but in earnest
A tragedy, with tragic end.

A slave is sent to the arena
When feeling has produced a line.

Then breathing soil and fate take over
And art has done and must resign.

## FROM EARLY DAWN . . .

From early dawn the thirtieth of April
Is given up to children of the town,
And caught in trying on the festive neck-
    lace,
By dusk it only just is settling down.

Like heaps of squashy berries under mus-
    lin
The town emerges out of crimson gauze.
Along the streets the boulevards are
    dragging
Their twilight with them, like a rank of
    dwarves.

The evening world is always eve and
    blossom,
But this one with a sprouting of its
    own
From May-day anniversaries will flower
One day into a commune fully blown.

For long it will remain a day of shifting,
Pre-festive cleaning, fanciful décor,
As once it used to be with Whitsun
    birches
Or pan-Athenian fires long before.

Just so they will go on, conveying actors
To their assembly points; beat sand; just
    so
Pull up towards illuminated ledges
The plywood boards, the crimson calico.

Just so in threes the sailors briskly walk-
    ing
Will skirt the grass in gardens and in
    parks,
The moon at nightfall sink into the pave-
    ments
Like a dead city or a burned-out hearth.

But with each year more splendid and
   more spreading
The taut beginning of the rose will
   bloom,
More clearly grow in health and sense of
   honor,
Sincerity more visibly will loom.

The living folksongs, customs and tradi-
   tions
Will ever spreading, many-petaled lay
Their scent on fields and industries and
   meadows
From early buddings on the first of May,

Until the full fermented risen spirit
Of ripened years will shoot up, like the
   smell
Of humid centifolia. It will have to
Reveal itself, it cannot help but tell.

---

   Pan-Athenian fires: torch processions etc.
during the Athenian festival.


## FALSE ALARM

From early morning—nonsense
With tubs and troughs and strain,
With dampness in the evening
And sunsets in the rain.

Deep sighing of the darkness
And choking swallowed tears,
A railway-engine's calling
Down from the sixteenth verst.

Outside and in the garden
A short fast-darkening day;
Small breakages and losses
In true September way.

In daytime autumn's vastness
Beyond the stream is rent
By wailing in the graveyard,
By anguish and lament.

But when the widow's sobbing
Is carried from the bank,

With all my blood I'm with her
And see my death point-blank.

As every year I see it
Out of the hall downstairs,
The long-delayed approaching
Of this my final year.

Through leaves in yellow terror,
Its way swept clear, I see
That winter from the hillside
Is staring down at me.


## SPRING 1944

This spring the world is new and differ-
   ent;
More lively is the sparrows' riot.
I do not even try expressing it,
How full my soul is and how quiet.

I think and write not as I did before;
And with their song of earth, entire
Freed territories add their mighty voice,
A booming octave in a choir.

The breath of spring within our mother-
   land
Is washing off the winter's traces,
Is washing off black rings and crevices
From tear-worn eyes of Slavic races.

The grass is everywhere in readiness;
And ancient Prague, in murk and
   smother
Still silent, soon will be awakening,
One street more crooked than the other.

Morave and Czech and Jugoslavian
Folk-lores in spring will rise and blos-
   som,
Tearing away the sheet of lawlessness
That winters past have laid across them.

It all will have the haze of fairy tales
Upon it, like the gilt and dazzle

Of ornaments in Boyar chambers and
On the cathedral of St. Basil.

A dreamer and a half-night-ponderer,
Moscow I love with all my power.
Here is the source of all the wonderful
With which the centuries will flower.

## HAMLET

The murmurs ebb; onto the stage I enter.
I am trying, standing in the door,
To discover in the distant echoes
What the coming years may hold in
    store.

The nocturnal darkness with a thousand
Binoculars is focused onto me.
Take away this cup, O Abba, Father,
Everything is possible to thee.

I am fond of this thy stubborn project,
And to play my part I am content.
But another drama is in progress,
And, this once, O let me be exempt.

But the plan of action is determined,
And the end irrevocably sealed.
I am alone; all round me drowns in false-
    hood:
Life is not a walk across a field.

———

The last line of the poem is a Russian
proverb.

## WIND

I am no more but you live on,
And the wind, whining and complaining,
Is shaking house and forest, straining
Not single fir trees one by one
But the whole wood, all trees together,
With all the distance far and wide,
Like sail-less yachts in stormy weather
When moored within a bay they lie.
And this not out of wanton pride

Or fury bent on aimless wronging,
But to provide a lullaby
For you with words of grief and longing.

## INTOXICATION

Under osiers with ivy ingrown
We are trying to hide from bad weather.
I am clasping your arms in my own,
In one cloak we are huddled together.

I was wrong. Not with ivy-leaves bound,
But with hops overgrown is the willow.
Well then, let us spread out on the
    ground
This our cloak as a sheet and a pillow.

———

The Russian title of this poem is a word
which means both 'hops' and 'intoxication.'

## FAIRY TALE

Once, in times forgotten,
In a fairy place,
Through the steppe, a rider
Made his way apace.

While he sped to battle,
Nearing from the dim
Distance, a dark forest
Rose ahead of him.

Something kept repeating,
Seemed his heart to graze:
Tighten up the saddle,
Fear the watering-place.

But he did not listen.
Heeding but his will,
At full speed he bounded
Up the wooded hill;

Rode into a valley,
Turning from the mound,
Galloped through a meadow,
Skirted higher ground;

Reached a gloomy hollow,
Found a trail to trace
Down the woodland pathway
To the watering-place.

Deaf to voice of warning,
And without remorse,
Down the slope, the rider
Led his thirsty horse.

Where the stream grew shallow,
Winding through the glen,
Eerie flames lit up the
Entrance to a den.

\* \* \*

Through thick clouds of crimson
Smoke above the spring,
An uncanny calling
Made the forest ring.

And the rider started,
And with peering eye
Urged his horse in answer
To the haunting cry.

Then he saw the dragon,
And he gripped his lance;
And his horse stood breathless
Fearing to advance.

Thrice around a maiden
Was the serpent wound;
Fire-breathing nostrils
Cast a glare around.

And the dragon's body
Moved his scaly neck,
At her shoulder snaking
Whiplike forth and back.

By that country's custom
Was a young and fair
Captive brought as ransom
To the dragon's lair.

This then was the tribute
That the people owed
To the worm—protection
For a poor abode.

Now the dragon hugged his
Victim in alarm,
And the coils grew tighter
Round her throat and arm.

Skyward looked the horseman
With imploring glance,
And for the impending
Fight he couched his lance.

\* \* \*

Tightly closing eyelids.
Heights and cloudy spheres.
Rivers. Waters. Boulders.
Centuries and years.

Helmetless, the wounded
Lies, his life at stake.
With his hooves the charger
Tramples down the snake.

On the sand, together—
Dragon, steed, and lance;
In a swoon the rider,
The maiden—in a trance.

Blue the sky; soft breezes
Tender noon caress.
Who is she? A lady?
Peasant girl? Princess?

Now in joyous wonder
Cannot cease to weep;
Now again abandoned
To unending sleep.

Now, his strength returning,
Opens up his eyes;
Now anew the wounded
Limp and listless lies.

[ 236 ]

But their hearts are beating.
Waves surge up, die down;
Carry them, and waken,
And in slumber drown.

Tightly closing eyelids.
Heights and cloudy spheres.
Rivers. Waters. Boulders.
Centuries and years.

## WINTER NIGHT

It swept, it swept on all the earth,
At every turning,
A candle on the table flared,
A candle, burning.

Like swarms of midges to a flame
In summer weather,
Snowflakes flew up towards the pane
In flocks together.

Snow molded arrows, rings and stars
The pane adorning.
A candle on the table shone
A candle, burning.

Entangled shadows spread across
The flickering ceiling,
Entangled arms, entangled legs,
And doom, and feeling.

And with a thud against the floor
Two shoes came falling,
And drops of molten candle wax
Like tears were rolling.

And all was lost in snowy mist,
Gray-white and blurring.
A candle on the table stood,
A candle, burning.

The flame was trembling in the draft;
Heat of temptation,
It lifted up two crossing wings
As of an angel.

All February the snow-storm swept.
Each time returning
A candle on the table wept,
A candle burning.

## PARTING

A man is standing in the hall
His house not recognizing.
Her sudden leaving was a flight,
Herself, maybe, surprising.

The chaos reigning in the room
He does not try to master.
His tears and headache hide in gloom
The extent of his disaster.

His ears are ringing all day long
As though he has been drinking.
And why is it that all the time
Of waves he keeps on thinking?

When frosty window-panes blank out
The world of light and motion,
Despair and grief are doubly like
The desert of the ocean.

She was as dear to him, as close
In all her ways and features,
As is the seashore to the wave,
The ocean to the beaches.

As over rushes, after storm
The swell of water surges,
Into the deepness of his soul
Her memory submerges.

In years of strife, in times which were
Unthinkable to live in,
Upon a wave of destiny
To him she had been driven,

Through countless obstacles, and past
All dangers never-ended,
The wave had carried, carried her,
Till close to him she'd landed.

And now, so suddenly, she'd left.
What power overrode them?
The parting will destroy them both,
The grief bone-deep corrode them.

He looks around him. On the floor
In frantic haste she'd scattered
The contents of the cupboard, scraps
Of stuff, her sewing patterns.

He wanders through deserted rooms
And tidies up for hours;
Till darkness falls he folds away
Her things into the drawers;

And pricks his finger on a pin
In her unfinished sewing,
And sees the whole of her again,
And silent tears come flowing.

### BAD DAYS

When Passion week started and Jesus
Came down to the city, that day
Hosannahs burst out at his entry
And palm leaves were strewn in his way.

But days grow more stern and more
    stormy.
No love can men's hardness unbend;
Their    brows    are    contemptuously
    frowning,
And now comes the postscript, the end.

Gray, leaden and heavy, the heavens
Were pressing on treetops and roofs.
The Pharisees, fawning like foxes,
Were secretly searching for proofs.

The lords of the Temple let scoundrels
Pass judgment, and those who at first
Had fervently followed and hailed him,
Now all just as zealously cursed.

The crowd on the neighboring sector
Was looking inside through the gate.

They jostled, intent on the outcome,
Bewildered and willing to wait.

And whispers and rumors were creeping,
Repeating the dominant theme.
The flight into Egypt, his childhood
Already seemed faint as a dream.

And Jesus remembered the desert,
The days in the wilderness spent,
The tempting with power by Satan,
That lofty, majestic descent.

He thought of the wedding at Cana,
The feast and the miracles; and
How once he had walked on the waters
Through mist to a boat, as on land;

The beggarly crowd in a hovel,
The cellar to which he was led;
How, startled, the candle-flame guttered,
When Lazarus rose from the dead . . .

### MARY MAGDALENE (I)

As soon as night descends, we meet.
Remorse my memories releases.
The demons of the past compete,
And draw and tear my heart to pieces,
Sin, vice and madness and deceit,
When I was slave of men's caprices
And when my dwelling was the street.

The deathly silence is not far;
A few more moments only matter,
Which the Inevitable bar.
But at the edge, before they scatter,
In front of thee my life I shatter,
As though an alabaster jar.

O what might not have been my fate
By now, my teacher and my savior,
Did not eternity await
Me at the table, as a late
New victim of my past behavior!

[ 238 ]

But what can sin now mean to me,
And death, and hell, and sulphur
    burning,
When, like a graft onto a tree,
I have—for everyone to see—
Grown into being part of thee
In my immeasurable yearning?

When pressed against my knees I place
Thy precious feet, and weep, despairing,
Perhaps I'm learning to embrace
The cross's rough four-sided face;
And, fainting, all my being sways
Towards thee, thy burial preparing.


## IT IS NOT SEEMLY

It is not seemly to be famous:
Celebrity does not exalt;
There is no need to hoard your writings
And to preserve them in a vault.

To give your all—this is creation,
And not—to deafen and eclipse.
How shameful, when you have no
    meaning,
To be on everybody's lips!

Try not to live as a pretender,
But so to manage your affairs
That you are loved by wide expanses,
And hear the call of future years.

Leave blanks in life, not in your papers,
And do not ever hesitate
To pencil out whole chunks, whole
    chapters
Of your existence, of your fate.

Into obscurity retiring
Try your development to hide,
As autumn mist on early mornings
Conceals the dreaming countryside.

Another, step by step, will follow
The living imprint of your feet;

But you yourself must not distinguish
Your victory from your defeat.

And never for a single moment
Betray your *credo* or pretend,
But be alive—this only matters—
Alive and burning to the end.


## JULY

A ghost is roaming through the building,
And shadows in the attic browse;
Persistently intent on mischief
A goblin roams about the house.

He gets into your way, he fusses,
You hear his footsteps overhead,
He tears the napkin off the table
And creeps in slippers to the bed.

With feet unwiped he rushes headlong
On gusts of draft into the hall
And whirls the curtain, like a dancer,
Towards the ceiling, up the wall.

Who is this silly mischief-maker,
This phantom and this double-face?
He is our guest, our summer lodger,
Who spends with us his holidays.

Our house is taken in possession
By him, while he enjoys a rest.
July, with summer air and thunder—
He is our temporary guest.

July, who scatters from his pockets
The fluff of blow-balls in a cloud,
Who enters through the open window,
Who chatters to himself aloud,

Unkempt, untidy, absent-minded,
Soaked through with smell of dill and
    rye,
With linden-blossom, grass and beet-
    leaves,
The meadow-scented month July.

[ 239 ]

## THE LINDEN AVENUE

A house of unimagined beauty
Is set in parkland, cool and dark;
Gates with an arch; then meadows, hillocks,
And oats and woods beyond the park.

Here, with their crowns each other hiding,
Enormous linden trees engage
In dusky, quiet celebration
Of their two hundred years of age.

And underneath their vaulted branches,
Across the regularly drawn
Symmetric avenues, grow flowers
In flower-beds upon a lawn.

Beneath the trees, on sandy pathways,
Not one bright spot relieves the dark,
Save—like an opening in a tunnel—
The distant entrance of the park.

But now the blossom-time is starting,
The walled-in linden trees reveal
And spread about within their shadow
Their irresistible appeal.

The visitors, in summer clothing,
While walking on the crunchy sand,
Breathe in unfathomable fragrance
Which only bees can understand.

This gripping scent is theme and subject,
Whereas—however well they look—
The flower-beds, the lawn, the garden,
Are but the cover of a book.

The clustered, wax-bespattered flowers
On massive trees, sedate and old,
Lit up by raindrops, burn and sparkle
Above the mansion they enfold.

In the first edition of my book I said in a
note to this poem that I recognized the park
and the estate described as the country place
Molody, where we spent several summers,

## AUTUMN FROST

The morning sun shows like a pillar
Of fire through smoke on frosty days.
As on a faulty snap, it cannot
Make out my features in the haze.

The distant trees will hardly see me
Until the sun at last can break
Out of the fog, and flash triumphant
Upon the meadows by the lake.

A passer-by in mist receding
Is recognized when he has passed.
You walk on hoarfrost-covered pathways
As though on mats of plaited bast.

The frost is covered up in gooseflesh,
The air is false like painted cheeks,
The earth is shivering, and sick of
Breathing potato-stalks for weeks.

## WHEN IT CLEARS UP

The lake is like a giant saucer;
Beyond—a gathering of clouds;
Like stern and dazzling mountain-ranges
Their massif the horizon crowds.

And with the light that swiftly changes,
The landscape never stays the same.
One moment clad in sooty shadows,
The next—the woods are all aflame.

When, after days of rainy weather,
The heavy curtain is withdrawn,

from 1913 onwards, and where Boris first
started to write poetry in earnest. During a
recent visit to Moscow, however, I saw there
some newly discovered variants of this poem,
which prove me to have been wrong: they
actually name the place described as the
former estate of the Princes Trubetskoy,
now a sanatorium of the Academy of
Sciences, where my brother spent some time
after an illness.

How festive is the sky, burst open!
How full of triumph is the lawn!

The wind dies down, the distance
    lightens,
And sunshine spreads upon the grass;
The steaming foliage is translucent
Like figures in stained-window glass.

Thus from the church's narrow windows
In glimmering crowns, on spreading
    wings
Gaze into time in sleepless vigil
Saints, hermits, prophets, angels, kings.

The whole wide world is a cathedral;
I stand inside, the air is calm,
And from afar at times there reaches
My ear the echo of a psalm.

World, Nature, Universe's Essence,
With secret trembling, to the end,
I will thy long and moving service
In tears of happiness attend.


NIGHT

The night proceeds and dwindling
Prepares the day's rebirth.
An airman is ascending
Above the sleeping earth.

And almost disappearing
In cloud, a tiny spark,
He now is like a cross-stitch,
A midget laundry-mark.

Beneath him are strange cities,
And heavy traffic-lanes,
And night-clubs, barracks, stokers,
And railways, stations, trains.

The shadow of his wing-span
Falls heavy on the cloud.
Celestial bodies wander
Around him in a crowd.

And there, with frightful listing
Through emptiness, away
Through unknown solar systems
Revolves the Milky Way.

In limitless expanses
Are headlands burning bright.
In basements and in cellars
The stokers work all night.

And underneath a rooftop
In Paris, maybe Mars
Or Venus sees a notice
About a recent farce.

And maybe in an attic
And under ancient slates
A man sits wakeful, working,
He thinks and broods and waits;

He looks upon the planet,
As if the heavenly spheres
Were part of his entrusted
Nocturnal private cares.

Fight off your sleep: be wakeful,
Work on, keep up your pace,
Keep vigil like the pilot,
Like all the stars in space.

Work on, work on, creator—
To sleep would be a crime—
Eternity's own hostage,
And prisoner of Time.


THE WIND
(4 fragments on Blok: fragment I)

The most influential of nitwits,
The sycophant toadies are used
To rule who should live and be lauded
And who should be dead and abused.

Thus no one, maybe, could be certain,
Is Pushkin a poet or not,
Without their elaborate theses
Explaining to us what is what.

But Blok is, thank Heaven, another,
A different matter for once.
He did not descend from Sinai
And did not accept us as sons.

Eternal and not manufactured,
Renowned not according to plan,
Outside schools and systems, he has not
Been foisted upon us by man.

---

Pasternak, like almost every creative artist, had no patience with the species of crawling literary digesters and commentators who, devoid of any talent of their own, live on (and off) the body of real art and alone have the power to decide on its recognition or destruction. He expresses similar sentiments in his autobiographical essay, in the chapter on Tolstoy's death.

## THE ROAD

Down into the ravine, then forward
Up the embankment to the top,
The ribbon of the road runs snaking
Through wood and field without a stop.

By all the precepts of perspective
Well-surfaced highway windings rush
Among the fields, among the meadows,
Not raising dust, nor stuck in slush.

The peaceful pond nearby ignoring
(On which a duck with ducklings swam)
The road once more is forward soaring
On having crossed and left the dam.

Now—down a slope again it hastens,
Now—on and upwards, in a climb,
As only life, maybe, is meant to
Strain up and onward all the time.

Through thousands of unheard-of
fancies,
Through times and countries, climb and
fall,

Through helps and hindrances it races
Relentless, too, towards a goal;

And this is to have lived your fullest,
Experienced all—at home, abroad—
Just as the landscape now is livened
By twists and turnings of the road.

## IN HOSPITAL

They stood, almost blocking the
pavement,
As though at a window display;
The stretcher was pushed in position,
The ambulance started away.

Past porches and pavements and people
It plunged with its powerful light
Through streets in nocturnal confusion
Deep into the blackness of night.

The headlights picked out single faces,
Militiamen, stretches of street.
The nurse with a smelling-salts phial
Was rocked to and fro on her seat.

A drain gurgled drearily. Cold rain
Was falling. The hospital-clerk
Took out a fresh form of admission
And filled it in, mark upon mark.

They gave him a bed by the entrance;
No room in the ward could be found.
Strong iodine vapor pervaded
The draft from the windows around.

His window framed part of the garden,
And with it a bit of the sky.
The newcomer studied the floorboards,
The ward and the objects nearby,

When, watching the nurse's expression
Of doubt, in her questioning drive,
He suddenly knew this adventure
Would hardly release him alive.

Then, grateful, he turned to the window
Behind which the wall, further down,
Was breathing like smoldering tinder,
Lit up by the glare of the town.

There, far off the city was glowing
All crimson-aflame; in its swell
A maple-branch, ragged, was bowing
To bid him a silent farewell.

'O Lord,' he was thinking, 'how perfect
Thy works are, how perfect and right;
The walls and the beds and the people,
This death-night, the city at night!

'I drink up a sedative potion,
And weeping, my handkerchief trace.
O Father, the tears of emotion
Prevent me from seeing thy face.

'Dim light scarcely touches my bedstead.
It gives me such comfort to drift
And feel that my life and my lot are
Thy priceless and wonderful gift.

'While dying in fading surroundings
I feel how thy hands are ablaze,
The hands that have made me and hold
      me
And hide like a ring in a case.'

### AFTER THE INTERVAL

About three months ago, when first
Upon our open, unprotected
And freezing garden snowstorms burst
In sudden fury, I reflected

That I would shut myself away
And in seclusion write a section
Of winter poems, day by day,
To supplement my spring collection.

But nonsense piled up mountain-high,
Like snow-drifts hindering and stifling
And half the winter had gone by,
Against all hopes, in petty trifling.

I understood, alas, too late
Why winter—while the snow was falling,
Piercing the darkness with its flakes—
From outside at my house was calling;

And while with numb white-frozen lips
It whispered, urging me to hurry,
I sharpened pencils, played with clips,
Made feeble jokes and did not worry.

While at my desk I dawdled on
By lamp-light on an early morning,
The winter had appeared and gone—
A wasted and unheeded warning.

### FIRST SNOW

Outside the snowstorm spins, and hides
The world beneath a pall.
Snowed under are the paper-girl,
The papers and the stall.

Quite often our experience
Has led us to believe
That snow falls out of reticence,
In order to deceive.

Concealing unrepentantly
And trimming you in white,
How often he has brought you home
Into the town at night!

While snowflakes blind and blanket out
The distance more and more,
A tipsy shadow gropes his way
And staggers to the door.

And then he enters hastily . . .
Again, for all I know,
Someone has something sinful to
Conceal in all this snow!

### PLOUGHING TIME

What is the matter with the landscape?
Familiar landmarks are not there.

Ploughed fields, like squares upon a
    chessboard,
Today are scattered everywhere.

The newly-harrowed vast expanses
So evenly are spread about,
As though the valley had been spring-
    cleaned
Or else the mountains flattened out.

And that same day, in one endeavor,
Outside the furrows every tree
Bursts into leaf, light green and downy,
And stretches skyward, tall and free.

No speck of dust on the new maples,
And colors nowhere are as clean
As is the light-gray of the ploughland
And as the silver-birch's green.

## AFTER THE STORM

The air is full of after-thunder freshness,
And everything rejoices and revives.
With the whole outburst of its purple
    clusters
The lilac drinks the air of paradise.

The gutters overflow; the change of
    weather
Makes all you see appear alive and new.
Meanwhile the shades of sky are growing
    lighter,
Beyond the blackest cloud the height is
    blue.

An artist's hand, with mastery still
    greater
Wipes dirt and dust off objects in his
    path.
Reality and life, the past and present,
Emerge transformed out of his color-
    bath.

The memory of over half a lifetime
Like swiftly passing thunder dies away.

The century is no more under wardship:
High time to let the future have its say.

It is not revolutions and upheavals
That clear the road to new and better
    days,
But revelations, lavishness and torments
Of someone's soul, inspired and ablaze.

## UNIQUE DAYS

How I remember solstice days
Through many winters long completed!
Each unrepeatable, unique,
And each one countless times repeated.

Of all these days, these only days,
When one rejoiced in the impression
That time had stopped, there grew in
    years
An unforgettable succession.

Each one of them I can evoke.
The year is to midwinter moving,
The roofs are dripping, roads are soaked,
And on the ice the sun is brooding.

Then lovers hastily are drawn
To one another, vague and dreaming,
And in the heat, upon a tree
The sweating nesting-box is steaming.

And sleepy clock-hands laze away
The clockface wearily ascending.
Eternal, endless is the day,
And the embrace is never-ending.

## GOD'S WORLD

Thin as hair are the shadows of sunset
When they follow drawn-out every tree.
On the road through the forest the post-
    girl
Hands a parcel and letters to me.

By the trail of the cats and the foxes,
By the foxes' and by the cats' trail,

I return with a bundle of letters
To the house where my joy will prevail.

Countries, continents, isthmuses, frontiers,
Lakes and mountains, discussions and
    news,
Children, grown-ups, old folk, adoles-
    cents,
Appreciations, reports and reviews.

O respected and masculine letters!
All of you, none excepted, have brought

A display of intelligent logic
Underneath a dry statement of thought.

Precious, treasured epistles of women!
Why, I also fell down from a cloud.
And eternally now and for ever
To be yours I have solemnly vowed.

Well and you, stamp-collectors, if even
Only one fleeting moment you had
Among us, what a marvelous present
You would find in my sorrowful stead!

# I REMEMBER

## SKETCH FOR AN AUTOBIOGRAPHY

## By BORIS PASTERNAK

*Translated, with notes, by* David Magarshack

---

### 1

In *Safe Conduct,* an autobiographical essay written in the twenties, I have analyzed the circumstances that made me what I am. Unfortunately, the book is spoiled by unnecessary mannerism, the common fault of those years.

In the present sketch I shall not be able to avoid retelling certain things, though I shall do my best not to repeat myself.

### 2

I was born in Moscow on January 29, 1890 (O.S.), in Lyzhin's house, opposite the Theological Seminary in Oruzheyny [Arsenal] Lane. I find it difficult to explain, but I can still remember something of my walks in the autumn with my wet nurse in the seminary park. The soaking wet paths under heaps of fallen leaves, the ponds, the artificial hillocks, and the painted iron railings of the seminary, the games and fights of laughing, boisterous seminarists during the longer breaks.

Straight across the gates of the seminary stood a two-storied brick house with a yard for cabbies and our apartment over the gateway above the arc of its vaulted ceiling.

### 3

My sensations of infancy are made up of the elements of panic and ecstasy. Their colorful fairyland atmosphere stems from two central images which united everything and dominated everything: the image of the stuffed bears in the carriage establishments in Coachmaker's Yard, and the image of P. P. Konchalovsky, the broad-shouldered, hirsute, low-voiced, good-natured giant of a publisher, his family, and the pencil, pen, and India ink drawings of Serov, Vrubel, the Vasnetsov father and brothers, which hung in the rooms of his apartment.

The district itself was rather disreputable. It included such slums as Tverskie and Yamskie Streets, the Truba, and the Tsvetnoy lanes. Again and again I found myself dragged away by the hand. Some things were not good for me to know, others were not good for me to hear. But my nurses and nannies could not bear solitude, and then we found ourselves surrounded by a motley company. At midday, too, the mounted police were drilled on the square of the Znamensky barracks.

From this intercourse with beggars and women pilgrims, from this neighboring world of the world's spurned and rejected and the things that happened to them and their hysterical wailings on the near-by boulevards, I acquired much too early—and retained for the rest of my life—a feeling of terrifying and breathtaking pity for woman and an even more unendurable pity for my parents, who would die before me and whom I would have to save from the tortures of hell by doing something unimaginably wonderful, something that had never, never been done before.

### 4

When I was three, we moved to a government apartment in the School of Painting, Sculpture, and Architecture in Myasnitsky Street, opposite the General Post Office. The apartment was in a wing of the house, inside the yard and standing apart from the main building.

The main building, which was old and beautiful, was remarkable in many ways. It had been spared by the fire of Moscow in 1812. A century earlier, in the reign of Catherine the Great, the house was the secret meeting place of a Masonic lodge. The house was at the corner of Myasnitsky Street and Yushkov Lane, and its curved façade had a semicircular balcony with columns. The spacious balcony formed a nichelike recess in the wall, communicating by a door with the assembly hall. From it one could look down the whole length of Myasnitsky Street, disappearing in the distance in the direction of the railway stations.

From this balcony the people who lived in the house watched in 1894 the funeral procession of Alexander III, and afterwards, two years later, separate scenes of the coronation celebrations at the beginning of the reign of Nicholas II.

Students and teachers were there. My mother held me by the hand in the crowd at the balcony railings. At her feet was a sheer drop into an abyss. At the bottom of the abyss, the empty street, strewn with sand, was in a state of suspended animation. The military bustled about rapping out orders, which, however, did not reach the ears of the spectators on the balcony, as though the dead silence of the thousands of people holding their breath, pushed back to the very edge of the pavements by the drawn-up lines of soldiers, absorbed every sound as completely as water is absorbed by sand. Church bells began ringing slowly and dolefully. A sea of hands rose like a wave in the distance which rolled on and on, farther and farther. Moscow was taking off her hat and crossing herself. To the accompaniment of the funereal ringing of church bells, which seemed to come from every direction, the head of an endless procession hove into sight: troops, clergy, black-caparisoned, plumed horses, a catafalque of fabulous splendor, heralds in strange costumes of another age. And the procession marched on and on and the façades of the buildings were covered in strip after strip of crepe and dressed all over in black cloth, and the mourning flags flew droopingly at half-mast.

The spirit of pageantry was inseparable from the school, which was under the authority of the Ministry of the Imperial Court. The Grand Duke Sergey Alexandrovich was its patron, and he was present at its speech-days and exhibitions. The Grand Duke was lean and lanky. Covering their sketchbooks with their hats, my father and Serov used to draw caricatures of him at the receptions given by the Golitzins and the Yakunchikovs, whenever he was present.

### 5

A small house stood in the yard, opposite the gate, leading into a small garden with very old trees among the outbuildings, sheds, and stables. Downstairs, in the basement, hot luncheons were served for the students. The staircase was always full of the fumes of fat in which the pasties and cutlets were fried. The door of our apartment was on the next landing. The registrar of the art school lived on the story above.

This is what I read fifty years later, quite recently, many years after the Soviet regime had come into being, in N. S. Rodionov's book, *Moscow in the Life and Work of L. N. Tolstoy,* on page 125, in a reference to the year 1894:

"On November 23rd, Tolstoy and his daughters paid a visit to the painter L. O. Pasternak at the School of Painting, Sculpture, and Architecture, where Pasternak was the Principal. They went to a concert in which Pasternak's wife and the Professors of the Conservatory, the violinist I. V. Grzhimali and the cellist A. A. Brandukov, took part."

Here everything is correct except for one small error. The Principal of the School was not my father but Prince Lvov.

I remember very well the night described by Rodionov. I was awakened in the middle of it by a sweetly poignant pain, more violent than any I had ever experienced before. I cried out and burst into tears from fear and anguish. But the music drowned my cries and it was only after the movement of the trio that had awakened me had come to an end that I was heard. The curtain behind which I was lying and which divided the room into two was parted. My mother appeared, bent over me, and quickly calmed me. They must have taken me out to show to our visitors, or I may have seen our drawing room through the frame of the open door. It was full of tobacco smoke. The candles flickered, blinking like eyelashes, just as though the

tobacco smoke had got into their eyes. They lit up brightly the polished red wood of the violin and cello. The grand piano loomed black. The frock coats of the men loomed black. The women emerged from dresses up to their shoulders, like birthday flowers out of flower baskets. The white hair of two or three old men blended with the rings of tobacco smoke. Afterwards I got to know one of them very well, and saw him often. It was the artist N. N. Ge. The image of the other passed through my whole life, as through the life of most people, particularly because my father illustrated his books, went to see him, revered him, and because our whole house was imbued with his spirit. It was Leo Nikolayevich [Tolstoy]. . . .

Why then did I cry and why can I still remember my suffering so clearly? I was accustomed to the sound of the piano in the house; my mother played it like a true artist. The voice of the grand piano seemed to me an integral part of music itself. But the timbres of stringed instruments, especially in their chamber music ensemble, were foreign to me, and they alarmed me like real cries for help and tidings of disaster coming from outside through the small ventilation window.

That, I believe, was the winter of two deaths: the deaths of Anton Rubinstein and of Tchaikovsky.* I suppose they must have been playing the famous Tchaikovsky trio.†

That night stood like a landmark between the unconscious state of infancy and my subsequent childhood. With it my memory became active and my consciousness was set into motion, hencefor-

---

* Actually, Tchaikovsky died in November, 1893, and Rubinstein in November, 1894.
† The trio "in memory of a great artist" (1881–82) composed to commemorate the death of Nikolay Rubinstein.

ward without any great gaps and inter-ruptions, as with grown-up people.

In spring the shows of the Society for Traveling Art Exhibitions, the so-called *Peredvizhniki,* were held in the rooms of the Moscow Art School. The exhibition was usually brought from Petersburg in winter. The crates with the paintings were put in the sheds which stood in a line behind our house opposite our windows. Before Easter they were brought out into the yard and unpacked in the open before the doors of the sheds. The caretakers of the school opened the crates, unscrewed the pictures in their heavy frames from the top and bottom of the crates, and two men carried each pic-ture across the yard to the exhibition. Perching on the window sills, we watched them eagerly. It was in this way that there passed before our eyes the most celebrated canvases of Repin, Myasoyedov, Makovsky, Surikov, and Polenov, a good half of the reserves of paintings of our present-day picture gal-leries and State storage depots.

The artists who were close to my father, as well as my father himself, exhibited at the traveling art shows only at the beginning and not for long. Soon Serov, Levitan, Korovin, Vrubel, Ivanov, my father, and others formed a new so-ciety, the Union of Russian Artists.

Toward the end of the nineties the sculptor Pavel Trubetskoy, who had spent all his life in Italy, arrived in Mos-cow. He was given a new studio with a glass roof. It was built against the wall of our house and one of its sides blocked up our kitchen window. Before, the window looked onto the garden, but now it faced Trubetskoy's sculpture studio. From the kitchen we watched his modeling and the work of his caster Robecchi as well as his models, including the small children and ballerinas who posed for him, and the carriages drawn by pairs of horses and the mounted Cossacks who rode in freely

through the wide gates of the lofty studio.

It was from the same kitchen that my father's remarkable illustrations to Tol-stoy's *Resurrection* were dispatched. After its final revision, the novel was serialized in the journal *Niva* by the Petersburg publisher Fyodor Marx. The work was feverish. I remember how pressed for time Father was. The issues of the journal came out regularly without delay. One had to be in time for each issue.

Tolstoy kept back the proofs, revising them again and again. There was the risk that the illustrations of the original text would be at variance with the corrections subsequently introduced into it. But my father's sketches came from the same source whence the author obtained his observations, the courtroom, the transit prison,* the country, the railway. It was the reservoir of living details, the identi-cal realistic presentation of ideas, that saved him from the danger of digressing from the spirit of the original.

In view of the urgency of the matter, special precautions were taken to prevent any delay in the sending of the illustra-tions. The services of the conductors of the express trains of the Nikolayevsky railway were enlisted. My childish imagi-nation was struck by the sight of a train conductor in his formal railway uniform, standing waiting at the door of the kitchen as if he were standing on a rail-way platform at the door of the compart-ment of a train that was just about to leave the station.

Joiner's glue was boiling on the stove. The illustrations were hurriedly wiped dry, fixed, glued on pieces of cardboard, rolled up, tied up. The parcels, once ready, were sealed with sealing wax and handed to the conductor.

---

* For prisoners going to Siberia.

## SCRIABIN

### 1

The first two decades of my life differ greatly from one another. In the nineties Moscow still preserved its old appearance of a fantastically picturesque provincial town with legendary features of the Third Rome or of the ancient capital city one reads about in the Russian epic poems, and with all the splendor of her famous "forty times forty" churches. Old customs were still observed. In the autumn, in Yushkov Lane, adjoining the yard of the School of Painting, in the yard of the Church of St. Florus and St. Laurus, who were regarded as the protectors of horse breeding, a service for the consecration of the horses took place, and the whole lane up to the gates of the school overflowed with horses and their drivers and stableboys, just as at a horse fair.

At the beginning of the new century everything was transformed in my memory as though by the wave of a magic wand. Moscow was seized by the business fever of the great capital cities. Big apartment houses were being rapidly put up with a view to getting larger returns on the invested capital. Brick giants, which seemed to grow imperceptibly, rose up to the very sky in all the streets. Together with them, Moscow, outstripping Petersburg, inaugurated a new Russian art, the art of a great city, a young, modern, new art.

### 2

The fever of the nineties had an effect on the School of Painting, too. The government grants were not sufficient for its maintenance. Businessmen were therefore entrusted with the raising of additional funds to cover its budget. It was decided to build on the land belonging to the school large apartment houses for letting to private persons, and to erect in the middle of the property, on the site of the former garden, glass exhibition galleries, also for letting. At the end of the 1890's began the work of pulling down the sheds and the cottages in the yard, and deep trenches were dug in the garden in place of its uprooted trees. The trenches became filled with water, and, as in ponds, drowned rats floated on the surface and frogs jumped and dived into them from the ground. Our house was also earmarked for demolition.

In winter a new apartment was fitted out for us in the main building of the school. It consisted of two or three classrooms and lecture rooms. We moved into it in 1901. As our new apartment, in which we spent ten years, had been made up of two large rooms one of which had been circular and the other of an even more fanciful form, our storeroom and bathroom were in the shape of a crescent, our kitchen was oval-shaped, and our dining room had a semicircular space cut out of it. Behind our front door we could always hear a subdued hubbub of voices from the corridors and the studios of the school, and from the last room on the other end we could hear the lectures on heating methods by Professor Chaplygin in the architecture class.

In the preceding years, in our old apartment, before I went to school, I was taught either by my mother or by some private tutor. At one time I was being prepared for entering the Petropavlovsk Grammar School and I studied all the subjects of the curriculum of the preparatory class in German.*

---

* The Petropavlovsk school was attached to the Moscow Lutheran Church and was meant for the children of the German community, but it was popular also with many Russian families.

Of all these teachers, whom I remember with gratitude, I shall mention my first teacher, Yekaterina Ivanovna Baratynskaya, a writer of children's stories and a translator of children's books from the English. She taught me reading and writing, elementary arithmetic and French, starting from the very beginning, that is, how to sit on a chair and how to hold a pen in my hand. I was taken to her for my lessons in the furnished bed-sitting room she lived in. The room was dark. It was filled from top to bottom with books. It exuded an atmosphere of cleanliness and severity and it smelled of boiled milk and roasted coffee. On the other side of the window, covered with a lace curtain, grimy, grayish-cream flakes of snow were falling, looking like stitches of knitting. It distracted me and I did not give the right answers to Yekaterina Ivanovna, who was talking to me in French. At the end of the lesson, Yekaterina Ivanovna wiped my pen on the inside of her blouse, and, after waiting for those who were to take me home, dismissed me.

In 1901 I joined the second class of the Fifth Moscow Grammar School, which remained a classical school after Vannovsky's reforms, and which in addition to the several newly introduced subjects, including natural sciences, retained classical Greek in the curriculum.

3

In the spring of 1903 my father rented a house in the country at Obolenskoye, near Malo-Yaroslavets, on the Bryansk (now Kiev) railway line. Our country neighbor turned out to be Scriabin. At that time we had not yet become acquainted with the Scriabins.

Our country houses stood on a little hill along the edge of a wood at some distance from one another. We arrived in the country, as usual, in the early morning. The sunlight broke up into dancing fragments of light as it came through the foliage of the woodland trees that hung low over our house. The large bales of matting were being unpacked and ripped open. Bedding, provisions, pails, and frying pans were taken out of the bales. I ran off into the wood.

Dear Lord, what a morning! The things it was full of! The sunlight streamed through it in every direction; the moving shade of the trees kept setting its cap now at one angle and now at another; on the upraised branches the birds burst into a chorus of chirping and twittering which always seems to be quite unexpected and which one can never get used to. It is loud and impetuous at first and dies down gradually, resembling in its passionate and repetitive persistence the trees of a thick forest that gradually fades away into the distance. And just as the light and shade followed upon each other in the forest and the birds sang and flew from one branch to another, so the passages and pieces of the Third Symphony or the *Divine Poem*, which was being composed on the piano in the country house next door, resounded and reverberated through it.

Lord, what music it was! The symphony was continually crumbling and tumbling like a city under artillery fire, and was all the time growing and being built up out of debris and wreckage. It was brimful of ideas minutely worked out to a point that was indistinguishable from frenzy, and at the same time as new as the forest, breathing life and freshness and, indeed, arrayed, surely, in the morning of the spring foliage of 1903 and not of 1803. And just as there was not a single leaf in that forest made of crimped paper or painted tin, so there was nothing in the symphony that was falsely profound or rhetorically respectable, "as in Beethoven," "as in Glinka," "like Ivan

Ivanovich," "like Princess Maria Alexevna"; but the tragic force of the composition in the process of creation put out its tongue triumphantly at everything that was decrepit and generally accepted and majestically obtuse, and was bold to a point of frenzy, to a point of mischievousness, playfully elemental, and free like a fallen angel.

It might be thought that a man composing such music would understand what sort of man he was and, after his work, would be lucidly serene and restfully calm, like God resting from His labors on the seventh day. And so he was.

He often went for walks with my father on the Warsaw highway, which cut across the district. Sometimes I accompanied them. Having started to run, Scriabin loved to go on running and skipping as though with his own momentum, just like a stone rebounding on the surface of the water, just as though had he run a little faster he would have become detached from the earth and sailed in the air. In general, he cultivated various forms of inspired lightness and unencumbered motion on the borderline of flight. It is to a phenomenon of that kind that one has to attribute his charming elegance, the air of fine breeding with which he avoided appearing seriousminded in society and tried to seem lighthearted and superficial. All the more striking were his paradoxes during the country walks in Obolenskoye.

He argued with Father about life, about art, about good and evil, he attacked Tolstoy, preached the Superman, amorality, Nietzscheism. They agreed about one thing—about the nature and the tasks of craftsmanship. About everything else they were poles apart.

I was twelve. Half of their arguments I did not understand. But Scriabin won me by the freshness of his spirit. I loved him to distraction. Without attempting to

grasp the essence of his views, I was always on his side. Soon he left for Switzerland, where he spent six years.

That autumn our return to town was delayed because I had met with an accident. Father had planned a painting, *Night Watch*. In it were depicted girls from the village of Bocharovo who, riding at full speed at sunset, were driving a drove of horses to the water meadows at the bottom of our hill. One day I insisted on accompanying him, and, as I took a jump over a wide stream, I was thrown by my horse, which was tearing along at breakneck speed, and broke a leg which did not knit well, one of my legs remaining shorter than the other, which later on exempted me from military service at each draft.

Even earlier, before the summer in Obolenskoye, I used to strum on the piano a little and made some feeble attempts to compose something of my own. Now, under the stimulus of my adoration of Scriabin, the craving for improvisation and composition flared up in me and grew into a passion. After that autumn I devoted the following six years of my life, all the years I spent at school, to a thorough study of the theory of composition, first under the supervision of the most excellent Y. D. Engel, a wellknown musicologist and music critic of those days, and later under the guidance of Professor R. M. Glier.

No one had any doubts about my future. My future had been settled, my path in life correctly chosen. I was meant to be a musician, everything was forgiven me for the sake of music, every shape and form of ingratitude and rudeness toward my elders I was not fit to hold a candle to, stubbornness, disobedience, negligence, and strangeness of behavior. Even at school when, during the Greek and math lessons, I was caught trying to solve some fugue or counterpoint problem and, asked to answer a question from my place, stood like a fool and did not know what to say, my classmates did their best to shield me and my teachers forgave me everything. And in spite of that, I gave up music.

I gave it up at a time when I had a right to be pleased with myself, when everyone around was congratulating me. My god and idol had returned from Switzerland with *Ecstasy* and his last works. Moscow celebrated his return and his victories. At the height of his triumphs, I had the effrontery to go and see him and play my compositions to him. His reception exceeded my expectations. Scriabin listened, encouraged, inspired, blessed.

But no one knew of my secret trouble and, were I to tell anyone about it, no one would have believed me. While the advance I made as a composer was pretty good, I was quite hopeless in a practical sense. I could scarcely play the piano and could not even read music with any fluency. I had to do it almost bar by bar. This discrepancy between the far from easy musical idea and its lagging technical support, transformed nature's gift, which could have served as a source of joy, into an object of constant torment which in the end I could no longer endure.

How was such a discrepancy possible? At its root lay something inadmissible, something that called for retribution, an unpardonable adolescent arrogance, a half-educated person's nihilistic disregard of everything that appears to him to be easily attainable and accessible. I despised everything uncreative, any kind of hack work, being conceited enough to imagine that I was a judge in these matters. In *real* life, I thought, everything must be a miracle, everything must be predestined from above, nothing must be deliberately designed or planned, nothing must be done to follow one's own fancies.

That was the negative side of Scriabin's influence, which in everything else became decisive for me. His egocentric nature was appropriate and justified only in his case. The seeds of his views, childishly misinterpreted, fell on favorable ground.

As it is, I was from early childhood inclined to mysticism and superstition and seized by a craving for the providential. Almost since the night described by Rodionov, I had believed in the existence of a higher heroic world, which must be served rapturously, though it might bring suffering. How many times at the age of six, seven, and eight was I near suicide!

I suspected all sorts of mysteries and deceptions around me. There was no absurdity in which I did not believe. At the dawn of life, when such idiocies are conceivable, perhaps because of the memories of the baby smocks in which I was arrayed still earlier, I imagined that at some time before I was born I had been a little girl and that I had to bring back that fascinating and delightful actuality by tightening my belt till I felt like fainting. And sometimes I imagined that I was not the son of my parents, but an adopted foundling.

In my misfortunes with music, too, it was the indirect, imaginary causes that were operative, such as belief in chance, expectation of signs and portents from above. I did not have perfect pitch; the faculty of recognizing the pitch of any arbitrarily taken note was an accomplishment that was absolutely unnecessary to me in my work. But the absence of this faculty depressed and humiliated me. I saw in it the proof that my music was against the will of fate and heaven. Under such a multitude of blows my spirits drooped and I lost heart.

Music, the beloved world of my labors, hopes, and anxieties for six years, I plucked out of myself and I parted from it as one parts from something most precious. For some time I kept up my improvisations on the piano from force of habit that was gradually growing weaker and weaker. But later on I decided to take stronger measures to enforce my abstinence. I stopped touching the piano, gave up going to concerts, and avoided meetings with musicians.

### 4

Scriabin's argument about the Superman was a characteristically Russian craving for the extraordinary. Actually, not only must music be supermusic to mean anything, but everything in the world must excel itself to be itself. Man, man's activity, must include an element of infinity which lends shape and style to a thing.

In view of my present backwardness so far as music is concerned and my atrophied and entirely extinct connections with it, all that is left of my memories of Scriabin, who meant so much to me and who was as important to me as my daily bread, is the Scriabin of the middle period, approximately from the Third to the Fifth Sonata.

The flashing harmonies of his *Prometheus* and his last works seem to me only the evidence of his genius and not daily food for the soul, and I am not in need of this evidence, because I believed in him without any proofs.

People on the verge of death, Andrey Bely, Khlebnikov, and some others, became absorbed before dying in the quest for new means of expression, in a pipe dream about a new language, they fumbled and rummaged about for its syllables, its vowels, and its consonants.

I could never understand those quests. In my opinion, the most striking discoveries are made when an artist is so full of his subject that it gives him no time to think about it and in his haste he

proclaims his new word in the old language, without bothering his head as to whether it is new or old.

So, in the old language of Mozart and Field, Chopin said so much that was astonishingly new in music that it seemed to be its second beginning.

So Scriabin also, with the means that were at the disposal of his predecessors, renewed our sensation of music from its very foundation at the very beginning of his career. In the Studies of Opus 8 and in his Preludes of Opus 11, everything is already contemporary, everything is full of those inner correspondences, accessible to music, with the surrounding external world, with the way in which people of those days lived, thought, felt, traveled, and dressed.

No sooner do the melodies of those works begin than tears start to your eyes and they flow from the corners of your eyes along your cheeks down to the corners of your lips. The melodies, mingling with the tears, run straight along your nerves to your heart, and you weep not because you feel sad, but because the way to your heart has been found so unerringly and so shrewdly.

And all of a sudden in the course of the melody an answer or an objection to it bursts in in another voice, a higher and more feminine voice, in another and simpler conversational tone, an unexpected dispute, a discord that is instantly settled, and a note of a shattering naturalness is introduced into the work, the sort of naturalness that decides everything in a work of art.

Art is full of things that everyone knows about, of generally acknowledged truths. Although everyone is free to use them, the generally accepted principles have to wait a long time before they find an application. A generally acknowledged truth must wait for a rare piece of luck, a piece of luck that smiles upon it only once in a hundred years, before it can find any application. Such a piece of luck was Scriabin. Just as Dostoevsky is not only a novelist and just as Blok is not only a poet, so Scriabin is not only a composer, but an occasion for perpetual congratulations, a personified festival and triumph of Russian culture.

## THE NINETEEN HUNDREDS

### 1

In response to the student demonstrations following the manifesto of the 17th of October, [1905], the rabble from Okhotny Ryad, the game market of Moscow, got out of hand, and began to smash up the higher educational institutions, the University and the Technological College. The School of Painting was also in danger of being attacked. On the instructions of the Principal of the School, heaps of cobblestones were piled up on the landings of the main staircase and hoses were screwed into the fire-cocks to repel any attack by the looters.

Demonstrators turned in to the school from the processions in the neighboring streets, held meetings in the Assembly Hall, took possession of rooms, went out on the balcony, and made speeches to those who stayed in the streets below. The students of the school formed militant organizations, and a fighting detachment made up of them kept watch over the building at night.

Among my father's papers are some sketches he made at the time: a woman agitator, who was making a speech on the balcony, is being shot at by dragoons who swooped down on the crowd. She is wounded, but she goes on with her speech, catching hold of a column to prevent herself from falling.

At the end of 1905 Gorky arrived in Moscow, which was in the grip of a general strike. The nights were frosty. Plunged in darkness, Moscow was lit by bonfires. Stray bullets flew whistling through the streets and mounted patrols galloped wildly over the noiseless, virginal snow, untrampled by pedestrians.

Father saw Gorky in connection with the political, satirical journals *The Whip, The Bugbear,* and others, whenever the latter invited him to their editorial offices.

I expect it must have been just then or later, after I had spent a year in Berlin with my parents, that I saw Blok's poems for the first time in my life. I cannot remember whether it was *Pussywillows* or some of his *Childhood Poems,* dedicated to Olenina d'Alheim, or something revolutionary, something about the city, but my impression I remember so distinctly that I can re-create it and I am going to attempt to describe it.

### 2

What is literature in the generally accepted and most widely understood meaning of the word? It is a world of eloquence, platitudes, rounded sentences, and venerable names of people who, when young, had observed life and who, on becoming famous, had passed on to abstractions, reiterations, and ratiocinations. And when in this realm of accepted, and only because of that unnoticed, artificiality, someone opens his mouth, not because of any inherent bent for literature, but because he knows something and wants to say it, this creates the impression of a revolution, just as though a door were flung open and the noise of the life going on outside came through it, just as though it were not a man explaining what was going on in the town, but the town itself announcing its presence through the lips of a man. So it was with Blok. Such was his solitary, unspoilt, childlike word, such was the powerful effect it produced.

A piece of paper contained a certain amount of information. It seemed as though the information had itself, without being asked, settled down on the sheet of printed paper, as though no one had composed and written the poem. It seemed as though the page were covered not with verses about wind and puddles, street lamps and stars, but the street lamps and the puddles themselves were spreading their wind-blown ripples on the surface of the journal, as though they themselves had left the damp imprints that exerted so powerful an influence on the reader.

3

A number of writers of my age as well as myself went through the years of our youth with Blok as our guide. Blok had everything that goes to make a great poet: fire, tenderness, emotion, his own image of the world, his own special gift for transforming everything he touched, and his own restrained, hidden, self-absorbed destiny. Of all these qualities and many more, I shall pause to consider only one side of his genius that has, perhaps, left the deepest impression on me and for that reason seems to me to be the most important one, namely Blok's impetuosity, his roving intentness, the rapidity of his observations.

*A gleam in the window,*
*A porch without light;*
*A Harlequin whispers*
*Alone with the night.*

*The snow in the streets is whirled and tossed*
*Round and round in faltering dance,*
*And here a hand is offered me,*
*And there a smile in someone's glance.*

*And there with a light one teases and flashes,*
*So often in winter night disguises*
*A shade, a shape that now appears*
*But soon departs and wholly vanishes.*

Adjectives without nouns, predicates without subjects, hide-and-seek, breathless agitation, nimbly darting little figures, abruptness—how that style seemed to agree with the spirit of the age, hiding, secretive, underground, barely emerged from the cellars, talking in the language of conspirators, of which the chief character was the city and the chief event the street.

These features permeate Blok's entire being, the fundamental and the predominant Blok, the Blok of the second volume of the Alkonost edition, the Blok of *The Terrible World, The Last Day, The Deception, Story, The Legends, The Political Meeting, The Stranger,* the poems: *In the Mists Above the Sparkling Dew, In the Pubs, Lanes and Winding Streets,* and *A Girl Sang in the Church Choir.*

The features of reality are brought into Blok's books like currents of air by the whirlwind of his sensibility. Even the most remote, which might appear to be mystical and might even be called "divine," that, too, is not a metaphysical fantasy but bits of reality culled from ecclesiastical life and scattered through all his poems, pieces out of the Greek Orthodox service, prayers before communion, and requiem psalms, known by heart and heard a thousand times during church services.

The sum total of this world, the bearer of this reality, was the city of Blok's poems, the chief hero of his *Story* and of his biography.

This city, this Petersburg of Blok's, is the most real of Petersburgs depicted by the artists of most recent times. It exists alike in life and imagination without any difference whatever. It is full of that everyday prose which feeds poetry with its drama and its anxieties, and in its streets resounds the everyday colloquial speech which is in general use and which enlivens the language of poetry.

At the same time the image of that city is composed of features selected by a hand so sensitive and is subjected to such inspired treatment, that it has all been transmuted into the most thrilling phenomenon of the rarest inner world.

4

I have had the occasion and the good luck to know many older poets who lived in Moscow: Bryusov, Andrey Bely, Khodasevich, Vyacheslav Ivanov, Baltrushaitis. I introduced myself to Blok for the first time during his last visit to Moscow,* in the corridor or on the staircase of the Polytechnic Museum on the evening of his address in the lecture theater of the Museum. Blok was nice to me, he said he had heard many good things about me, he complained of not feeling well and asked me to postpone my visit to him till he felt better.

That evening he read his poems in three places: at the Polytechnic Museum, at the Press Club, and at the Society of Dante Alighieri, where the most zealous of his admirers had gathered and where he read his *Italian Poems*.

Mayakovsky was present at the Polytechnic Museum. In the middle of the reading he told me that an anti-Blok demonstration was being organized at the Press Club under the pretext of critical integrity, and that at that "benefit" performance Blok would be booed and shouted down. He suggested that the two

---

* Blok arrived in Moscow on May 1, 1921. During his visit he gave six readings of his poetry. He died on August 7th in Petersburg.

of us should go there and try to prevent that contemptible attack planned by Blok's enemies.

We left the Blok meeting and walked to the Press Club. But Blok was taken to his second meeting by car, and by the time we made our way to the Nikitsky Boulevard, where the Press Club was, the reading was over and Blok had gone to the Society of friends of Italian literature. The hostile demonstration which we feared had in the meantime taken place. After his reading at the Press Club, Blok had been told a lot of monstrous things; some of his attackers were not even ashamed to tell him to his face that he was out of date and had been dead without realizing it for many years, with which he calmly agreed. That was said to him only a few months before his real death.

5

In those years of our first attempts to challenge the accepted conventions of poetic expression only two poets, Aseyev and Marina Tsvetayeva, possessed the mastery over a mature and completely formed poetic style. The acclaimed originality of the others, including my own, arose from our utter helplessness and inarticulateness, which did not, however, prevent us from writing, publishing, and translating. Among my depressingly incompetent writings of that time, the most awful ones were my translations of Ben Jonson's *Alchemist* and Goethe's poem *The Mysteries*. There is extant a review of them by Blok published in the last volume of his collected works among his other reviews written for the publishing house World Literature. This scornful and scathing criticism is well deserved and justified in its final appraisal.

However, from all these digressions it is time we returned to our story, which we interrupted at the years long since passed, the early nineteen hundreds.

## 6

When a schoolboy in the third or fourth class, I traveled by myself to Petersburg for the Christmas vacation on a free ticket given me by my uncle, the stationmaster of the Petersburg freight station of the Nikolayevsky line. For days on end I wandered about the streets of the immortal city, as though devouring with my feet and eyes a sort of magnificent stone book, and the evenings I spent at Kommissarzhevskaya's theater. I was intoxicated with the newest literature, raved about Andrey Bely, Hamsun, Przybyszewski.

A still greater and more real idea of travel I got from the trip of our whole family to Berlin in 1906. This was the first time that I found myself abroad. Everything was unusual, everything different. I felt as though I were not awake, but dreaming, taking part in some imaginary theatrical performance which no one was really obliged to take part in. You don't know anyone, no one can lay down the law for you. A long row of slamming and opening doors along the entire wall of the railway carriage, a separate door for each compartment. Four tracks on the elevated belt railway, suspended over the streets, canals, racehorse stables, and the back yards of the gigantic city. Trains overtaking other trains, driving alongside or crossing the paths of other trains. A double line of street lights, crisscrossing and intersecting lights under the bridges, lights in the second and third floors of houses level with the overhead railway lines, the multicolored lights of the automatic machines in the station buffets, ejecting cigars, sweets, sugared almonds. I soon got used to Berlin, loafed about its numberless streets and immense park, spoke German, tried to imitate the Berlin dialect, breathed a mixture of locomotive smoke, coal gas, and beer foam, listened to Wagner.

Berlin was full of Russians. The composer Rebikov played his *Christmas Tree* to his friends and divided music into three periods: animal music before Beethoven, human music during the next period, and the music of the future after himself.

Gorky, too, was in Berlin. Father made a drawing of him. Andreyeva objected to the cheekbones on the drawing's being so prominent that they looked angular. She said: "You haven't understood him. He is Gothic." That was how most people talked in those days.

## 7

It was, I think, after this trip abroad, on my return to Moscow, that another great lyric poet of the century entered into my life, a lyric poet who was scarcely known at the time, but who has now been acknowledged by the entire world: the German poet, Rainer Maria Rilke.

In 1900 he went to see Tolstoy in Yasnaya Polyana; he knew my father and corresponded with him. One summer he spent with the peasant poet Drozhzhin in Zavidovo, near Klin.

In those far-off days, he used to present his early collections of poems to Father with warm inscriptions. Two of these books fell into my hands rather late during one of the winters I have described, and I was struck by the same things that amazed me in the first poems of Blok I ever saw: the urgency of what they had to say, the absoluteness, the gravity, the direct purposefulness of their language.

## 8

Rilke is entirely unknown in Russia. The few attempts to render him into Russian have not been successful. The translators are not to blame. They are accustomed to translate the meaning and not the tone of a poem, and with Rilke the tone is everything.

In 1913 Verhaeren was in Moscow. Father painted his portrait. A few times Father asked me to keep the poet entertained so as to prevent his face from growing stiff and lifeless. Once I had diverted the historian V. O. Klyuchevsky in this way. Now came my turn to divert Verhaeren. With understandable enthusiasm I told him how I admired his poetry and then I asked him timidly if he had heard of Rilke. I never thought that Verhaeren would know him. The poet looked transformed. Father could not have asked for anything better. The name of Rilke alone revived his model more than any of my conversations. "He is the best European poet," said Verhaeren, "and my favorite spiritual brother."

With Blok prose remains the source of the poem. It does not form any part of his means of expression. With Rilke the true-to-life and psychological methods of our contemporary novelists (Tolstoy, Flaubert, Proust, and the Scandinavians) are inseparable from the style and the language of his poetry.

## 9

Somewhere about the beginning of 1907 new publishing houses began popping out of the ground like mushrooms, concerts of new music were given much oftener than before, one after another there opened exhibitions of pictures by painters belonging to different groups, such as the World of Art, the Golden Fleece, the Jack of Diamonds, the Donkey's Tail, and the Blue Rose. Beside the Russian names of Somov, Sapunov, Sudeikin, Krymov, Larionov, and Goncharova there appeared the names of Bonnard and Vuillard. At the exhibitions of the Golden Fleece, in rooms shaded by curtains, where, as in hothouses, it smelled of earth from the flowerpots of hyacinths, one could see the works of Rodin and Matisse. The young people joined these movements.

In the courtyard of one of the new houses in Razgulyay Square was preserved an old wooden cottage belonging to the general who owned the house. The general's son, the poet and artist Julian Pavlovich Anissimov, used to hold parties in the attic of the cottage for young people who held the same views as he. He had weak lungs. He spent the winters abroad. His friends gathered at his place when the weather was good in spring and autumn. They read, made music, painted, talked, ate snacks, and drank tea with rum. There I made the acquaintance of a large number of people.

Our host, a highly talented man of excellent taste, who spoke several foreign languages as fluently as he did Russian, was himself an embodiment of poetry, but as he was only an amateur of great charm it was rather difficult for him to be, in addition, a strong creative personality, a character out of which a master of his craft is eventually produced. We had similar interests, we admired the same people. I liked him very much.

The late Sergey Nikolayevich Durylin, who at that time used to write under the pseudonym of Sergey Rayevsky, used to go there. It was he who persuaded me to give up music in favor of literature and who, out of the kindness of his heart, was able to find something worthy of attention in my first literary efforts. He was poor, keeping his mother and his aunt on

what he earned from private lessons, and by his enthusiastic candor and furious conviction of the rightness of his ideas reminded me of Belinsky as tradition paints him.

It was there that my university colleague K. G. Loks, whom I had known before, showed me for the first time the poems of Innokenty Annensky, because he seemed to find a certain kinship between my writings and ramblings and the work of the remarkable poet who was quite unknown to me at the time.

This circle of friends had its own name. It was christened Serdarda, a name whose meaning no one knew. This word was said to have been heard one day on the Volga by a member of our circle, the poet and bass Arkady Guryev. He had heard it at night during a commotion on the quay created by two river steamers after one of them had made fast to the other and the passengers of the second steamer had disembarked with their baggage by walking through the saloon of the first steamer, which had made fast to the quay earlier, and mingled with her passengers and their baggage.

Guryev was a native of Saratov. He had a powerful and soft voice and he gave highly artistic renderings of the dramatic and vocal subtleties of whatever he happened to be singing. Like all born but untrained artists, he struck you equally by his perpetual buffoonery and the rudiments of genuine originality which one glimpsed through his affectation. His far from mediocre poems anticipated the future unrestrained candor of Mayakovsky and the clear-cut images of Esenin so easily grasped by the reader. He was a natural operatic and dramatic actor, the sort of born actor who was more than once depicted by Ostrovsky.

His head was rounded like an onion, his forehead was large, his nose barely perceptible, and there were unmistakable signs that he would end up with a skull as bare as the back of his hand. He was all movement, expressiveness. He did not gesticulate or wave his arms about, but when he engaged in arguments or recited, though he might be standing still, the upper part of his body seemed to be walking, acting, and talking. He inclined his head, threw back his body, and put his feet far apart as though caught tapping his heels in the middle of a folk dance. He was a little given to drink and when drunk believed in his own inventions. At the end of his turns he pretended that his heel had stuck to the floor and he could not tear it away, and he assured his audience that the devil was trying to catch him by the foot.

There were poets and artists in Serdarda: B. B. Krasin, who set Blok's *Pussywillows* to music, Sergey Bobrov, the future partner of my early debuts, whose appearances in Razgulyay Square were preceded by rumors that he was a newly arisen Russian Rimbaud, A. I. Kozhebatkin, editor of *Musaget,* and Sergey Makovsky, editor of *Apollon,* whenever he was on a visit to Moscow.

I myself joined Serdarda on the strength of my standing as a musician and improvised on the piano a musical description of every new arrival at the beginning of the evening.

The short spring nights passed quickly. The cold morning breeze wafted through the open window. It raised the skirts of the curtains, stirred the flames of the guttering candles, rustled the sheets of paper on the table. And everyone—the guests and our host—was yawning. Empty vistas, a gray sky, rooms, staircases. We each went our way, overtaking in the wide streets, which seemed to go on forever because of the absence of people, the interminable lines of the rumbling night carts of the Public Health Department. "Centaurs," someone remarked in the language of the period.

## 10

Around the *Musaget* publishing house there was formed something in the nature of an academy. Andrey Bely, Stepun, Rachinsky, Boris Sadovsky, Emile Metner, Shenrok, Petrovsky, Ellis, and Nilender taught the young people who were interested in the subjects of poetic rhythm, the history of the German romantic movement, Russian lyric poetry, the aesthetics of Goethe and Richard Wagner, Baudelaire and the French symbolists, and ancient Greek pre-Socratic philosophy.

The mind behind all these undertakings was Andrey Bely, the unchallenged authority of that circle in those days, a first-class poet and author of the particularly striking *Symphonies in Prose* and of the novels *The Silver Dove* and *Petersburg,* which created an upheaval in the pre-Revolutionary taste of his contemporaries and gave rise to the first Soviet prose.

Andrey Bely possessed all the marks of genius that refused to be driven into a rut by the petty worries of everyday life, by family, by the lack of understanding of those near and dear to him, a genius that ran amok and from a productive force was transformed into a destructive and barren one. This flaw of superabundant inspiration did not discredit him, but aroused one's sympathy and added a martyrlike touch to his charm.

He gave lectures on the practical study of the Russian classical iambic verse and by the method of statistical calculation analyzed, together with his students, its rhythmic figures and variations. I did not go to his lectures because I have been, and am now too, of the opinion that the music of the word is not an acoustic phenomenon and does not consist of the euphony of vowels and consonants, taken by themselves, but of the relationship between the meaning and the sound of the words.

The young people did not always meet in the offices of *Musaget,* but in all sorts of other places. Such a meeting place was the studio of the sculptor Kracht in the Presnya section.

The studio had a living space on top in the form of an enclosed gallery high up near the ceiling; below, dressed in ivy leaves and other decorative greenery, were the white casts of fragments of antique sculpture, plaster-of-Paris masks, and the original works of the owner of the studio.

One day in late autumn I read in this studio a paper under the title of "Symbolism and Immortality." Part of my audience was sitting below and another part was listening above, lying on the floor of the gallery with their heads sticking out over its edge.

My paper was based on the idea that our perceptions are subjective, on the fact that the sounds and colors we perceive in nature correspond to something else, namely to the objective vibrations of the sound and light waves. In my paper I argued that this subjectivity was not the attribute of every individual human being, but was a generic and suprapersonal quality, that it was the subjectivity of the world of man and of humanity at large. I suggested in my paper that after his death every person leaves behind him a part of that undying, generic subjectivity which he possessed during his lifetime and with which he participated in the history of mankind's existence. The main object of my paper was to advance the theory that perhaps this preeminently subjective and universally human corner or separate part of the soul had since time immemorial been the sphere of action and the main subject of art. That, besides, though the artist was of course mortal like the rest of mankind, the joy of living experienced by him was immortal, and that other people a century later might through his works be able to experience something approaching the personal and vital form of his original sensations.

My paper was entitled "Symbolism and Immortality" because in it I affirmed the symbolic, conventional quiddity of every art in the general sense in which one can talk of the symbolism of algebra.

My paper created a stir. It was talked about. I came back home late. At home I learned that Tolstoy, stopped by illness after his flight from Yasnaya Polyana, had died at the railway station of Astapovo and that Father had been summoned there by telegram. We packed our things quickly and drove to Paveletsky Station to catch the night train.*

### 11

At that time one noticed the departure from town more than now. The landscape of the countryside looked more different from the urban landscape than at the present time. From the morning, and for the rest of the day, the window of our compartment was filled with the vast expanse of fields, some fallow and some under winter corn, enlivened only by a glimpse of an occasional village, the vast, thousand-mile expanse of arable Russia, the Russia of peasant villages, which feed the small area of urban Russia and work for it. The first frosts had already silvered the earth and the gold that still hung on the birch trees framed it all along the boundaries of the fields, and this silver of the frosts and the gold of the birch trees lay on her like a modest ornament, like gold leaf and

---

* Tolstoy left Yasnaya Polyana on the early morning of November 10, 1910. He travelled third-class by train. He caught a chill and died of pneumonia in the station-master's house at Astapovo on November 20.

silver foil on her sacred and meek antiquities.

The plowed and fallow land that flashed by in the windows of the carriage was not conscious that somewhere close by, somewhere not very far away, her last giant lay dead, a man who because of his high birth could have been her Tsar, and because of the richness of his intellect, saturated with all the subtleties of the world, could have been the greatest darling and the grandest gentleman of them all. But out of love for her and out of a sense of justice toward her he walked behind the plow and dressed and girt himself with a belt like a peasant.

### 12

I expect it must have become known that artists would make drawings of the deceased and that afterwards a caster, who had arrived with Merkurov, would take his death mask, for those who had come to bid a last farewell were asked to leave the room. When we entered it, it was empty. Sofia Andreyevna, with a tear-stained face, stepped forward rapidly from a far corner of the room and, seizing my father's hands, cried spasmodically in a voice choked with tears: "Oh, Leonid Osipovich, you can't imagine what I've been through! You, at least, know how much I loved him!" And she began telling him how after Tolstoy had left she had tried to commit suicide by throwing herself into a pond and how she had been dragged out of it more dead than alive.

In the room lay a mountain like Elbrus, and she was one of its large, detached crags; the room was filled by a storm cloud the size of half the sky, and she was one of its separate lightnings. And she did not realize that she had the privilege of a crag and of a sheet of lightning to be silent and to crush by the mysteriousness of her conduct; that she need not enter into arguments with those who were the most un-Tolstoyan in the world—the Tolstoyans; that she need not join in a pygmy battle with those people.

But she tried to justify herself and appealed to my father to be a witness that she excelled her rivals in her devotion and her intellectual understanding, and that she would have taken care of her late husband better than they. Good Lord, I thought, to what a state can a human being be reduced, and a wife of Tolstoy, at that!

It is, in fact, strange. A modern man who rejects the duel as an outworn convention writes an enormous work on the subject of Pushkin's duel and Pushkin's death. Poor Pushkin! He should have married Shchegolev and the latest Pushkiniana and everything would have been perfect! He would have lived to our own days and would have composed several continuations of *Eugene Onegin* and written five Poltava poems instead of one. And yet, it always seemed to me that I would have ceased to understand Pushkin if I were to admit that he was more in need of our understanding than of Natalya Nikolayevna.

### 13

It was not, however, a mountain that lay in the corner of the room, but a little, wizened old man, one of the old men created by Tolstoy, one of those he had described and scattered over his pages by the dozen. Little Christmas trees stood all around the place. The setting sun cut across the room with four slanting shafts of light and formed a cross over the corner where the body was lying with the thick shadow of the window-bars and other little baby crosses with the traceries of the young Christmas trees.

The railway hamlet of Astapovo was transformed that day into a discordantly noisy encampment of world journalism. The station buffet did a roaring trade, the waiters were run off their feet, too busy to carry out all the orders of their customers and serving underdone beefsteaks at a run. Rivers of beer were consumed.

Tolstoy's sons Ilya and Andrey were at the station. His other son Sergey arrived by the train which had come to take Tolstoy's remains to Yasnaya Polyana.

To the chanting of a requiem, the students and the young people carried the coffin across the little yard and the garden of the stationmaster's house to the railway platform and put it in the freight car, and to the accompaniment of the resumed singing, the train slowly moved off in the direction of Tula.

It seemed natural, somehow, that Tolstoy was at peace and that he should have found peace by the wayside like a pilgrim, near the main lines of communication of the Russia of those days, which his heroes and heroines continued to fly past and pass and repass, looking through the windows of the train at the insignificant railway station they were passing through, without realizing that the eyes which had watched them all their lives, the eyes which had seen through them and immortalized them, had closed forever in it.

### 14

If we were to take only one quality from every writer—for instance, if we were to characterize Lermontov by passionateness, Tyutchev by the richness of his subject matter, Chekhov by his poetic qualities, Gogol by his dazzling brilliance, Dostoevsky by his imaginative powers—what are we to say of Tolstoy, if we must limit the definition to one characteristic only?

The chief quality of this moralist, leveller, and preacher of a system of justice that would embrace everybody without fear or favor would be an originality that distinguished him from everyone else and that verged on the paradoxical.

All his life and at any given moment he possessed the faculty of seeing things in the detached finality of each separate moment, in sharp relief, as we see things only on rare occasions, in childhood, or on the crest of an all-embracing happiness, or in the triumph of a great spiritual victory.

To see things like that it is necessary that one's eye should be directed by passion. For it is passion that by its flash illuminates an object, intensifying its appearance.

Such a passion, the passion of creative contemplation, Tolstoy constantly carried about within himself. Indeed, it was in its light that he saw everything in its pristine freshness, in a new way, as though for the first time. The authenticity of what he saw differs so much from what we are used to that it may appear strange to us. But Tolstoy was not looking for this strangeness, he was not pursuing it as an aim in itself, and he most certainly did not use it in his works as a literary method.

## BEFORE THE
## FIRST WORLD WAR

1

During the first half of 1912, the spring and summer, I lived abroad. Our school vacations coincide with the summer se-

mester of the West. This semester I spent in the old University of Marburg.

It was at this university that Lomonosov often attended the lectures of the mathematician and philosopher Christian Wolff. A century and a half before him, Giordano Bruno had read the essay on his new astronomy there before his return from his foreign tour to Italy and his death at the stake in Rome.

Marburg is a small medieval town. In those days it numbered twenty-nine thousand inhabitants. Half of these were students. It clings picturesquely to the side of a mountain, from which are quarried the stones that were used for the building of its houses, churches, castles, and university, and it is buried in dense orchards, dark as the night.

Of the money that had been assigned for my living expenses and studies in Germany, I had only a little left over. On this unspent remainder of my funds I went to Italy. I saw Venice, brick-pink and aquamarine-green, like the transparent pebbles which the sea casts ashore, and I paid a visit to Florence, dark, narrow, slender—a living extraction from Dante's tercets. I had no money left for a sight-seeing tour of Rome.

The following year I completed my course at Moscow University. I was assisted in passing my examinations by Mansurov, a young postgraduate research student in history. He supplied me with a whole collection of textbooks and lecture notes which he had used himself before passing his finals the year before. The professorial library greatly exceeded the examination requirements, and in addition to general textbooks it contained reference books on classical antiquities and separate monographs on all sorts of subjects. It was with difficulty that I took away all those riches in a cab.

Mansurov was a relative and a friend

of the young Trubetskoy and Dmitry Samarin. I knew them from the Fifth Grammar School, where they used to pass their examinations every year after having been taught at home.

The elder Trubetskoys, the father and uncle of the student Nikolay, were one a professor of jurisprudence, and the other Rector of the University and a well-known philosopher. Both were notable for their vast corpulence and, elephants in frock coats without waists, used to clamber up to the rostrum in the lecture hall and read their remarkable lectures in whining, beseeching, muffled, aristocratically burring voices.

The three inseparable young men, who used always to drop in at the university together, were of the same breed: tall, gifted youths with eyebrows growing right across their foreheads and with high-sounding voices and names.

The Marburg school of philosophy was held in high honor in that circle. Trubetskoy wrote about it and sent his more gifted students there to perfect themselves. Dmitry Samarin, who had been there before me, was quite at home there. He was a zealot of Marburg. I went there on his advice.

Dmitry Samarin belonged to a famous Slavophile family, on whose former estate there is now situated the writers' village of Peredelkino and the Peredel-kino Tuberculosis Sanatorium for Children.

Philosophy, dialectics, and a knowledge of Hegel were in his blood. He had inherited it. He was untidy, absent-minded, and possibly not quite normal. As a result of his strange behavior when his fits came over him he was very difficult to live with and quite unbearable in society. It is impossible to blame his family, who could not get on with him and with whom he was constantly quarrelling.

At the beginning of NEP he returned to Moscow from Siberia, where he had spent a long time carried hither and thither during the Civil War. He had grown much more simple and more understanding. He had swollen up from starvation and become covered with lice during his journey. He fell ill with typhus, at a time when the epidemic was on the wane, and died.

I do not know what became of Mansu-rov, but the famous philosopher Nikolay Trubetskoy became a world celebrity and died in Vienna a short time ago.

2

The summer after my finals I spent with my parents at their country house at Molodya near the Stolbovaya railway station on the Moscow-Kursk line.

From our house, according to tradition, the Cossacks of our retreating army returned the fire of the advancing forward detachments of Napoleon's troops. On the grounds, which merged with the adjoining cemetery, their graves were sunk and overgrown.

Inside the house the rooms were narrow in proportion to their high ceilings and high windows. The oil lamp on the table threw immense shadows in the corners of the dark red walls and on the ceiling.

At the bottom of the park meandered a little stream with many deep eddies. A large old birch tree, half broken, continued to grow lopsidedly over one of the eddies. The green tangle of its branches formed an overhead summerhouse. It was quite safe to make oneself comfortable in their strong interlacement either by sitting or half lying down. Here I made myself a place to work in.

I read Tyutchev and for the first time

in my life wrote poetry not as a rare exception, but often and continuously, as one paints or composes music.

In the thicket of that tree I wrote the poems of my first book in two or three summer months.

The book was, with quite stupid pretentiousness, entitled *A Twin in the Clouds,* in imitation of the cosmological ingenuities which were characteristic of the book titles of the symbolists and the names of their publishing houses.

To write those poems, to cross out, revise, and correct them and then rewrite them again, was something that I felt to be an absolute necessity and gave me immense pleasure that brought me to the verge of tears.

I did my best to avoid any romantic affectation, any attempt to engage the interest of the reader by something that was not germane to the main theme of the poem. I had no desire to declaim these poems from the stage at the top of my voice so that people engaged in intellectual pursuits should shy away from them, crying indignantly: "What degradation! What barbarity!" I did not want flies and wives of professors to expire because of their discreet elegance, or that after reading them to a small audience of six or seven admirers I should be told: "Permit me to shake hands with an honest man!" I was not trying to achieve the clear-cut rhythms of a song or a dance, under whose influence almost without the participation of words hands and feet begin to move by themselves. I did not express, reflect, represent, or depict anything at all.

Later on, as a result of quite unnecessary attempts to find some sort of affinity between Mayakovsky and myself, people discovered oratorical and melodic tendencies in my poems. This is not correct. They are there no more than in the speech of any ordinary person.

Quite the contrary, the subject matter of my poems was my constant preoccupation, my constant dream was that my poem itself should have something in it, that it should have a new idea or a new picture, that it should be engraved with all its peculiarities in the book and should speak from its pages with all its silence and with all the colors of its black colorless print.

For instance, I wrote a poem *Venice* and a poem *The Railway Station.* The city on the water stood before me and the circles and figures of eight of its reflections widened and multiplied, swelling like a rusk in tea. Or, far away, at the end of the tracks and platforms, there arose before me, all in clouds and smoke, a railway farewell horizon, behind which the trains were hidden, and which contained the history of relationships, meetings and partings, and the events before and after them.

There was nothing I demanded from myself, from my readers, or from the theory of art. All I wanted was that one poem should contain the city of Venice and the other the Brest (now the Belorussko-Baltiysky) railway station.

Bobrov liked the lines, "Sometimes the West moved apart in shuntings of trains and sleepers" from my *Railway Station.* Aseyev and I, together with a few other young writers, founded a small co-operative publishing house by pooling all our available resources. Bobrov, who knew all there was to know about typography from his work at the *Russian Archives,* published his own things with our publishing house and edited our things for it. He published the *Twin* with a friendly preface by Aseyev.

Maria Ivanovna Baltrushaitis, the wife of the poet, used to say: "One day you will be sorry to have published an immature book." She was right. I was often sorry to have done so.

## 3

I spent the hot summer of 1914 with its drought and full eclipse of the sun at the country cottage of the Baltrushaitises on a large estate on the Oka near the town of Alexin. I was their son's tutor and I was also translating Kleist's comedy *The Broken Jug* for the newly founded Kamerny Theater, of which Baltrushaitis was the literary director.

There were many people from the world of art on the estate, such as Vyacheslav Ivanov, the artist Ulyanov, and the wife of the writer Muratov. Not far away, in Tarussa, Balmont was translating *Sakuntala* by Kalidasa for the same theater. In July I was called up and went to Moscow for my medical and obtained a "white ticket," that is to say, complete exemption from military service because of my shortened leg which I had broken as a boy. I then returned to the Baltrushaitises' summer place on the Oka.

Shortly after that, something of this sort happened one evening. From behind a curtain of mist that hung over the rushes in the river Oka, the strains of a military band playing some sort of regimental music, a polka or a march, were slowly floating toward us from below and coming nearer and nearer. Then a little tug with three barges in tow appeared from behind a promontory. They must have sighted the estate on the top of the hill from the tug and decided to land. The tug sailed straight across the river and brought the barges to our bank. There were soldiers on them, a large unit of a grenadier regiment. They disembarked and lit campfires at the foot of the hill. The officers were invited to the house to dine and spend the night there. In the morning they sailed away. It was one of the episodes of the general mobilization. The war began.

## 4

Then I spent about a year, in two separate stages with a few breaks between them, in the family of a rich businessman, Moritz Philippe, as tutor of their son Walter, a nice and affectionate boy.

During the anti-German riots in the summer, Philippe's offices and private house were looted together with the biggest private firms, such as Einem and Verrein. The destruction was proceeding according to plan and with the knowledge of the police. The property belonging to the employees was not touched, only the things belonging to the owners of the German firms. In the ensuing confusion my linen, clothes, and other things were saved, but my books and manuscripts were destroyed in the general turmoil.

Later on, many of the things I had written got lost under more peaceful conditions. I do not like my style up to 1940, I reject half of Mayakovsky, and I do not like everything of Esenin's. The general disintegration of form in those days, the impoverishment of thought, the uneven and impure style are foreign to me. I am not worried about the disappearance of imperfect and faulty works. But neither was I ever sorry for the loss of successful works, though for quite a different reason.

In life it is more necessary to lose than to gain. A seed will only germinate if it dies. One has to live without getting tired, one must look forward and feed on one's living reserves, which oblivion no less than memory produces.

At different times I have lost for different reasons: the text of my paper "Symbolism and Immortality," the articles of my futuristic period, a fairy tale for children in prose, two poems, a notebook of verses, intermediate between

*Above the Barriers* and *My Sister, Life,* the rough copy of a novel in several foolscap notebooks, the revised beginning of which was published as a long short story under the title *The Childhood of Luverse,* and, finally, my translation of one whole tragedy from Swinburne's dramatic trilogy on Mary Stuart.

We moved to a new rented apartment from Philippe's looted and half-burned house. There I had a room to myself. I remember it very well. The rays of the setting autumn sun furrowed the room and the book I was looking through. There were two kinds of evening in the book. One lay across it with a light rosy hue. The other was made up of the contents and the soul of the poems published in it.

I envied its author, who was able to retain the bits of reality she had put into it with such simple means. It was one of Akhmatova's first books, probably *The Plantain.*

5

During the same years, in the intervals between my work at the Philippes', I traveled to the Urals and the Kama district. One winter I lived in Vsevolodo-Vilva in the north of the province of Perm, which, according to the reminiscences of A. N. Tikhonov, who described those places, Chekhov and Levitan had once upon a time visited. Another winter I spent in the Quiet Mountains on the Kama River at the chemical works of the Ushkovs.

In the offices of the works, I was for some time in charge of the draft board and freed whole districts of people attached to factories and doing defense work from military service.

In winter the factories kept in communication with the outside world by antediluvian methods. The mail came by sledges drawn by teams of three horses from Kazan, about two hundred miles away, as in the days of Pushkin's *Captain's Daughter.* Once I took part in this winter journey.

When, in March, 1917, the news that the Revolution had broken out in Petersburg reached the factories, I left for Moscow.

At the Izhev factory I had to find and take with me a remarkable man, an engineer by the name of Zbarsky, who had been sent there on a special mission. I had to put myself under his orders and go with him.

From the Quiet Mountains we traveled in a *kibitka,* a covered cart on runners, a whole night and part of the following day. Wrapped in three long peasant overcoats and buried in hay, I rolled round and round like a big, heavy sack on the bottom of the sledge, bereft of all freedom of movement. I dozed, nodded, fell asleep and woke up, closed and opened my eyes.

I saw the road through the forest, the stars of the frosty night. The high snowdrifts formed humps of snowy hillocks across the narrow track. The top of the covered sledge often knocked against the overhanging branches of the silver firs, shook the hoarfrost from them, trailing noisily under them and dragging them after it. The white surface of the snowy waste reflected the twinkling starlight and lighted up the road. Inside, in the depths of the dense forest, the glittering pall of snow sent a cold shiver through me; it was just as though a lighted candle had been stuck in the snow.

Three horses, harnessed in single file, drew the sledge at a spanking pace, but from time to time one or the other strayed from the road and left the file. The coachman drew them back into line again and again, and when the sledge leaned over to one side he jumped off it, ran alongside, and supported it with his shoulder to prevent it from overturning.

I fell asleep again, totally oblivious of the passage of time, and suddenly woke up from a jolt and the cessation of movement.

The coachmen's inn in the forest was just like one in a fairy tale about brigands. A dim light in the cottage, the hissing of the samovar and the ticking of the clock, the coachman who had just arrived with the sledge is divesting himself of his coat, thawing himself out, and talking softly, as one does at night, so as not to wake the sleepers behind the partition, to the innkeeper's wife who is about to serve him supper; meanwhile, another coachman wipes his mustache, buttons up his peasant overcoat, and goes out into the frost to harness a team of three horses to another sledge.

And once more a drive at a spanking pace, the hissing of the runners, dozing, sleep. And then, next day—a far horizon with factory chimneys, the limitless snowy desert of a large frozen river, and a railway.

## 6

Bobrov treated me with quite undeserved cordiality. He watched unwearyingly over my futuristic purity and protected me from harmful influences. By these he meant the sympathy shown by older people. The moment he noticed any signs of interest on their part, he hastened, fearful lest their kindness should cause me to lapse into academicism, to destroy the suspected bonds of friendship by any means at his disposal. Thanks to him, I never ceased quarrelling with everybody.

I was very fond of Julian Anissimov and his wife, Vera Stanevich. I had to be an involuntary participant of Bobrov's rupture with them.

Vyacheslav Ivanov presented me with one of his books with a moving inscription. In Bryusov's circle of friends, Bobrov made fun of this inscription in a way that suggested that it was I who was responsible for his sneering remarks. Vyacheslav Ivanov stopped speaking to me.

The *Contemporary Review* published my translation of Kleist's comedy *The Broken Jug*. The work was both immature and uninteresting. I should have been deeply grateful to the journal for publishing it. And I ought to have been even more grateful to its editorial board for letting some unknown hand go over my manuscript and improve it beyond recognition.

But the feeling of fairness, modesty, and gratitude was not fashionable among the young people of the left-wing artistic movements and was looked upon as a sign of sentimentality and spinelessness. The proper thing was to have a high opinion of oneself and one's talents, to strut about, to be impudent, and, however much I hated it, I strove to keep in step with them all so as not to fall behind my friends.

Something had happened to the proofs of the comedy. They were late and they included all sorts of words added by the typesetters which had no relation to the text.

To be fair to Bobrov, it must be stated that in the present case he had no idea what it was all about, and really did not know what he was doing. He said that I should not let such a disgraceful thing as scribbled remarks in the proofs and unasked-for stylistic improvements of the original pass without protest and that I must complain to Gorky, who, according to his information, was in some secret, unofficial way connected with the running of the periodical. I did so. Instead of expressing my thanks to the editorial board of the *Contemporary*, I wrote a stupid letter, full of studied and ignorant arrogance, complaining to Gorky because they had been anxious to help me and had done me a kindness. Years passed and it seems that I complained to Gorky about Gorky. The comedy was published at his recommendation and he corrected it with his own hand.

Finally, my acquaintance with Mayakovsky began with a polemical meeting of two hostile futuristic groups, he being a member of one of them and I of the other. According to the idea of the organizers of the meeting, it should have ended in a brawl, but a quarrel was averted by the mutual understanding we showed to one another from the very first words.

## 7

I will not describe my relations with Mayakovsky. We were never on intimate terms. His recognition of myself has been exaggerated. His point of view with regard to my works has been distorted. He disliked my *Year 1905* and *Lieutenant Schmidt* and considered them a mistake. He liked two of my books: *Above the Barriers* and *My Sister, Life.*

I will not describe our meetings and our disagreements. I shall try, as well as I am able, to give a general characterization of Mayakovsky and his significance. Needless to say, both the one and the other will be colored by subjectivity and prejudice.

## 8

Let us begin with the most important. We have no idea of the mental agony that precedes suicide. Under physical torture on the rack, people lose consciousness every minute, the sufferings inflicted by torture being so great that they bring the end near by the very fact of being so unendurable. Subjected to torture by a hangman, a man is not yet utterly destroyed; though unconscious from pain, he is nevertheless present at his own end, his past belongs to him, his memories are with him, and, if he so desires, he can make use of them and they may be of some help to him before he dies.

Having arrived at the thought of suicide, one abandons all hope, one turns away from one's past, one declares oneself a bankrupt and one's memories as nonexistent. These memories are no longer capable of reaching the would-be suicide to save him, to sustain him. The continuity of one's inner existence is destroyed, the personality has ceased to exist. In the end, perhaps, one kills oneself not out of loyalty to the decision one has made, but because one can no longer endure the agony that does not seem to belong to anyone in particular, the suffering in the absence of a sufferer, the empty suspense which is not filled up by a life that still goes on.

It seems to me that Mayakovsky shot himself out of pride because he had condemned something in himself or around himself with which his self-respect could not be reconciled. Esenin hanged himself without any clear realization of the consequences, wondering at heart whether or not it was the end; for you never can tell, it might not be the end after all. Marina Tsvetayeva all her life shielded herself by her work against the humdrum affairs of everyday existence. When it seemed to her that it was an inadmissible luxury and that for the sake of her son she must for a time sacrifice her all-absorbing passion, she cast a sober look around her and she saw the chaos that had not filtered through her creative work, immovable, stagnant, monstrous, and recoiled in panic. Not knowing how to protect herself from that horror, she hurriedly hid herself in death, putting her head into a noose as under a pillow. I can't help feeling that Paolo Yashvili was no longer capable of comprehending anything at all when, bewitched by the ideas first enunciated by Shigalyov [in Dostoevsky's *The Devils*], which were so prevalent in 1937, he gazed at his sleeping daughter at night and imagined that he was no longer worthy of looking at her and in the morning went to his comrades and blew out his brains with the shot from his double-barrelled gun. And it seems to me that Fadeyev, with that guilty smile which he managed to preserve through all the cunning intricacies of politics, could bid farewell to himself at the last moment before pulling the trigger with, I should imagine, words like these: "Well, it's all over! Good-bye, Sasha!"

But all of them suffered beyond description, their suffering reaching the point where the feeling of anguish became a mental illness. Let us bow our heads with compassion for their talents and their bright memory as well as for their sufferings.

## 9

And so there was to be a clash between two literary groups in the summer of 1914 in a coffeeshop in the Arbat. Bobrov and I represented one group and Tretyakov and Shershenevich were to represent the other group. But they brought Mayakovsky with them.

It seemed that, contrary to expectation, I was familiar with the appearance of the young man whom I had seen in the corridors of the Fifth Grammar School, where he was two classes below me, and in lobbies of concert halls where I had caught sight of him during the intermissions.

A little earlier one of his future blind admirers had shown me some of Mayakovsky's first published work. In those days that man not only did not understand his future god, but showed me this printed novelty with a scornful laugh as an unmistakably nonsensical piece by a third-rater. But I liked the poems very much. They were his first brightest experiments, which were afterwards published in his collection of poems, *Simple as Mooing*.

Now in the coffeehouse I liked their author no less. Before me sat a handsome youth of gloomy aspect with the bass voice of a deacon and the fist of a pugilist, inexhaustibly, deadly witty, something between a mythical hero of Alexander Grin and a Spanish toreador.

One could see at once that if he was handsome, witty, talented, perhaps supertalented, that was not the main thing about him; the main thing was his innate iron self-control, a kind of inherited principle of nobility, a feeling of duty which did not permit him to be different, less handsome, less witty, less talented.

And this resoluteness of his and his tousled mane of hair, which he kept ruffling with all his five fingers, at once made me think of the young terrorist conspirator, a composite image of the minor provincial characters in Dostoevsky's novels.

The provinces did not always lag behind the Russian capital cities to their own disadvantage. At times, during the period of decadence of the main centers of population, the remote parts of the country were saved by the beneficent old traditions that were preserved there. So, during the reign of the tango and the skating rinks, Mayakovsky brought from the remote Transcaucasian forest district where he was born the conviction, which was still firmly held in out-of-the-way places, that education in Russia could only be revolutionary.

To his natural attributes the young Mayakovsky added, in quite a wonderful fashion, an artistic disorder which he affected and a rather coarse and careless ponderousness of mind and body, and rebellious features of Bohemianism in which he draped himself and with which he played about so tastefully. His taste was so mature and fully developed that it seemed older than himself. He was twenty-two, and his taste was, as it were, a hundred and twenty-two.

## 10

I liked Mayakovsky's early lyrical poetry very much. Against the background of buffoonery that was so characteristic of those days, its seriousness—so heavy, so menacing, and so plaintive—was quite unusual. It was a poetry beautifully modeled, majestic, demonic, and, at the same time, infinitely doomed, perishing and almost calling for help.

*Time, I beseech you: though you be*
*A blind ikon painter, my image paint*
*In the shrine of this century's*
    *abortion!*
*I am solitary like the one-eyed*
*Man who goes to lead the blind.*

Time obliged and did what he asked. His image is written in the shrine of our century. But what one had to possess to see and divine it!
Or he says:

*Not for you to understand why, calm*
*Amid the storm of gibes,*
*My soul I carry on a plate*
*For the feast of coming years. . . .*

It is impossible not to think of parallels from the liturgy: "Be silent, all flesh of man, and stand in fear and trembling and think not of earthly things. For the King of Kings and the Lord of Lords cometh to offer Himself as a sacrifice and as food to the faithful."

In contradiction to the classics, to whom the sense of the hymns and prayers was important, to Pushkin, who paraphrased St. Yefrem of Syria in his *Desert Fathers,* and to Alexey Tolstoy, who put into verse the funeral lamentations of St. John of Damascus, the fragments of Church canticles and lessons are dear to Blok, Mayakovsky, and Esenin in their literal sense, as fragments of everyday life, in the same way as the street, the house, and any words of colloquial speech are dear to them.

These ancient literary deposits suggested to Mayakovsky the parodical structure of his poems. One can find in him a great many analogies with canonical ideas, hidden or underlined. They called for something vast and mighty, they demanded strong hands and trained the poet's audacity.

It is a very good thing that Mayakovsky and Esenin did not ignore what they knew and remembered from childhood, that they raised these familiar strata, made use of the beauty contained in them and did not leave them under lock and key.

## 11

When I got to know Mayakovsky more intimately, we discovered that there were unforeseen, technical coincidences in our poems, a similar construction of images, a similarity of rhyme structure. I liked the beauty and the felicity of his movements. I did not want anything better. Not to repeat him and not to seem to be his imitator, I began to suppress in myself everything I had in common with him, the heroic tone, which would have been false in my case, and the desire for effects. This narrowed down my style and purified it.

Mayakovsky had neighbors. He was not a solitary figure in poetry, he was not in a desert. Before the Revolution his rival on the concert platform was Igor Severyanin and, in the arena of the people's revolution and in the hearts of men—Sergey Esenin.

Severyanin was the dictator of the concert halls and when he appeared the house, to use a theatrical term, was sold out. He used to sing his verses to two or three popular tunes from French operas, without its becoming vulgar or offending the ear.

His lack of culture, his bad taste and vulgar coinage of words in combination with the pure and unimpeded flow of his poetic diction created a special strange genre representing, under the cloak of banality, a belated appearance of Turgenev's influence in poetry.

Since the days of Koltsov, Russia has not produced anything so native, natural, appropriate, and inalienable as Sergey Esenin, having made him a present to our times with unexampled freedom and without burdening her present with tons of ultranationalistic zeal. At the same time, Esenin was a living, palpitating particle of that spirit of pure art which, after Pushkin, we call the highest Mozartean principle, the Mozartean element.

Esenin treated his life like a fairy tale. He was Ivan the Crown Prince who flew over the ocean on a gray wolf and, like the Firebird, caught Isadora Duncan by the tail. His verses, too, he wrote by fairy tale methods, sometimes arranging his words like cards in a game of patience and sometimes writing them with his heart's blood. The most precious thing in him is the image of his native countryside, the woodlands of central Russia, of the Ryazan province, described with amazing freshness as it appeared to him in childhood.

Compared with Esenin, Mayakovsky's genius was coarser and more ponderous but, to make up for it, perhaps vaster and more profound. The place nature occupies in Esenin is occupied in Mayakovsky's poetry by the labyrinth of a modern big city, where the solitary soul of modern man has lost its way and become morally entangled and whose passionate and inhuman situations he depicts.

## 12

As I have said already, my intimacy with Mayakovsky has been exaggerated. Once, at Aseyev's, where we had a discussion about our differences, which have become more acute since then, he characterized our dissimilarity in these words: "Well, what does it matter? We really are different. You love lightning in the sky and I in an electric iron!"

I could not understand his propagandist zeal, the worming of himself and his friends by force into the public's consciousness, his idea that a poem could be written by several hands, by an association of craftsmen, and his complete subordination to the demand for topical subjects.

Even more incomprehensible to me was the journal *Lef* which he edited, its contributors and the system of ideas which was defended in it. The only consistent and honest man in this group of negationists was Sergey Tretyakov, who drove his negation to its natural conclusion. Like Plato, Tretyakov considered that there was no place for art in a young socialist state, or, at any rate, not at the moment of its birth, and that the commonplace pseudo-art, uncreative and vitiated by the corrections made in accordance with the dictates of the times, which flourished in *Lef*, was not worth the worries and labors lavished on it, and that it could be easily sacrificed.

With the exception of the immortal document *At the Top of the Voice*, written on the eve of his death, the later

Mayakovsky, beginning with *Mystery Buffo,* is inaccessible to me. I remain indifferent to those clumsily rhymed sermons, that cultivated insipidity, those commonplaces and platitudes, set forth so artificially, so confusedly, and so devoid of humor. This Mayakovsky is in my view worthless, that is, nonexistent. And the remarkable thing about it is that this worthless, nonexistent Mayakovsky has come to be accepted as revolutionary.

But it was a general mistake to consider that Mayakovsky and I were friends. Thus, for instance, Esenin, at the period of his dissatisfaction with imagism, asked me to arrange a meeting with Mayakovsky because he was anxious to become reconciled with him and because he thought that I was the right man for the job.

Though I was on familiar terms with Esenin, and not with Mayakovsky, my meetings with the former were even more infrequent. They could be counted on the fingers of the hands and they always ended in stormy scenes. We either shed tears and vowed to be true to one another, or engaged in violent fights and had to be separated by force.

### 13

During the last years of Mayakovsky's life, when all poetry had ceased to exist, either his or anybody else's, when Esenin had hanged himself, when, to put it more simply, literature had stopped—for even the beginning of *Quiet Flows the Don* and the first works of Pilnyak and Babel, Fedin and Vsevolod Ivanov, were poetry —in those years Mayakovsky's closest friend and his principal supporter was Aseyev, a perfect comrade, intelligent, talented, inwardly free, and unblinded by anything.

I, on the other hand, had completely broken with him, but for some reason, in spite of my announcement about my resignation from *Lef* and my ceasing to be a member of their circle, my name continued to appear among the names of contributors. I wrote a sharply worded letter to Mayakovsky which should have made him boil with rage.

A little earlier, during the years when I was still under the spell of his fire, his inner force, and his immense creative powers, and when he returned my devotion with the same warmth, I inscribed eight lines of verse in his copy of my *My Sister, Life.* In these I deplored his preoccupation with the national balance sheet and the tragedy of the Supreme Council of National Economy, and expressed my surprise that he should have strayed from his true and sincere path and allowed himself to be inveigled "under the arches of such an almshouse."

### 14

There are two famous sayings about that period: that life had become easier and more cheerful; and that Mayakovsky was and remained the best and most talented poet of the epoch. For the second saying I thanked the author in a personal letter, for it protected me from the inflation of my role, to which I had become assigned in the mid-thirties, at the time of the Writers' Conference. I like my life and I am satisfied with it. I am not in need of any additional gilding of it. Life without privacy and without obscurity, life reflected in the splendor of a plate-glass show case is inconceivable to me.

Mayakovsky was beginning to be propagated compulsorily, like potatoes in the reign of Catherine the Great. That was his second death. For that he is not to blame.

## THREE SHADOWS

### 1

In July, 1917, Ehrenburg got in touch with me on the advice of Bryusov. It was then that I got to know this clever writer, active and unreserved and with a cast of mind so different from mine.

It was then that the great influx began of political *émigrés* returning from abroad, people who had been caught abroad by the war and interned, and many others. Andrey Bely arrived from Switzerland. Ehrenburg arrived.

Ehrenburg spoke to me in high terms of Marina Tsvetayeva and showed me her poems. I was present at a literary meeting at the beginning of the Revolution at which she, among other writers, read her verses. During one of the winters of the Civil War I went to see her with some kind of message. I talked about all sorts of unimportant things and listened to all sorts of trivialities in turn. Marina Tsvetayeva made no impression on me.

My ear was at the time perverted by the pretentious extravagances and the break from everything natural that were in vogue in those days. Everything spoken in a normal way rebounded from me. I forgot that words by themselves can mean and contain something apart from the cheap toys with which they are strung.

It was just the harmony of Marina Tsvetayeva's verses, the clarity of their meaning, the presence of fine qualities and absence of defects that interfered with and barred the way to my understanding of their true nature. It was not the essential I looked for in everything, but some nicety which had nothing to do with it.

For a long time I underestimated Marina Tsvetayeva as in different ways I had underestimated Bagritsky, Khlebnikov, Mandelstam, and Gumilyov.

I have already said that among the young people who could not express themselves intelligibly and who raised their tongue-tied babblings into a virtue and tried to be original at all costs, only two, Aseyev and Marina Tsvetayeva, expressed themselves in human language and wrote in a classical style and language.

And suddenly both of them renounced their skill. Aseyev was tempted by Khlebnikov's example. Marina Tsvetayeva had undergone some inward changes of her own. But it was the original, the traditional Marina Tsvetayeva who in the end prevailed over me long before she suffered a rebirth.

### 2

One had to read oneself into her. When I had done so, I was amazed to discover such an abyss of purity and power. Nothing at all comparable existed anywhere else. Let me be brief. I don't think I shall go far wrong if I say that with the exception of Annensky and Blok and, with certain reservations, Andrey Bely, the early Marina Tsvetayeva was what all the rest of the symbolists taken together wanted to be but were not. Where their literary efforts floundered helplessly in a world of artificial contrivances and lifeless archaisms, Marina Tsvetayeva skimmed with the greatest of ease over the difficulties of true creative art, solving its problems with remarkable facility and with incomparable technical brilliance.

In the spring of 1922, when she was already abroad, I bought in Moscow her little volume *Versts*. I was instantly won over by the great lyrical power of the form of her poetry, which stemmed from personal experience, which was not weak-chested but wonderfully compact and condensed, which did not get out of breath at the end of each separate line, but which by the development of its periods without interruption of rhythm sustained itself for a whole succession of strophes.

These peculiarities seemed to conceal a sort of closeness or, perhaps, a community of experienced influences, or a similarity of stimuli in the formation of character, a resemblance in the part played by family and music, a homogeneity of points of departure, aims, and preferences.

I wrote a letter to Marina Tsvetayeva in Prague full of expressions of my enthusiasm and my surprise that I had failed to recognize her genius for so long and had made myself familiar with her work so late. She replied to my letter. We began a correspondence which grew particularly frequent in the middle of the twenties after the appearance of her *Craftsmanship*. In Moscow her other poems became known in manuscript, poems that were outstanding for the sweep of their ideas and brilliant and quite extraordinary for their novelty, such as *The Poem of the End, The Poem of the Mountain,* and *The Ratcatcher.* We became friends.

In the summer of 1935, feeling ill and on the point of a breakdown from insomnia lasting for almost a year, I found myself at an anti-Fascist congress in Paris. There I became acquainted with Marina Tsvetayeva's husband, a charming, refined, and steadfast man, and I grew fond of him as if he were my own brother.

The members of Marina Tsvetayeva's family insisted that she should return to Russia. They were prompted partly by homesickness and sympathy with Communism and the Soviet Union and partly by the consideration that Marina Tsvetayeva could never be happy in Paris and that she would perish living in a sort of vacuum without any readers to respond to her.

Marina Tsvetayeva asked me what I thought of it. I had no definite opinion to offer. I did not know what to say to her and I was very much afraid that she and her remarkable family would find things rather difficult and not very peaceful in Russia. The general tragedy of the family infinitely exceeded my fears.

### 3

At the beginning of this autobiographical sketch, in the section referring to my childhood, I gave some descriptions of real scenes and pictures and related a number of true events, and in the middle I went over to generalizations and began to limit my story to rapid characterizations. I am afraid this had to be done for the sake of compactness.

Had I begun to relate the story of my friendship with Marina Tsvetayeva incident by incident, the history of the aspirations and interests that created the common bond between her and myself, I should have digressed too far from the limits which I had imposed upon myself. I should have had to devote a whole book to it, so many things had we experienced in common, changes, joyful and tragic events, always unexpected, and time after time enlarging the mental outlook of us both.

But here, too, and in the remaining chapters, I shall refrain from anything personal and limit myself to what is essential and of general interest.

Marina Tsvetayeva was a woman with the soul of an active man, determined, militant, indomitable. In her life and in her work she rushed impetuously, eagerly, and almost rapaciously toward the achievement of finality and definitiveness, in the pursuit of which she had gone far and was ahead of everybody else.

In addition to the small number of her known poems, she wrote a great number of things that are not generally known, immense, violent works, some in the style of Russian fairy tales, others on subjects of well-known historical legends and myths.

Their publication would be a great triumph and a great find for Russian poetry. It would be a belated gift that would enrich it all at once.

I think that a thorough re-examination of her work and the fullest possible recognition of her genius await Marina Tsvetayeva.

We were friends. I had about a hundred letters from her in reply to mine. In spite of the place that losses and disappearances, as I have explained earlier, occupied in my life, I could never have visualized the loss of these carefully kept precious letters. They were lost because of overcarefulness in guarding them.

During the war years and my visits to my evacuated family, one of the members of the staff of the Scriabin Museum, a great admirer of Marina Tsvetayeva and a great friend of mine, proposed to me that I should give her these letters, together with the letters of my parents and several letters from Gorky and Romain Rolland, for safekeeping. She put them in the museum safe, but kept Marina Tsvetayeva's letters with her, not wishing to let them out of her hands and distrusting the strength of the walls of the fireproof safe.

She lived all the year round outside Moscow and every evening she carried the letters home with her in an attaché case and took them back to the museum in the morning. One winter night she was going back to her house in the country in a state of utter exhaustion. Halfway from the station, in the woods, she suddenly realized that she had left the attaché case

with the letters in the train. That is how Marina Tsvetayeva's letters went astray and got lost.

4

During the decades since the publication of *Safe Conduct,* I often thought that if I were to republish it I would add a chapter on the Caucasus and two Georgian poets. Time passed and the need for other additions did not arise. The only gap that remained was this missing chapter. I am going to write it now.

About 1930, in winter, Paolo Yashvili and his wife paid me a visit in Moscow. Yashvili was a brilliant man of the world, a cultured and entertaining conversationalist, a "European," a tall and handsome man.

Soon after their visit all sorts of upheavals, complications, and changes took place in two families, that of a friend of mine and my own. They were very painful to those implicated in them. For some time my companion, who was afterwards to become my second wife, and I had no roof over our heads. Yashvili offered us a place of refuge at his house in Tiflis.

At that time the Caucasus, Georgia, the life of the Georgian people and some of its individual representatives were a complete revelation to me. Everything was new, everything was surprising. Dark bulks of overhanging mountains towered at the end of all the street vistas of Tiflis. The life of the city's poorest inhabitants, brought out from the yards into the streets, was bolder and less concealed than in the North. It was brighter and more candid. It was full of mysticism and the messianic symbolism of folk legends which are so favorable to the life of the imagination and which, as in Catholic Poland, turn every man into a poet. The more advanced section of the population showed a high level of cultural and intellectual life that was seldom to be met with in those days. The fine buildings of certain parts of Tiflis reminded me of Petersburg; some had railings outside the first-floor windows which were bent in the shape of baskets or lyres. The city also abounded in picturesque back lanes. Big tambourines beating to the rhythm of the *lezginka* followed you about everywhere and always seemed to catch up with you. In addition, there were the goatlike bleatings of the bagpipes and some other musical instruments. Nightfall in a Southern town was full of stars and the scent of flowers from the gardens mingled with the smells from coffeehouses and confectioners' shops.

Paolo Yashvili is a remarkable poet of the post-symbolist period. His poetry is constructed on exact data and the evidence of the senses. It is akin to the modern European prose of Bely, Hamsun, and Proust and, like that prose, is fresh with unexpected and accurate observations. It is creative poetry *par excellence*. It is not cluttered up with tightly crammed effects. It is spacious and airy. It moves and breathes.

## 5

The First World War caught Yashvili in Paris. He was a student at the Sorbonne. He returned to his native country by a roundabout route. At a remote Norwegian railway station, Yashvili, lost in a daydream, did not notice that his train had left. A young Norwegian married couple, a farmer and his wife, who had come by sledge from their remote village for the post, saw the daydreaming, fiery Southerner and the unfortunate result of his daydreams. They were sorry for Yashvili and, after succeeding somehow or other in making themselves understood, took him with them to their farm where he was to stay till the next train which was only expected in two days' time.

Yashvili was a marvelous raconteur. He was a born teller of adventure stories. He was always beset by the sort of surprises that one only reads about in novels. Chance played a prominent part in his life. He had a gift for it. He was lucky that way.

In his company one could not help feeling that one was in the presence of a highly gifted man. His eyes blazed with the fire of his soul, his lips were seared by the fire of his passions. His face was scorched and blackened by the heat of experience, so that he seemed to be older than his age, a man who had been through a great deal, a man who was a little the worse for wear.

On the day of our arrival he collected his friends, the members of the group whose leader he was. I don't remember who came on that occasion. His next-door neighbor, Nikolay Nadiradze, must quite certainly have been there. Titian Tabidze was there too with his wife.

## 6

I can see that room just as if I were there now. And how could I forget it? On that very evening, without suspecting the horrors that lay in store for it, I lowered it very gently so that it should not get broken to the bottom of my soul with all the terrible things that happened in it and near it.

Why were those two men sent to me? How shall I describe our relations? Both became integral parts of my personal world. I did not prefer one to the other because they were inseparable and complementary to one another. The fate of these two men, and that of Marina Tsvetayeva, was to become my greatest sorrow.

7

If Yashvili was turned outwards, all in a centrifugal direction, Titian Tabidze was turned inwards and every line he wrote and every step he took called you into the depths of his rich soul, so full of intuitions and forebodings.

The main thing in his poetry is the feeling of an inexhaustible fund of lyrical potentialities that is implied in every one of his poems, the preponderance of unsaid things and of those he would still say over those he had said already. This presence of an untouched store of spiritual reserves creates the background and lends depth to his poems and imparts that special mood with which they are imbued and which constitutes their principal and bitter charm. There is as much soul in his poems as there was in himself, a complex, esoteric soul, directed wholly toward good, capable of clairvoyance and self-sacrifice.

When I think of Yashvili all sorts of urban scenes come to my mind, rooms, arguments, addresses delivered at public meetings, Yashvili's dazzling eloquence at crowded parties at night.

The thought of Tabidze brings to mind the elements of nature, in my imagination arise all sorts of country scenes, the freedom of flowering meadows, the waves of the sea.

Clouds are sailing along, and in the distance, in a line with them, mountains rise up. And the thickset, compact figure of the smiling poet merges with them. He has a somewhat wavering gait. He shakes all over when he laughs. Now he gets up, stands sideways to the table, and taps his glass with a knife before making a speech. His habit of raising one shoulder higher than the other makes him look a little crooked.

His house in Kodzhary stands at the bend of the road. The road rises along the front and then, bending round the house, goes past its back wall. From that house one can see those who walk and those who drive past it twice.

It was at the height of the period when, according to Bely's witty definition, the triumph of materialism had abolished matter. There was nothing to eat; there was nothing to wear. There was nothing tangible around, only ideas. If we kept alive, it was thanks to our Tiflis friends, miracle workers who all the time managed to get something and bring something and provide us with advances from publishing houses for something we had no idea of.

We met, exchanged news, dined, read something to each other. The light, cool breezes played, as though with fingers, with the poplar's silvery foliage, velvety and white on the underside. The air, as with rumors, was full of the heavy scents of the South. Like the front of a cart on its coupling-pole, the night on high slowly turned the whole body of its starry chariot. And on the road bullock-carts and automobiles drove and moved along and every one of them could be seen from the house twice.

Or we were on the Georgian military road, or in Borzhom, or in Abastuman. Or after trips into the countryside, to beauty spots, adventures, and libations, we, each one of us with something or other, and I with a black eye from a fall, stopped in Bakuriany at the house of Leonidze, a most original poet, more than anyone else closely bound up with the mysteries of the language in which he wrote, and for that reason least of all amenable to translation.

A midnight feast on the grass in a wood, a beautiful hostess, two charming little daughters. Next day the unexpected arrival of a *mestvir*, a wandering minstrel with a bagpipe, and an impromptu glorification of everyone at the table in turn, with an appropriate text and an ability to seize on any excuse, like my black eye, for instance, for a toast.

Or we went to the seaside in Kabuleti. Rains and storms. In the same hotel Simon Chikovani, the future master of bright, picturesque verse, at the time still a member of the Communist Youth League. And above the line of all the mountains and horizons, the head of the smiling poet walking beside me, and the bright, luminous signs of his prodigious talent, and the shadow of sadness and destiny in his smile. And once more I bid farewell to him now on these pages. Let me, in his person, bid a farewell to all my other memories.

## CONCLUSION

This concludes my autobiographical sketch. I do not cut it short by leaving it unfinished, but put a full stop where I had intended to put it from the very first. It was not my intention to write the history of the last fifty years in many volumes and with many characters.

I have not analyzed the works of Martynov, Zabolotsky, Selvinsky, Tikhonov—all good poets. I have not said anything about the poets of the generation of Simonov and Tvardovsky, so numerous.

I proceeded from the center of the narrowest circle of life, limiting myself by it deliberately.

What I have written here is enough to give an idea of how life in my own case was transmuted into art, how it was born of chance and experience. . . .

Above I have described my ambivalent attitude toward my own poetic past and to that of others. I would never lift a finger to bring back from oblivion three fourths of what I have written. Why

then, it may be objected, do I let someone else publish it?

There are two reasons for it. First, there are often grains of truth, aptness, and acute observation in the mass of what is deplorable and annoying about those things of mine. Secondly, quite recently, I completed my chief and most important work, the only one I am not ashamed of and for which I can answer with the utmost confidence, a novel in prose with a supplement in verse, *Doctor Zhivago*.

I have now come to the end of my autobiographical sketch. To continue it would be exceedingly difficult. To keep up the sequence of events I should have had to speak of years, circumstances, people, and destinies within the framework of the Revolution. Of a world of hitherto unknown aims and aspirations, problems and exploits, a new self-restraint, a new strictness—new trials with which this world confronts the human personality and man's honor, pride, and endurance.

This unique world, the like of which has never been known before, has now receded into the faraway distance of memories and hangs suspended on the horizon like mountains seen from a plain or like a faraway big city against the smoky background of a red sunset.

One would have to write about it in a way to make the heart stop beating and the hair stand on end. To write about it in an ordinary and commonplace way, to write about it unemotionally, to write about it less colorfully than Gogol and Dostoevsky have depicted Petersburg, is not only senseless and useless; to write like that would be both dishonest and base.

We are far from that ideal.

November, 1957

# NOTES

*An alphabetical list of names mentioned in the text, with the exception of names of internationally known writers. [Dates given are as of 1960.—ED.]*

ACMEISM. Movement in Russian poetry founded in 1912 as a reaction against symbolism. The acmeists objected to the mysticism and vagueness of symbolist poetry and called for a return to clarity, precision, and concreteness. They also emphasized the virile and heroic aspects of life.

AKHMATOVA, pseudonym of Anna Arkadyevna Gorenko (1888–    ). Poet. Began to publish poetry in 1907. Love lyrics published in 1912–15 established her popularity. After the Revolution she published one book in 1923, *A.D. 1921*, then fell silent; after a gap of seventeen years, published another book of poems in 1940. Married to Gumilyov, whom she divorced in 1918. During her long period of silence as a poet, she published some important studies of Pushkin. In 1940 she took advantage of the greater leniency of the war years to publish a selection of her poems, new and old. Zhdanov launched an attack on her in 1946 which led to her expulsion from the Union of Soviet Writers. In 1950 she published a number of patriotic verses of rather poor quality. Her poems show some of the best qualities of acmeism. Her range of subject matter is small, concerned chiefly with the themes of love and death, treated with a tinge of mysticism reminiscent of symbolism. Her works show no marked development of style or ideas.

ALKONOST. Publishers of Blok's works. Volume II of this edition appeared in 1922, in Petersburg. *Alkonost:* a folktale bird with a human face.

ANDREYEVA, MARIA FYODOROVNA (1872–1953). Actress. Joined Stanislavsky's amateur theatrical group in 1894 and afterwards became a member of the Moscow Art Theater. Stanislavsky admired her as a "Gothic" actress. Played Irina in *The Three Sisters*, Varya in *The Cherry Orchard*, Natasha in *The Lower Depths*, etc. Joined Marxist student organization. From 1903 associated with Gorky, acting as his secretary. Visited a number of European countries and the U.S.A. along with Gorky, 1906. Accompanied Gorky to London in 1907. Returned to the stage in 1913. Helped to establish Petersburg Bolshoi Theater in 1919, acting in it 1919–26. From 1931 to 1948 was Director of Moscow Scientists' and Scholars' Club.

ANNENSKY, INNOKENTY FYODOROVICH (1856–1909). Symbolist poet. Tried to introduce the impressionism of Verlaine and Mallarmé into Russia. Translator of Euripides, Rimbaud, and Baudelaire. First appeared in print as writer of reviews and articles on educational subjects in the 1880's. In 1904 published a book of lyric poems, *Quiet Songs,* under the pseudonym Nik-to (*nikto*—nobody). His second book of poems, *The Cypress Chest,* was published posthumously in 1910. Tried to depict the world of the "sick soul," described nightmares, etc. His verse became known long before his death in the circle around the journal *Apollon,* then was forgotten. Revived interest in him about 1923.

*Apollon.* A symbolist review.

ASEYEV, NIKOLAI NIKOLAYEVICH (1889–    ). Poet. Began writing symbolist poetry in 1913. Met Mayakovsky and much influenced by him. Published collections of verse during the First World War. During Civil War published revolutionary verses. In 1923 was one of the founders of the journal *Lef.* Notable poems on revolutionary themes: *The 26* (i.e., the 26 Baku Commissars executed in 1918) (1926). Poem in honor of Mayakovsky awarded Stalin Prize, 1941. Aseyev tries to distinguish Mayakovsky sharply from such futurists as Khlebnikov. During the 1941–45 war wrote patriotic verses, and after the war wrote anti-American verses and songs.

BABEL, ISAAK EMANUILOVICH (1894–1938). Outstanding Soviet short-story writer. Born in Odessa, Jewish; his first stories were published by Gorky in his *Annals* in 1915. They were highly erotic, and Babel was prosecuted for pornography. Took part in the Polish campaign with Budyony's Cossack cavalry. His short stories of the early Soviet period began to appear in 1923 and he was immediately recognized as an outstanding writer. His stories are stories of blood and death, of cold-blooded crime, of heroism and cruelty. There is always a grain of irony in them which does not destroy but only enhances the heroic pathos. They deal with the Polish campaign (*The Red Cavalry,* 1923) and with the Odessa underworld. (Probably killed in the purge of 1937–38. His stories were republished in Russia and his work discussed for the first time since 1937 in 1956.)

BAGRITSKY, EDUARD GEORGIEVICH, pseudonym of Dzubin (1895–1934). Poet. Born in Odessa; Jewish. Wrote verses during First World War under influence of Gumilyov and acmeism. Verses written in the 1920's deal with Civil War themes and with life of fishermen and sailors. The setting of his major work, *The Epic of Apanas,* 1926, is the Civil War of the Ukraine. Poems written in the 1930's hail the constructive labor of ordinary people (*The New Knights*) and especially the Soviet young generation (*Death of a Pioneer Girl*).

BALMONT, KONSTANTIN DMITRIEVICH (1867–1943). Poet. Leader of early symbolist movement in Russia. Collections of poems: *Under the Northern Light* (1894); *Shoreless* (1895); *Silence* (1898); *Burning Building* (1900); *Let's Be Like the Sun* (1903); *Liturgy of Beauty* (1905); *Evil Charms* (1906); *Bird of Flame* (1906). Traveled in South Africa, Mexico, New Zealand, Spain. Translated Shelley, Whitman, Poe, and Calderón. Emigrated in 1918 and died in Paris.

BALTRUSHAITIS, JURGIS (1873–1945). Poet. Born in a Lithuanian peasant family. Wrote poetry from 1899 onward, in both Russian and Lithuanian. Associated with the symbolists, and one of the founders of their publishing house Skorpion. Distinguished as translator of Byron, Ibsen, D'Annunzio, Hamsun, Wilde, and Strindberg.

BELINSKY, VISSARION GRIGORYEVICH (1811–48). Famous Russian literary critic, who has greatly influenced Russian contem-

porary writings. A close friend of Turgenev. Was the first literary critic to appreciate Dostoevsky's genius.

BELY, ANDREY, pseudonym of Bugayev, Boris Nikolayevich (1880–1934). Poet and novelist. One of the principal representatives of Russian symbolism. Born in Moscow, son of a professor of mathematics. Studied in Moscow. In 1904 began to contribute to Bryusov's journal *Vessy* (Scales) and soon became one of the most outstanding theoreticians of symbolism, which he conceived not merely as a literary school but as a world outlook. Became a follower of Rudolf Steiner, the anthroposophist, in 1912. His first writings appeared in 1902 under the title *Symphony (Second, Dramatic)*, followed by the *First* (1904), *Third* (1905), and *Fourth* "Symphonies." Most famous of his prose works is his novel *Petersburg.* He is also the author of works on the history of literature. Recognized as a master of meter and rhythm, some of his works being written in rhythmic, musical prose.

BLOK, ALEXANDER ALEXANDROVICH (1880–1921). Greatest Russian poet of modern times. Began publishing verses in 1903. Contributed to symbolist journal *The Golden Fleece,* as poet, playwright, and critic. Served in the army during the First World War. After the Revolution, worked in the Commission for Publishing the Classics, and in the theatrical section of the Commissariat of Education. His early poems are full of mysticism and the sense of impending catastrophe. In his first poems, *Verses About a Beautiful Woman,* he gives an ideal picture of a woman who is the incarnation of the "eternal feminine." The 1905 Revolution made a big impression on him, and after that he wrote on social themes, such as the contrasts and antagonisms of rich and poor, etc. He greeted the October Revolution as a cleansing storm. He entered the Soviet poetic scene with his great poem *The Twelve,* an apocalyptic vision of the Revolution, personified in twelve Red Army men as the apostles of the new world, headed by Christ crowned with a wreath of white roses, and marching invisible and unscathed through the raging storm. In the same period *The Scythians* (1918) expresses Russia's "love-hatred" for the West.

BLUE ROSE, THE. Name given to a Moscow art exhibition of 1907, the participants in which were decorative impressionists.

BOBROV, SERGEY PAVLOVICH (1881–    ). Futurist poet, and author of works on versification and the theory of literature. Also prose writer: *The Uprising of the Misanthropes,* a fantasy of world revolution.

BRYUSOV, VALERY YAKOVLEVICH (1873–1924). One of the founders of the symbolist movement in Russia. Born in Moscow. His grandfather and father were serfs who later became small tradesmen. Educated in private schools and Moscow University, where he studied philosophy. He provides a living link between Soviet poetry and the great Russian poetry of the past. At the age of twenty-two, in 1895 he issued his manifesto to the world: "Incapable of entreaties and tears, I have locked my door and cursed our days." These first poems, published in *Russian Symbolists,* made him famous. Followed it up with two more volumes, *Chef d'oeuvre* (1894–95) and *Me Eum Esse* (1896–97). The hero of his lyric poems is a militant individualist, an enemy of materialism. He was much influenced by Baudelaire and Verlaine. The chief aim of symbolism, according to the young Bryusov, was to make his readers see the world in a new light and stimulate their imaginations. By 1903 he was the recognized head of the symbolist movement. He edited the symbolist review *Vessy* (Scales) from 1904 to 1909. During the First World War acted as war correspondent of a Moscow paper. Author of several plays as well as translations of plays performed on the Petersburg and Moscow stages. After the October Revolution he rallied to the new regime, and did much to instruct the young Soviet poets in the art of poetry.

CHIKOVANI, SIMON IVANOVITCH (1902–    ). Soviet poet glorifying benefits of Revolu-

tion in Georgia. Awarded the Stalin Prize in 1947.

CONSTRUCTIVISTS. Group of poets formed in 1924 around Selvinsky. From the futurists they took their interest in technology and other contemporary themes, but they were not so antitraditional. Their central idea was that all the images and devices of a poem must be directed toward the poem's subject: e.g., a poem about war should have a marching rhythm. The group broke up in 1930.

D'ALHEIM OLENINA, MARIA ALEXEYEVNA (1871–    ). Mezzo-soprano. Made her debut in Paris in 1897 at Musorgsky concerts. First performed in Russia in 1901. Founded the music society Dom Pesni (The House of Song) in 1908 in Moscow. This played a notable role in development of musical taste in Moscow and Petersburg. Wrote a book, *The Legacy of Musorgsky.* After 1918 lived in Paris. Married to the French critic Pierre D'Alheim, who did much to make Musorgsky's music known in France.

DONKEY'S TAIL, THE. Name assumed by a group of surrealist painters.

DROZHZHIN, SPIRIDON DMITRIEVICH (1848–1930). Poet, of peasant origin. Began publishing verse 1873. From 1896 lived in his native village in Tver province, occupied with farming and writing. Wrote verse depicting the hard life of the peasants. Much influenced by Nekrasov. Welcomed the October Revolution and wrote verse in its honor, notably *In Memory of Lenin,* 1924.

DURYLIN, SERGEY NIKOLAYEVICH (1881–    ). Poet. Pseudonyms: S. Severny, S. Rayevsky. Best known for his writings about literature. Early works much influenced by symbolism. In 1916 wrote a study of the poet Lermontov, examining his verses from the standpoint of Andrey Bely's theories. Important later books: *Repin and Garshin,* 1926, *From Gogol's Family Chronicle,* 1928, *About Tolstoy,* 1928.

EHRENBURG, ILYA GEORGIEVICH (1891–    ). Poet and novelist. Left Russia in

1909 for Paris, where he entered the Bohemian literary world. His first poetry appeared in 1911. During the First World War remained in France as war correspondent. Returned to Russia in 1917, and lived in the South, under the Whites. In 1921 was arrested by the Soviet authorities but released on "accepting" the Revolution. Returned to Paris and spent most of his time in the West until 1941. Was Soviet war correspondent in Spain in 1936–37. During Second World War wrote much patriotic propaganda. First successful novel, *Julio Jurenito*, 1922, satirical and cynical. *Trust D.E.*, 1923, a fantasy of the conquest of Europe by America. *The Second Day*, 1933 depicts the construction of a steel works in Siberia. His *Storm and The Ninth Wave* were translated into English and widely read in England and America. His latest novel, *The Thaw*, met with violent attacks in Soviet Russia and involved him in heated polemics with several writers, especially Konstantin Simonov. He is now under a cloud.

ELLIS-KOBYLINSKY, LEV LVOVICH (1874–1947). Poet and critic. Member of the Society of Religious Philosophy. Emigrated and died in Locarno.

ENGEL, YURI DMITRIEVICH (1868–1927). Studied at Moscow Conservatory. From 1897 in charge of the music column in *Russkyie Vyedomosti*. One of the founders of the People's Conservatory, 1906, and of the Society for Jewish Folk Music, 1908. First biographer of Scriabin. After October Revolution active in musical education work for the schools. After 1924 lived at Tel-Aviv.

ESENIN, SERGEY ALEXANDROVICH (1895–1925). One of the greatest modern Russian lyric poets. Son of a peasant. Worked in Moscow as a proofreader. Influenced by Blok and Bely. Equally unsurpassable as a nature poet and as a poet of love lyrics; in both nature and love he depicted the eternally true and the eternally different. The peculiar charm of his poetry is its freshness. Joined the imagists and led a rowdy café life with them. Married the famous dancer, Isadora Duncan, in 1922 and went abroad with her, but they separated and he returned to Russia in 1923. Suffered a mental collapse in 1925, wrote a farewell poem in his own blood, and hanged himself.

FADEYEV, ALEXANDER ALEXANDROVICH (1901–56). Novelist. Of peasant origin, grew up in Far Eastern Siberia. Served on the Red side in the Civil War. His first important work was his short novel *The Rout*, 1927, set among the partisans of the Far East. Another novel, *The Last of the Udegs*, 1928–36, depicts the changes brought about by the Revolution in the life of an almost extinct Far Eastern tribe. In 1939 he was made Secretary of the Union of Soviet Writers. In 1945 he wrote *The Young Guard*, a war novel. He rewrote sections of this novel after strong Communist Party criticism. Committed suicide in 1956 after a strongly worded attack on him by Sholokhov, who accused him of having been corrupted by his "love of power," at the Communist Party Congress.

FEDIN, KONSTANTIN ALEXANDROVICH (1892– ). Prominent Russian novelist. A member of the Serapion group. Published *The Orchard* in 1920, which was attacked by Soviet critics. His first novel, *Cities and Years*, 1924, was one of the earliest attempts to depict the impact of the Revolution on an intellectual. Soviet critics accused Fedin of sharing his hero's "doubts." His second novel, *Brothers*, 1928, deals with the mission of the artist, whose right to individualism is opposed to the obligations of Soviet life, and again Fedin seemed to sympathize with his nonconforming hero. In the 1930's Fedin appears to have overcome his objections to the Soviet regime. *The Rape of Europe*, 1934–35, contrasts "decadent" Western Europe with progressive Russia. His postwar novels, *Early Joys*, 1945–46, and *Extraordinary Summer*, 1948, are his best work.

FIELD, JOHN (1782–1837). Composer and pianist. Born in Dublin and settled in Moscow. Chopin used his nocturnes as models.

FUTURISM. Poetry movement founded in

1910 by Khlebnikov. A manifesto published by him, Mayakovsky, and others in 1912 was entitled *A Slap in the Face of Public Taste*. In revolt against symbolism, especially against its mysticism and aestheticism, the futurists were fascinated by the most modern features of modern life. They wanted to scrap the whole cultural tradition of the past and to wake everybody up by shock methods. In 1923 they formed an organization and a journal called *Lef* (Left Front) to oppose the tendency toward a return to conservative realism. They did not have much success, and the journal closed down in 1925. A new *Lef* was begun in 1927, but it, too, soon ceased publication.

GE, NIKOLAY NIKOLAYEVICH (1831–94). Russian painter. Studied in Italy. His paintings on themes from the New Testament show remarkable psychological insight and dramatic power. On return to Petersburg in 1869 was active in *Peredvizhniki* group. Historical paintings, notably *Peter the Great with the Tsarevich Alexey* (1871); portraits of Turgenev, Antokolsky, Saltykov-Shchedrin, Nekrasov, and other eminent contemporaries. Left Petersburg to live in the country and painted a series of scenes from the life of Christ. Fell under the influence of Tolstoy, whose portrait he painted in 1884.

GLIER, REINHOLD MORITSOVICH (1874– ). Composer. Born in Kiev of a musical family. Studied music in Kiev and at Moscow Conservatory. Began conducting, 1908. In 1914–20 director of Kiev Conservatory. In 1920–41 director of Moscow Conservatory. Already known for his symphonies before the Revolution, Glier's best period began after it. He was one of the first composers of the older generation to rally to the Soviet regime and help it in its educational and cultural work. His *Red Poppy* (1927) was the first ballet on a contemporary revolutionary theme. He devoted special attention to the folk music of Azerbaijan and Central Asia and composed operas based on their folklore. Prokofiev, Myaskovsky, and several other famous composers studied under Glier.

*Golden Fleece, The*. A monthly review (1906–09) of the symbolists of the second generation, including Blok.

GOLITZIN, DMITRI PETROVICH, PRINCE (1860–1919). Published tales, novels, and poems under the pseudonym of Muravlin. Influenced by Dostoevsky.

GOLITZIN, NIKOLAY DMITRIEVICH, PRINCE (1850–1925). Last chairman of the Tsar's council of ministers, 1916–17.

GONCHAROVA, NATALYA SERGEYEVNA (1883– ). Painter. Studied under Trubetskoy in Moscow, 1899–1902. As artist, fell under influence of most "extreme" tendencies of her time, such as cubism, etc., 1911–13. Futurist pictures include *Airplane over a Train*. Growing interest in Eastern folk art; influence of Henri Rousseau. Together with Larionov, whom she married, tried to found a new theory, *Luchism* (*Luch*— "ray"), related to cubism, but nothing came of this. In later works, e.g., *Spanish Girls,* Goncharova tried to combine the traditions of the great painters of the West with the methods of ancient Russian fresco painters. Participated in *World of Art* exhibitions. Went to Paris on Diaghilev's invitation, and was responsible for sets for a number of his productions, such as *Le Coq d'Or* and others. Exhibited in Paris and America.

GRIN, ALEXANDER STEPANOVICH, pseudonym of Grinevsky (1890–1932). Author of fantastic novels and stories.

GUMILYOV, NIKOLAY STEPANOVICH (1886–1921). Poet and critic. Educated at the Sorbonne and at Petersburg University. Traveled in Abyssinia and Somaliland. Served as volunteer in 1914 war. Fought on the Salonika front. Went to France after the February Revolution, became Provisional Government Commissioner for the affairs of Russian troops in France. In 1918 returned to Russia. Shot in 1921 for alleged participation in White Guard conspiracy. As poet, Gumilyov began under the influence of the symbolists. Following Bryusov, he wrote about exotic, savage countries: *The Giraffe*. He then became the leader of the acmeist group. After the October Revolution he returned to symbolism and mysticism. His best works are *The Pyre,* 1918, and *The Pillar of Fire,* 1921. Translated Théophile Gautier.

HAMSUN, KNUT, pseudonym of Knut Pedersen (1859–1952). Norwegian novelist. His novel *Hunger,* published in 1890, in which he described irrational processes in the mind of a starving man in a lyric ecstatic style influenced by Dostoevsky, made him famous. Wrote a trilogy, 1906–09–12, about a vagabond dreamer. A neoromantic individualist in revolt against civilization. His *Growth of the Soil,* 1917, was an epic of the simple life for which he was awarded the Nobel Prize. His novels were very popular in Russia, and at one time he was read more avidly there than Ibsen. His extremely reactionary views led to collaboration with the Nazi occupiers of Norway. He was tried for treason after the war and fined the greater part of his fortune.

IMAGISTS. A group of Moscow poets whose theory was that the principal thing in poetry is "imagery." Their poetry is therefore an agglomeration of "images" of the most far-fetched and exaggerated description. They made it a special point not to distinguish between "pure" and "impure," and to introduce the coarsest and crudest images side by side with the pathetic and the sublime. The group was founded in 1919 and fell apart after 1924.

IVANOV, SERGEY VASILYEVICH (1846–1910). A genre painter and a member of the Society for Traveling Art Exhibitions.

IVANOV, VSEVOLOD VYACHESLAVICH (1895–    ). Soviet novelist and playwright. Was actor, sailor, printshop-worker. Took part in Civil War in Siberia and wrote stories about it: *Partisans,* 1921. His play *Armored Train 14–69* (1922) was produced by Stanislavsky for the Moscow Art Theater in 1927. Associated for a time with the Serapion Fraternity. Another play of his, *Blockade* (1929), deals with the suppression of the Baltic Fleet mutiny in Kronstadt in 1921. At the end of the 1930's returned to Civil War themes and wrote the novel *Parkhomenko* (1938–39), about one of the heroes of the Red Army.

In addition, wrote patriotic articles and tales during the 1941–45 war, and in 1947 published *Encounters with Maxim Gorky.*

IVANOV, VYACHESLAV IVANOVICH (1866–1949). Symbolist poet. Appointed professor of Greek at Baku in 1921. In 1924 left the Soviet Union on an official mission. Remained in Italy, becoming a convert to Roman Catholicism. In *Guiding Stars,* a book of poetry published in 1903, he proclaimed the equation of Christ and Dionysos. According to him, "ecstasy for ecstasy's sake" was to be found in "symphonic" culture and nonacceptance of the world.

JACK OF DIAMONDS, THE (1910–26). Name of a group of formalist painters hostile to realism in painting.

KHLEBNIKOV, VELEMIR (Viktor Vladimirovich) (1886–1922). Experimental poet. His first verses (1906–08) showed the influence of symbolism, but later he became connected with the futurists and went in for word-creation. He idealized the patriarchal past of the Slavs. He hailed the October Revolution, which, however, he conceived as a sort of "Stenka Razin" affair, an elemental revolt. In his last poems he attempted a fantastic picture of the society of the future. Mayakovsky admired Khlebnikov's experimental efforts. Russian futurism dates from 1910, when Khlebnikov published his famous etymological poem, which was nothing but a series of freshly coined derivatives of one word, *smekh* (laughter).

KHODASEVICH, VLADISLAV FELITSIANOVICH (1886–1939). Poet. First volume of symbolist poems, *Youth,* published in 1908. Fascinated by death, disintegration, and monstrosity. A successor to Annensky. In exile from 1922. His latest poems (*The Way of the Grain,* 1920, and *The Heavy Lyre,* 1923) show a return to the Russian classical traditions.

KLEIST, HEINRICH WILHELM VON (1777–1811). German poet and playwright, associated with Goethe, Schiller, and Wieland. Most important North German dramatist of the romantic movement. Lived mainly in Berlin. Infatuated with a woman of brilliant musical talent and died in a suicide pact with her.

KLYUCHEVSKY, VASILY OSIPOVICH (1841–1911). Professor of history at Moscow University. A right-wing liberal. His most important work was his *Course of Russian History*, in five volumes, published between 1904 and 1911.

KOLTSOV, ALEXEY VASILYEVICH (1809–42). Poet. Born in Voronezh in a cattle merchant's family. Had a hard childhood, spent only two years at the parish school. His father tried to suppress the boy's literary aspirations. At sixteen, however, began to write verse. Dealt mainly with peasant life and the countryside—*The Forest*, 1838.

KOMMISSARZHEVSKAYA, VERA (1864–1910). Famous Russian dramatic actress. Began career in 1892 in amateur dramatics and a year later went to the provinces as a professional actress. In 1896 joined the Petersburg Alexandrinsky Theater and in 1902 left it for the provinces. Founded her own theater in Petersburg in 1904. Sister of famous producer Fyodor Kommissarzhevsky.

KOROVIN, KONSTANTIN ALEXEYEVICH (1861–1939). Landscape painter, but particularly famous as designer of scenery for the theater and opera, especially for productions of *A Life for the Tsar*, 1904, *Sadko*, 1906, *The Snow Maiden*, 1907, *Khovanshchina*, 1912. Later became impressionist. Died in exile.

KRYMOV, NIKOLAY PETROVICH (1884–    ). Painter. Studied in Moscow, 1904–11. Began as journalist, member of Blue Rose group. Later turned to realistic painting. Famous as a landscape painter—*A Summer Day, A Dull Day, Dawn in the Gorky Park of Culture and Rest*, 1937. Also did much theatrical scene designing.

*Lef* (Left-Wing Front). A left-wing literary journal of futurist writers published with interruptions from 1923 to 1930. Mayakovsky broke with *Lef* in 1928.

LEONIDZE, GEORGI NIKOLAYEVICH (1899–    ). Georgian poet. Studied at theological seminary and at Tiflis University. His first poems show influence of symbolists, but later he abandoned this school and wrote in honor of triumphs of socialist construction in Georgia—*To Lenin*, 1936. Also poems about the Georgian countryside and the history of Georgia. Awarded Stalin Prize for a poem about Stalin, 1941. Awarded further Stalin Prize in 1952.

LEVITAN, ISAAK ILYICH (1860–1900). One of the most famous Russian landscape painters and one of Anton Chekhov's closest friends. Studied in Moscow in 1884 under Polenov. His famous series of scenes along the Volga painted in the 1880's and 1890's. Some of his works have indirect social and political criticism—e.g., *Vladimirka* (1892), showing the road along which exiles to Siberia were taken. Taught in Moscow from 1898. In 1889 visited Paris, where he discovered the Barbizon painters and impressionists, whose style he assimilated.

LOMONOSOV, MIKHAIL VASILYEVICH (1711–65). Poet and scientist. Son of a peasant, born near Archangel. Walked to Moscow in 1730 in search of an education, living in very difficult circumstances. Attracted attention by his outstanding abilities. Taken into the secondary school attached to the Academy of Sciences. In 1736 sent to Germany to study chemistry and metallurgy. Was at Marburg University, 1736–40, where he married. Traveled in Germany and Holland. Returned to Russia, 1741. Given a post in the Academy of Sciences. In 1745 made professor of chemistry; in 1757 put in charge of the Academy's Geographical Department. Later became head of Moscow University. Author of important works on physics and chemistry. Also distinguished as a poet. Called "the father of modern Russian literature." Wrote an important *Letter on the Rules of Russian Versification*, and works on Russian grammar and style.

MAKOVSKY, SERGEY KONSTANTINOVICH (1878–    ). Poet, critic, and editor of Petersburg review *Apollon* (1909–17). Emigrated in 1922, living in Paris.

MAKOVSKY, VLADIMIR YEGOROVICH (1846–1920). Painter, member of the Society for Traveling Art Exhibitions. Prominent in realist revolt against academicism. Paintings of urban life in which emphasis is laid on social contrasts and sympathy shown for the poor and the oppressed. His pictures include *The Condemned,* 1879, *Bank Crash,* 1881, *Examination of a Revolutionary,* 1904.

MANDELSTAM, OSIP EMILIEVICH (1892–1938). An acmeist poet associated with Gumilyov and Akhmatova. First poem published in *Apollon* in 1910. Influenced by French classical poets. First book of poems, entitled *Kamen* (Stone), appeared in 1913. Another volume of poems, *Tristia,* published in 1922. Between 1920 and 1926 published three books of children's poems and translations from French and English prose. Own prose works include a book of essays, *On Poetry,* 1928, *The Noise of Time,* 1925, and *The Egyptian Stamp,* 1928. His last known original poems include the cycle *Armenia, Leningrad,* and *Midnight in Moscow.* Bitterly opposed to Bolshevism, and in 1932, at an informal gathering at the Moscow apartment of Boris Pasternak, recited a satirical piece derogatory to Stalin. Some days later arrested and banished. Released in 1937, but soon arrested again and believed to have died in Vladivostok hospital in December, 1938.

MANIFESTO OF OCTOBER 17, 1905. The Tsar issued a manifesto promising a constitution, and a procession of students carrying Red flags was attacked by Cossacks, on this day. One of the students was killed. His funeral procession a few days later turned into a mass demonstration by students and workers. The same evening Cossacks and the reactionary, terroristic Black Hundreds beat and killed a number of students.

MARIA ALEXEVNA, PRINCESS. A fictitious character mentioned in Griboyedov's famous comedy, *The Misfortune of Being Clever.* The Russian Mrs. Grundy.

MARTYNOV, LEONID NIKOLAYEVICH (1905–        ). Poet and journalist. Traveled in Siberia and Central Asia. From 1922 on, published poems about those parts, especially on Civil War themes.

MAYAKOVSKY, VLADIMIR VLADIMIROVICH (1893–1930). Famous Soviet poet. Studied painting and came under futurist influ-

ence. Signed futurist manifesto in 1912. In 1917 was one of the few established writers who rallied at once to the Soviet regime. Wrote *Mystery Buffo,* 1918, a verse play prophesying victory of Revolution over capitalism, but his later satirical plays, *The Bedbug,* 1928, and *The Bath House,* 1929, show disillusionment with the growing philistinism and bureaucracy of Soviet life. He was a poet of action and had a great passion for truth, but the shafts of his satire were directed equally against friend and foe. In 1918–20 contributed drawings and texts for thousands of propaganda posters. In 1923 joined the Russian Association of Proletarian Writers (Rapp), the agency of Party control over literature, and made a tremendous effort to do what was officially wanted, fervently promising to write "a hundred Party books." Only two months later, however, he shot himself without having written another line except his death-note (in which he said: "The boat of love has crashed on the rocks of everyday life").

METNER, EMILE KARLOVICH (1872–1936). Philosopher and philologist. Emigrated and died in Dresden.

MOSCOW. Moscow is encircled by two "rings" —the Boulevard, near the center of town, and, beyond that, the Sadovaya. Before the Revolution the industrial and working-class were mainly in the outskirts, beyond the Sadovaya ring. The area inside this ring was mostly occupied by offices, shops, theaters, hotels, the University, etc. Two main working-class areas were the Presnya district to the west of the Sadovaya ring, and the "railway district" around the main-line termini, to the northwest (these were the chief storm centers during the 1905 Revolution). Tverskie and Yamskie Streets, and Oruzheyny Lane are just beyond the Sadovaya ring to the northwest, and Razgulyay Square is to the east. The Arbat, running west from the Boulevard ring through the Sadovaya ring, and Myasnitsky Street, cutting through both rings in the opposite direction, are mentioned in 1898 and 1903 guides to Moscow as lively streets with elegant houses and foreign shops. "Truba" is what Muscovites called the area around Trubnaya

Square, on the north sector of the Boulevard ring. There was a market there, for birds, fishermen's equipment, etc. The Tsvetnoi Boulevard, just north of the Truba, is divided into two lanes with gardens between them; the Circus and the Central Market were in this boulevard. Yushkov Lane was a turning off Myasnitsky Street just before it crossed the Boulevard ring. Okhotny Ryad was the game market, near the very center of Moscow. The Church of Sts. Florus and Laurus was on Myasnitsky Street. The saints are recognized only by the Greek orthodox Church. They are said to have been stonemasons who were martyred in Illyria in the second century because they erected a cross on a heathen temple that they had been ordered to build. Their saints' day is August 18th.

MURATOV, PAVEL PAVLOVICH (1881–1950). Novelist and critic. Associated with the periodical *The World of Art,* which was founded in 1898 by Diaghilev and became the center of the aesthetic movement in art and literature. Author of a *History of Old Russian Painting,* 1914. Emigrated.

MUSAGET (i.e., Musagetes, Apollo, leader of the Muses). Publishing house, founded in 1909, which published a symbolist review of the same name.

MYASOYEDOV, GRIGORY GRIGORIEVICH (1835–1911). Painter. Studied abroad. On return he became one of the organizers of the Society for Traveling Art Exhibitions. His paintings deal with peasant life and historical episodes. Members of the Academy of Art from 1893.

NADIRADZE, KOLAU (NIKOLAY) (1894–    ), Georgian poet. Born at Kutais, studied at Moscow University. First verses appeared in 1916 in the journal of the Georgian symbolists, *Blue Horns.* There is a great deal of mysticism and nationalistic romanticism in his writings. After Sovietization of Georgia, Nadiradze was at first hostile, but later wrote on revolutionary themes.

NATALYA NIKOLAYEVNA (PUSHKIN), NÉE GONCHAROV. Alexander Pushkin's wife. Pushkin met her in Moscow when she was only seventeen and married her a year later, on February 18, 1831. There were two sons and two daughters of the marriage. Pushkin was killed six years later, on January 29, 1837, in a duel with a cavalry officer, Dantès, an adopted son of the Dutch ambassador, whom he suspected of having an affair with his wife.

NEP. The New Economic Policy of the Soviet government, promulgated in May, 1921, by which the rigid state control of industry and agriculture was relaxed.

NILENDER, V. O. Poet and translator. Member of Society of Religious Philosophy.

*Niva.* Weekly illustrated magazine for family reading, published in Petersburg from 1870 to 1918 by A. F. Marx. Attained a circulation exceeding 200,000. Published supplements, including works of Turgenev, Goncharov, and Dostoevsky. Published works by L. N. Tolstoy, including *Resurrection,* which was serialized in 1899, Nos. 11–52.

OSTROVSKY, ALEXANDER NIKOLAYEVICH (1823–86). Famous Russian dramatist closely associated with the Maly Theater in Moscow.

PASTERNAK, BORIS LEONIDOVICH (1890–1960). Poet and novelist. Born in Moscow, eldest son of Leonid Pasternak, the painter, and Rosa Pasternak, née Kaufman, the pianist. In 1901 enters secondary school in Moscow. Meets Scriabin in summer of 1903 and decides to take up music as a career. First visit abroad, to Germany, with family in 1906. Enters Moscow University (Faculty of Law) in 1908. Scriabin returns to Russia in 1909 and Pasternak changes over from Law to Philosophy on his advice. Becomes member of Serdarda circle and the Musaget group of writers, poets, and critics in 1910. Spends summer term at Marburg University, studying Kantian philosophy under Hermann Cohen, 1912. After abortive love affair, which he describes in *Safe Conduct,* decides to give up philosophy and devote himself to poetry. Graduates from Moscow University in spring, 1913, and in summer of the same year writes most of his first book of poems, *A Twin in the Clouds,* published in the autumn of 1914. Joins the Centrifuge futurists' association in spring and meets Mayakovsky in May, 1914. Tutor to son of Moscow manufacturer, 1914 to 1916. Meets Khlebnikov, founder of Russian futurism in October, 1915. Spends two winters (1915–1917) doing clerical work in ordnance factories in the Urals and returns to Moscow in March, 1917. Publishes second book of verse, *Above the Barriers,* and writes and loses ms. of the *Reverse of the Medal.* Writes third book of verse, *My Sister, Life,* in summer, 1917. Writes two short stories, *The Childhood of Luverse* and *Letters from Tula,* in 1918. Breaks with Mayakovsky in 1920, meets Alexander Blok in Moscow in 1921. Pasternak's parents and sisters leave for Berlin in 1921, and Pasternak works as salesman in Writers' Bookshop in Moscow. *My Sister, Life,* published in 1921. First marriage, 1922; leaves with wife for Berlin to visit parents and prepare publication of fourth book of verse; revisits Marburg. Publishes fourth collection of verse, *Themes and Variations,* in Berlin and Moscow and returns to Moscow in autumn. In 1924, works in library of People's Commissariat of Foreign Affairs; 1925, publishes four short stories in book form, *Childhood of Luverse, Letters from Tula, Il Tratto di Apelle,* and *Aerial Ways.* In 1927, publishes in book form two revolutionary poems: *The Year 1905* and *Lieutenant Schmidt,* as well as *A Story.* In 1929–31, publishes first autobiography, *Safe Conduct,* in serial form. Mayakovksy commits suicide, February 14, 1930. Friendship with Paolo Yashvili, 1930–31. Divorce and remarriage, early 1930's. Stays in Georgia and works on translations of Georgian poets. Publishes *Spektorsky,* a novel in verse, in 1931, as well as a collection of verse for children, *The Zoo.* In 1932, publishes a volume of collected poems, *Second Birth.* During the years from 1932 to 1943 works mainly as translator. In June, 1935, attends first anti-Fascist congress in Paris and meets Marina Tsvetayeva and her family. In 1937, death of Paolo Yashvili and of Titian Tabidze. Publishes translation of *Hamlet,* 1940. Suicide of Marina Tsvetayeva, 1941. During Second World War

(1941–45) publishes patriotic war poems and continues work on translations of Shakespeare. In 1943, publication of collected poems, *In Early Trains,* and 1945 publication of collected poems, *Wide Open Spaces of the Earth.* In 1946 Zhdanov's attack on cosmopolitanism in literature imposes renewed silence on Pasternak as poet. In 1950, publication of translation of Goethe's *Faust.* Publishes ten poems from *Doctor Zhivago* in *Znamya.* Submits manuscript of *Doctor Zhivago* to the editorial board of *Novy Mir* in summer, 1956; novel rejected by *Novy Mir* editors in September, 1956. *Doctor Zhivago* first published abroad in Italian in autumn, 1957, and a year later in English in the United States and England. Expelled from the Union of Soviet Writers in November, 1958, after award of Nobel Prize for Literature.

PASTERNAK, LEONID OSIPOVICH (1862–1945). Father of Boris Pasternak. Well-known painter and illustrator. After leaving Russia in 1921 lived first in Germany (Berlin and Munich) and from 1938 in England. Died in Oxford.

PASTERNAK, ROSA ISODOROVNA, née Kaufman (1867–1940). Mother of Boris Pasternak. Well-known concert pianist. Gave up professional career when she married.

PETROVSKY, MIKHAIL ALEXEYEVICH (1887–   ). Critic and translator.

PILNYAK, pseudonym of Vogau, Boris Andreyevich (1894–1937). Novelist. First works published in 1915. His novel *The Naked Year,* 1922, deals with the Civil War, shows life degenerating to an animal level. His *Tale of the Unextinguished Moon,* 1926, gives an account of the death of Frunze, War Commissar, on the operating table in 1925, hinting that it was a "medical murder" ordered by Stalin. This got him into trouble from which he never recovered. His novel *Mahogany* was refused publication in Russia and he had it published in Berlin in 1929. This led to his expulsion from the Union of Soviet Writers. In 1937 he disappeared, and it is believed that he has been shot.

POLENOV, VASILY DMITRIEVICH (1844–1927). Painter. Paintings of country life. Took part as volunteer in Serbo-Turkish war of

1876 and as war artist in Russo-Turkish war of 1877–78. A member of the Society for Traveling Art Exhibitions. In the 1880's he painted a series of scenes from the life of Christ. Was elected a member of the Academy of Art in 1893. After the October Revolution lived in the country in a village now called Polenovo. Made People's Artist in 1926.

PRZYBYSZEWSKI, STANISLAW (1868–1927). Outstanding Polish romantic poet, of the 1890's and 1900's. After spending several years in Scandinavia and Germany he returned to Poland in 1898 and became editor of *Zycie,* the leading weekly of the modern poets. He wrote plays full of fatalistic terror and prose poems dealing with the mystical and tragic side of love and death, and these became the fashion of the day.

REBIKOV, VLADIMIR IVANOVICH (1866–1920). Composer. One of the first representatives of modernism in Russian music. Composed *Fables,* based on Krylov, and the opera *Christmas Tree,* based on Dostoevsky, as well as a number of lyrical pieces for the piano; performed as pianist both in Russia and abroad.

REPIN, ILYA YEFIMOVICH (1844–1930). Famous Russian painter. Studied in Petersburg, Italy, and Paris. Active in the Society for Traveling Art Exhibitions. His paintings deal with peasant life and many historical subjects, as *Ivan the Terrible with His Son Ivan,* 1885; *The Zaporozhian Cossacks Write to the Sultan,* 1891. His portraits include several of well-known Russian writers, composers, painters, and, among foreign celebrities, one of Eleonora Duse.

SADOVSKY, BORIS ALEXANDROVICH (1881–
). Symbolist poet and critic.
SAPUNOV, NIKOLAY NIKOLAYEVICH (1880–1912). Painter. Studied under Levitan, Korovin, and Serov. Visited Italy in 1902. Joined the Blue Rose group. Painted landscapes in Levitan's manner. Designed scenery for productions of Ibsen's *Hedda Gabler,* Blok's *Balalaika Player,* Gozzi's *Turandot,* etc.
SCRIABIN, ALEXANDER NIKOLAYEVICH (1872–

1915). Composer. Born in Moscow, son of diplomat and pianist. Attended the aristocratic Cadet School. In 1882–92 at the Moscow Conservatory studied composition with Taneyev and piano with Safonov, winning a gold medal as a pianist in 1892. In 1898–1903 professor of the piano at Moscow Conservatory. His earlier compositions show a kinship with Chopin. His *Poème Satanique* of 1903 echoes Liszt's *Malediction* and shows Scriabin committing himself to the view of art as magic. His First Symphony in 1901 already shows a taste for the grandiose and the religious. With the fourth of the piano sonatas, written in 1903, he has thrown off the drawing-room elegance of his earlier compositions and reveals the fragmentation of melody and ecstatic trills of his maturer period. His idea of a musical performance as a magic rite, a liturgical incantation and the calling to life of hidden cosmic forces, is explicit in the inscription over the orgiastic Fifth Piano Sonata: "I call you forth to life, hidden influences, sunk in the obscure depths of the Creative Spirit, timid germs of life, I bring you boldness!" He soon developed an interest in theosophy and saw himself as the messiah destined to bring about the Final Act, "the act of Union between the Male-Creator and the Woman World," by which Spirit was to redeem Matter, a great liturgical rite in which all the arts were to play a part and which was to usher in a new era. The nearest he approached to his idea was "the poem of fire," *Prometheus,* for orchestra, piano, and *clavier à lumières*— the first attempt to achieve a synthesis of the arts and a "counterpoint of the senses." He dreamed of "a musical phrase ending in a scent, a chord that resolved itself into a color, a melodic line whose climax becomes a caress." He saw himself as Prometheus, the Free Redeemer, rescuing the world of Matter by the power of Spirituality, hence his *Poem of Ecstasy* (*Poème de l'extase*), his most famous composition. Between 1904 and 1910 he toured Switzerland, France (where he first became acquainted with the writings of Blavatsky and Annie

Besant), Italy, and the United States. In 1910 he performed in Holland and in 1914 in Britain. Died prematurely of an infection of the blood. In 1922 his apartment in Moscow was made a museum of his life and work.

SELVINSKY, ILYA LVOVICH (1899–   ). Poet. Leader of the "constructivist" group which sought to subordinate the imagery and vocabulary of poetry to its theme. In 1929–30 the constructivist movement rallied a number of poets to a program of active support for the regime. At one time it seemed that Selvinsky might take Mayakovsky's place. His first poems appeared in 1926. Of his later work, his ballads and songs have been the most successful. In 1933–34 he took part in the Arctic expedition of the *Chelyuskin* and wrote a poem about this. During the 1941–45 war, wrote patriotic verses.

SERAPION FRATERNITY. The Serapion group came together in 1921, taking their name from the hermit Serapion in Hoffmann's stories, in whose cave a variety of people gather and tell each other their experiences. The group included Tikhonov, Fedin, and Vsevolod Ivanov. It played an important part in restoring normal literary activity after a period of chaos and disorder and in bringing together older and experienced writers with young writers who, demobilized from the Civil War, were determined to pursue a literary career.

SEROV, VALENTIN ALEXANDROVICH (1865–1911). Painter. Born in Petersburg, son of the composers A. N. Serov and V. S. Serova. Pupil of Repin. Especially distinguished as portrait painter, but also painted scenes of country life and dramatic compositions, such as *The Meeting: An Exile's Wife Arrives.* At the end of the nineteenth century, Serov joined the World of Art group. During the 1905 Revolution drew caricatures for the revolutionary press, sent protest to the Academy of Art against the massacre of January 9th, and resigned from the Academy when it was rejected. Portraits of actresses Yermolova and Feodotova, also of Chaliapin and Stanislavsky.

SEVERYANIN, IGOR, pseudonym of Lotaryov,

Igor Vasilyevich (1887–1941). Poet. Leader of the symbolist group called "Ego-Futurists." Emigrated after the Revolution. Was in Estonia when it was occupied by the Soviet Union in 1940, and wrote verses hailing the Soviet power. His poetry idealizes the aspirations of the average townsman. His claim to be a futurist was based on his love of such things as cars and luxury hotels, and on his profuse coining of new words—most of which were in complete disharmony with the genius of the language.

SHCHEGOLEV, PAVEL YELISEYEVICH (1877–1931). Historian of Russian literature.

SHENROK, VLADIMIR IVANOVICH (1853–1910). Historian of literature. Specialized in the study of Gogol.

SHERSHENEVICH, VADIM GAVRILOVICH (1893–1942). Poet. First works were close to the symbolists. Later wrote about urban life in the futurist manner. In 1919–24 joined the imagists, wrote verses which are catalogues of metaphors, not linked by any unity of poetic idea. Translator of Shakespeare, Corneille, and Baudelaire. Author of film scenarios, libretti for operettas, etc.

SIMONOV, KONSTANTIN MIKHAILOVICH (1915–   ). Soviet poet, novelist, and playwright. His earlier verse was mostly love poetry. Graduated from the literary institute of the Union of Soviet Writers in 1938. Wrote a patriotic poem about Suvorov, 1939. During the Second World War became the most popular lyric poet. Wrote novels about the war: *Days and Nights, Comrades in Arms,* as well as plays, including the anti-American play, *The Russian Question.* Since the war mainly active in journalism as editor of *Literaturnaya Gazeta* and *Novy Mir.* Is now under a cloud, following the disgrace of Fadeyev.

SOCIETY FOR TRAVELING ART EXHIBITIONS (*Peredvizhniki*). On November 9, 1863, thirteen pupils of the Academy of Art who were all Gold Medalist candidates refused to paint a picture on the set subject of *Odin in Valhalla.* They grouped themselves into an Artists' Co-operative Society, and in 1870, thanks to the financial assistance of Tretyakov, a rich patron of the arts, founded the Society for

Traveling Art Exhibitions. The society undertook to educate the masses by means of their exhibitions, which they held in the capitals, in Kiev, Odessa, Riga, Kazan, etc. The critical writings of V. V. Stasov were sympathetic to this activity and indeed furnished its ideology. Members of the society included the brothers Vasnetsov, Levitan, V. E. Makovsky, Polenov, Repin, Serov, Surikov.

SOLOVYOV, VLADIMIR SERGEYEVICH (1853–1900). Poet, critic, and most influential of nineteenth-century Russian religious philosophers. Was the son of a distinguished historian. He had apocalyptic dreams of the end of the world, and appears to have believed literally in the coming of Antichrist. His poetry gave expression to the symbolist belief that the world is a system of symbols which express the existence of the abstract metaphysical realities. While working at the Reading Room of the British Museum he had a vision of Sophia, Divine Wisdom. He had another such vision later in Egypt. His idea of the World Soul is satirized by Chekhov in *The Seagull*.

SOMOV, KONSTANTIN NIKOLAYEVICH (1869–1939). Painter and art critic. Member of the World of Art group.

STASOV, VLADIMIR VASILYEVICH (1824–1906). Art and music critic. Keen supporter of the Society for Traveling Art Exhibitions. In the 1880's wrote a number of works on the history of art. Edited the published letters of Musorgsky and Glinka.

STEPUN, F. A. (1885–    ). Producer. One of the founders in 1919 of the State Exemplary Theater in Moscow, with the aim of educating the masses through the great classics, including Shakespeare and the tragedies of antiquity. Author of an adaptation of Sophocles' *Oedipus Rex* intended to demonstrate that ancient Thebes showed the tragedy of contemporary Russia. Attacked by Meyerhold for his reactionary ideology, Stepun left the Exemplary Theater. He now lives in Germany. Author of *The Russian Soul and Revolution* and articles on stagecraft.

SUDEIKIN, SERGEY YURIEVICH (1883–    ). Artist, participant in the exhibitions of the Blue Rose and the World of Art groups. His pictures, mainly landscapes, are mostly studies for theatrical scenery. Exhibited in Paris, 1921.

SUPREME COUNCIL OF NATIONAL ECONOMY (V.S.N.). Set up in 1917 as supreme economic organ of the dictatorship of the proletariat. Reorganized in 1932 into separate People's Commissariats of Heavy Industry, Light Industry, and Timber Industry.

SURIKOV, VASILY IVANOVICH (1848–1916). Painter. A member of the Society for Traveling Art Exhibitions. Studied in Petersburg but quarreled with his conservative professors and moved to Moscow in 1877. Great historical pictures are *The Morning of the Execution of the Streltsi*, 1881, *Menshikov at Beryozov*, 1883, *The Boyarina Morozova*, 1887. Scenes from the careers of Stenka Razin and Pugachov.

TABIDZE, TITIAN JUSTINOVICH (1895–1937). Poet. One of the founders of the Georgian symbolist group Blue Horns, 1915. Rallied to the Soviet power after 1921, and wrote poetry glorifying the struggle to transform the Colchis marshes into citrus fruit plantations. The Blue Horns group was criticized at Congress of Soviet Writers in 1934 as "fellow-travelers." Tabidze was shot in one of the purges of the thirties.

THIRD ROME. After the Grand Duke of Russia had assumed the title of Tsar, Moscow (then the capital) was called the "Third Rome," the "First" being Rome itself and the "Second" Byzantium.

TIKHONOV, A. N. Editor. Published some of Pasternak's poetry and prose in his journal *Russky Sovremennik* in the 1920's.

TIKHONOV, NIKOLAI SEMYONOVICH (1896–    ). Prominent Soviet poet. Fought in the First World War and the Civil War (on the Red side). His first poems were war poems written in 1916 and 1917. His next two books of poems, *The Horde* and *Country Beer*, came out in 1922. Characteristic feature of his later poetry is its universality. His volume of poems *The Shadow of a Friend* includes poems written in Poland, Austria, France, Belgium, and England, while in his two volumes of verse *Yurga* and *Poems of Kakhetia* are contained his experiences in the Caucasus and Soviet Central Asia. He is greatly attracted by strong personalities, grandiose scenery, and enterprises involving risk and danger. His experiences in beleaguered Leningrad are described in the volume of his war poems, *The Fiery Year.*

TOLSTOY, ALEXEY KONSTANTINOVICH (1817–1875). Poet and dramatist. Moscow Art Theater opened its first season with his play *Tsar Fyodor Ivanovich* in October, 1898.

TOLSTOY, ANDREY LVOVICH (1877–1916). Leo Tolstoy's ninth child.

TOLSTOY, ILYA LVOVICH (1866–1933). Leo Tolstoy's third child, second son. Author of *Reminiscences of My Father.*

TOLSTOY, SERGEY LVOVICH (1863–1947). Leo Tolstoy's eldest son. Author of monograph on father, *My Father in the Seventies.*

TRETYAKOV, SERGEY MIKHAILOVICH (1892–1939). Soviet dramatist, author of *Roar, China!*, produced by Meyerhold. Arrested during the purges of 1937–38 and disappeared.

TRUBETSKOY, PAVEL PETROVICH (1867–1938). Born and died in Italy. Famous Russian sculptor. Lived in Russia 1897–1906, also paid some visits to Russia in 1907–14. Worked in France and U.S.A. Statuettes: *L. N. Tolstoy on Horseback,* 1899; *A Moscow Cabby,* 1898; *Girl with a Dog,* 1901. The equestrian monument to Alexander III in Petersburg, unveiled in 1909.

TSVETAYEVA, MARINA IVANOVNA (1892–1941). Poet. Began her literary work in 1910. Left Russia in 1922, to be with her husband, a former White officer, first in Czechoslovakia, later in Paris. Returned with family to Russia in 1939. Her husband was arrested and punished. Their daughter, too, was arrested, and their son was killed early in the war. Tsvetayeva was banished to the provinces, where she could find no employment, and hanged herself. Her poems are distinguished by their exhilarating rhythm, fire, and passion, and by their strong folk-song influences.

TVARDOVSKY, ALEXANDER TRIFONOVICH (1910–    ). Soviet poet. First publication of his poems was in 1930. He achieved fame with his three long narrative poems, *The Land of Muravia, Vasily Tyorkin,* and *The House by the Roadside.* His realism is highly imaginative, the realism of pure poetry where everything is possible, where, for instance, the agony of war, which is the main theme of *Vasily Tyorkin,* finds expression in the dialogue between the Soldier and Death, and in *The House by the Roadside* where the rights of the human personality are voiced by the new-born baby in its dialogue with its mother.

TYUTCHEV, FYODOR IVANOVICH (1803–73). Russian lyric poet. He wrote about three hundred short lyric poems. His poetry is rich in imagery of vision and sound.

ULYANOV, NIKOLAY PAVLOVICH (1875–1949). Painter. Studied in Moscow under Serov, who influenced him a great deal. His portraits include one of Chekhov and one of Stanislavsky. He did a great deal of work for the theater, designing the sets for *Les Fourberies de Scapin, The Days of the Turbins, Carmen.* His memoirs were published posthumously in 1952.

VANNOVSKY, PYOTR SEMYONOVICH (1822–1904). Minister of Education who, in his modernization program, added to the science curriculum.

VASNETSOV, APPOLLINARY MIKHAILOVICH (1856–1933). Painter. Born in Vyatka province, son of a village priest. Joined the Society for Traveling Art Exhibitions and became well known as a landscape painter, especially of Ural and Siberian scenes. From 1890 lived in Moscow and painted pictures illustrating the city's historic past. Elected to Academy in 1900. Designed scenery for operas *Khovanshchina, Sadko,* etc. Published a book on art, 1908, in which he attacked impressionism. After the October Revolution became chairman of the Commission for the Study of Old Moscow and devoted himself mainly to archaeological work.

VASNETSOV, VIKTOR MIKHAILOVICH (1848–1926). Painter. Born in Vyatka province, son of a village priest. Elder brother of Appollinary. Associated with Repin and V. V. Stasov. Painted scenes of the life of the city poor in a realistic vein. In 1878 moved to Moscow. Painted subjects from Russian folklore and medieval history, notably a portrait of *Ivan the Terrible,* and the group *Bogatyri,* reproduced often. In the 1880's did scenery and costumes for the theater and opera. Elected to the Academy in 1893.

VERHAEREN, EMILE (1855–1916). Belgian poet. Began publishing verse in Brussels in the 1880's. Much influenced by the impressionist painters. Some of his verses described the Belgian countryside and lamented the flight of population to the towns and the expansion of the great industrial towns into the countryside. His chief work, *Toute la Flandre,* is a series of poems in which autobiography is mingled with Flemish history and descriptions of the Flemish scene. He also wrote love poems, and some plays on historical and classical themes.

VRUBEL, MIKHAIL ALEXANDROVICH (1856–1910). Painter. Member of the Academy of Art from 1905. Well known as book illustrator and theatrical designer.

WORLD OF ART, THE. A group of painters and writers including all the symbolists supporting the review of the same name (1899–1904). Had no common program but were all united against the tendencies prevalent in the Russian Academy of Art and the Society for Traveling Art Exhibitions.

YAKUNCHIKOVA, MARIA VASILYEVNA (1870–1902). Artist, studied in Moscow and Paris. Turned to decorative art, and did many drawings for book covers, designs for toys, etc. Painted a number of landscape pictures in a style similar to Levitan's.

YASHVILI, PAOLO DZHIBRAELOVICH (1895–1937). Georgian poet. Studied at Kutais *gymnasium,* wrote verses while still a schoolboy. On eve of First World War went to Paris. Returning home in 1916, Yashvili was one of the initiators of a group of Georgian symbolist poets. His poems—*Letter to Mother, The Red Bull* —were outstanding representative works of this group. Yashvili welcomed the establishment of Soviet power, and wrote poetry celebrating it. His verses on the death of Lenin were especially appreciated. In the 1930's he wrote about triumphs of socialist construction in Georgia, new hydroelectric plants, etc. Translated Pushkin, Lermontov, and Mayakovsky into Georgian. Committed suicide.

YEFREM OF SYRIA, ST. (Ephraem Syrus). A fourth-century Churchman who was born in Mesopotamia. Widely famous as a poet and a defender of orthodoxy against heretics. His writings were translated into Greek, Armenian, Coptic, Arabic, and Ethiopic. Most of his works were written in meter, and they include a number of hymns; he was distinguished among contemporary theological writers for the richness of his diction and his skill in the use of metaphors and illustrations.

ZABOLOTSKY, NIKOLAY (1903–    ). Poet. His early poems sounded like parodies or nonsense verse, but after a disappearance of several years he returned and wrote in a more orthodox style.

# DOCTOR ZHIVAGO

## By BORIS PASTERNAK

*Translated by* Max Hayward *and* Manya Harari

[ Excerpt ]

---

CHAPTER FIVE

### Farewell to the Old

The small town was called Meliuzeievo and lay in the fertile, black-soil country. Black dust hung over its roofs like a cloud of locusts. It was raised by the troops and convoys passing through the town; they moved in both directions, some going to the front and others away from it, and it was impossible to tell whether the war were still going on or had ceased.

Every day newly created offices sprang up like mushrooms. And they were elected to everything—Zhivago, Lieutenant Galiullin, and Nurse Antipova, as well as a few others from their group, all of them people from the big cities, well-informed and experienced.

They served as temporary town officials and as minor commissars in the army and the health department, and they looked upon this succession of tasks as an outdoor sport, a diversion, a game of blindman's buff. But more and more they felt that it was time to stop and to get back to their ordinary occupations and their homes.

Zhivago and Antipova were often brought together by their work.

2

The rain turned the black dust into coffee-colored mud and the mud spread over the streets, most of them unpaved.

The town was small. At the end of almost every street you could see the steppe, gloomy under the dark sky, all the vastness of the war, the vastness of the revolution.

Yurii Andreievich wrote to his wife:

"The disintegration and anarchy in the army continue. Measures are being taken to improve discipline and morale. I have toured units stationed in the neighborhood.

"By way of a postscript, though I might have mentioned it much earlier, I must tell that I do a lot of my work with a certain Antipova, a nurse from Moscow who was born in the Urals.

"You remember the girl student who shot at the public prosecutor on that terrible night of your mother's death? I believe she was tried later. I remember telling you that Misha and I had once seen her, when she was still a schoolgirl, at some sordid hotel where your father took us. I can't remember why we went, only that it was a bitterly cold night. I think it was at the time of the Presnia uprising. Well, that girl was Antipova.

"I have made several attempts to go home, but it is not so simple. It is not so much the work—we could hand that over easily enough—the trouble is the trip. Either there are no trains at all or else they are so overcrowded that there is no way of finding a seat.

"But of course it can't go on like this forever, and some of us, who have resigned or been discharged, including Antipova, Galiullin, and myself, have made up our minds that whatever happens we shall leave next week. We'll go separately; it gives us a better chance.

"So I may turn up any day out of the blue, though I'll try to send a telegram."

Before he left, however, he received his wife's reply. In sentences broken by sobs and with tear stains and ink spots for punctuation, she begged him not to come back to Moscow but to go straight to the Urals with that wonderful nurse whose progress through life was marked by portents and coincidences so miraculous that her own, Tonia's, modest life could not possibly compete with it.

"Don't worry about Sasha's future," she wrote. "You will never need to be ashamed of him. I promise you to bring him up in those principles which as a child you saw practiced in our house."

Yurii Andreievich wrote back at once: "You must be out of your mind, Tonia! How could you imagine such a thing? Don't you know, don't you know well enough, that if it were not for you, if it were not for my constant, faithful thoughts of you and of our home, I could never have survived these two terrible, devastating years of war? But why am I writing this—soon we'll be together, our life will begin again, everything will be cleared up.

"What frightens me about your letter is something else. If I really gave you cause to write in such a way, my behavior must have been ambiguous and I am at fault not only before you but before that other woman whom I am misleading. I'll apologize to her as soon as she is back. She is away in the country. Local councils, which formerly existed only in provincial capitals and county seats, are being set up in the villages, and she has gone to help a friend of hers who is acting as instructor in connection with these legislative changes.

"It may interest you to know that although we live in the same house I don't know to this day which is Antipova's room. I've never bothered to find out."

### 3

Two main roads ran from Meliuzeievo, one going east, the other west. One was a mud track leading through the woods to Zybushino, a small grain center that was administratively a subdivision of Meliuzeievo although it was ahead of it in every way. The other was graveled and went through fields, boggy in winter but dry in summer, to Biriuchi, the nearest railway junction.

In June Zybushino became an independent republic. It was set up by the local miller Blazheiko and supported by deserters from the 212th Infantry who had left the front at the time of the upheavals, kept their arms, and come to Zybushino through Biriuchi.

The republic refused to recognize the Provisional Government and split off from the rest of Russia. Blazheiko, a religious dissenter who had once corresponded with Tolstoy, proclaimed a new millennial Zybushino kingdom where all work and property were to be collectivized, and referred to the local administration as an Apostolic Seat.

Zybushino had always been a source of legends and exaggerations. It is mentioned in documents dating from the

Times of Troubles[1] and the thick forests surrounding it teemed with robbers even later. The prosperity of its merchants and the fabulous fertility of its soil were proverbial. Many popular beliefs, customs, and oddities of speech that distinguished this whole western region near the front originated in Zybushino.

Now amazing stories were told about Blazheiko's chief assistant. It was said that he was deaf and dumb, that he acquired the gift of speech at moments of inspiration, and then lost it again.

The republic lasted two weeks. In July a unit loyal to the Provisional Government entered the town. The deserters fell back on Biriuchi. Several miles of forest had once been cleared along the railway line on both sides of the junction, and there, among the old tree stumps overgrown with wild strawberries, the piles of timber depleted by pilfering, and the tumble-down mud huts of the seasonal laborers who had cut the trees, the deserters set up their camp.

4

The hospital in which Zhivago convalesced and later served as a doctor, and which he was not preparing to leave, was housed in the former residence of Countess Zhabrinskaia. She had offered it to the Red Cross at the beginning of the war.

It was a two-story house on one of the best sites of the town, at the corner of the main street and the square, known as the *Platz,* where soldiers had drilled in the old days and where meetings were held now.

Its position gave it a good view of the neighborhood; in addition to the square and the street it overlooked the adjoining farm (owned by a poor, provincial family who lived almost like peasants) as well as the Countess's old garden at the back.

The Countess had a large estate in the district, Razdolnoie, and had used the house only for occasional business visits to the town and as a rallying point for the guests who came from near and far to stay at Razdolnoie in summer.

Now the house was a hospital, and its owner was in prison in Petersburg, where she had lived.

Of the large staff, only two women were left, Ustinia, the head cook, and Mademoiselle Fleury, the former governess of the Countess's daughters, who were now married.

Gray-haired, pink-cheeked, and disheveled, Mademoiselle Fleury shuffled about in bedroom slippers and a floppy, worn-out housecoat, apparently as much at home in the hospital as she had been in the Zhabrinsky family. She told long stories in her broken Russian, swallowing the ends of her words in the French manner, gesticulated, struck dramatic poses, and burst into hoarse peals of laughter that ended in coughing fits.

She believed that she knew Nurse Antipova inside out and thought that the nurse and the doctor were bound to be attracted to each other. Succumbing to her passion for matchmaking, so deep-rooted in the Latin heart, she was delighted when she found them in each other's company, and would shake her finger and wink slyly at them. This puzzled Antipova and angered the doctor; but, like all eccentrics, Mademoiselle cherished her illusions and would not be parted from them at any price.

Ustinia was an even stranger character. Her clumsy, pear-shaped figure gave her the look of a brood hen. She was dry and sober to the point of maliciousness, but her sober-mindedness went hand in hand with an imagination unbridled in everything to do with superstition. Born

[1] Period of interregnum and civil war in the seventeenth century.

[ 299 ]

in Zybushino and said to be the daughter of the local sorcerer, she knew countless spells and would never go out without first muttering over the stove and the keyhole to protect the house in her absence from fire and the Evil One. She could keep quiet for years, but once she was roused nothing would stop her. Her passion was to defend the truth.

After the fall of the Zybushino republic, the Meliuzeievo Executive Committee launched a campaign against the local anarchistic tendencies. Every night peaceful meetings were held at the *Platz,* attended by small numbers of citizens who had nothing better to do and who, in the old days, used to gather for gossip outside the fire station. The Meliuzeievo cultural soviet encouraged them and invited local and visiting speakers to guide the discussions. The visitors believed the tales about the talking deaf-mute to be utter nonsense and were anxious to say so. But the small craftsmen, the soldiers' wives, and former servants of Meliuzeievo did not regard these stories as absurd and stood up in his defense.

One of the most outspoken of his defenders was Ustinia. At first held back by womanly reserve, she had gradually become bolder in heckling orators whose views were unacceptable in Meliuzeievo. In the end she developed into an expert public speaker.

The humming of the voices in the square could be heard through the open windows of the hospital, and on quiet nights even fragments of speeches. When Ustinia took the floor, Mademoiselle often rushed into any room where people were sitting and urged them to listen, imitating her without malice in her broken accent: "Disorder . . . Disorder . . . Tsarist, bandit . . . Zybushi- . . . deaf-mute . . . traitor! traitor!"

Mademoiselle was secretly proud of the spirited and sharp-tongued cook. The two women were fond of each other although they never stopped bickering.

## 5

Yurii Andreievich prepared to leave, visiting homes and offices where he had friends, and applying for the necessary documents.

At that time the new commissar of the local sector of the front stopped at Meliuzeievo on his way to the army. Everybody said he was completely inexperienced, a mere boy.

A new offensive was being planned and a great effort was made to improve the morale of the army masses. Revolutionary courts-martial were instituted, and the death penalty, which had recently been abolished, was restored.

Before leaving, the doctor had to obtain a paper from the local commandant.

Usually crowds filled his office, overflowing far out into the street. It was impossible to elbow one's way to the desks and no one could hear anything in the roar caused by hundreds of voices.

But this was not one of the reception days. The clerks sat writing silently in the peaceful office, disgruntled at the growing complication of their work, and exchanging ironic glances. Cheerful voices came from the commandant's room; it sounded as if, in there, people had unbuttoned their tunics and were having refreshments.

Galiullin came out of the inner room, saw Zhivago, and vigorously beckoned to him.

Since the doctor had in any case to see the commandant, he went in. He found the room in a state of artistic disorder.

The center of the stage was held by the new commissar, the hero of the day and the sensation of the town, who, instead of being at his post, was addressing the rulers of this paper kingdom quite unconnected with staff and operational matters.

"Here's another of our stars," said the commandant, introducing the doctor. The commissar, completely self-absorbed, did not look around, and the commandant turned to sign the paper that the doctor put in front of him and waved him politely to a low ottoman in the center of the room.

The doctor was the only person in the room who sat normally. All the rest were lolling eccentrically with an air of exaggerated and assumed ease. The commandant almost lay across his desk, his cheek on his fist, in a thoughtful, Byronic pose. His aide, a massive, stout man, perched on the arm of the sofa, his legs tucked on the seat as if he were riding side saddle. Galiullin sat astride a chair, his arms folded on its back and his head resting on his arms, and the commissar kept hoisting himself up by his wrists onto the window sill and jumping off and running up and down the room with small quick steps, buzzing about like a wound-up top, never still or silent for a moment. He talked continuously; the subject of the conversation was the problem of the deserters at Biriuchi.

The commissar was exactly as he had been described to Zhivago. He was thin and graceful, barely out of his teens, aflame with the highest ideals. He was said to come of a good family (the son of a senator, some people thought) and to have been one of the first to march his company to the Duma in February. He was called Gints or Gintse—the doctor had not quite caught the name—and spoke very distinctly, with a correct Petersburg accent and a slight Baltic intonation.

He wore a tight-fitting tunic. It probably embarrassed him to be so young, and in order to seem older he assumed a sneer and an artificial stoop, hunching his shoulders with their stiff epaulettes and keeping his hands deep in his pockets; this did in fact give him a cavalryman's silhouette which could be drawn in two straight lines converging downward from the angle of his shoulders to his feet.

"There is a Cossack regiment stationed a short distance down the railway," the commandant informed him. "It's Red, it's loyal. It will be called out, the rebels will be surrounded, and that will be the end of the business. The corps commander is anxious that they should be disarmed without delay."

"Cossacks? Out of the question!" flared the commissar. "This is not 1905. We're not going back to prerevolutionary methods. On this point we don't see eye to eye. Your generals have outsmarted themselves."

"Nothing has been done yet. This is only a plan, a suggestion."

"We have an agreement with the High Command not to interfere with operational matters. I am not canceling the order to call out the Cossacks. Let them come. But I, for my part, will take such steps as are dictated by common sense. I suppose they have a bivouac out there?"

"I guess so. A camp, at any rate. Fortified."

"So much the better. I want to go there. I want to see this menace, this nest of robbers. They may be rebels, gentlemen, they may even be deserters, but remember, they are the people. And the people are children, you have to know them, you have to know their psychology. To get the best out of them, you must have the right approach, you have to play on their best, most sensitive chords.

"I'll go, and I'll have a heart-to-heart talk with them. You'll see, they'll go back to the positions they have deserted. You don't believe me? Want to bet?"

"I wonder. But I hope you're right."

"I'll say to them, 'Take my own case, I am an only son, the hope of my parents, yet I haven't spared myself. I've given up everything—name, family, position. I have done this to fight for your freedom, such freedom as is not enjoyed by any other people in the world. This I did, and so did many other young men like myself, not to speak of the old guard of our glorious predecessors, the champions of the people's rights who were sent to hard labor in Siberia or locked up in the Schlüsselburg Fortress. Did we do this for ourselves? Did we have to do it? And you, you who are no longer ordinary privates but the warriors of the first revolutionary army in the world, ask yourselves honestly: Have you lived up to your proud calling? At this moment when our country is being bled white and is making a supreme effort to shake off the encircling hydra of the enemy, you have allowed yourselves to be fooled by a gang of nobodies, you have become a rabble, politically unconscious, surfeited with freedom, hooligans for whom nothing is enough. You're like the proverbial pig that was allowed in the dining room and at once jumped onto the table.' Oh, I'll touch them to the quick, I'll make them feel ashamed of themselves."

"No, that would be risky," the commandant objected halfheartedly, exchanging quick, meaningful glances with his aide.

Galiullin did his best to dissuade the commissar from his insane idea. He knew the reckless men of the 212th, they had been in his division at the front. But the commissar refused to listen.

Yurii Andreievich kept trying to get up and go. The commissar's naïveté embarrassed him, but the sly sophistication of the commandant and his aide—two sneering and dissembling opportunists—was no better. The foolishness of the one was matched by the slyness of the others.

And all this expressed itself in a torrent of words, superfluous, utterly false, murky, profoundly alien to life itself.

Oh, how one wishes sometimes to escape from the meaningless dullness of human eloquence, from all those sublime phrases, to take refuge in nature, apparently so inarticulate, or in the wordlessness of long, grinding labor, of sound sleep, of true music, or of a human understanding rendered speechless by emotion!

The doctor remembered his coming talk with Antipova. Though it was bound to be unpleasant, he was glad of the necessity of seeing her, even at such a price. She was unlikely to be back. But he got up as soon as he could and went out, unnoticed by the others.

6

She was back. Mademoiselle, who gave him the news, added that she was tired, she had had a quick meal and had gone up to her room saying she was not to be disturbed. "But I should go up and knock if I were you," Mademoiselle suggested. "I am sure she is not asleep yet."— "Which is her room?" the doctor asked. Mademoiselle was surprised beyond words by his question. Antipova lived at the end of the passage on the top floor, just beyond several rooms in which all of the Countess's furniture was kept locked, and where the doctor had never been.

It was getting dark. Outside, the houses and fences huddled closer together in the dusk. The trees advanced out of the depth of the garden into the light of the lamps shining from the windows. The night was hot and sticky. At the slightest effort one was drenched with sweat. The light of the kerosene lamps streaking into the yard went down the trees in a dirty, vaporous flow.

The doctor stopped at the head of the stairs. It occurred to him that even to knock on Antipova's door when she was only just back and tired from her journey would be discourteous and embarrassing. Better leave the talk for tomorrow. Feeling at a loss as one does when one changes one's mind, he walked to the other end of the passage, where a window overlooked the neighboring yard, and leaned out.

The night was full of quiet, mysterious sounds. Next to him, inside the passage, water dripped from the washbasin regularly and slowly. Somewhere outside the window people were whispering. Somewhere in the vegetable patch they were watering cucumber beds, clanking the chain of the well as they drew the water and poured it from pail to pail.

All the flowers smelled at once; it was as if the earth, unconscious all day long, were now waking to their fragrance. And from the Countess's centuries-old garden, so littered with fallen branches that it was impenetrable, the dusty aroma of old linden trees coming into bloom drifted in a huge wave as tall as a house.

Noises came from the street beyond the fence on the right—snatches of a song, a drunken soldier, doors banging.

An enormous crimson moon rose behind the crows' nest in the Countess's garden. At first it was the color of the new brick mill in Zybushino, then it turned yellow like the water tower at Biriuchi.

And just under the window, the smell of new-mown hay, as perfumed as jasmine tea, mixed with that of belladonna. Below there a cow was tethered; she had been brought from a distant village, she had walked all day, she was tired and homesick for the herd and would not yet accept food from her new mistress.

"Now, now, whoa there, I'll show you how to butt," her mistress coaxed her in a whisper, but the cow crossly shook her head and craned her neck, mooing plaintively, and beyond the black barns of Meliuzeievo the stars twinkled, and invisible threads of sympathy stretched between them and the cow as if there were cattle sheds in other worlds where she was pitied.

Everything was fermenting, growing, rising with the magic yeast of life. The joy of living, like a gentle wind, swept in a broad surge indiscriminately through fields and towns, through walls and fences, through wood and flesh. Not to be overwhelmed by this tidal wave, Yurii Andreievich went out into the square to listen to the speeches.

### 7

By now the moon stood high. Its light covered everything as with a thick layer of white paint. The broad shadows thrown by the pillared government buildings that surrounded the square in a semicircle spread on the ground like black rugs.

The meeting was being held across the square. Straining one's ears, one could hear every word. But the doctor was stunned by the beauty of the spectacle; he sat down on the bench outside the fire station and instead of listening looked about him.

Narrow dead-end streets ran off the square, as deep in mud as country lanes and lined with crooked little houses. Fences of plaited willows stuck out of the mud like bow nets in a pond, or lobster pots. You could see the weak glint of open windows. In the small front gardens, sweaty red heads of corn with oily whiskers reached out toward the rooms, and single pale thin hollyhocks looked out over the fences, like women in night clothes whom the heat had driven out of their stuffy houses for a breath of air.

The moonlit night was extraordinary, like merciful love or the gift of clairvoyance. Suddenly, into this radiant, legendary stillness, there dropped the measured, rhythmic sound of a familiar, recently heard voice. It was a fine ardent voice and it rang with conviction. The doctor listened and recognized it at once. Commissar Gints was addressing the meeting on the square.

Apparently the municipality had asked him to lend them the support of his authority. With great feeling he chided the people of Meliuzeievo for their disorganized ways and for giving in to the disintegrating influence of the Bolsheviks, who, he said, were the real instigators of the Zybushino disorders. Speaking in the same spirit as at the commandant's, he reminded them of the powerful and ruthless enemy, and of their country's hour of trial. Then the crowd began to heckle.

Calls of protest alternated with demands for silence. The interruptions grew louder and more frequent. A man who had come with Gints, and who now assumed the role of chairman, shouted that speeches from the floor were not allowed and called the audience to order. Some insisted that a citizeness who wished to speak should be given leave.

A woman made her way through the crowd to the wooden box that served as a platform. She did not attempt to climb on the box but stood beside it. The woman was known to the crowd. Its attention was caught. There was a silence. This was Ustinia.

"Now you were saying, Comrade Commissar, about Zybushino," she began, "and about looking sharp—you told us to look sharp and not to be deceived —but actually, you yourself, I heard you, all you do is to play about with words like 'Bolsheviks, Mensheviks,' that's all you talk about—Bolsheviks, Mensheviks. Now all that about no more fighting and all being brothers, I call that being godly, not Menshevik, and about the works and factories going to the

poor, that isn't Bolshevik, that's just human decency. And about that deaf-mute, we're fed up hearing about him. Everybody goes on and on about the deaf-mute. And what have you got against him? Just that he was dumb all that time and then he suddenly started to talk and didn't ask your permission? As if that were so marvelous! Much stranger things than that have been known to happen. Take the famous she-ass, for instance. 'Balaam, Balaam,' she says, 'listen to me, don't go that way, I beg you, you'll be sorry.' Well, naturally, he wouldn't listen, he went on. Like you saying, 'A deaf-mute,' he thought 'a she-ass, a dumb beast, what's the good of listening to her.' He scorned her. And look how sorry he was afterwards. You all know what the end of it was."

"What?" someone asked curiously.

"That's enough," snapped Ustinia. "If you ask too many questions you'll grow old before your time."

"That's no good. You tell us," insisted the heckler.

"All right, all right, I'll tell you, you pest. He was turned into a pillar of salt."

"You've got it wrong, that was Lot. That was Lot's wife," people shouted. Everyone laughed. The chairman called the meeting to order. The doctor went to bed.

## 8

He saw Antipova the following evening. He found her in the pantry with a pile of linen, straight out of the wringer; she was ironing.

The pantry was one of the back rooms at the top, looking out over the garden. There the samovars were got ready, food was dished out, and the used plates were stacked in the dumb-waiter to be sent down to the kitchen. There too the lists of china, silver, and glass were kept and checked, and there people spent their moments of leisure, using it as a meeting place.

The windows were open. In the room, the scent of linden blossoms mingled, as in an old park, with the caraway-bitter smell of dry twigs and the charcoal fumes of the two flatirons that Antipova used alternately, putting them each in turn in the flue to keep them hot.

"Well, why didn't you knock last night? Mademoiselle told me. But it's a good thing you didn't. I was already in bed. I couldn't have let you in. Well, how are you? Look out for the charcoal, don't get it on your suit."

"You look as if you've been doing the laundry for the whole hospital."

"No, there's a lot of mine in there. You see? You keep on teasing me about getting stuck in Meliuzeievo. Well, this time I mean it, I'm going. I'm getting my things together, I'm packing. When I've finished I'll be off. I'll be in the Urals and you'll be in Moscow. Then one day somebody will ask you: 'Do you happen to know a little town called Meliuzeievo?' and you'll say: 'I don't seem to call it to mind.'—'And who is Antipova?'—'Never heard of her.' "

"That's unlikely. Did you have a good trip? What was it like in the country?"

"That's a long story. How quickly these irons cool! Do hand me the other, do you mind? It's over there, look, just inside the flue. And could you put this one back? Thanks. Every village is different, it depends on the villagers. In some the people are industrious, they work hard, then it isn't bad. And in others I suppose all the men are drunks. Then it's desolate. A terrible sight."

"Nonsense! Drunks? A lot you understand! It's just that there is no one there, all the men are in the army. What about the new councils?"

"You're wrong about the drunks, I don't agree with you at all. The councils? There's going to be a lot of trouble with the councils. The instructions can't be applied, there's nobody to work with. All the peasants care about at the moment is the land question. . . . I stopped at Razdolnoie. What a lovely place, you should go and see it. . . . It was burned a bit and looted last spring, the barn is burned down, the orchards are charred, and there are smoke stains on some of the houses. Zybushino I didn't see, I didn't get there. But they all tell you the deaf-mute really exists. They describe what he looks like, they say he's young and educated."

"Last night Ustinia stood up for him on the square."

"The moment I got back there was another lot of old furniture from Razdolnoie. I've asked them a hundred times to leave it alone. As if we didn't have enough of our own. And this morning the guard from the commandant's office comes over with a note—they must have the silver tea set and the crystal glasses, it's a matter of life and death, just for one night, they'll send it back. Half of it we'll never see again. It's always a loan—I know these loans. They're having a party —in honor of some visitor or something."

"I can guess who that is. The new commissar has arrived, the one who's appointed to our sector of the front. They want to tackle the deserters, have them surrounded and disarmed. The commissar is a greenhorn, a babe in arms. The local authorities want to call out the Cossacks, but not he—he's planning to speak to their hearts. The people, he says, are like children, and so on; he thinks it's a kind of game. Galiullin tried to argue with him, he told him to leave the jungle alone, not to rouse the wild beast. 'Leave us to deal with it,' he said. But you can't do anything with a fellow like that once he's got a thing in his head. I do wish you'd listen to me. Do stop ironing a minute. There will be an unimaginable mess here soon; it's beyond our power to avert it. I do wish you'd leave before it happens."

"Nothing will happen, you're exaggerating. And anyway, I am leaving. But I can't just snap my fingers and say goodbye. I have to hand in a properly checked inventory. I don't want it to look as if I've stolen something and run away. And who is to take over? That's the problem, I can't tell you what I've been through with that miserable inventory, and all I get is abuse. I listed Zhabrinskaia's things as hospital property, because that was the sense of the decree. Now they say I did it on purpose to keep them for the owner! What a dirty trick!"

"Do stop worrying about pots and rugs. To hell with them. What a thing to fuss about at a time like this! Oh, I wish I'd seen you yesterday. I was in such good form that I could have told you all about everything, explained the whole celestial mechanics, answered any accursed question! It's true, you know, I'm not joking, I really did want to get it all off my chest. And I wanted to tell you about my wife, and my son, and myself. . . . Why the hell can't a grown-up man talk to a grown-up woman without being at once suspected of some ulterior motive? Damn all motives—ulterior ones and others.

"Please, go on with your ironing, make the linen nice and smooth, don't bother about me, I'll go on talking. I'll talk a long time.

"Just think what's going on around us! And that you and I should be living at such a time. Such a thing happens only once in an eternity. Just think of it, the whole of Russia has had its roof torn off, and you and I and everyone else are out in the open! And there's nobody to spy on us. Freedom! Real freedom, not just talk about it, freedom, dropped out of the sky, freedom beyond our expectations, freedom by accident, through a misunderstanding.

"And how great everyone is, and completely at sea! Have you noticed? As if crushed by his own weight, by the discovery of his greatness.

"Go on ironing, I tell you. Don't talk. You aren't bored. Let me change your iron for you.

"Last night I was watching the meeting in the square. An extraordinary sight! Mother Russia is on the move, she can't stand still, she's restless and she can't find rest, she's talking and she can't stop. And it isn't as if only people were talking. Stars and trees meet and converse, flowers talk philosophy at night, stone houses hold meetings. It makes you think of the Gospel, doesn't it? The days of the apostles. Remember St. Paul? You will speak with tongues and you will prophesy. Pray for the gift of understanding."

"I know what you mean about stars and trees holding meetings. I understand that. It's happened to me too."

"It was partly the war, the revolution did the rest. The war was an artificial break in life—as if life could be put off for a time—what nonsense! The revolution broke out willy-nilly, like a sigh suppressed too long. Everyone was revived, reborn, changed, transformed. You might say that everyone has been through two revolutions—his own personal revolution as well as the general one. It seems to me that socialism is the sea, and all these separate streams, these private, individual revolutions, are flowing into it—the sea of life, the sea of spontaneity. I said life, but I mean life as you see it in a great picture, transformed by genius, creatively enriched. Only now people have decided to experience it not in books and pictures but in themselves, not as an abstraction but in practice."

The sudden trembling of his voice betrayed his rising agitation. Antipova stopped ironing and gave him a grave, astonished look. It confused him and he forgot what he was saying. After a moment of embarrassed silence he rushed on, blurting out whatever came into his head.

"These days I have such a longing to live honestly, to be productive. I so much want to be a part of all this awakening. And then, in the middle of all this general rejoicing, I catch your mysterious, sad glance, wandering God knows where, far away. How I wish it were not there! How I wish your face to say that you are happy with your fate and that you need nothing from anyone. If only someone who is really close to you, your friend or your husband—best of all if he were a soldier—would take me by the hand and tell me to stop worrying about your fate and not to weary you with my attentions. But I'd wrest my hand free and take a swing. . . . Ah, I have forgotten myself. Please forgive me."

Once again the doctor's voice betrayed him. He gave up struggling and, feeling hopelessly awkward, got up and went to the window. Leaning on the sill, his cheek on his hand, he stared into the dark garden with absent, unseeing eyes, trying to collect himself.

Antipova walked round the ironing board, propped between the table and the other window, and stopped in the middle of the room a few steps behind him. "That's what I've always been afraid of," she said softly, as if to herself. "I shouldn't have . . . Don't, Yurii Andreievich, you mustn't. Oh, now just look at what you've made me do!" she exclaimed. She ran back to the board, where a thin stream of acrid smoke came from under the iron that had burned through a blouse.

She thumped it down crossly on its stand. "Yurii Andreievich," she went on, "do be sensible, go off to Mademoiselle

for a minute, have a drink of water and come back, please, as I've always known you till now and as I want you to be. Do you hear, Yurii Andreievich? I know you can do it. Please do it, I beg you."

They had no more talks of this kind, and a week later Larisa Feodorovna left.

9

Some time later, Zhivago too set out for home. The night before he left there was a terrible storm. The roar of the gale merged with that of the downpour, which sometimes crashed straight onto the roofs and at other times drove down the street with the changing wind as if lashing its way step by step.

The peals of thunder followed each other uninterruptedly, producing a steady rumble. In the blaze of continual flashes of lightning the street vanished into the distance, and the bent trees seemed to be running in the same direction.

Mademoiselle Fleury was waked up in the night by an urgent knocking at the front door. She sat up in alarm and listened. The knocking went on.

Could it be, she thought, that there wasn't a soul left in the hospital to get up and open the door? Did she always have to do everything, poor old woman, just because nature had made her reliable and endowed her with a sense of duty?

Well, admittedly, the house had belonged to rich aristocrats, but what about the hospital—didn't that belong to the people, wasn't it their own? Whom did they expect to look after it? Where, for instance, had the male nurses got to, she'd like to know. Everyone had fled— no more orderlies, no more nurses, no doctors, no one in authority. Yet there were still wounded in the house, two legless men in the surgical ward where the drawing room used to be, and downstairs next to the laundry the storeroom full of dysentery cases. And that devil Ustinia had gone out visiting. She knew perfectly well that there was a storm coming, but did that stop her? Now she had a good excuse to spend the night out.

Well, thank God the knocking had stopped, they realized that nobody would answer, they'd given it up. Why anybody should want to be out in this weather . . . Or could it be Ustinia? No, she had her key. Oh God, how terrible, they've started again.

What pigs, just the same! Not that you could expect Zhivago to hear anything, he was off tomorrow, his thoughts were already in Moscow or on the journey. But what about Galiullin? How could he sleep soundly or lie calmly through all this noise, expecting that in the end she, a weak, defenseless old woman, would go down and open for God knows whom, on this frightening night in this frightening country.

Galiullin!—she remembered suddenly. No, such nonsense could occur to her only because she was half asleep, Galiullin wasn't there, he should be a long way off by now. Hadn't she herself, with Zhivago, hidden him, and disguised him as a civilian, and then told him about every road and village in the district to help him to escape after that horrible lynching at the station when they killed Commissar Gints and chased Galiullin all the way from Biriuchi to Meliuzeievo, shooting at him and then hunting for him all over the town!

If it hadn't been for those automobiles, not a stone would have been left standing in the town. An armored division happened to be passing through, and stopped those evil men.

The storm was subsiding, moving away. The thunder was less continuous, duller, more distant. The rain stopped occasionally, when the water could be heard splashing softly off the leaves and down the gutters. Noiseless reflections of distant lightning lit up Mademoiselle's room, lingering as though looking for something.

Suddenly the knocking at the front door, which had long since stopped, was resumed. Someone was in urgent need of help and was knocking repeatedly, in desperation. The wind rose again and the rain came down.

"Coming," shouted Mademoiselle to whoever it was, and the sound of her own voice frightened her.

It had suddenly occurred to her who it might be. Putting down her feet and pushing them into slippers, she threw her dressing gown over her shoulders and hurried to wake up Zhivago, it would be less frightening if he came down with her. But he had heard the knocking and was already coming down with a lighted candle. The same idea had occurred to both of them.

"Zhivago, Zhivago, they're knocking on the front door, I'm afraid to go down alone," she called out in French, adding in Russian: "You will see, it's either Lar or Lieutenant Gaiul."

Roused by the knocking, Yurii Andreievich had also felt certain that it was someone he knew—either Galiullin, who had been stopped in his flight and was coming back for refuge, or Nurse Antipova, prevented from continuing her journey for some reason.

In the hallway the doctor gave the candle to Mademoiselle, drew the bolts, and turned the key. A gust of wind burst the door open, putting out the candle and showering them with cold raindrops.

"Who is it? Who is it? Anybody there?"

Mademoiselle and the doctor shouted in turn into the darkness but there was no reply. Suddenly the knocking started again in another place—was it at the back door, or, as they now thought, at the French window into the garden?

"Must be the wind," said the doctor.

"But just to make sure, perhaps you'd have a look at the back. I'll stay here in case there really is someone."

Mademoiselle disappeared into the house while the doctor went out and stood under the entrance roof. His eyes had become accustomed to the darkness, and he could make out the first signs of dawn.

Above the town, clouds raced dementedly as if pursued, so low that their tatters almost caught the tops of the trees, which bent in the same direction so that they looked like brooms sweeping the sky. The rain lashed the wooden wall of the house, turning it from gray to black.

Mademoiselle came back. "Well?" said the doctor.

"You were right. There's no one." She had been all around the house; a branch knocking on the pantry window had broken one of the panes and there were huge puddles on the floor, and the same thing in what used to be Lara's room—there was a sea, a real sea, an ocean. "And on this side, look, there's a broken shutter knocking on the casement, do you see it? That's all it was."

They talked a little, locked the door, and went back to their rooms, both regretting that the alarm had been a false one.

They had been sure that when they opened the door Antipova would come in, chilled through and soaked to the skin, and they would ask her dozens of questions while she took off her things, and she would go and change and come down and dry herself in front of the kitchen stove, still warm from last night, and would tell them her adventures, pushing back her hair and laughing.

They had been so sure of it that after locking the front door they imagined that she was outside the house in the form of a watery wraith, and her image continued to haunt them.

### 10

It was said that the Biriuchi telegrapher, Kolia Frolenko, was indirectly responsible for the trouble at the station.

Kolia, the son of a well-known Meliuzeievo clockmaker, had been a familiar figure in Meliuzeievo from his earliest childhood. As a small boy he had stayed with some of the servants at Razdolnoie and had played with the Countess's daughters. It was then that he learned to understand French. Mademoiselle Fleury knew him well.

Everyone in Meliuzeievo was used to seeing him on his bicycle, coatless, hatless, and in canvas summer shoes in any weather. Arms crossed on his chest, he free-wheeled down the road, glancing up at the poles and wires to check the condition of the network.

Some of the houses in Meliuzeievo were connected by a branch line with the exchange at the station. The calls were handled by Kolia at the station switchboard. There he was up to his ears in work, for not only the telephone and telegraph were in his charge, but, if the stationmaster Povarikhin was absent for a few moments, also the railway signals, which were operated from the same control room.

Having to look after several mechanical instruments at once, Kolia had evolved a special style of speech, obscure, abrupt, and puzzling, which enabled him, if he chose, to avoid answering questions or getting involved in a conversation. He was said to have abused the advantage this gave him on the day of the disorders.

It is true that, by suppressing information, he had defeated Galiullin's good intentions and, perhaps unwittingly, had given a fatal turn to the events.

Galiullin had called up from town and asked for Commissar Gints, who was somewhere at the station or in its vicinity, in order to tell him that he was on his way to join him and to ask him to wait for him and do nothing until he arrived. Kolia, on the pretext that he was busy signaling an approaching train, refused to call the commissar. At the same time he did his utmost to delay the train, which was bringing up the Cossacks summoned to Biriuchi.

When the troops arrived nevertheless he did not conceal his dismay.

The engine, crawling slowly under the dark roof of the platform, stopped in front of the huge window of the control room. Kolia drew the green serge curtain with the initials of the Company woven in yellow into the border, picked up the enormous water jug standing on the tray on the window ledge, poured some water into the plain, thick, straight-sided glass, drank a few mouthfuls, and looked out.

The engineer saw him from his cab and gave him a friendly nod.

"The stinker, the louse," Kolia thought with hatred. He stuck out his tongue and shook his fist. The engineer not only understood him but managed to convey by a shrug of the shoulders and a nod in the direction of the train: "What was I to do? I'd like to know what you'd have done in my place. He's the boss."—"You're a filthy brute all the same," Kolia replied by gestures.

The horses were taken, balking, out of the freight cars. The thud of their hoofs on the wooden gangways was followed by the ring of their shoes on the stone platform. They were led, rearing, across the tracks.

At the end of the tracks were two rows of derelict wooden coaches. The rain had washed them clean of paint, and worms and damp had rotted them from inside, so that now they were reverting to their original kinship with the wood of the forest, which began just beyond the roll-

ing stock, with its lichen, its birches, and the clouds towering above it.

At the word of command, the Cossacks mounted their horses and galloped to the clearing.

The rebels of the 212th were surrounded. In woods, horsemen always seem taller and more formidable than in an open field. They impressed the infantrymen, although they had rifles in their mud huts. The Cossacks drew their swords.

Within the ring formed by the horses, some timber was piled up. Gints mounted it and addressed the surrounded men.

As usual, he spoke of soldierly duty, of the fatherland, and many other lofty subjects. But these ideas found no sympathy among his listeners. There were too many of them. They had suffered a great deal in the war, they were thick-skinned and exhausted. They had long been fed up with the phrases Gints was giving them. Four months of wooing by the Left and Right had corrupted these unsophisticated men, who, moreover, were alienated by the speaker's foreign-sounding name and Baltic accent.

Gints felt that his speech was too long and was annoyed at himself, but he thought that he had to make himself clear to his listeners, who instead of being grateful rewarded him with expressions of indifference or hostile boredom. Gradually losing his temper, he decided to speak straight from the shoulder and to bring up the threats he had so far held in reserve. Heedless of the rising murmurs, he reminded the deserters that revolutionary courts-martial had been set up, and called on them, on pain of death, to disarm and give up their ringleaders. If they refused, he said, they would prove that they were common traitors, and irresponsible swollen-headed rabble. The

men had become unused to being talked to in such a tone.

Several hundred voices rose in an uproar. Some were low pitched and almost without anger: "All right, all right. Pipe down. That's enough." But hate-filled, hysterical trebles predominated:

"The nerve! Just like in the old days! These officers still treat us like dirt. So we're traitors, are we? And what about you yourself, Excellency? Why bother with him? Obviously he's a German, an infiltrator. Show us your papers, blueblood. And what are you gaping at, pacifiers?" They turned to the Cossacks. "You've come to restore order, go on, tie us up, have your fun."

But the Cossacks, too, liked Gints' unfortunate speech less and less. "They are all swine to him," they muttered. "Thinks himself the lord and master!" At first singly, and then in ever-growing numbers, they began to sheathe their swords. One after another they got off their horses. When most of them had dismounted, they moved in a disorderly crowd toward the center of the clearing, mixed with the men of the 212th, and fraternized.

"You must vanish quietly," the worried Cossack officers told Gints. "Your car is at the station, we'll send for it to meet you. Hurry."

Gints went, but he felt that to steal away was beneath his dignity, so he turned quite openly toward the station. He was terribly agitated but out of pride forced himself to walk calmly and unhurriedly.

He was close to the station. At the edge of the woods, within sight of the tracks, he looked back for the first time. Soldiers with rifles had followed him. "What do they want?" he wondered. He quickened his pace.

So did his pursuers. The distance between them remained unchanged. He saw the double wall of derelict coaches, stepped behind them, and ran. The train that had brought the Cossacks had been shunted. The lines were clear. He crossed them at a run and leaped onto the steep platform. At the same moment the soldiers ran out from behind the old coaches. Povarikhin and Kolia were shouting and waving to him to get into the station building, where they could save him.

But once again the sense of honor bred in him for generations, a city-bred sense of honor, which impelled him to self-sacrifice and was out of place here, barred his way to safety. His heart pounding wildly, he made a supreme effort to control himself. He told himself: "I must shout to them, 'Come to your senses, men, you know I'm not a spy.' A really heart-felt word or two will bring them to their senses."

In the course of the past months his feeling for a courageous exploit or a heart-felt speech had unconsciously become associated with stages, speakers' platforms, or just chairs onto which you jumped to fling an appeal or ardent call to the crowds.

At the very doors of the station, under the station bell, there stood a water butt for use in case of fire. It was tightly covered. Gints jumped up on the lid and addressed the approaching soldiers with an incoherent but gripping speech. His unnatural voice and the insane boldness of his gesture, two steps from the door where he could so easily have taken shelter, amazed them and stopped them in their tracks. They lowered their rifles.

But Gints, who was standing on the edge of the lid, suddenly pushed it in. One of his legs slipped into the water and the other hung over the edge of the butt.

Seeing him sitting clumsily astride the edge of the butt, the soldiers burst into laughter and the one in front shot Gints in the neck. He was dead by the time the others ran up and thrust their bayonets into his body.

## 11

Mademoiselle called up Kolia and told him to find Dr. Zhivago a good seat in the train to Moscow, threatening him with exposure if he did not.

Kolia was as usual conducting another conversation and, judging by the decimal fractions that punctuated his speech, transmitting a message in code over a third instrument.

"Pskov, Pskov, can you hear me? What rebels? What help? What are you talking about, Mademoiselle? Ring off, please. Pskov, Pskov, thirty-six point zero one five. Oh hell, they've cut me off. Hello, hello, I can't hear. Is that you again, Mademoiselle? I've told you, I can't. Ask Povarikhin. All lies, fictions. Thirty-six . . . Oh hell . . . Get off the line, Mademoiselle."

And Mademoiselle was saying:

"Don't you throw dust in my eyes, Pskov, Pskov, you liar, I can see right through you, tomorrow you'll put the doctor on the train, and I won't listen to another word from any murdering little Judases."

## 12

The day Yurii Andreievich left, it was sultry. A storm like the one that had broken two days earlier was brewing. Near the station, at the outskirts of the town, littered with the shells of sunflower seeds, the clay huts and the geese looked white and frightened under the still menace of the black sky.

The grass on the wide field in front of the station and stretching to both sides of it was trampled and entirely covered by a countless multitude who had for weeks been waiting for trains.

Old men in coarse gray woolen coats wandered about in the hot sun from group to group in search of news and rumors. Glum fourteen-year-old boys lay on their elbows twirling peeled twigs, as if they were tending cattle, while their small brothers and sisters scuttled about with flying shirts and pink bottoms. Their legs stretched straight in front of them, their mothers sat on the ground with babies packed into the tight shapeless bosoms of their brown peasants coats.

"All scattered like sheep as soon as the shooting began. They didn't like it," the stationmaster told the doctor unsympathetically as they walked between the rows of bodies lying on the ground in front of the entrance and on the floors inside the station. "In a twinkling everybody cleared off the grass. You could see the ground again; we hadn't seen it in four months with all this gypsy camp going on, we'd forgotten what it looked like. This is where he lay. It's a strange thing, I've seen all sorts of horror in the war, you'd think I'd be used to anything. But I felt so sorry somehow. It was the senselessness of it. What had he done to them? But then they aren't human beings. They say he was the favorite son. And now to the right, if you please, into my office. There isn't a chance on this train, I'm afraid, they'd crush you to death. I'm putting you on a local one. We are making it up now. But not a word about it until you're ready to get on it, they'd tear it apart before it was made up. You change at Sukhinichi tonight."

## 13

When the "secret" train backed into the station from behind the railway sheds, the whole crowd poured onto the tracks. People rolled down the hills like marbles, scrambled onto the embankment, and, pushing each other, jumped onto the steps and buffers or climbed in through the windows and onto the roofs. The train filled in an instant, while it was still moving, and by the time it stood by the platform, not only was it crammed but passengers hung all over it, from top to bottom. By a miracle, the doctor managed to get into a platform and from there, still more unaccountably, into the corridor.

There he stayed, sitting on his luggage, all the way to Sukhinichi.

The stormy sky had cleared. In the hot, sunny fields, crickets chirped loudly, muffling the clatter of the train.

Those passengers who stood by the windows shaded the rest from the light. Their double and triple shadows streaked across the floor and benches. Indeed, these shadows went beyond the cars. They were crowded out through the opposite windows, and accompanied the moving shadow of the train itself.

All around people were shouting, bawling songs, quarreling, and playing cards. Whenever the train stopped, the noise of the besieging crowds outside was added to this turmoil. The roar of the voices was deafening, like a storm at sea, and, as at sea, there would be a sudden lull. In the inexplicable stillness you could hear footsteps hurrying down the platform, the bustle and arguments outside the freight car, isolated words from people, farewells spoken in the distance, and the quiet clucking of hens and rustling of trees in the station garden.

Then, like a telegram delivered on the train, or like greetings from Meliuzeievo addressed to Yurii Andreievich, there drifted in through the windows a familiar fragrance. It came from somewhere to one side and higher than the level of either garden or wild flowers, and it quietly asserted its excellence over everything else.

Kept from the windows by the crowd, the doctor could not see the trees; but he imagined them growing somewhere very near, calmly stretching out their heavy branches to the carriage roofs, and their foliage, covered with dust from the passing trains and thick as night, was sprinkled with constellations of small, glittering waxen flowers.

This happened time and again throughout the trip. There were roaring crowds at every station. And everywhere the linden trees were in blossom.

This ubiquitous fragrance seemed to be preceding the train on its journey north as if it were some sort of rumor that had reached even the smallest, local stations, and which the passengers always found waiting for them on arrival, heard and confirmed by everyone.

### 14

That night at Sukhinichi a porter who had preserved his pre-war obligingness took the doctor over the unlit tracks to the back of some unscheduled train that had just arrived, and put him in a second-class carriage.

Hardly had he unlocked it with the conductor's key and heaved the doctor's luggage inside when the conductor came and tried to throw it out. He was finally appeased by Yurii Andreievich and withdrew and vanished without a trace.

The mysterious train was a "special" and went fairly fast, stopping only briefly at stations, and had some kind of armed guard. The carriage was almost empty.

Zhivago's compartment was lit by a guttering candle that stood on the small table, its flame wavering in the stream of air from the half-open window.

The candle belonged to the only other occupant of the compartment, a fair-haired youth who, judging by the size of his arms and legs, was very tall. His limbs seemed to be attached too loosely at the joints. He had been sprawling nonchalantly in a corner seat by the window, but when Zhivago came in he politely rose and sat up in a more seemly manner.

Something that looked like a floor cloth lay under his seat. One corner of it stirred and a flop-eared setter scrambled out. It sniffed Yurii Andreievich over and ran up and down the compartment throwing out its paws as loosely as its lanky master crossed his legs. Soon, at his command, it scrambled back under the seat and resumed its former likeness to a floor rag.

It was only then that Yurii Andreievich noticed the double-barreled gun in its case, the leather cartridge belt, and the hunter's bag tightly packed with game that hung on a hook in the compartment.

The young man had been out shooting.

He was extremely talkative, and, smiling amiably, at once engaged the doctor in conversation, looking, as he did so, fixedly at his mouth.

He had an unpleasant, high-pitched voice that now and then rose to a tinny falsetto. Another oddity of his speech was that, while he was plainly Russian, he pronounced one vowel, *u*, in a most outlandish manner, like the French *u*. To utter even this garbled *u*, he had to make a great effort, and he pronounced it louder than any other sound, accompanying it each time with a slight squeal. At moments, apparently by concentrating, he managed to correct this defect but it always came back.

"What is this?" Zhivago wondered. "I'm sure I've read about it, as a doctor I ought to know, but I can't think what it is. It must be some brain trouble that causes defective speech." The squeal struck him as so funny that he could hardly keep a straight face. "Better go to bed," he told himself.

He climbed up onto the rack which was used as a berth. The young man offered to blow out the candle lest it keep him awake. The doctor accepted, thanking him, and the compartment was plunged into darkness.

"Shall I close the window?" Yurii Andreievich asked. "You are not afraid of thieves?"

There was no reply. He repeated his question louder, but there was still no answer.

He struck a match to see if his neighbor had gone out during the brief interval. That he had dropped off to sleep in so short a time seemed even more improbable.

He was there, however, sitting in his place with his eyes open. He smiled at the doctor, leaning over him from his berth.

The match went out. Yurii Andreievich struck another, and while it was alight repeated his question for the third time.

"Do as you wish," the young man replied at once. "I've got nothing a thief would want. But perhaps leave it open. It's stuffy."

"What an extraordinary character!" thought Zhivago. "An eccentric, evidently. Doesn't talk in the dark. And how distinctly he pronounced everything now, without any slur. It's beyond me."

## 15

Tired out by the events of the past week, the preparations for the trip, and the early start, the doctor expected to go to sleep the moment he had stretched comfortably, but he was mistaken. His exhaustion made him sleepless. Only at daybreak did he fall asleep.

His thoughts swarmed and whirled in the dark. But they all fell clearly into two distinct groups, as it were, two main threads that kept getting tangled and untangled.

One group of thoughts centered around Tonia, their home, and their former, settled life where everything, down to the smallest detail, had an aura of poetry and was permeated with affection and warmth. The doctor was concerned about this life, he wanted it safe and whole and in his night express was impatient to get back to it after two years of separation.

In the same group were his loyalty to the revolution and his admiration for it. This was the revolution in the sense in which it was accepted by the middle classes and in which it had been understood by the students, followers of Blok, in 1905.

These familiar, long-held ideas also included the anticipations and promises of a new order which had appeared on the horizon before the war, between 1912 and 1914, which had emerged in Russian thinking, in Russian art, in Russian life, and which had a bearing on Russia as a whole and on his own future.

It would be good to go back to that climate, once the war was over, to see its renewal and continuation, just as it was good to be going home.

New things were also in the other group of his thoughts, but how different, how unlike the first! These new things were not familiar, not led up to by the old, they were unchosen, determined by an ineluctable reality, and as sudden as an earthquake.

Among these new things was the war with its bloodshed and its horrors, its homelessness and savagery, its ordeals and the practical wisdom that it taught. So, too, were the lonely little towns to which the war washed you up, and the people you met in them. And among these new things too was the revolution —not the idealized intellectuals' revolution of 1905, but this new upheaval, today's, born of the war, bloody, ruthless, elemental, the soldiers' revolution led by those professional revolutionaries, the Bolsheviks.

And among the new thoughts, too, was Nurse Antipova, stranded by the war God knows where, about whose past he knew nothing, who never blamed anyone but whose very silence seemed to be a complaint, who was mysteriously reserved and so strong in her reserve. And so was Yurii Andreievich's honest endeavor not to love her, as wholehearted as his striving throughout his life until now to love everyone, not only his family and his friends, but everyone else as well.

The train rushed on at full speed. The head wind, coming through the open window, ruffled and blew dust on Yurii Andreievich's hair. At every station, by night as by day, the crowds stormed and the linden trees rustled.

Sometimes carts or gigs rattled up to the station out of the darkness, and voices and rumbling wheels mingled with the rustling of trees.

At such moments Yurii Andreievich felt he understood what it was that made these night shadows rustle and put their heads together, and what it was they whispered to each other, lazily stirring their leaves heavy with sleep, like faltering, lisping tongues. It was the very thing he was thinking of, turning restlessly in his berth—the tidings of the ever-widening circles of unrest and excitement in Russia, the tidings of the revolution, of its difficult and fateful hour and its probable ultimate greatness.

### 16

The doctor did not wake up until after eleven. "Prince, Prince," his neighbor was calling softly to his growling dog. To Yurii Andreievich's astonishment, they still had the compartment to themselves; no other passenger had got in.

The names of the stations were familiar to him from childhood. They were out of the province of Kaluga and well into that of Moscow.

He washed and shaved in prewar comfort and came back to the compartment in time for breakfast, to which his strange companion had invited him. Now he had a better look at him.

What struck him most were his extreme garrulousness and restlessness. He liked to talk, and what mattered to him was not communicating and exchanging ideas but the function of speech itself, pronouncing words and uttering sounds. As he spoke he kept jumping up as if he were on springs; he laughed deafeningly for no reason, briskly rubbing his hands with contentment, and, when all this seemed inadequate to express his delight, he slapped his knees hard, laughing to the point of tears.

His conversation had the same peculiarities as the night before. He was curiously inconsistent, now indulging in uninvited confidences, now leaving the most innocent questions unanswered. He poured out incredible and disconnected facts about himself. Perhaps he lied a little; he obviously was out to impress by his extremism and by his rejection of all commonly accepted opinions.

It all reminded Zhivago of something long familiar to him. Similar radical views were advanced by the nihilists of the last century, and a little later by some of Dostoievsky's heroes, and still more recently by their direct descendants, the provincial educated classes, who were often ahead of the capitals because they still were in the habit of going to the root of things while in the capitals such an approach was regarded as obsolete and unfashionable.

The young man told him that he was the nephew of a well-known revolutionary, but that his parents were incorrigible reactionaries, real dodoes, as he called them. They had a fairly large estate in a place near the front, where he had been brought up. His parents had been at swords' points with his uncle all their lives, but the uncle did not bear them a grudge and now used his influence to save them a good deal of unpleasantness.

His own views were like his uncle's, the talkative man informed Zhivago; he was an extremist in everything, whether in life, politics, or art. This too reminded the doctor of Piotr Verkhovensky[1]—not so much the leftism as the frivolity and the shallowness. "He'll be telling me he's a futurist next," thought Yurii Andreievich, and indeed they spoke of modern art. "Now it'll be sport—race horses, skating rinks, or French wrestling." And the conversation turned to shooting.

The young man had been shooting in his native region. He was a crack shot, he boasted, and if it had not been for the physical defect that had kept him out of the army he would have distinguished himself by his marksmanship. Catching Zhivago's questioning glance, he exclaimed: "What? Haven't you noticed anything? I thought you had guessed what was the matter with me."

He took two cards out of his pocket and handed them to Yurii Andreievich. One was his visiting card. He had a double name; he was called Maxim Aristarkhovich Klintsov-Pogorevshikh— or just Pogorevshikh, as he asked Zhivago to call him, in honor of his uncle who bore this name.

The other card showed a table with squares, each containing a drawing of two hands variously joined and with fingers differently folded. It was an alphabet for deaf-mutes. Suddenly everything became clear. Pogorevshikh was a phenomenally gifted pupil of the school of either Hartman or Ostrogradov, a deaf-mute who had reached an incredible facility in speaking and understanding speech by observing the throat muscles of his teachers.

Putting together what he had told him

_____
[1] Character in Dostoievski's *The Possessed*.

of the part of the country he came from and of his shooting expedition, the doctor said:

"Forgive me if this is indiscreet; you needn't tell me. Did you have anything to do with setting up the Zybushino republic?"

"But how did you guess . . . Do you know Blazheiko? Did I have anything to do with it? Of course I did!" Pogorevshikh burst forth joyfully, laughing, rocking from side to side, and frenziedly slapping his knees. And once again he launched on a long and fantastic discourse.

He said that Blazheiko had provided the opportunity and Zybushino the place for the application of his own theories. Yurii Andreievich found it hard to follow his exposition of them. Pogorevshikh's philosophy was a mixture of the principles of anarchism and hunter's tall stories.

Imperturbable as an oracle, he prophesied disastrous upheavals in the near future. Yurii Andreievich inwardly agreed that this was not unlikely, but the calm, authoritative tone in which this unpleasant boy was making his forecasts angered him.

"Just a moment," he said hesitantly. "True, all this may happen. But it seems to me that with all that's going on—the chaos, the disintegration, the pressure from the enemy—this is not the moment to start dangerous experiments. The country must be allowed to recover from one upheaval before plunging into another. We must wait till at least relative peace and order are restored."

"That's naïve," said Pogorevshikh. "What you call disorder is just as normal a state of things as the order you're so keen about. All this destruction—it's a natural and preliminary stage of a broad creative plan. Society has not yet disintegrated sufficiently. It must fall to pieces completely, then a genuinely revolution-

ary government will put the pieces together and build on completely new foundations."

Yurii Andreievich felt disturbed. He went out into the corridor.

The train, gathering speed, was approaching Moscow. It ran through birch woods dotted with summer houses. Small roofless suburban stations with crowds of vacationers flew by and were left far behind in the cloud of dust raised by the train, and seemed to turn like a carrousel. The engine hooted repeatedly, and the sound filled the surrounding woods and came back in long, hollow echoes from far away.

All at once, for the first time in the last few days, Yurii Andreievich understood quite clearly where he was, what was happening to him, and what awaited him in an hour or so.

Three years of changes, moves, uncertainties, upheavals; the war, the revolution; scenes of destruction, scenes of death, shelling, blown-up bridges, fires, ruins—all this turned suddenly into a huge, empty, meaningless space. The first real event since the long interruption was this trip in the fast-moving train, the fact that he was approaching his home, which was intact, which still existed, and in which every stone was dear to him. This was real life, meaningful experience, the actual goal of all quests, this was what art aimed at—homecoming, return to one's family, to oneself, to true existence.

The woods had been left behind. The train broke out of the leafy tunnels into the open. A sloping field rose from a hollow to a wide mound. It was striped horizontally with dark green potato beds; beyond them, at the top of the mound, were cold frames. Opposite the field, beyond the curving tail of the train, a dark purple cloud covered half the sky. Sunbeams were breaking through it, spreading like wheel spokes and reflected by the glass of the frames in a blinding glare.

Suddenly, warm, heavy rain, sparkling in the sun, fell out of the cloud. The drops fell hurriedly and their drumming matched the clatter of the speeding train, as though the rain were afraid of being left behind and were trying to catch up.

Hardly had the doctor noticed this when the Church of Christ the Savior showed over the rim of the hill, and a minute later the domes, chimneys, roofs, and houses of the city.

"Moscow," he said, returning to the compartment. "Time to get ready."

Pogorevshikh jumped up, rummaged in his hunter's bag, and took out a fat duck. "Take it," he said. "As a souvenir. I have rarely spent a day in such pleasant company."

Zhivago's protests were unavailing. In the end he said: "All right, I'll take it as a present from you to my wife."

"Splendid, splendid, your wife," Pogorevshikh kept repeating delightedly, as though he had heard the word for the first time, jerking and laughing so much that Prince jumped out and took part in the rejoicing.

The train drew into the station. The compartment was plunged into darkness. The deaf-mute held out the wild duck, wrapped in a torn piece of some printed poster.

CHAPTER SIX

## The Moscow Encampment

### 1

In the train it had seemed to Zhivago that only the train was moving but that time stood still and it was not later than noon.

But the sun was already low by the time his cab had finally made its way through the dense crowd in Smolensky Square.

In later years, when the doctor recalled this day, it seemed to him—he did not know whether this was his original impression or whether it had been altered by subsequent experiences—that even then the crowd hung about the market only by habit, that there was no reason for it to be there, for the empty stalls were shut and not even padlocked and there was nothing to buy or sell in the littered square, which was no longer swept.

And it seemed to him that even then he saw, like a silent reproach to the passers-by, thin, decently dressed old men and women shrinking against the walls, wordlessly offering for sale things no one bought and no one needed—artificial flowers, round coffee pots with glass lids and whistles, black net evening dresses, uniforms of abolished offices.

Humbler people traded in more useful things—crusts of stale rationed black bread, damp, dirty chunks of sugar, and ounce packages of coarse tobacco cut in half right through the wrapping.

And all sorts of nondescript odds and ends were sold all over the market, going up in price as they changed hands.

The cab turned into one of the narrow streets opening from the square. Behind them, the setting sun warmed their backs. In front of them a draft horse clattered along, pulling an empty, bouncing cart. It raised pillars of dust, glowing like bronze in the rays of the low sun. At last they passed the cart which had blocked their way. They drove faster. The doctor was struck by the piles of old newspapers and posters, torn down from the walls and fences, littering the sidewalks and streets. The wind pulled them one way and hoofs, wheels, and feet shoved them the other.

They passed several intersections, and soon the doctor's house appeared at a corner. The cab stopped.

Yurii Andreievich gasped for breath

and his heart hammered loudly as he got out, walked up to the front door, and rang the bell. Nothing happened. He rang again. As there was still no reply, he went on ringing at short, anxious intervals. He was still ringing when he saw that the door had been opened by Antonina Alexandrovna and that she stood holding it wide open. The unexpectedness of it so dumfounded them both that neither of them heard the other cry out. But as the door held wide open by Tonia was in itself a welcome and almost an embrace, they soon recovered and rushed into each other's arms. A moment later they were both talking at once, interrupting each other.

"First of all, is everybody well?"

"Yes, yes, don't worry. Everything is all right. I wrote you a lot of silly nonsense, forgive me. But we'll talk about that later. Why didn't you send a telegram? Markel will take your things up. I suppose you got worried when Egorovna didn't let you in! She is in the country."

"You're thinner. But how young you look, and so pretty! Wait a minute, I'll pay the driver."

"Egorovna has gone to get some flour. The other servants have been discharged. There's only one girl now, Niusha, you don't know her, she's looking after Sashenka, there's no one else. Everybody has been told you're coming, they're all longing to see you—Gordon, Dudorov, everyone."

"How is Sashenka?"

"All right, thank God. He's just waked up. If you weren't still dirty from the train we could go to him at once."

"Is Father at home?"

"Didn't anyone write to you? He's at the borough council from morning till night, he's the chairman. Yes, can you believe it! Have you settled with the driver? Markel! Markel!"

They were standing in the middle of the street with wicker hamper and suit-case blocking the way, and the passers-by, as they walked around them, looked them over from head to foot, and stared at the cab as it pulled away from the curb and at the wide-open front door, to see what would happen next.

But Markel was already running up from the gate to welcome the young master, his waistcoat over his cotton shirt and his porter's cap in his hand, shouting as he ran:

"Heavenly powers, if it isn't Yurochka! It's our little falcon in person! Yurii Andreievich, light of our eyes, so you haven't forgotten us and our prayers, you've come home! And what do you want?" he snapped at the curious. "Be off with you. What's there to goggle at?"

"How are you, Markel? Let's embrace. Put your cap on, you eccentric. Well, what's new? How's your wife? How are the girls?"

"How should they be? They're growing, thanks be to God. As for news, you can see for yourself, while you were busy at the front we were not idle either. Such a mess they made, such bedlam, the devil couldn't sort it out! The streets unswept, roofs unrepaired, houses unpainted, bellies empty as in Lent. Real peace there—no annexations and no reparations, as they say."

"I'll tell on you, Markel. He's always like that, Yurochka. I can't stand that foolishness. He's talking like that only because he thinks you like it, but he's a sly one. All right, all right, Markel, don't argue with me, I know you. You're a deep one, Markel. Time you were sensible. After all, you know what kind of people we are."

They went in. Markel carried the doctor's things inside, shut the front door behind him, and went on confidentially:

"Antonina Alexandrovna is cross, you heard what she said. It's always like that. She says, You're all black inside, Markel, she says, like that stovepipe. Nowadays, she says, every little child, maybe even every spaniel or any other lap dog knows what's what. That, of course, is true, but all the same, Yurochka, believe it or not, those who know have seen the book, the Mason's prophecies, one hundred and forty years it's been lying under a stone, and now, it's my considered opinion, Yurochka, we've been sold down the river, sold for a song. But can I say a word? See for yourself, Antonina Alexandrovna is making signs to me, she wants me to go."

"Do you wonder? That's enough, Markel, put the things down, and that will be all, thank you. If Yurii Andreievich wants anything, he'll call you."

## 2

"At last we've got rid of him! All right, all right, you can listen to him if you like, but I can tell you, it's all make-believe. You talk to him and you think he's the village idiot, butter wouldn't melt in his mouth, and all the time he's secretly sharpening his knife—only he hasn't quite decided yet whom he'll use it on, the charming fellow."

"Isn't that a bit far-fetched? I expect he's just drunk, that's all."

"And when is he sober, I'd like to know. Anyway, I've had enough of him. What worries me is, Sasha might go to sleep again before you've seen him. If it weren't for typhus on trains . . . You haven't any lice on you?"

"I don't think so. I traveled comfortably—the same as before the war. I'd better have a quick wash, though; I'll wash more thoroughly afterwards. Which way are you going? Don't we go through the drawing room any more?"

"Oh, of course, you don't know. Father and I thought and thought and we decided to give up a part of the ground floor to the Agricultural Academy. It's too much to heat in winter, anyway.

Even the top floor is too big. So we've offered it to them. They haven't taken it over yet, but they've moved in their libraries and their herbariums and their specimens of seed. I only hope we don't get rats—it's grain, after all. But at the moment they're keeping the rooms spick-and-span. By the way, we don't say 'rooms' any more, it's called 'living space' now. Come on, this way. Aren't you slow to catch on! We go up the back stairs. Understand? Follow me, I'll show you."

"I'm very glad you've given up those rooms. The hospital I've been in was also in a private house. Endless suites of rooms, here and there the parquet flooring still left. Potted palms sticking out their paws like ghosts over the beds— some of the wounded from the battle zone used to wake up screaming—they weren't quite normal, of course—shell-shocked—we had to remove the plants. What I mean is, there really was something unhealthy in the way rich people used to live. Masses of superfluous things. Too much furniture, too much room, too much emotional refinement, too many circumlocutions. I'm very glad we're using fewer rooms. We should give up still more."

"What's that parcel you've got? There's something sticking out of it, it looks like a bird's beak. It's a duck! How lovely! A wild drake! Where did you get it? I can't believe my eyes. It's worth a fortune these days."

"Somebody made me a present of it on the train. I'll tell you later, it's a long story. What shall I do? Shall I leave it in the kitchen?"

"Yes, of course. I'll send Niusha down at once to pluck and clean it. They say there will be all sorts of horrors this winter, famine, cold."

"Yes, that's what they are saying everywhere. Just now, I was looking out of the window in the train—I thought, what is there in the whole world worth more than a peaceful family life and work? The rest isn't in our hands. It does look as if there is a bad time coming for a lot of people. Some are trying to get out, they talk of going south, to the Caucasus, or farther still. I wouldn't want to do that, myself. A grown-up man should share his country's fate. To me it's obvious. But for you it's different. I wish you didn't have to go through it all. I'd like to send you away to some safe place—to Finland, perhaps. But if we stand gossiping half an hour on every step we'll never get upstairs."

"Wait a minute. I forgot to tell you. I've got news for you—and what news! Nikolai Nikolaievich is back."

"What Nikolai Nikolaievich?"

"Uncle Kolia."

"Tonia! It can't be! Is it really true?"

"It is true. He was in Switzerland. He came all the way around through London and Finland."

"Tonia! You're not joking? Have you seen him? Where is he? Can't we get him now, at once?"

"Don't be so impatient. He's staying with someone in the country. He promised to be back the day after tomorrow. He's changed a lot. You'll be disappointed. He stopped in Petersburg on the way, he's got Bolshevized. Father gets quite hoarse arguing with him. But why do we stop on every step. Let's go. So you too have heard there's a bad time ahead—hardships, dangers, anything might happen."

"I think so myself. Well, what of it? We'll manage, it can't be the end of everything. We'll wait and see, the same as other people."

"They say there won't be any firewood, or water, or light. They'll abolish money. No supplies will be coming in. Now we've stopped again! Come along. Listen, they say there are wonderful iron stoves for sale in the Arbat. Small ones. You can burn a newspaper and cook a meal. I've got the address. We must get one before they're all gone."

"That's right. We'll get one. Good idea. But just think of it, Uncle Kolia! I can't get over it."

"Let me tell you what I want to do. We'll set aside a corner somewhere on the top floor, say two or three rooms, communicating ones, and we'll keep those for ourselves and Father and Sashenka and Niusha, and we'll give up all the rest of the house. We'll put up a partition and have our own door, and it will be like a separate apartment. We'll put one of those iron stoves in the middle room, with a pipe through the window, and we'll do all our laundry, and our cooking, and our entertaining, all in this one room. That way we'll get the most out of the fuel, and who knows, with God's help, we'll get through the winter."

"Of course we'll get through it. There's no question. That's a fine idea. And you know what? We'll have a housewarming. We'll cook the duck and we'll invite Uncle Kolia."

"Lovely. And I'll ask Gordon to bring some drink. He can get it from some laboratory or other. Now look, this is the room I was thinking of. All right? Put your suitcase down and go get your hamper. We could ask Dudorov and Shura Shlesinger to the housewarming as well. You don't mind? You haven't forgotten where the washroom is? Spray yourself with some disinfectant. In the meantime I'll go in to Sashenka, and send Niusha down, and when we're ready I'll call you."

3

The most important thing for him in Moscow was his little boy. He had been mobilized almost as soon as Sashenka was born. He hardly knew him.

One day, while Tonia was still in hospital, he went to see her; he was already in uniform and was about to leave Moscow. He arrived at the babies' feeding time and was not allowed in.

He sat down in the waiting room. From the nursery, at the end of the passage beyond the maternity ward, came the squealing chorus of ten or twelve babies' voices. Several nurses came down the corridor, hurrying so that the newborn babies should not catch cold, taking them to their mothers, bundled up like shopping parcels, one under each arm.

"Wa, wa," yelled the babies all on one note, almost impassively, without feeling, as if it were all in the day's work. Only one voice stood out from the others. It was also yelling "wa, wa," and it did not express any more suffering than the rest, but it was deeper and seemed to shout less out of duty than with a deliberate, sullen hostility.

Yurii Andreievich had already decided that his child was to be called Alexander in honor of his father-in-law. For some reason he imagined that the voice he had singled out was that of his son; perhaps it was because this particular cry had its own character and seemed to foreshadow the future personality and destiny of a particular human being; it had its own sound-coloring, which included the child's name, Alexander, so Yurii Andreievich imagined.

He was not mistaken. It turned out later that this had in fact been Sashenka's voice. It was the first thing he had known about his son.

The next thing was the photographs Tonia sent to him at the front. They showed a cheerful, handsome, chubby little fellow with a cupid's-bow mouth, standing up on a blanket, bandy-legged and with its fist up as if it were doing a peasant dance. Sashenka had been a year old at the time and trying to take his first steps; now he was two and was beginning to talk.

Yurii Andreievich picked up his suitcase, put it on to the card table by the window, and began to unpack. What had the room been used for in the past, he wondered. He could not recognize it. Tonia must have changed the furniture or the wallpaper or redecorated it in some way.

He took out his shaving kit. A bright full moon rose between the pillars of the church tower exactly opposite the window. When it lit up the top layer of clothes and books inside the suitcase, the light in the room changed and he realized where he was.

It had been Anna Ivanovna's storeroom, where she used to put broken chairs and tables and old papers. Here she had kept her family archives and, in the summer, the trunks of winter clothes. During her lifetime the corners were cluttered up to the ceiling with junk, and the children were not allowed in. Only at Christmas or Easter, when huge crowds of children came to parties and the whole of the top floor was thrown open to them, was it unlocked and they played bandit in it, hiding under the tables, dressing up, and blackening their faces with cork.

The doctor stood thinking of all this, then he went down the back stairs to get his wicker hamper from the hall.

In the kitchen Niusha squatted in front of the stove, plucking the duck on a piece of newspaper. When he came in carrying his hamper she jumped up with a shy, graceful movement, blushing crimson, shook the feathers from her apron, and, after greeting him respectfully, offered to help him. He thanked her, saying he could manage, and went up. His wife called him from a couple of rooms farther on: "You can come in now, Yura."

He went into the room, which was Tonia's and his old classroom. The boy in the crib was not nearly so handsome as in his photograph, but he was the exact image of Yurii Andreievich's mother, Maria Nikolaievna Zhivago, a more striking likeness than any of her portraits.

"Here's Daddy, here's your Daddy, wave your hand like a good boy," Antonina Alexandrovna was saying. She lowered the net of the crib to make it easier for the father to kiss the boy and pick him up.

Sashenka, though doubtless frightened and repelled, let the unshaven stranger get quite close and bend over him, then he jerked himself upright, clutching the front of his mother's dress with one hand, and angrily swung the other arm and slapped him in the face. Terrified by his own daring, he then threw himself into his mother's arms and burst into bitter tears.

"No, no," Tonia scolded him. "You mustn't do that, Sashenka. What will Daddy think? He'll think Sasha is a bad boy. Now, show how you can kiss, kiss Daddy. Don't cry, silly, it's all right."

"Let him be, Tonia," the doctor said. "Don't bother him, and don't upset yourself. I know the kind of nonsense you are thinking—that it's not accidental, it's a bad sign—but that's all rubbish. It's only natural. The boy has never seen me. Tomorrow he'll have a good look at me and we'll become inseparable."

Yet he went out of the room depressed and with a feeling of foreboding.

### 4

Within the next few days he realized how alone he was. He did not blame anyone. He had merely got what he had asked for.

His friends had become strangely dim and colorless. Not one of them had preserved his own outlook, his own world. They had been much more vivid in his memory. He must have overestimated them in the past. Under the old order, which enabled those whose lives were secure to play the fools and eccentrics at the expense of the others while the majority led a wretched existence, it had been only too easy to mistake the foolishness and idleness of a privileged minority for genuine character and originality. But the moment the lower classes had risen, and the privileges of those on top had been abolished, how quickly had those people faded, how unregretfully had they renounced independent ideas—apparently no one had ever had such ideas!

The only people to whom Yurii Andreievich now felt close were his wife, her father, and two or three of his colleagues, modest rank-and-file workers, who did not indulge in grandiloquent phrases.

The party with duck and vodka was given as planned, a few days after his return. By then he had seen all those who came to it, so that the dinner was not in fact the occasion of their reunion.

The large duck was an unheard-of luxury in those already hungry days, but there was no bread with it, and because of this its splendor was somehow pointless—it even got on one's nerves.

The alcohol (a favorite black-market currency) had been brought by Gordon in a medicine bottle with a glass stopper. Antonina Alexandrovna never let go of the bottle, and now and then diluted a small portion of the alcohol with more or less water, according to her inspiration. It was discovered that it is easier to hold a number of consistently strong drinks than ones of varying strength. This, too, was annoying.

But the saddest thing of all was that their party was a kind of betrayal. You could not imagine anyone in the houses across the street eating or drinking in the same way at the same time. Beyond the windows lay silent, dark, hungry Moscow. Its shops were empty, and as for game and vodka, people had even forgotten to think about such things.

And so it turned out that only a life similar to the life of those around us, merging with it without a ripple, is genuine life, and that an unshared happiness is not happiness, so that duck and vodka, when they seem to be the only ones in town, are not even duck and vodka. And this was most vexing of all.

The guests too inspired unhappy reflections. Gordon had been all right in the days when he was given to gloomy thoughts and expressed them sullenly and clumsily. He was Zhivago's best friend, and in the gymnasium many people had liked him.

But now he had decided to give himself a new personality, and the results of his efforts were unfortunate. He played the merry fellow, he was jovial, cracked jokes, and often exclaimed, "What fun!" and "How amusing!"—expressions that did not belong to his vocabulary, for Gordon had never looked upon life as an entertainment.

While they were waiting for Dudorov he told the story of Dudorov's marriage, which he thought was comical, and which was circulating among his friends. Yurii Andreievich had not yet heard it.

It turned out that Dudorov had been married for about a year and then divorced his wife. The improbable gist of this story consisted in the following:

Dudorov had been drafted into the army by mistake. While he was serving and his case was being investigated, he was constantly punished for absentmindedly forgetting to salute officers in the street. For a long time after his discharge he would raise his arm impulsively whenever an officer came in sight, and often he imagined epaulettes where there were none.

In this latter period his behavior was erratic in other ways as well. At one point—so the rumor went—while waiting for a steamer at a Volga port, he made the acquaintance of two young women, sisters, who were waiting for the same steamer. Confused by the presence of a large number of army men and the memories of his misadventures as a soldier, he fell in love with the younger sister, and proposed to her on the spot. "Amusing, isn't it?" Gordon said. But he had to interrupt his story when its hero was heard at the door. Dudorov entered the room.

Like Gordon, he had become the opposite of what he had been. He had always been flippant and featherbrained: now he was a serious scholar. As a schoolboy he had been expelled for helping political prisoners escape; he had then tried several art schools, but in the end had become a student of the humanities. During the war he graduated from the university a few years behind his schoolmates. Now he held two chairs—those of Russian history and of general history. He was even the author of two books, one on the land policies of Ivan the Terrible, the other a study of Saint-Just.

Here at the party he spoke amiably about everyone and everything, in a voice that was muffled as though by a cold, staring dreamily at a certain fixed point in the distance like a man delivering a lecture.

Toward the end of the evening, when Shura Shlesinger burst in and added to the general noise and excitement, Dudorov, who had been Zhivago's childhood friend, asked him several times, addressing him with the formal "you" rather than the usual "thou," whether he had read Mayakovsky's *War and the World* and *Flute-Spine*.

Missing Yurii Andreievich's reply in all the noise, he asked him again a little later: "Have you read *Flute-Spine* and *Man?*"

[ 324 ]

"I told you, Innokentii. It's not my fault that you don't listen. Well, all right, I'll say it again. I've always liked Mayakovsky. He is a sort of continuation of Dostoievsky. Or rather, he's a Dostoievsky character writing lyrical poems—one of his young rebels, the 'Raw Youth' or Hippolyte or Raskolnikov. What an all-devouring poetic energy! And his way of saying a thing once and for all, uncompromisingly, straight from the shoulder! And above all, with what daring he flings all this in the face of society and beyond, into space!"

But the main attraction of the evening was, of course, Uncle Kolia. Antonina Alexandrovna had been mistaken in thinking that he was out of town; he had come back the day of his nephew's return. They had met a couple of times already and had got over their initial exclamations and had talked and laughed together to their heart's content.

The first time had been on a dull, gray night with a drizzle, fine as watery dust. Yurii Andreievich went to see him at his hotel. The hotels were already refusing to take people in except at the recommendation of the town authorities, but Nikolai Nikolaievich was well known and had kept some of his old connections.

The hotel looked like a lunatic asylum abandoned by its staff—the stairways and corridors empty, everything in a state of chaos.

Through the large window of his unswept room the huge square of those mad days looked in, deserted and frightening, more like a square in a nightmare than the one plainly to be seen in front of the hotel.

For Yurii Andreievich the encounter was a tremendous, unforgettable event. He was seeing the idol of his childhood, the teacher who had dominated his mind as a boy.

His gray hair was becoming to him, and his loose foreign suit fitted him well.

He was very young and handsome for his years.

Admittedly, he was overshadowed by the grandeur of the events; seen beside them, he lost in stature. But it never occurred to Yurii Andreievich to measure him by such a yardstick.

He was surprised at Nikolai Nikolaievich's calm, at his light and detached tone in speaking of politics. He was more self-possessed than most Russians could be at that time. It marked him as a new arrival, and it seemed old-fashioned and a little embarrassing.

But it was something very different from politics that filled those first few hours of their reunion, that made them laugh and cry and throw their arms around each other's necks, and punctuated their first feverish conversation with frequent moments of silence.

Theirs was a meeting of two artists, and although they were close relatives, and the past arose and lived again between them and memories surged up and they informed each other of all that had happened during their separation, the moment they began to speak of the things that really matter to creative minds, all other ties between them vanished, their kinship and difference of age were forgotten, all that was left was the confrontation of elemental forces, of energies and principles.

For the last ten years Nikolai Nikolaievich had had no opportunity to speak about the problems of creative writing as freely and intimately as now. Nor had Yurii Andreievich ever heard views as penetrating, apt, and inspiring as on that occasion.

Their talk was full of exclamations, they paced excitedly up and down the room, marveling at each other's perspicacity, or stood in silence by the window drumming on the glass, deeply moved by the exalting discovery of how completely they understood each other.

Such was their first meeting, but later the doctor had seen his uncle a few times in company, and then Nikolai Nikolaievich was completely different, unrecognizable.

He felt that he was a visitor in Moscow and persisted in acting like one. Whether it was Petersburg that he regarded as his home, or some other place, remained uncertain. He enjoyed his role of a social star and political oracle, and possibly he imagined that Moscow would have political salons in the style of Madame Roland's in Paris on the eve of the Convention.

Calling on his women friends at their hospitable apartments in quiet Moscow back streets, he amiably teased them and their husbands on their backwardness and parochialism. He showed off his familiarity with newspapers, as he had done formerly with books forbidden by the Church, and Orphic texts.

It was said that he had left a new young love, much unfinished business, and a half-written book in Switzerland, and had only come for a dip into the stormy waters of his homeland, expecting, if he came out safe and sound, to hasten back to his Alps.

He was pro-Bolshevik, and often mentioned two left-wing Social Revolutionaries who shared his views, a journalist who wrote under the pseudonym of Miroshka Pomor and a pamphleteer, Sylvia Koteri.

"It's frightful, what you've come down to, Nikolai Nikolaievich," Alexander Alexandrovich chided him. "You and your Miroshkas! What a cesspool! And then that Lydia Pokori."

"Koteri," corrected Nikolai Nikolaievich, "and Sylvia."

"Pokori or Potpourri, who cares. Names won't change anything."

"All the same, it happens to be Koteri," Nikolai Nikolaievich insisted patiently. They had dialogues of this sort:

"What are we arguing about? It's so obvious that it makes you blush to have to prove it. It's elementary. For centuries the mass of the people have lived impossible lives. Take any history textbook. Whatever it was called—feudalism and serfdom or capitalism and industrial workers, it was unnatural and unjust. This has been known for a long time, and the world has been preparing for an upheaval that would bring enlightenment to the people and put everything in its proper place.

"You know perfectly well that it's quite useless tinkering with the old structure, you have to dig right down to the foundations. I don't say the whole building mayn't collapse as a result. What of it? The fact that it's frightening doesn't mean it won't happen. It's a question of time. How can you dispute it?"

"That's not the point, that's not what I was talking about," Alexander Alexandrovich said angrily, and the argument flared up. "Your Potpourris and Miroshkas are people without a conscience. They say one thing and do another. Anyway, where's your logic? It's a complete nonsequitur. No, wait a minute, I'll show you something," and he would begin hunting for some newspaper with a controversial article, banging the drawers of his desk and stimulating his eloquence with this noisy fuss.

Alexander Alexandrovich liked something to get in his way when he was talking; the distraction served as an excuse for his mumbling and his hems and haws. His fits of talkativeness came on him when he was looking for something he had lost—say, hunting for a matching snow boot in the dimly lighted cloakroom—or when he stood at the bathroom door with a towel over his arm, or when he was passing a heavy serving dish or pouring wine into the glasses of his friends.

Yurii Andreievich enjoyed listening to

his father-in-law. He adored the familiar, old-Moscow singsong and the soft, purring Gromeko r's.

Alexander Alexandrovich's upper lip with its little cropped mustache protruded above the lower lip in just the same way as his butterfly tie stuck out from his neck. There was something in common between the lip and the tie, and it somehow gave him a touching, childishly trusting look.

On the night of the party Shura Shlesinger appeared very late. She had come straight from a meeting and was wearing a suit and a worker's cap. She strode into the room and, shaking everyone's hand in turn, at once burst into complaints and accusations.

"How are you, Tonia? Hello, Alexander. You must admit it's disgusting. The whole of Moscow knows he's back, everyone is talking about it, and I am the last to be told. Well, I suppose I'm not good enough. Where is he, anyway? Let me get at him, you surround him like a wall. Well, how are you? I've read it, I don't understand a word, but it's brilliant, you can tell at once. How are you, Nikolai Nikolaievich? I'll be back in a moment, Yurochka, I've got to talk to you. Hello, young men. You're here too, Gogochka, Goosey-Goosey-Gander" (this to a distant relative of the Gromekos', an enthusiastic admirer of all rising talents, known as Goosey because of his idiot laugh and as the Tapeworm on account of his lankiness). "So you're eating and drinking? I'll soon catch up with you. Well, my friends, you've simply no idea what you're missing. You don't know anything, you haven't seen a thing. If you only knew what's going on! You go and have a look at a real mass meeting, with real workers, real soldiers, not out of books. Just try to let out a squeak to them about fighting the war to a victorious end! They'll give you a victorious end! I've just been listening to a

sailor—Yurochka, you'd simply rave! What passion! What single-mindedness!"

Shura was interrupted time and again. Everyone shouted. She sat next to Yurii Andreievich, took his hand in hers, and, moving her face close to his, shouted like a megaphone above the din:

"Let me take you along someday, Yurochka. I'll show you real people. You must, you simply must get your feet on the ground, like Antaeus. Why are you staring at me like that? I'm an old war horse, didn't you know? An old Bestuzhevist.[1] I've seen the inside of a prison, I've fought on the barricades.—Well of course, what did you think? Oh, we don't know the people at all. I've just come from there, I was right in the thick of it. I'm collecting a library for them."

She had had a drink and was obviously getting tipsy. But Yurii Andreievich's head was also spinning. He never noticed how it happened that Shura was now at one end of the room and he at the other; he was standing at the head of the table and apparently, quite unexpectedly to himself, making a speech. It took him some time to get silence.

"Ladies and gentlemen . . . I should like . . . Misha! Gogochka! Tonia, what am I to do, they won't listen! Ladies and gentlemen, let me say a word or two. Unprecedented, extraordinary events are approaching. Before they burst upon us, here is what I wish you: May God grant us not to lose each other and not to lose our souls. Gogochka, you can cheer afterwards, I haven't finished. Stop talking in the corners and listen carefully.

"In this third year of the war the people have become convinced that the difference between those on the front line and those at the rear will sooner or later

---

[1] A student taking the Bestuzhev university courses for women. Many of the students were left-wing.

vanish. The sea of blood will rise until it reaches every one of us and submerge all who stayed out of the war. The revolution is this flood.

"During the revolution it will seem to you, as it seemed to us at the front, that life has stopped, that there is nothing personal left, that there is nothing going on in the world except killing and dying. If we live long enough to read the chronicles and memoirs of this period, we shall realize that in these five or ten years we have experienced more than other people do in a century. I don't know whether the people will rise of themselves and advance spontaneously like a tide, or whether everything will be done in the name of the people. Such a tremendous event requires no dramatic proof of its existence. I'll be convinced without proof. It's petty to explore causes of titanic events. They haven't any. It's only in a family quarrel that you look for beginnings—after people have pulled each other's hair and smashed the dishes they rack their brains trying to figure out who started it. What is truly great is without beginning, like the universe. It confronts us as suddenly as if it had always been there or had dropped out of the blue.

"I too think that Russia is destined to become the first socialist state since the beginning of the world. When this comes to pass, the event will stun us for a long time, and after awakening we shall have lost half our memories forever. We'll have forgotten what came first and what followed, and we won't look for causes. The new order of things will be all around us and as familiar to us as the woods on the horizon or the clouds over our heads. There will be nothing else left."

He said a few more things, and by then he had sobered up completely. As before, he could not hear clearly what people were saying, and answered them pointlessly. He saw that they liked him, but could not rid himself of the sadness that oppressed him. He said:

"Thank you, thank you. I appreciate your feelings, but I don't deserve them. It's wrong to bestow love in a hurry, as though otherwise one would later have to give much more of it."

They all laughed and clapped, taking it for a deliberate witticism, while he did not know where to escape from his forebodings of disaster and his feeling that despite his striving for the good and his capacity for happiness, he had no power over the future.

The guests began to leave. They had long, tired faces. Their yawns, snapping and unsnapping their jaws, made them look like horses.

Before going, they drew the curtains and pushed the windows open. There was a yellowish dawn in the wet sky filled with dirty, pea-colored clouds. "Looks as if there's been a storm while we were chattering," said someone. "I was caught in the rain on my way here, I only just made it," Shura confirmed.

In the deserted street it was still dark and the drip-drip of the water from the trees alternated with the insistent chirruping of drenched sparrows.

There was a roll of thunder, as if a plow had been dragged right across the sky. Then silence. Then four loud, delayed thuds, like overgrown potatoes in autumn being flung out with a shovel from the soft ground.

The thunder cleared the dusty, smoke-filled room. Suddenly the element of life became distinguishable, as apprehensible as electric currents, air and water, desire for happiness, earth, sky.

The sky filled with the voices of the departing guests. They had begun a heated argument in the house and continued arguing just as hotly in the street. Gradually the voices grew fainter in the distance and died out.

"How late it is," said Yurii Andreievich. "Let's go to bed. The only people I love in the world are you and Father."

## 5

August had gone by and now September was almost over. The inevitable was approaching. Winter was near and, in the human world, something like a state of suspended animation, which was in the air, and which everyone was talking about.

This was the time to prepare for the cold weather, to store up food and wood. But in those days of the triumph of materialism, matter had become a disembodied idea, and the problems of alimentation and fuel supply took the place of food and firewood.

The people in the cities were as helpless as children in the face of the unknown—that unknown which swept every established habit aside and left nothing but desolation in its wake, although it was itself the offspring of the city and the creation of city-dwellers.

All around, people continued to deceive themselves, to talk endlessly. Everyday life struggled on, by force of habit, limping and shuffling. But the doctor saw life as it was. It was clear to him that it was under sentence. He looked upon himself and his milieu as doomed. Ordeals were ahead, perhaps death. Their days were counted and running out before his eyes.

He would have gone insane had he not been kept busy by the details of daily life. His wife, his child, the necessity to earn money, the humble daily ritual of his practice—these were his salvation.

He realized that he was a pygmy before the monstrous machine of the future; he was anxious about this future, and loved it and was secretly proud of it, and as though for the last time, as if in farewell, he avidly looked at the trees and clouds and the people walking in the streets, the great Russian city struggling through misfortune—and was ready to sacrifice himself for the general good, and could do nothing.

He most often saw the sky and the people from the middle of the street when he crossed the Arbat at the corner of Old Coachyard Row, near the pharmacy of the Russian Medical Society.

He resumed his duties at his old hospital. It was still called the Hospital of the Holy Cross, although the society of that name had been dissolved. So far no one had thought of a new name for the hospital.

The staff had already divided up into camps. To the moderates, whose obtuseness made the doctor indignant, he seemed dangerous; to those whose politics were advanced, not Red enough. Thus he belonged to neither group, having moved away from the former and lagging behind the latter.

In addition to his normal duties, the medical chief had put him in charge of general statistics. Endless questionnaires and forms went through his hands. Death rate, sickness rate, the earnings of the staff, the degree of their political consciousness and of their participation in the elections, the perpetual shortage of fuel, food, medicines, everything had to be checked and reported.

Zhivago worked at his old table by the staff-room window, stacked with charts and forms of every size and shape. He had pushed them to one side; occasionally, in addition to taking notes for his medical works, he wrote in snatches his "Playing at People, a Gloomy Diary or Journal Consisting of Prose, Verse, and What-have-you, Inspired by the Realization that Half the People Have Stopped Being Themselves and Are Acting Unknown Parts."

The light, sunny room with its white painted walls was filled with the creamy light of the golden autumn days that follow the Feast of the Assumption, when the mornings begin to be frosty and titmice and magpies dart into the bright-leaved, thinning woods. On such days the sky is incredibly high, and through the transparent pillar of air between it and the earth there moves an icy, dark-blue radiance coming from the north. Everything in the world becomes more visible and more audible. Distant sounds reach us in a state of frozen resonance, separately and clearly. The horizons open, as if to show the whole of life for years ahead. This rarefied light would be unbearable if it were not so short-lived, coming at the end of the brief autumn day just before the early dusk.

Such was now the light in the staff room, the light of an early autumn sunset, as succulent, glassy, juicy as a certain variety of Russian apple.

The doctor sat at his desk writing, pausing to think and to dip his pen while some unusually quiet birds flew silently past the tall windows, throwing shadows on his moving hands, on the table with its forms, and on the floor and the walls, and just as silently vanished from sight.

The prosector came in; he was a stout man who had lost so much weight that his skin hung on him in bags. "The maple leaves are nearly all gone," he said. "When you think how they stood up to all the rain and wind, and now a single morning frost has done it."

The doctor looked up. The mysterious birds darting past the window had in fact been wine-red maple leaves. They flew away from the trees, gliding through the air, and covered the hospital lawn, looking like bent orange stars.

"Have the windows been puttied up?" the prosector asked.

"No," Yurii Andreievich said, and went on writing.

"Isn't it time they were?"

Yurii Andreievich, absorbed in his work, did not answer.

"Pity Taraska's gone," went on the prosector. "He was worth his weight in gold. Patch your boots or repair your watch—he'd do anything. And he could get you anything in the world. Now we'll have to do the windows ourselves."

"There's no putty."

"You can make some. I'll give you the recipe." He explained how you made putty with linseed oil and chalk. "Well, I'll leave you now. I suppose you want to get on with your work."

He went off to the other window and busied himself with his bottles and specimens. "You'll ruin your eyes," he said a minute later. "It's getting dark. And they won't give you any light. Let's go home."

"I'll work another twenty minutes or so."

"His wife is a nurse here."

"Whose wife?"

"Taraska's."

"I know."

"Nobody knows where he is himself. He prowls about all over the country. Last summer he came twice to see his wife, now he's in some village. He's building the new life. He's one of those soldier-Bolsheviks, you see them everywhere, walking about in the streets, traveling in trains. And do you know what makes them tick? Take Taraska. He can turn his hand to anything. Whatever he does, he has to do it well. That's what happened to him in the army—he learned to fight, just like any other trade. He became a crack rifleman. His eyes and hands—first-class! All his decorations were awarded him, not for courage, but for always hitting the mark. Well, anything he takes up becomes a passion with him, so he took to fighting in a big way. He could see what a rifle does for a man—it gives him power, it brings him distinction. He wanted to be a power himself. An armed man isn't just a man like any other. In the old days such men turned from soldiers into brigands. You just try to take Taraska's rifle away from him now! Well, then came the slogan 'Turn your bayonets against your masters,' so Taraska turned. That's the whole story. There's Marxism for you."

"That's the most genuine kind—straight from life. Didn't you know?"

The prosector went back to his test tubes.

"How did you make out with the stove specialist?" he asked after a while.

"I'm most grateful to you for sending him. A most interesting man. We spent hours talking about Hegel and Croce."

"Naturally! Took his doctorate in philosophy at Heidelberg. What about the stove?"

"That's not so good."

"Still smoking?"

"Never stops."

"He can't have fixed the stovepipe right. It ought to be connected with a flue. Did he let it out through the window?"

"No, the flue, but it still smokes."

"Then he can't have found the right air vent. If only we had Taraska! But you'll get it right in the end. Moscow wasn't built in a day. Getting a stove to work isn't like playing the piano, it takes skill. Have you laid in your firewood?"

"Where am I to get it from?"

"I'll send you the church janitor. He's an expert at stealing wood. Takes fences to pieces and turns them into firewood. But you'll have to bargain with him. No, better get the exterminator."

They went down to the cloakroom, put their coats on, and went out.

"Why the exterminator? We don't have bedbugs."

"That's got nothing to do with it. I'm talking about wood. The exterminator is an old woman who is doing a big busi-

ness in wood. She's got it all set up on a proper business footing—buys up whole houses for fuel. It's dark, watch your step. In the old days I could have taken you blindfold anywhere in this district. I knew every stone. I was born near here. But since they've started pulling down the fences I can hardly find my way about, even by day. It's like being in a strange town. On the other hand, some extraordinary places have come to light. Little Empire houses you never knew were there, with round garden tables and half-rotten benches. The other day I passed a place like that, a sort of little wilderness at an intersection of three streets, and there was an old lady poking about with a stick—she must have been about a hundred. 'Hello, Granny,' I said, 'are you looking for worms to go fishing?' I was joking, of course, but she took it quite seriously. 'No, not worms,' she said, 'mushrooms.' And it's true, you know, the town is getting to be like the woods. There's a smell of decaying leaves and mushrooms."

"I think I know where you mean—between Serebriany and Molchanovka, isn't it? The strangest things are always happening to me there—either I meet someone I haven't seen in twenty years, or I find something. They say it's dangerous, and no wonder, there's a whole network of alleys leading to the old thieves' dens near Smolensky. Before you know where you are, they've stripped you to the skin and vanished."

"And look at those street lamps—they don't shine at all. No wonder they call bruises shiners. Be careful you don't bump yourself."

6

All sorts of things did indeed happen to the doctor at that place. One cold dark night, shortly before the October fighting, he came across a man lying unconscious on the sidewalk, his arms flung out, his head against a curbstone, and his feet in the gutter. Occasionally he uttered weak groans. When the doctor tried to rouse him he muttered a few words, something about a wallet. He had been attacked and robbed. His head was battered and covered with blood, but a casual examination revealed that the skull was intact.

Zhivago went to the pharmacy in the Arbat, telephoned for the cab that the hospital used in emergencies, and took the patient to the emergency ward.

The wounded man proved to be a prominent political leader. The doctor treated him till he recovered, and for years afterwards this man acted as his protector, getting him out of trouble several times in those days that were so heavy with suspicion.

### 7

Antonina Alexandrovna's plan had been adopted and the family had settled for the winter in three rooms on the top floor.

It was a cold, windy Sunday, dark with heavy snow clouds. The doctor was off duty.

The fire was lit in the morning, and the stove began to smoke. Niusha struggled with the damp wood. Antonina Alexandrovna, who knew nothing about stoves, kept giving her absurd and bad advice. The doctor, who did know, tried to interfere, but his wife took him gently by the shoulders and pushed him out of the room, saying: "Don't you meddle in this. You'll only pour oil on the fire."

"Oil wouldn't be so bad, Toniechka, the stove would be ablaze at once! The trouble is, there is neither oil nor fire."

"This is no time for jokes. There are moments when they are out of place."

The trouble with the stove upset everyone's plans. They had all hoped to get their chores done before dark and have a free evening, but now dinner would be late, there was no hot water, and various other plans might have to be dropped.

The fire smoked more and more. The strong wind blew the smoke back into the room. A cloud of black soot stood in it like a fairy-tale monster in a thick wood.

Finally Yurii Andreievich drove everyone out into the two other rooms, and opened the top pane of the window. He removed half the wood from the stove, and spaced out the rest with chips and birchwood shavings between them.

Fresh air rushed in through the window. The curtain swayed and flew up. Papers blew off the desk. A door banged somewhere down the hall, and the wind began a cat-and-mouse game with what was left of the smoke.

The logs flared up and crackled. The stove was ablaze. Its iron body was covered with red-hot spots like a consumptive flush. The smoke in the room thinned out and soon vanished.

The room grew lighter. The windows, which Yurii Andreievich had recently fixed according to the prosecutor's recipe, gave off the warm, greasy smell of putty. An acrid smell of charred fir bark and the fresh, toilet-water scent of aspen came from the wood drying by the stove.

Nikolai Nikolaievich burst into the room as impetuously as the wind coming through the open window.

"They're fighting in the street," he reported. "There is a regular battle between the cadets who support the Provisional Government and the garrison soldiers who support the Bolsheviks. There is skirmishing all over the city. I got into trouble coming here—once at the corner of Bolshaia Dmitrovka and once at the Nikitsky Gate. Now you can't get through directly, you have to go around.

Hurry up, Yura! Put your coat on, let's go. You've got to see it. This is history. This happens once in a lifetime."

But he stayed talking for a couple of hours. Then they had dinner, and by the time he was ready to go home and was dragging the doctor out, Gordon burst in, in exactly the same way as Nikolai Nikolaievich and with much the same news.

Things had progressed, however. There were new details. Gordon spoke of increasing rifle fire and of passers-by killed by stray bullets. According to him, all traffic had stopped. He had got through by a miracle, but now the street was cut off.

Nikolai Nikolaievich refused to believe him and dashed out but was back in a minute. He said bullets whistled down the street knocking chips of brick and plaster off the corners. There was not a soul outside. All traffic had stopped.

That week Sashenka caught a cold.

"I've told you a hundred times, he's not to play near the stove," Yurii Andreievich scolded. "It's much worse to let him get too hot than cold."

Sashenka had a sore throat and a fever. He had a special, overwhelming terror of vomiting, and when Yurii Andreievich tried to examine his throat he pushed away his hand, clenching his teeth, yelling and choking. Neither arguments nor threats had the slightest effect on him. At one moment, however, he inadvertently yawned, and the doctor quickly took advantage of this to insert a spoon into his son's mouth and hold down his tongue for long enough to get a look at his raspberry-colored larynx and swollen tonsils covered with alarming white spots.

A little later, by means of a similar maneuver, he got a specimen and, as he had a microscope at home, was able to examine it. Fortunately, it was not diphtheria.

But on the third night Sashenka had an attack of nervous croup. His temperature shot up and he could not breathe. Yurii Andreievich was helpless to ease his suffering and could not bear to watch it. Antonina Alexandrovna thought the child was dying. They carried him about the room in turn, and this seemed to make him feel better.

They needed milk, mineral water, or soda water for him. But the street fighting was at its height. Gun and rifle fire never ceased for a moment. Even if Yurii Andreievich had crossed the battle zone at the risk of his life, he would not have found anyone about in the streets beyond it. All life in the city was suspended until clarified.

Yet there could be no doubt about the outcome. Rumors came from all sides that the workers were getting the upper hand. Small groups of cadets were fighting on, but they were cut off from each other and from their command.

The Sivtzev quarter was held by soldiers' units who were pressing on toward the center. Soldiers who had fought against Germany and young working boys sat in a trench they had dug down the street; they were already getting to know the people who lived in the neighborhood and joked with them as they came and stood outside their gates. Traffic in this part of the town was being restored.

Gordon and Nikolai Nikolaievich, who had got stuck at the Zhivagos', were released from their three days' captivity. Zhivago had been glad of their presence during Sashenka's illness, and his wife forgave them for adding to the general disorder. But they had felt obliged to repay the kindness of their hosts by entertaining them with ceaseless talk. Yurii Andreievich was so exhausted by three days of pointless chatter that he was happy to see them go.

[ 333 ]

*8*

They learned that their guests had got home safely. But military operations continued, several streets were still closed, and the doctor could not yet go to his hospital. He was impatient to return to his work and the manuscript he had left in the drawer of the staff-room desk.

Only here and there did people come out in the morning and walk a short distance to buy bread. When they saw a passer-by carrying a milk bottle, they would surround him trying to find out where he had got it.

Occasionally the firing resumed all over the town, and the streets were cleared again. It was said that the two sides were engaged in negotiations, whose course, favorable or unfavorable, was reflected in the varying intensity of the firing.

At about 10 P.M. one evening in late October (Old Style) Yurii Andreievich went without any particular necessity to call on one of his colleagues. The streets he passed were deserted. He walked quickly. The first thin powdery snow was coming down, scattered by a rising wind.

He had turned down so many side streets that he had almost lost count of them when the snow thickened and the wind turned into a blizzard, the kind of blizzard that whistles in a field covering it with a blanket of snow, but which in town tosses about as if it had lost its way.

There was something in common between the disturbances in the moral and in the physical world, near and far on the ground and in the air. Here and there resounded the last salvoes of islands of resistance. Bubbles of dying fires rose and broke on the horizon. And the snow swirled and eddied and smoked at Yurii's feet, on the wet streets and pavements.

A newsboy running with a thick batch of freshly printed papers under his arm and shouting "Latest news!" overtook him at an intersection.

"Keep the change," said the doctor. The boy peeled a damp sheet off the batch, thrust it into his hand, and a minute later was engulfed in the snowstorm.

The doctor stopped under a street light to read the headlines. The paper was a late extra printed on one side only; it gave the official announcement from Petersburg that a Soviet of People's Commissars had been formed and that Soviet power and the dictatorship of the proletariat were established in Russia. There followed the first decrees of the new government and various brief news dispatches received by telegraph and telephone.

The blizzard lashed at the doctor's eyes and covered the printed page with gray, rustling pellets of snow. But it was not the snowstorm that prevented him from reading. The historic greatness of the moment moved him so deeply that it took him some time to collect himself.

To read the rest of the news he looked around for a better lit, sheltered place. He found that he was standing once again at that charmed spot, the intersection of Serebriany and Molchanovka, in front of a tall, five-story building with a glass door and a spacious, well-lit lobby.

He went in and stood under the electric light, next to the staircase, reading the news.

Footsteps sounded above him. Someone was coming down the stairs, stopping frequently, as though hesitating. At one point, he actually changed his mind and ran up again. A door opened somewhere and two voices welled out, so distorted by echoes that it was impossible to tell whether men or women were speaking. Then the door banged and the same steps ran down, this time resolutely.

Yurii Andreievich was absorbed in his

paper and had not meant to look up, but the stranger stopped so suddenly at the foot of the stairs that he raised his head.

Before him stood a boy of about eighteen in a reindeer cap and a stiff reindeer coat worn, as in Siberia, fur side out. He was dark and had narrow Kirghiz eyes. His face had an aristocratic quality, the fugitive spark and reticent delicacy that give an impression of remoteness and are sometimes found in people of a complex, mixed parentage.

The boy obviously mistook Yurii Andreievich for someone else. He looked at him, puzzled and shy, as if he knew him but could not make up his mind to speak. To put an end to the misunderstanding Yurii Andreievich measured him with a cold, discouraging glance.

The boy turned away confused and walked to the entrance. There he looked back once again before going out and banging the heavy glass door shut behind him.

Yurii Andreievich left a few minutes after him. His mind was full of the news; he forgot the boy and the colleague he had meant to visit, and set out straight for home. But he was distracted on the way by another incident, one of those details of everyday life that assumed an inordinate importance in those days.

Not far from his house he stumbled in the dark over an enormous pile of timber near the curb. There was an institution of some sort in the street, to which the government had probably supplied fuel in the form of boards from a dismantled house in the outskirts of the town. Not all of it would go into the yard, and the rest had been left outside. A sentry with a rifle was on duty by this pile; he paced up and down the yard and occasionally went out into the street.

Without thinking twice, Yurii Andreievich took advantage of a moment when the sentry's back was turned and the wind had raised a cloud of snow into the

air to creep up on the dark side, avoiding the lamplight, carefully loosen a heavy beam from the very bottom, and pull it out. He loaded it with difficulty on his back, immediately ceasing to feel its weight (your own load is not a burden), and, hugging the shadow of the walls, took the wood safely home.

Its arrival was timely; they had run out of firewood. The beam was chopped up, and the pieces were stacked. Yurii Andreievich lit the stove and squatted in front of it in silence, while Alexander Alexandrovich moved up his armchair and sat warming himself.

Yurii Andreievich took the newspaper out of the side pocket of his coat and held it out to him.

"Seen that? Have a look."

Still squatting on his heels and poking the fire, he talked to himself.

"What splendid surgery! You take a knife and with one masterful stroke you cut out all the old stinking ulcers. Quite simply, without any nonsense, you take the old monster of injustice, which has been accustomed for centuries to being bowed and scraped and curtsied to, and you sentence it to death.

"This fearlessness, this way of seeing the thing through to the end, has a familiar national look about it. It has something of Pushkin's uncompromising clarity and of Tolstoy's unwavering faithfulness to the facts."

"Pushkin, you said? Wait a second. Let me finish. I can't read and listen at the same time," said Alexander Alexandrovich under the mistaken impression that his son-in-law was addressing him.

"And the real stroke of genius is this. If you charged someone with the task of creating a new world, of starting a new era, he would ask you first to clear the ground. He would wait for the old centuries to finish before undertaking to build the new ones, he'd want to begin a new paragraph, a new page.

"But here, they don't bother with anything like that. This new thing, this marvel of history, this revelation, is exploded right into the very thick of daily life without the slightest consideration for its course. It doesn't start at the beginning, it starts in the middle, without any schedule, on the first weekday that comes along, while the traffic in the street is at its height. That's real genius. Only real greatness can be so unconcerned with timing and opportunity."

9

Winter came, just the kind of winter that had been foretold. It was not as terrifying as the two winters that followed it, but it was already of the same sort, dark, hungry, and cold, entirely given to the breaking up of the familiar and the reconstruction of all the foundations of existence, and to inhuman efforts to cling to life as it slipped out of your grasp.

There were three of them, one after the other, three such terrible winters, and not all that now seems to have happened in 1917 and 1918 really happened then— some of it may have been later. These three successive winters have merged into one and it is difficult to tell them apart.

The old life and the new order had not yet come in contact. They were not yet openly hostile to each other, as when the civil war broke out a year later, but there was no connection between the two. They stood apart, confronting each other, incompatible.

There were new elections everywhere —in administration of buildings, organizations of all kinds, government offices, public services. Commissars invested with dictatorial powers were appointed to each, men of iron will in black leather jackets, armed with means of intimidation and guns, who shaved rarely and slept even more rarely.

They knew the slinking bourgeois breed, the ordinary holders of cheap government bonds, and they spoke to them without the slightest pity and with Mephistophelean smiles, as to petty thieves caught in the act.

These were the people who reorganized everything in accordance with the plan, and company after company, enterprise after enterprise became Bolshevized.

The Hospital of the Holy Cross was now known as the Second Reformed. Many things had changed in it. Part of the staff had been dismissed and others had resigned because they did not find work sufficiently rewarding. These were doctors with a fashionable practice and high fees, and glib talkers. They left out of self-interest but asserted that they had made a civic gesture of protest and looked down on those who had stayed on, almost boycotting them. Zhivago had stayed.

In the evenings husband and wife had conversations of this sort:

"Don't forget Wednesday, at the Doctors' Union; they'll have two sacks of frozen potatoes for us in the basement. I'll let you know what time I can get away. We'll have to go together and take the sled."

"All right, Yurochka, there's plenty of time. Why don't you go to bed now, it's late. I wish you'd rest, you can't do everything."

"There's an epidemic. Exhaustion is lowering resistance. You and Father look terrible. We must do something. If only I knew what. We don't take enough care of ourselves. Listen. You aren't asleep?"

"No."

"I'm not worried about myself, I've got nine lives, but if by any chance I should get ill, you will be sensible, won't you, you mustn't keep me at home. Get me into the hospital at once."

"Don't talk like that. Pray God you'll keep well. Why play Cassandra?"

"Remember, there aren't any honest people left, or any friends. Still less any experts. If anything should happen don't trust anyone except Pichuzhkin. That is if he's still there, of course. You aren't asleep?"

"No."

"The pay wasn't good enough, so off they went; now it turns out they had principles and civic sentiments. You meet them in the street, they hardly shake hands, just raise an eyebrow: 'So you're working for *them?*'—'I am,' I said, 'and if you don't mind, I am proud of our privations and I respect those who honor us by imposing them on us.' "

### 10

For a long time most people's daily food consisted of thin millet boiled in water and soup made of herring heads; the herring itself was used as a second course. A sort of kasha was also made of unground wheat or rye.

A woman professor who was a friend of Antonina Alexandrovna's taught her to bake bread in an improvised Dutch oven. The idea was to sell some of the bread and so cover the cost of heating the tile stove as in the old days, instead of using the iron stove, which continued to smoke and gave almost no heat.

Antonina Alexandrovna's bread was good but nothing came of her commercial plans. They had to go back to the wretched iron stove. The Zhivagos were hard up.

One morning, after Yurii Andreievich had gone to work, Antonina Alexandrovna put on her shabby winter coat—she was so run down that she shivered in it even in warm weather—and went out "hunting." There were only two logs left. For about half an hour she wandered through the alleys in the neighborhood where you could sometimes catch a peasant from one of the villages outside

Moscow selling vegetables and potatoes. In the main streets, peasants with loads were liable to be arrested. Soon she found what she was looking for. A sturdy young fellow in a peasant's coat walked back with her, pulling a sleigh that looked as light as a toy, and followed her cautiously into the yard.

Covered up by sacking inside the sleigh was a load of birch logs no thicker than the balusters of an old-fashioned country house in a nineteenth-century photograph. Antonina Alexandrovna knew their worth—birch only in name, the wood was of the poorest sort and too freshly cut to be suitable for burning. But as there was no choice, it was pointless to argue.

The young peasant carried five or six armloads up to the living room and took in exchange Tonia's small mirror wardrobe. He carried it down and packed it in his sleigh to take away as a present for his bride. In discussing a future deal in potatoes, he asked the price of the piano.

When Yurii Andreievich came home he said nothing about his wife's purchase. It would have been more sensible to chop up the wardrobe, but they could never have brought themselves to do it.

"There's a note for you on the table, did you see it?" she said.

"The one sent on from the hospital? Yes, I've had the message already. It's a sick call. I'll certainly go. I'll just have a little rest first. But it's pretty far. It's somewhere near the Triumphal Arch, I've got the address."

"Have you seen the fee they are offering you? You'd better read it. A bottle of German cognac or a pair of stockings! What sort of people are they, do you imagine? Vulgar. They don't seem to have any idea of how we live nowadays. *Nouveaux riches,* I suppose."

"Yes, that's from a supplier."

Suppliers, concessionaires, and authorized agents were names then given to small businessmen to whom the government, which had abolished private trade, occasionally made concessions at moments of economic difficulties, charging them with the procurement of various goods.

They were not former men of substance or dismissed heads of old firms—such people did not recover from the blow they had received. They were a new category of businessmen, people without roots who had been scooped up from the bottom by the war and the revolution.

Zhivago had a drink of hot water and saccharin whitened with milk and went off to see his patient.

Deep snow covered the street from wall to wall, in places up to the level of the ground-floor windows. Silent half-dead shadows moved all over this expanse carrying a little food or pulling it along on sleds. There was almost no other traffic.

Old shop signs still hung here and there. They had no relation to the small new consumer shops and co-operatives, which were all empty and locked, their windows barred or boarded up.

The reason they were locked and empty was not only that there were no goods but that the reorganization of all aspects of life, including trade, had so far remained largely on paper and had not yet affected such trifling details as the boarded-up shops.

## 11

The house to which the doctor went was at the end of Brest Street near the Tver Gate.

It was an old barracklike stone building with an inside courtyard, and three wooden staircases rose along the courtyard walls.

That day the tenants were at their general meeting, in which a woman delegate from the borough council participated, when a military commission suddenly turned up to check arms licenses and to confiscate unlicensed weapons. The tenants had to go back to their flats, but the head of the commission asked the delegate not to leave, assuring her that the search would not take long and the meeting could be resumed within a short time.

When the doctor arrived, the commission had almost finished but the flat where he was going had not yet been searched. Zhivago was stopped on the landing by a soldier with a rifle, but the head of the commission heard them arguing and ordered the search to be put off until after the doctor had examined his patient.

The door was opened by the master of the house, a polite young man with a sallow complexion and dark, melancholy eyes. He was flustered by a number of things—because of his wife's illness, the impending search, and his profound reverence for medical science and its representatives.

To save the doctor time and trouble he tried to be as brief as possible, but his very haste made his speech long and incoherent.

The flat was cluttered with a mixture of expensive and cheap furniture, hastily bought as an investment against the rapid inflation. Sets were supplemented by odd pieces.

The young man thought his wife's illness had been caused by nervous shock. He explained with many digressions that they had recently bought an antique clock. It was a broken-down chiming clock, and they had bought it for a song merely as a remarkable example of the clockmaker's art (he took the doctor into the next room to see it). They had even doubted whether it could be repaired.

Then, one day, suddenly the clock, which had not been wound for years, had started of itself, played its complicated minuet of chimes, and stopped. His wife was terrified, the young man said; she was convinced that her last hour had struck, and now there she was delirious, refused all food, and did not recognize him.

"So you think it's nervous shock," Yurii Andreievich said doubtfully. "May I see her now?"

They went into another room, which had a porcelain chandelier, a wide double bed, and two mahogany bedside tables. A small woman with big black eyes lay near the edge of the bed, the blanket pulled up above her chin. When she saw them she freed one arm from under the bedclothes and waved them back, the loose sleeve of her dressing gown falling back to her armpit. She did not recognize her husband, and as if she were alone in the room, she began to sing something sad in a low voice, which upset her so much that she cried, whimpering like a child and begging to "go home." When the doctor went up to the bed she turned her back on him and refused to let him touch her.

"I ought to examine her," he said, "but it doesn't really matter. It's quite clear that she's got typhus—a severe case, poor thing; she must be feeling pretty wretched. My advice to you is to put her in a hospital. I know you'd see to it that she had everything she needed at home, but it's most important that she should have constant medical supervision in the first few weeks. Could you get hold of any sort of transportation—a cab or even a cart? Of course she'll have to be well wrapped up. I'll give you an admission order."

"I'll try, but wait a moment. Is it really typhus? How horrible!"

"I am afraid so."

"Look, I know I'll lose her if I let her go—couldn't you possibly look after her here? Come as often as you possibly can—I'll be only too happy to pay you anything you like."

"I am sorry—I've told you: what she needs is constant supervision. Do as I say—I really am advising you for her good. Now, get a cab at any cost and I'll write out the order. I'd better do it in your house committee room. The order has to have the house stamp on it, and there are a few other formalities."

### 12

One by one the tenants, in shawls and fur coats, had returned to the unheated basement, which had once been a wholesale egg store and was now used by the house committee.

An office desk and several chairs stood at one end of it. As there were not enough chairs, old empty egg crates turned upside down had been placed in a row to form a bench. A pile of them as high as the ceiling towered at the far end of the room; in a corner was a heap of shavings stuck into lumps with frozen yolk that had dripped from broken eggs. Rats scurried noisily inside the heap, making an occasional sortie into the middle of the stone floor and darting back.

Each time this happened a fat woman climbed squealing onto a crate and, holding up her skirt daintily and tapping her fashionable high shoes, shouted in a deliberately hoarse, drunken voice:

"Olia, Olia, you've got rats all over the place. Get away, you filthy brute. Ai-ai-ai! look at it, it understands, it's mad at me. Ai-ai-ai! it's trying to climb up, it'll get under my skirt, I'm so frightened! Look the other way, gentlemen. Sorry, I forgot, you're comrade citizens now, not gentlemen."

Her astrakhan cape hung open over the three quaking layers of her double chin and rich, silk-swathed bosom and stomach. She had once been the belle of her circle of small tradesmen and salesmen, but now her little pig eyes with their swollen lids could scarcely open. A rival had once tried to splash her with vitriol but had missed and only a drop or two had plowed traces on her cheek and at the corner of her mouth, so slight as to be almost becoming.

"Stop yelling, Khrapugina. How can we get on with our work?" said the delegate of the borough council, who had been elected chairman and was sitting behind the desk.

The delegate had known the house and many of the tenants all her life. Before the meeting she had had an unofficial talk with Aunt Fatima, the old janitress who had once lived with her husband and children in a corner of the filthy basement but had now only her daughter with her and had been moved into two light rooms on the first floor.

"Well, Fatima, how are things going?" the delegate asked.

Fatima complained that she could not cope with such a big house and so many tenants all by herself and that she got no help because, although each family was supposed to take turns cleaning the yard and the sidewalks, not one of them did it.

"Don't worry, Fatima, we'll show them. What kind of committee is this, anyway? They're hopeless. Criminal elements are given shelter, people of doubtful morals stay on without registration. We'll get rid of them and elect another. I'll make you house-manageress, only don't make a fuss."

The janitress begged to be let off, but the delegate refused to listen.

Looking around the room and deciding that enough people were present, she called for quiet and opened the meeting with a short introductory speech. She condemned the committee for slackness, proposed that candidates should be put up for the election of a new one, and went on to other business.

In conclusion she said:

"So that's how it is, comrades. Frankly speaking, this is a big house, it's suitable for a hostel. Look at all the delegates who come to town to attend conferences, and we don't know where to put them. It's been decided to take over the building for a district soviet hostel for visitors from the country and to call it the Tiverzin Hostel, in honor of Comrade Tiverzin, who lived here before he was deported, as everyone knows. No objections? Now, as to dates. There's no hurry, you've got a whole year. Working people will be rehoused; others must find accommodations for themselves and are given a year's notice."

"We're all working people? Every one of us! We're all workers," people shouted from every side, and one voice sobbed out: "It's Great-Russian chauvinism! All the nations are equal now! I know what you're hinting at."

"Not all at once, please. Whom am I to answer first? What have nations got to do with it, Citizen Valdyrkin? Look at Khrapugina, you can't think there's a question of nationality involved in her case, and we are certainly evicting her."

"You are, are you! Just you try and evict me, we'll see about that! You crushed sofa! You crumpled bedsheet!" Khrapugina screamed, calling the delegate every meaningless name she could think of in the heat of the quarrel.

"What a she-devil!" the janitress was indignant. "Haven't you any shame?"

"Don't you meddle in this, Fatima, I can look after myself," said the delegate. "Stop it, Khrapugina, I know all about you. Shut up, I tell you, or I'll hand you over at once to the authorities before they catch you brewing vodka and running an illegal bar."

[ 340 ]

The uproar was at its height when the doctor came into the room. He asked the first man he ran into at the door to point out to him a member of the house committee. The other held up his hands like a trumpet in front of his mouth and shouted above the noise:

"Ga-li-iul-li-na! Come here. You're wanted."

The doctor could not believe his ears. A thin elderly woman with a slight stoop, the janitress, came up to him. He was struck by her likeness to her son. He did not, however, identify himself at once, but said: "One of your tenants has got typhus" (he told her the name). "There are various precautions that have to be taken to prevent its spreading. Moreover, the patient must go to the hospital. I'll make out an admission order, which the house committee has to certify. How and where can we get that done?"

She thought he meant "How is the patient to get to the hospital?" and replied: "There's a cab coming from the soviet for Comrade Demina, that's the delegate. She's very kind, Comrade Demina, I'll tell her, she's sure to let your patient have the cab. Don't worry, Comrade Doctor, we'll get her there all right."

"That's wonderful. Actually, I only meant where could I write out the order. But if there's a cab as well . . . May I ask you, are you the mother of Lieutenant Galiullin? We were in the same unit at the front."

Galiullina started violently and grew pale. She grasped the doctor's hand. "Come outside," she said. "We'll talk in the yard."

As soon as they were outside the door she said quickly: "Talk softly, for God's sake. Don't ruin me. Yusupka's gone wrong. Judge for yourself—what is he? He was an apprentice, a worker. He ought to understand—simple people are much better off now, a blind man can see that, nobody can deny it. I don't know

what you feel yourself, maybe it would be all right for you, but it's a sin for Yusupka, God won't forgive him. Yusupka's father was a private, he was killed, they say his face was shot off, and his arms and legs."

Her voice broke, she waited till she was more calm, then she went on: "Come. I'll get you the cab. I know who you are. He was here for a couple of days. He told me. He said you knew Lara Guishar. She was a good girl, I remember her, she used to come and see us. What she's like now, I don't know—who can tell with you people? After all, it's natural for the masters to stick together. But for Yusupka it's a sin. Come, let's ask for the cab. I'm sure Comrade Demina will let you have it. You know who Comrade Demina is? She's Olia Demina, a seamstress she was, worked for Lara's mother, that's who she is, and she's from this house. Come along."

### 13

Night had fallen. All around them was darkness. Only the small round patch of light from Demina's pocket flashlight jumped from snowdrift to snowdrift four or five paces ahead, confusing more than lighting the way. The darkness was all around them, and they had left behind them the house where so many people had known Lara, where she had often come as a girl, and where, they said, Antipov, her husband, had grown up.

"Will you really find your way without a flashlight, Comrade Doctor?" Demina was facetiously patronizing. "If not, I'll lend you mine. It's a fact, you know, I had a real crush on her when we were little girls. They had a dressmaking establishment, I was an apprentice in the workshop. I've seen her this year. She stopped on her way through Moscow. I said, 'Where are you off to, silly? Stay here. Come and live with us. We'll find you a job.' But it wasn't any good, she wouldn't. Well, it's her business. She married Pasha with her head, not with her heart, she's been crazy ever since. Off she went."

"What do you think of her?"

"Careful—it's slippery. I don't know how many times I've told them not to throw the slops out of the door—might as well talk to a wall. What do I think of her? How do you mean, think? What should I think? I haven't any time to think. Here's where I live. One thing I didn't tell her—her brother, who was in the army, I think they've shot him. As for her mother, my mistress she used to be—I'll save her, I'm seeing to it. Well, I've got to go in, goodbye."

They parted. The light of Demina's little flashlight shot into the narrow stone entrance and ran on, lighting up the stained walls and the dirty stairs while the doctor was left surrounded by the darkness. On his right lay Sadovaia Triumphalnaia Street, on his left Sadovaia Karetnaia Street. Running into the black snowy distance, they were no longer streets but cuttings in the jungle of stone buildings, like cuttings through the impassable forests of Siberia or the Urals.

At home it was light and warm.

"Why are you so late?" asked Antonina Alexandrovna. "An extraordinary thing happened while you were out," she went on before he could reply. "Really quite unaccountable. Yesterday Father broke the alarm clock—I forgot to tell you—he was terribly upset, it was our only clock. He tried to repair it, he tinkered and tinkered with it, but he got nowhere. The clockmaker around the corner wanted a ridiculous price—three pounds of bread. I didn't know what to do and Father was completely dejected. Well, about an hour ago—can you believe it—there was sudden ringing—such a piercing, deafening noise, we were

all frightened out of our wits. It was the alarm clock! Can you imagine such a thing? It had started up again, all by itself."

"My hour for typhus has struck," said Yurii Andreievich, laughing. He told her about his patient and the chiming clock.

## 14

But he did not get typhus until much later. In the meantime the Zhivagos were tried to the limits of endurance. They had nothing and they were starving. The doctor went to see the Party member he had once saved, the one who had been the victim of a robbery. This man did everything he could for the doctor, but the civil war was just beginning and he was hardly ever in Moscow; moreover, he regarded the privations people had to suffer in those days as only natural, and he himself went hungry, though he concealed it.

Yurii Andreievich tried to get in touch with the supplier in Brest Street. But in the intervening months the young man had disappeared and nothing was known about his wife, who had recovered. Galiullina was out when Yurii Andreievich called, most of the tenants were new, and Demina was at the front.

One day he received an allocation of wood at the official price. He had to bring it from the Vindava Station. Walking home along the endless stretches of Meshchanskaia Street—keeping an eye on the cart loaded with his unexpected treasure—he noticed that the street looked quite different; he found that he was swaying from side to side, his legs refusing to carry him. He realized that he was in for a bad time, that he had typhus. The driver picked him up when he fell down and slung him on top of the wood. The doctor never knew how he got home.

### 15

He was delirious off and on for two weeks. He dreamed that Tonia had put two streets on his desk, Sadovaia Karetnaia on his left and Sadovaia Triumphalnaia on his right, and had lit the table lamp; its warm orange glow lit up the streets and now he could write. So he was writing.

He was writing what he should have written long ago and had always wished to write but never could. Now it came to him quite easily, he wrote eagerly and said exactly what he wanted to say. Only now and then a boy got in his way, a boy with narrow Kirghiz eyes, in an unbuttoned reindeer coat worn fur side out, as in the Urals or Siberia.

He knew for certain that this boy was the spirit of his death or, to put it quite plainly, that he was his death. Yet how could he be his death if he was helping him to write a poem? How could death be useful, how was it possible for death to be a help?

The subject of his poem was neither the entombment nor the resurrection but the days between; the title was "Turmoil."

He had always wanted to describe how for three days the black, raging, worm-filled earth had assailed the deathless incarnation of love, storming it with rocks and rubble—as waves fly and leap at a seacoast, cover and submerge it—how for three days the black hurricane of earth raged, advancing and retreating.

Two lines kept coming into his head: "We are glad to be near you," and "Time to wake up."

Near him, touching him, were hell, dissolution, corruption, death, and equally near him were the spring and Mary Magdalene and life. And it was time to awake. Time to wake up and to get up. Time to arise, time for the resurrection.

### 16

He began to get better. At first he took everything for granted, like a halfwit. He remembered nothing, he could see no connection between one thing and another and was not surprised at anything. His wife fed him on white bread and butter and sugared tea; she gave him coffee. He had forgotten that such things did not exist, and he enjoyed their taste like poetry or like fairy tales, as something right and proper for a convalescent. Soon, however, he began to think and wonder.

"How did you get all this?" he asked his wife.

"Your Grania got it for us."

"What Grania?"

"Grania Zhivago."

"Grania Zhivago?"

"Well, yes, your brother Evgraf, from Omsk. Your half brother. He came every day while you were ill."

"Does he wear a reindeer coat?"

"That's right. So you did see him. You were unconscious nearly all the time. He said he had run into you on the stairs in some house or other. He knew you—he meant to speak to you, but apparently you frightened him to death! He worships you, he reads every word you write. The things he got for us! Rice, raisins, sugar! He's gone back now. He wants us to go there too. He's a strange boy, a bit mysterious. I think he must have some sort of connection with the government out there. He says we ought to get away for a year or two, get away from the big towns, 'go back to the land' for a bit, he says. I thought of the Krueger place and he said it was a very good idea. We could grow vegetables and there's the forest all around. There isn't any point in dying without a struggle, like sheep."

In April that year Zhivago set out with his whole family for the former Varykino estate, near the town of Yuriatin, far away in the Urals.

## CHAPTER SEVEN

## Train to the Urals

### 1

The end of March brought the first warm days of the year, false heralds of spring which were always followed by a severe cold spell.

The Zhivagos were hurriedly getting ready to leave. To disguise the bustle, the tenants—there were more of them now than sparrows in the street—were told that the apartment was having a spring cleaning for Easter.

Yurii Andreievich had opposed the move. So far, he had thought that it would come to nothing and had not interfered with the preparations, but they had advanced and were about to be completed. The time had come to discuss the matter seriously.

He reiterated his doubts at a family council made up of himself, his wife, and his father-in-law. "Do you think I'm wrong?" he asked them after stating his objections. "Do you still insist on going?"

"You say that we must manage as best we can for the next couple of years," said his wife, "until land conditions are settled, then we might get a vegetable garden near Moscow. But how are we to endure until then? That's the crucial point, and you haven't told us."

"It's sheer madness to count on such things," her father backed her up.

"Very well then, you win," Yurii Andreievich said. "What bothers me is that we are going blindfold, to a place we know nothing about. Of the three people who lived at Varykino, Mother and Grandmother are dead, and Grandfather

Krueger is being held as a hostage—that is, if he is still alive.

"You know he made a fictitious sale in the last year of the war, sold the forests and the factories or else put the title deeds in the name of someone else, a bank or a private person, I don't know. We don't know anything, in fact. To whom does the estate belong now? I don't mean whose property it is, I don't care if we lose it, but who is in charge there? Who runs it? Is the timber being cut? Are the factories working? And above all, who is in power in that part of the country, or rather, who will be by the time we get there?

"You are relying on the old manager, Mikulitsyn, to see us through, but who is to tell us if he is still there? Or whether he is still alive? Anyway what do we know about him except his name—and that we only remember because Grandfather had such difficulty in pronouncing it.

"However, what is there to argue about? You have made up your minds, and I've agreed. Now we must find out exactly what one does about traveling these days. There is no point in putting it off."

### 2

Yurii Andreievich went to the Yaroslavsky Station to make inquiries.

Endless queues of passengers moved along raised gangways between wooden handrails. On the stone floors lay people in gray army coats who coughed, spat, shifted about, and spoke in voices that resounded incongruously loudly under the vaulted ceilings.

Most of these people had recently had typhus and been discharged from the overcrowded hospitals as soon as they were off the critical list. Yurii Andreievich, as a doctor, knew the necessity for this, but he had had no idea that there

could be so many of these unfortunates or that they were forced to seek refuge in railway stations.

"You must get a priority," a porter in a white apron told him. "Then you must come every day to ask if there is a train. Trains are rare nowadays, it's a question of luck. And of course" (he rubbed two fingers with his thumb) "a little flour or something . . . Wheels don't run without oil, you know, and what's more" (he tapped his Adam's apple) "you won't get far without a little vodka."

## 3

About that time Alexander Alexandrovich was asked several times to act as consultant to the Higher Economic Council, and Yurii Andreievich to treat a member of the government who was dangerously ill. Both were paid in what was then the highest currency—credit slips for an allotment of articles from the first of the newly opened distribution centers.

The center was an old army warehouse next to the Simonov Monastery. The doctor and his father-in-law went through the monastery and the barrack yard and straight through a low stone door into a vaulted cellar. It sloped down and widened at its farther end, where a counter ran across from wall to wall; behind it stood an attendant, weighing, measuring, and handing out goods with calm unhurried movements, crossing off the items on the list with broad pencil strokes and occasionally replenishing his stock from the back of the store.

There were not many customers. "Containers," said the storekeeper, glancing at the slips. The professor and the doctor held out several large and small pillowcases and, with bulging eyes, watched them being filled with flour, cereals, macaroni, sugar, suet, soap, matches, and something wrapped in paper that was later found to be Caucasian cheese.

Overwhelmed by the storekeeper's generosity and anxious not to waste his time, they hurriedly stuffed their bundles into big sacks and slung them over their shoulders.

They came out of the vault intoxicated not by the mere thought of food but by the realization that they too were of use in the world and did not live in vain and had deserved the praise and thanks that Tonia would shower on them at home.

## 4

While the men disappeared for whole days into government offices, seeking travel documents and registering the apartment so that they should be able to go back to it on their return to Moscow, Antonina Alexandrovna sorted the family belongings.

Walking up and down the three rooms now officially assigned to the Zhivagos, she weighed even the smallest article twenty times in her hand before deciding whether to put it into the pile of things they were taking with them. Only a small part of their luggage was intended for their personal use; the rest would serve as currency on the way and in the first weeks after their arrival.

The spring breeze came in through the partly open window, tasting faintly of newly cut white bread. Cocks were crowing and children playing and shouting in the yard. The more the room was aired the more noticeable became the smell of mothballs from the open trunks in which the winter clothes had been packed.

As for the choice of things to be taken or left behind, there existed a whole theory, developed by those who had left earlier and communicated their observations to friends at home. The simple, indisputable rules of this theory were so distinctly present in Antonina Alexandrovna's mind that she imagined hearing them repeated by some secret voice coming from outside with the chirruping of sparrows and the cries of playing children.

"Lengths for dresses," she pondered, "but luggage is checked on the way, so this is dangerous unless they are tacked up to look like clothes. Materials and fabrics, clothes, preferably coats if they're not too worn. No trunks or hampers (there won't be any porters); be sure to take nothing useless and tie up everything in bundles small enough for a woman or a child to carry. Salt and tobacco have been found very useful but risky. Money in Kerenkas.[1] Documents are the hardest thing to carry safely." And so on and so on.

## 5

On the day before they left there was a snowstorm. Gray clouds of spinning snow swept into the sky and came back to earth as a white whirlwind, which ran off into the black depths of the street and covered it with a white shroud.

All the luggage was packed. The apartment, with such things as remained in it, was being left in the care of an elderly former salesclerk and his wife, relatives of Egorovna's who, the preceding winter, had helped Antonina Alexandrovna to trade old clothes and furniture for potatoes and wood.

Markel could not be trusted. At the militia post which he had selected as his political club he did not actually say that his former masters sucked his blood, but he accused them, instead, of having kept him in ignorance all these years and deliberately concealed from him that man is descended from apes.

Antonina Alexandrovna took the

---

[1] Kerenkas: paper money introduced by the Kerensky government and still in circulation at that time.

couple on a final survey of the house, fitting keys to locks, opening and shutting drawers and cupboards, and giving them last-minute instructions.

The chairs and tables had been pushed against the walls, the curtains taken down, and there was a pile of bundles in the corner. The snowstorm, seen through the bare windows of the rooms stripped of their winter. comfort, reminded each of them of past sorrows. Yurii Andreievich thought of his childhood and his mother's death, and Antonina Alexandrovna and her father of the death and funeral of Anna Ivanovna. They felt that this was their last night in the house, that they would never see it again. They were mistaken on this point, but under the influence of their thoughts, which they kept to themselves in order not to upset each other, they looked back over the years spent under this roof, struggling against the tears that came to their eyes.

In spite of all this, Antonina Alexandrovna kept within the rules of propriety in the presence of strangers. She talked endlessly with the woman in whose care she was leaving everything. She overestimated the favor the couple were doing her. Anxious not to seem ungrateful, she kept apologizing, going next door and coming back with presents for the woman—blouses and lengths of cotton and silk prints. And the dark materials, with their white check or polka-dot patterns, were like the dark snow-bound street checkered with bricks and covered with white dots which, that farewell night, looked in through the uncurtained windows.

## 6

They left for the station at dawn. The other tenants were usually asleep at this hour, but one of them, Zevorotnina, incurably fond of organizing any social occasion, roused them all shouting: "At-

[ 346 ]

tention! Attention! Comrades! Hurry up! The Gromeko people are going. Come and say goodbye!"

They all poured out onto the back porch (the front door was kept boarded up) and stood in a semicircle as though for a photograph. They yawned and shivered and tugged at the shabby coats they had thrown over their shoulders and stamped about in the huge felt boots they had hastily pulled on over their bare feet.

Markel had already managed to get drunk on some murderous brew he had succeeded in obtaining even in those dry days, and he hung like a corpse over the worn porch railings, which threatened to collapse under him. He insisted on carrying the luggage to the station and was offended when his offer was refused. At last they got rid of him.

It was still dark. The wind had fallen and the snow fell thicker than the night before. Large, fluffy flakes drifted down lazily and hung over the ground, as though hesitating to settle.

By the time they had left the street and reached the Arbat it was lighter. Here the snow came down like a white, slowly descending stage curtain as wide as the street, its fringe swinging around the legs of the passers-by so that they lost the sense of moving forward and felt they were marking time.

There was not a soul about except the travelers, but soon they were overtaken by a cab with a snow-white nag and a driver who looked as if he had been rolled in dough. For a fabulous sum (worth less than a kopek in those days) he took them to the station with their luggage, except for Yurii Andreievich, who at his own request was allowed to walk.

### 7

He found Antonina Alexandrovna and her father standing in one of the endless queues squeezed between the wooden handrails. Niusha and Sashenka were walking about outside and occasionally looking in to see if it were time to join the grown-ups. They gave off a strong smell of kerosene, which had been thickly smeared on their necks, wrists, and ankles as a protection against lice.

The queues went up to the gates of the platforms, but in fact the passengers had to board the train a good half mile farther down the line. With not enough cleaners, the station was filthy and the tracks in front of the platforms were unusable because of dirt and ice. The trains stopped farther out.

Antonina Alexandrovna waved to her husband and when he was close enough shouted instructions as to where he was to get their travel papers stamped.

"Show me what they've put," she said when he came back. He held out a batch of papers across the handrail.

"That's for the special coach," said the man behind her in the queue, reading over her shoulder.

The man in front of her was more explicit. He was one of those sticklers for form who seem to be familiar with and accept without question every regulation in the world.

"This stamp," he explained, "gives you the right to claim seats in a classified coach, that is to say a passenger coach, if there is a passenger coach on the train."

The whole queue joined in at once.

"Passenger coach indeed! If you can get a seat on the buffers you must be thankful nowadays!"

"Don't listen to them," said the other. "I'll explain, it's quite simple. Today there is only one type of train, and it always includes army, convict, cattle, and passenger cars. Why mislead the man?" he said, turning to the crowd. "Words don't cost anything, you can say what you like, but you should say it clearly so that he can understand."

"A lot you've explained." He was shouted down. "A lot you've said when you've told him he's got stamps for the special coach! You should look at a man first, before you start explaining. How can anyone with such a face go in the special coach? The special coach is full of sailors. A sailor has a trained eye and a gun. He takes a look at him and what does he see? A member of the propertied classes—worse than that: a doctor, former quality. He pulls out his gun—and goodbye."

There is no knowing to what lengths the sympathy aroused by the doctor's case would have gone if the crowd had not turned its attention to something else.

For some time people had been looking curiously through the enormous plate-glass windows at the tracks, which were roofed in for several hundred yards. The falling snow could be seen only beyond the far end of the roofs; seen so far away, it looked almost still, sinking to the ground as slowly as bread crumbs thrown to fishes sink through water.

For some time, figures had been strolling into the distance along the tracks, singly or in groups. At first they were taken for railwaymen attending to their duties, but now a whole mob rushed out, and from the direction in which they were running there appeared a small cloud of smoke.

"Open up the gates, you scoundrels," yelled voices in the queue. The crowd stirred and swung against the gates, those at the back pushing those in front.

"Look what's going on! They've locked us in here and through there some people have found a way around and jumped the queue. Open up, you bastards, or we'll smash the gates. Come on, let's give it a push."

"They needn't envy that lot, the fools," said the know-it-all stickler for form. "Those men are conscripts, called up for forced labor from Petrograd. They were supposed to be sent to Vologda, but now they're being taken to the eastern front. They're not traveling of their own choice. They're under escort. They'll be digging trenches."

## 8

They had been traveling three days but had not got far from Moscow. The landscape was wintry. Tracks, fields, woods, and village roofs—everything was covered with snow.

The Zhivagos had been lucky enough to get a corner to themselves on the upper bunks, right up against the long bleary window close under the ceiling.

Antonina Alexandrovna had never traveled in a freight car before. The first time they got in Yurii Andreievich lifted her up to the high floor and pushed open the heavy sliding doors for her, but later she learned to climb in and out by herself.

The car looked to Antonina Alexandrovna no better than a pigsty on wheels, and she had expected it to fall apart at the first jar. But for three days now they had been jolted back and forth and from side to side as the train had changed speed or direction, for three days the wheels had rattled underneath them like the sticks on a mechanical toy drum, and there had been no accident. Her fears had been groundless.

The train had twenty-three cars (the Zhivagos were in the fourteenth). When it stopped at country stations, only a few front, middle, or end cars stood beside the short platform.

Sailors were in front, civilian passengers in the middle, and the labor conscripts in eight cars at the back. There were about five hundred of the latter, people of all ages, conditions, and professions.

They were a remarkable sight—rich, smart lawyers and stockbrokers from

Petrograd side by side with cab drivers, floor polishers, bath attendants, Tartar ragpickers, escaped lunatics, shop-keepers, and monks, all lumped in with the exploiting classes.

The lawyers and stockbrokers sat on short thick logs in their shirt sleeves around red-hot iron stoves, told endless stories, joked, and laughed. They were not worried, they had connections, influential relatives were pulling strings for them at home, and at the worst they could buy themselves off later on.

The others, in boots and unbuttoned caftans, or barefoot and in long shirts worn outside their trousers, with or without beards, stood at the half-open doors of the airless cars, holding on to the sides or to the boards nailed across the openings, and gazed sullenly at the peasants and villages by the wayside, speaking to no one. These had no influential friends. They had nothing to hope for.

There were too many conscripts for the cars allotted to them, and the overflow had been put among the civilian passengers, including those of the fourteenth car.

9

Whenever the train stopped, Antonina Alexandrovna sat up cautiously to avoid knocking her head on the ceiling and looked down through the slightly open door to see if it were worth while to go out. This depended on the size of the station, the probable length of the halt, and the consequent likelihood of profitable barter.

So it was on this occasion. The train had wakened her from a doze by slowing down. The number of switches over which it bumped and rattled suggested that the station was fairly large, and that they would stop for a long time.

She rubbed her eyes, tidied her hair, and after rummaging at the bottom of a bundle pulled out a towel embroidered with cockerels, oxbows, and wheels.

The doctor, who had waked up in the meantime, jumped down first from his bunk, and helped his wife to get to the floor. Guard's shelters and lampposts drifted past the door, followed by trees bending under heavy piles of snow, which they held out toward the train as though in sign of welcome. Long before it had stopped, sailors jumped off into the untrodden snow and raced around the corner of the station building where peasant women were usually to be found trading illegally in food.

Their black uniforms with bell-bottom trousers and ribbons fluttering from their visorless caps gave an air of reckless speed to their advance and made other people give way as before the onrush of racing skiers or skaters.

Around the corner, girls and women from near-by villages, as excited as if they were at the fortuneteller's, stood one behind the other in single file in the shelter of the station wall selling cucumbers, cottage cheese, and platters of boiled beef and rye pancakes kept hot and tasty by quilted napkins. Muffled up in shawls tucked inside their sheepskins, the women blushed a fiery red at the sailors' jokes but at the same time were terrified of them, for it was generally sailors who formed the units organized to fight against speculation and the forbidden free market.

The apprehensions of the peasant women were soon dispelled. When the train stopped and civilian passengers joined the crowd, trade became brisk.

Antonina Alexandrovna walked down the line inspecting the wares, her towel flung over her shoulder as if she were going to the back of the station to wash in the snow. Several women had called out: "Hey, what do you want for your towel?" but she continued on her way, escorted by her husband.

At the end of the row there was a woman in a black shawl with a scarlet pattern. She saw the towel and her bold eyes lit up. Glancing around cautiously, she sidled up to Antonina Alexandrovna and, uncovering her wares, whispered eagerly: "Look at this. Bet you haven't seen that in a long while. Tempting, isn't it? Don't think about it too long or it will be gone. Like to give me your towel for a half?"

Antonina Alexandrovna missed the last word.

"What do you mean, my good woman?"

The woman meant half a hare, roasted whole from head to tail and cut in two. She held it up. "I'm telling you, I'll give you a half for your towel. What are you staring at? It isn't dog meat. My husband is a hunter. It's hare, all right."

They exchanged their goods. Each believed that she had had the best of the bargain. Antonina Alexandrovna felt as ashamed as if she had swindled the peasant woman, while she, delighted with her deal, called a friend who had also sold out her wares and made off with her, home to their village, striding down the snowy path into the distance.

At this moment there was an uproar in the crowd. An old woman was screaming: "Hey, you! Where are you off to? Where's my money? When did you pay me, you cheat? Look at him, greedy pig, you call him and he doesn't even bother to turn around. Stop! Stop, I tell you, Mister Comrade! I've been robbed! Stop, thief! There he goes, that's him, catch him!"

"Which one?"

"That one, the one who's clean-shaven and grinning."

"Is that the one with the hole in his sleeve?"

"Yes, yes, catch him, the heathen!"

"The one with the patched elbow?"

"Yes, yes. Oh, I've been robbed."

"What's going on here?"

"Fellow over there bought some milk and pies, stuffed himself, and went off without paying, so the old woman is crying."

"That shouldn't be allowed. Why don't they go after him?"

"Go after him! He's got straps and cartridge belts all over him. He'll go after you."

10

There were several labor conscripts in car fourteen. With them was their guard, Private Voroniuk. Three of the men stood out from the rest. They were Prokhor Kharitonovich Prituliev, who had been cashier in a government liquor store in Petrograd—the cashier, as he was called in the car; Vasia Brykin, a sixteen-year-old boy apprenticed to an ironmonger; and Kostoied-Amursky, a gray-haired revolutionary co-operativist, who had been in all the forced-labor camps of the old regime and was now discovering those of the new.

The conscripts, who had all been strangers when they were impressed, were gradually getting to know each other. It turned out that the cashier and Vasia, the apprentice, came from the same part of the country, the Viatka government, and also that the train would be going through their native villages.

Prituliev came from Malmyzh. His hair was cropped and he was pockmarked, squat, and hideous. His gray sweater, black with sweat under the arms, fitted him snugly like a fleshy woman's blouse. He would sit for hours as silent as a statue, lost in thought, scratching the warts on his freckled hands until they bled and suppurated.

One day last autumn, he was going down the Nevsky when he walked into a militia roundup at the corner of Liteiny Street. He had to show his papers and was found to hold a fourth-class ration book, the kind issued to nonworkers, on which nothing could ever be bought. He was consequently detained, with many others who were arrested for the same reason, and taken under escort to barracks. His group was to be sent, like the one preceding it, to dig trenches on the Archangel front, but was diverted on its way and sent east through Moscow.

Prituliev had a wife in Luga, where he had worked before the war. She heard indirectly of his misfortune and rushed off to Vologda (the junction for Archangel) to look for him and obtain his release. But the unit had not gone there, her labors had been in vain, and she lost track of him.

In Petrograd Prituliev lived with a certain Pelagia Nilovna Tiagunova. At the time he was arrested he had just said goodbye to her, preparing to go in a different direction to keep an appointment, and looking down Liteiny Street he could still see her back disappearing among the crowd.

She was a plump woman with a stately carriage, beautiful hands, and a thick braid which she tossed from time to time, with deep sighs, over her shoulder. She was now with the convoy, having volunteered to accompany Prituliev.

It was difficult to know what it was that attracted women to such an ugly man, but certainly they clung to him. In a car farther forward there was another woman friend of his, Ogryzkova, a bony girl with white eyelashes who had somehow made her way onto the train and whom Tiagunova called "the squirt," "the nozzle," and many other insulting names. The rivals were at swords' points and took good care to avoid each other. Ogryzkova never went to the other's car. It was a mystery to know how she ever met the object of her passion. Perhaps she contented herself with seeing him from afar, when the engine was being

refueled with the help of all the passengers.

## 11

Vasia's story was quite different. His father had been killed in the war and his mother had sent him to Petrograd to be apprenticed to his uncle.

The uncle kept a private shop in Apraksin Yard. One day last winter he had been summoned by the local soviet to answer a few questions. He mistook the door and walked into the office of the labor corps selection board. The room was full of conscripts; after a while soldiers came in, surrounded the men, and took them to the Semenov barracks for the night, and escorted them to the Vologda train in the morning.

The news of so many arrests spread and the prisoners' families came to say goodbye to them at the station. Among them were Vasia and his aunt. His uncle begged the guard (Voroniuk, who was now in car fourteen) to let him out for a minute to see his wife. The guard refused without a guarantee that he would return. The uncle and aunt offered Vasia as a hostage. Voroniuk agreed. Vasia was brought in and his uncle was let out. This was the last he ever saw of his aunt or uncle.

When the fraud was discovered, Vasia, who had suspected nothing, burst into tears. He threw himself at Voroniuk's feet, kissed his hands, and begged him to let him go, but to no avail. The guard was inexorable not because he was cruel, but discipline was very strict in those troubled times. The guard answered for the number of his charges with his life, and the numbers were checked by roll call. That was how Vasia came to be in the labor corps.

The co-operativist, Kostoied-Amursky, who had enjoyed the respect of his jailors under both Tsarism and the present government and who was always on good terms with them, repeatedly spoke to the head of the convoy about Vasia's predicament. The officer admitted that it was a terrible misunderstanding but said there were formal difficulties in the way of examining the case until they arrived; he promised to do his best at that moment.

Vasia was an attractive boy with regular features who looked like a royal page or an angel of God in a picture. He was unusually innocent and unspoiled. His favorite occupation was to sit on the floor at the feet of his elders, looking up at them, his hands clasped around his knees, and listen to their discussions and stories. By watching the muscles of his face, as he just barely restrained himself from tears or choked with laughter, you could almost follow the conversation.

## 12

The Zhivagos had invited the co-operativist Kostoried to dinner. He sat in their corner sucking a leg of hare with a loud wheezing noise. He dreaded drafts and chills, and changed his place several times, looking for a sheltered spot. At last he found a place where he did not feel the draft. "That's better," he said. He finished his bone, sucked his fingers clean, wiped them on his handkerchief, thanked his hosts, and said: "It's your window. It has to be cemented. But to go back to our discussion: You're mistaken, Doctor. Roast hare is an excellent thing, but to conclude that the peasants are prosperous is rash, to say the least, if you'll forgive my saying so."

"Oh, come," said Yurii Andreievich. "Look at all these stations. The trees aren't cut, the fences are intact. And these markets! These women! Think how wonderful! Somewhere life is still going on, some people are happy. Not everyone

is wretched. This justifies everything."

"It would be good if that were true. But it isn't. Where did you get all those ideas? Take a trip to any place that is fifty miles from the railway. You'll find that there are peasant rebellions everywhere. Against whom? you'll ask. Well, they're against the Reds or against the Whites, whoever happens to be in power. You'll say, Aha, that's because the peasants are enemies of all authority, they don't know what they want. Allow me to differ. The peasant knows very well what he wants, better than you or I do, but he wants something quite different.

"When the revolution woke him up, he decided that his century-old dream was coming true—his dream of living on his own land by the work of his hands, in complete independence and with no obligations to anyone. Instead, he found he had only exchanged the oppression of the former state for the new, much harsher yoke of the revolutionary superstate. Can you wonder that the villages are restless and can't settle down? And you say they are prosperous! No, there are a lot of things you don't know, my dear fellow, and as far as I can see you don't want to know them."

"All right, it's true, I don't. Why on earth should I know and worry myself sick over every blessed thing? History hasn't consulted me. I have to put up with whatever happens, so why shouldn't I ignore the facts? You tell me my ideas don't correspond to reality. But where is reality in Russia today? As I see it, reality has been so terrorized that it is hiding. I want to believe that the peasants are better off and flourishing. If it is an illusion, what am I to do? What am I to live by; whom am I to believe? And I have to go on living, I've got a family."

He made a despairing gesture and, leaving the argument to his father-in-law, moved away, and hung his head over the edge of the bunk to look at what was going on below.

Prituliev, Tiagunova, Vasia, and Voroniuk were talking together. As the train was approaching his native province, Prituliev recalled the way to his village, the station, and the road you took according to whether you went by horse or on foot, and at the mention of familiar village names, Vasia repeated them with shining eyes, as if they were a marvelous fairy tale.

"You get off at Dry Ford?" he asked, choking with excitement. "Our station! Of course! And then you go on to Buisky, right?"

"That's right, you take the Buisky road."

"That's what I say—Buisky—Buisky village. Of course I know it, that's where you get off the main road, you turn right and right again. That's to get to us, to Veretenniki. And your way must be left, away from the river, isn't it? You know the river Pelga? Well, of course! That's our river. You keep following the river, on and on, and away up on the cliff on the right, overhanging that same river Pelga, there's our village, Veretenniki! It's right up on the edge, and it's stee-eep! It makes you giddy, honest to God it does. There's a quarry down below, for millstones. That's where my mother lives, in Veretenniki, and my two little sisters. Alenka and Arishka . . . Mother is a bit like you, Aunt Pelagia, she's young and fair. Uncle Voroniuk! Please, Uncle Voroniuk, for the love of Christ, please, I beg you, for God's sake . . . Uncle Voroniuk!"

"Well, what? Uncle, uncle, I know I'm not your aunt. What do you expect me to do? Am I mad? If I let you go that would be the end of me, amen, they'd put me up against a wall."

Pelagia Tiagunova sat looking thoughtfully out of the window, stroking Vasia's reddish hair. Now and then she bent down to him and smiled as if she were telling him: "Don't be silly. This isn't something to talk to Voroniuk about in front of everyone. Don't worry, have patience, it will be all right."

### 13

Peculiar things began to happen when they left Central Russia behind on their way east. They were going through a restless region infested with armed bands, past villages where uprisings had recently been put down.

The train stopped frequently in the middle of nowhere and security patrols checked the passengers' papers and luggage.

Once they stopped at night, but no one came in and no one was disturbed. Yurii Andreievich wondered if there had been an accident and went out to see.

It was dark. For no apparent reason the train had stopped between two stations, in a field, with a row of firs on either side of the track. Other passengers who had come out and were stamping their feet in the snow told Yurii Andreievich that there was nothing wrong, but that the engineer refused to go on, saying that this stretch was dangerous and should first be inspected by handcar. Spokesmen of the passengers had gone to reason with him and if necessary to grease his palm. It was said that sailors were also taking a hand in it and would undoubtedly get their way.

The snow at the head of the train was lit up at intervals, as from a bonfire, by fiery flashes from the smokestack or the glowing coals in the firebox. By this light several dark figures were now seen running to the front of the engine.

The first of them, presumably the engineer, reached the far end of the

[ 353 ]

running board, leapt over the buffers, and vanished as if the earth had swallowed him. The sailors who were chasing him did exactly the same thing: they too flashed for a moment through the air and vanished.

Curious about what was going on, several passengers including Yurii Andreievich went to see.

Beyond the buffers, where the track opened out before them, they were met with an astonishing sight. The engineer stood in the snow up to his waist. His pursuers surrounded him in a semicircle, like hunters around their quarry; like him, they were buried in snow up to the waist.

"Thank you, comrades, fine stormy petrels you are,"[1] the engineer was shouting. "A fine sight, sailors chasing a fellow worker with guns! All because I said the train must stop. You be my witnesses, comrade passengers, you can see what kind of place this is. Anybody might be roaming around unscrewing the bolts. Do you think I'm worrying about myself, you God-damned bastards? To hell with you. It's for you I was doing it, so that nothing should happen to you, and that's all the thanks I get for my trouble! Go on, go on, why don't you shoot? Here I am. You be my witnesses, comrade passengers, I'm not running away."

Bewildered voices rose from the group. "Pipe down, old man . . . They don't mean it . . . Nobody would let them . . . They don't really mean it.. . ." Others urged him on: "That's right, Gavrilka, stand up for yourself! Don't let them bully you!"

The first sailor to scramble out of the snow was a red-haired giant with a head so huge that it made his face look flat.

_____
[1] Stormy petrels: The reference is to the sailors in the *Potemkin* mutiny and is also an allusion to Gorky's story of that name.

He turned to the passengers and spoke in a deep, quiet, unhurried voice with a Ukrainian accent, like Voroniuk's, his composure oddly out of keeping with the scene.

"Beg pardon, what's all this uproar about? Be careful you don't catch a chill in this cold, citizens. It's windy. Why not go back to your seats and keep warm?"

The crowd gradually dispersed. The giant went to the engineer, who was still worked up, and said:

"Enough hysterics, comrade engineer. Get out of the snow, and let's get going."

### 14

Next day the train, creeping at a snail's pace lest it run off the tracks, powdered by the wind with unswept snow, pulled up beside a lifeless, burned-out ruin. This was all that was left of the station, Nizhni Kelmes, its name still faintly legible on its blackened façade.

Beyond it lay a deserted village blanketed in snow. This too was damaged by fire. The end house was charred, the one next to it sagged where its corner timbers had fallen in; broken sleighs, fences, rusty pieces of metal, and smashed furniture were scattered all over the street; the snow was dirty with soot, and black patches of earth showed through the frozen puddles with half-burnt logs sticking out of them—all evidence of the fire and of the efforts to put it out.

The place was not in fact as dead as it looked; there were a few people still about. The stationmaster rose out of the ruins and the guard jumped down from the train and commiserated with him. "The whole place was burned down?"

"Good day to you, and welcome. Yes, we certainly had a fire, but it was worse than that."

"I don't follow."

"Better not try."

"You don't mean Strelnikov!"

"I do."

"Why? What had you done?"

"We didn't do anything, it was our neighbors; we got it too for good measure. You see that village over there? Nizhni Kelmes is in the Ust-Nemdinsk county—it was all because of them."

"And what crime had they committed?"

"Just about all the seven deadly sins: Dissolved their Poor Peasants' Committee, that's one; refused to supply horses to the Red Army, that's two (and they're all Tartars, mind you, horsemen); resisted the mobilization decree, that makes three. Well, there you are."

"Yes, I see. I quite see. So they were shelled?"

"Naturally."

"From the armored train?"

"Of course."

"That's bad. All our sympathy. Still, it's none of our business."

"Besides, it's an old story. And the news I have isn't very good either. You'll have to stop here for a couple of days."

"You're joking! I'm taking replacements to the front. This is an urgent matter."

"I'm not joking at all. We've had a blizzard for a solid week—snowdrifts all along the line, and no one to clear it. Half the village has run away. I'll put the rest of them on the job, but it won't be enough."

"Damn. What am I to do?"

"We'll get it cleared, somehow."

"How deep is the snow?"

"Not too bad. It varies. The worst patch is in the middle—about two miles long; we'll certainly have trouble there. Farther on the forest has kept the worst of the snow off the tracks. And on this side it's open country, so the wind has blown away some of it."

"Hell, what a pain in the neck! I'll mobilize all the passengers."

"That's what I was thinking."

"We mustn't use the sailors and Red Army men. But there's a whole corps of labor conscripts—including the other passengers, there are about seven hundred in all."

"That's more than enough. We'll start the moment we get the shovels. We're a bit short of them, so we've sent to the near-by villages for more. We'll manage."

"God, what a blow! Do you think we can do it?"

"Of course we can. With plenty of troops you can take a city, they say, and this is only a bit of tracks. Don't worry."

## 15

Clearing the line took three days, and all the Zhivagos, even Niusha, took part in it. They were the best three days of their journey.

The landscape had a withdrawn, secretive quality. It made one think of Pushkin's story about the Pugachev uprising and of some places described by Aksakov. The ruins added to the air of mystery; so did the wariness of the remaining villagers, who, afraid of informers, avoided the passengers and were silent even among themselves.

The workers were divided into gangs, with the labor conscripts and the civilians kept apart. Armed soldiers guarded each working group.

The tracks were cleared in several places at the same time by separate gangs. Mounds of snow between the sections hid the gangs from one another and were left untouched until the last.

The workers spent all day in the open, going back only to sleep. The days were clear and frosty, and the shifts were short because there were not enough shovels. It was sheer pleasure.

Zhivago's section of the track had a fine view. The country to the east dipped down into a valley and rose in gentle hills as far as the horizon.

On the top of a hill there was a house exposed to all the winds; its park must have been luxuriant in summer but could not give it any shelter now with its frosty lacework.

The snow smoothed and rounded all contours. It could not quite conceal the winding bed of a stream which in spring would rush down to the viaduct below the railway bank but at present was tucked up in the snow like a child in its cot with its head under the eiderdown.

Was anyone living in the house on the hill, Zhivago wondered, or was it standing empty and falling into ruins, held by some land committee? What had happened to the people who had once lived there? Had they fled abroad? Or been killed by the peasants? Or had they been popular and were they allowed to settle in the district as technical specialists? If they had stayed, had they been spared by Strelnikov or shared the fate of the kulaks?

The house teased his curiosity but kept its sorrowful silence. Questions were not in order in these days, and no one ever answered them. But the sun sparkled on the pure whiteness with a glare that was almost blinding. How cleanly his shovel cut into its smooth surface! How dry, how iridescent, like diamonds, was each shovelful. He was reminded of the days when, as a child in their yard at home, dressed in a braided hood and a black sheepskin fastened with hooks and eyes sewn in the curly fleece, he cut the dazzling snow into cubes and pyramids and cream puffs and fortresses and the cities of cave dwellers. Life had had zest in those far-off days, everything was a feast for the eyes and the stomach!

But these three days in the air, too, gave the impression of a feast. And no wonder! At night the workers received loaves of hot fresh bread, which was brought no one knew from where or by whose orders. The bread had a tasty crisp crust, shiny on top, cracked at the side, and with bits of charcoal baked into it underneath.

### 16

They became fond of the ruined station, as one becomes attached to a shelter used for a few days on a climbing trip in a snow-bound mountain. Its shape, its site, the details of its damage, remained imprinted in their memory.

They returned to it every evening just as the sun, as if out of loyalty to the past, set at its usual place behind an old birch tree outside a telegrapher's window.

At that spot the wall had caved into the room, but the corner facing the window had remained intact, with its coffee-colored wallpaper, the tiled stove with the round vent and the copper lid closed with a chain, and the inventory of the office furniture hanging on the wall in a black frame. As before the collapse, the setting sun brushed the tiles, brought out the warm brown glow on the wallpaper, and hung the shadow of the birch on the wall as if it were a woman's scarf.

At the rear of the building, on the nailed door to the ruins of the waiting room, there was still an announcement, put up in the first days of the February revolution, or shortly before it, which said:

"Sick passengers are temporarily requested not to bother about medicines and bandages. For obvious reasons, am sealing door, of which am giving notice hereby.

"Medical Assistant
"Ust-Nemdinsk District"

When finally the last piles of snow between the cleared tracks were leveled, the entire line of rails came into view, flying into the distance like an arrow. On each side stretched white mountains of shovelled snow, bordered all along by the black walls of the forest.

As far as the eye could reach, groups of people with shovels in hand stood at intervals along the line. Seeing themselves for the first time in full force, they were astonished at their numbers.

### 17

It was learned that the train would leave shortly, despite the lateness of the hour and the approaching night. Yurii Andreievich and Antonina Alexandrovna went out to enjoy the sight of the cleared line once again. No one else was on the tracks. The doctor and his wife stood a while, gazing into the distance, exchanged a few words, and turned back to their car.

On the way they heard the angry voices of two quarreling women. They recognized them at once as those of Ogryzkova and Tiagunova, who were walking in the same direction as they were, from the head to the end of the train, but on the station side, while the doctor and his wife walked on the wooded side. The endless line of cars screened the two couples from each other. The women seemed hardly ever to be abreast of the doctor and Antonina Alexandrovna, but always to be ahead of them or falling behind.

They seemed to be in a state of great agitation, and it was as though their strength failed them. Judging from the way their voices rose to a shriek or died down to a whisper, either their legs refused to carry them or else they kept stumbling and falling into snowdrifts. Tiagunova seemed to be chasing Ogryzkova, perhaps belaboring her with her fists whenever she caught up with her. She showered her rival with choice abuse, and her genteel, melodious voice made the insults sound infinitely more obscene than the coarse and unmusical swearing of men.

"You slut, you drag-tailed whore," Tiagunova screamed. "I can't move an inch without seeing you flouncing up and down, and ogling. Isn't my old fool enough for you without your having to make eyes at a babe in arms, to seduce a minor?"

"So Vasia too is your legal husband?"

"I'll give you legal husband, you filthy plague! One more word from you, and I'll kill you, don't tempt me."

"Now, now, keep your hands to yourself. What do you want of me?"

"I want to see you dead, you lecherous louse, you cat in heat, you shameless bitch!"

"That's what I am, is it? Naturally, I'm nothing but a cat, a bitch, compared with such a grand lady as you! Born in the gutter, married in a ditch, a rat in your belly, and a hedgehog for a brat! . . . Help! Help! She'll kill me! Help a poor orphan, help a poor defenseless girl!"

"Come along," Antonina Alexandrovna urged her husband. "I can't bear to listen to it, it's too disgusting. It will end badly."

### 18

Suddenly everything changed—the weather and the landscape. The plains ended, and the track wound up hills through mountain country. The north wind that had been blowing all the time dropped, and a warm breath came from the south, as from an oven.

Here the woods grew on escarpments projecting from the mountain slopes, and when the track crossed them, the train had to climb sharply uphill until it reached the middle of the wood, and then go steeply down again.

The train creaked and puffed on its

way into the wood, hardly able to drag itself along, as if it were an aged forest guard walking in front and leading the passengers, who turned their heads from side to side and observed whatever was to be seen.

But there was nothing yet to see. The woods were still deep in their winter sleep and peace. Only here and there a branch would rustle and shake itself free of the remaining snow, as though throwing off a choker.

Yurii Andreievich was overcome with drowsiness. All these days he lay in his bunk and slept and woke and thought and listened. But there was nothing yet to hear.

## 19

While Yurii Andreievich slept his fill, the spring was heating and melting the masses of snow that had fallen all over Russia, first in Moscow on the day they had left and since then all along the way—all that snow they had spent three days clearing off the line at Ust-Nemdinsk, all that thick, deep layer of snow that had settled over the immense distances.

At first the snow thawed quietly and secretly from within. But by the time half the gigantic labor was done it could not be hidden any longer and the miracle became visible. Waters came rushing out from below with a roar. The forest stirred in its impenetrable depth, and everything in it awoke.

There was plenty of room for the water to play. It flung itself down the rocks, filled every pool to overflowing, and spread. It roared and smoked and steamed in the forest. It streaked through the woods, bogging down in the snow that tried to hinder its movement, it ran hissing on level ground or hurtled down and scattered into a fine spray. The earth was saturated. Ancient pine trees perched on dizzy heights drank the moisture almost from the clouds, and it foamed and dried a rusty white at their roots like beer foam on a mustache.

The sky, drunk with spring and giddy with its fumes, thickened with clouds. Low clouds, drooping at the edges like felt, sailed over the woods and rain leaped from them, warm, smelling of soil and sweat, and washing the last of the black armor-plating of ice from the earth.

Yurii Andreievich woke up, stretched, raised himself on one elbow, and looked and began to listen.

## 20

As they approached the mining region, there were more and more settlements, the runs were shorter, the stations more frequent. More people got on and off at the small stations. Instead of settling down and going to sleep, those who had only a short way to go found seats anywhere—near the door or in the middle of the car—and sat up arguing in low voices about local matters intelligible only to themselves.

From the hints dropped by such local passengers in the past three days Yurii Andreievich gathered that in the north the Whites were getting the upper hand and had seized or were about to occupy Yuriatin. Moreover, unless he had misheard the name or his old friend had a namesake, the White forces were led by Galiullin, whom he had last seen in Meliuzeievo.

Not to worry his family, he said nothing to them about these unconfirmed rumors.

## 21

Yurii Andreievich woke up shortly after midnight brimming with a vague feeling of happiness, which was, however, strong enough to have aroused him. The train was standing still. The station bathed in the glassy dusk of a white night. Something subtle and powerful in this luminous darkness suggested a vast and open landscape and that the station was situated high up.

People walked along the platform past the carriage speaking softly and treading as silently as shadows. Zhivago was touched by this evidence of a prewar consideration for the sleeping passengers.

The doctor was mistaken. There was the same din of shouting voices and stamping boots on this platform as on any other. But there was a waterfall near by. It widened the expanse of the white night by a breath of freshness and freedom; that was what had filled him with happiness in his sleep. Its incessant noise dominated all other sounds and gave an illusion of stillness.

Knowing nothing of its existence but soothed and braced by it, the doctor fell fast asleep.

Two men were talking underneath his bunk.

"Well, have they had their tails twisted yet? Are they keeping quiet now?"

"The shopkeepers, you mean?"

"That's right. The grain merchants."

"Feed out of your hand! As soon as a few were bumped off by way of example, all the others piped down. A fine has been imposed on the district."

"How much?"

"Forty thousand."

"You're lying!"

"Why should I lie?"

"Forty thousand—that isn't even chicken feed!"

"Not forty thousand rubles, of course —forty thousand bushels."

"That was smart!"

"Forty thousand of the finest ground."

"Well, that's not such a miracle, after all. It's rich soil. Right in the thick of the corn belt. From here on, along the Rynva till you get to Yuriatin, it's village

to village, harbor to harbor, one whole-sale after another."

"Don't shout. You'll wake people up."

"All right." He yawned.

"How about going to sleep? Looks as if we're moving."

The train, however, stayed where it was. But the rumble of another train came from behind, bursting into a deafening thunder and obliterating the sound of the waterfall as it approached, and an old-fashioned express rushed past at full speed on the parallel track, roared, hooted, winked its tail lights, and vanished into the distance ahead.

The conversation was resumed.

"Well, we're in for it. Now we'll never go."

"Yes. It won't be soon."

"It's an armored express—must be Strelnikov."

"Must be him."

"He's a wild beast when it comes to counterrevolutionaries."

"He's after Galeiev."

"Who's that?"

"Hetman Galeiev. They say he's out-side Yuriatin with a Czech covering force. He's seized the harbors, the pest, and he's hanging on. Hetman Galeiev."

"Never heard of him."

"Or it may be Prince Galileiev. I can't quite remember the name."

"There aren't any such princes. Must be Ali Kurban. You've mixed them up."

"May be Kurban."

"That's more like it."

## 22

Toward morning Yurii Andreievich woke up a second time. He had had a pleasant dream. The feeling of bliss and liberation was still with him. Again the train was standing still, perhaps at the same station as before, possibly at another. Once more there was the sound of the waterfall, perhaps a different waterfall but more probably the same one.

He went back to sleep almost at once, and as he was dozing off he dimly heard the sound of running feet and of some commotion. Kostoied was quarreling with the commander of the convoy and they were shouting at each other. The air was even more pleasant than before. It had a breath of something new in it, something that had not been there earlier —something magical, springlike, white, blackish, thin and insubstantial, like a snow flurry in May when the wet, melting flakes falling on the earth make it seem black rather than white. It was something transparent, blackish-white, sweet-smelling—"Wild cherry," Yurii Andreievich decided in his sleep.

### 23

Next morning Antonina Alexandrovna said:

"Really, Yura, you're extraordinary, you're a mass of contradictions. Sometimes a fly will wake you up and you can't get back to sleep till morning, and here you slept through all this row and I simply couldn't get you to wake up. Prituliev and Vasia have escaped, just think of it! And so have Tiagunova and Ogryzkova! Can you imagine such a thing! Wait, that isn't all. Voroniuk as well. It's true, I tell you, he's run away. Now listen. How they managed it, together or separately, and in what order— it's all a complete mystery. Voroniuk, of course, I understand—once he found the others had gone, he would have to try to save his skin. But what about the rest? Did they really all vanish of their own free will, or was somebody done away with? For instance, if the women are to be suspected, did Tiagunova kill Ogryzkova or was it the other way around? Nobody knows. The commander of the escort has been running up and down the

train like a lunatic. 'You're not to start the train. I order you in the name of the law not to move till I've caught my prisoners.' And the commanding officer shouts back: 'I'm taking replacements up to the front, I'm not waiting for your lousy crew. What an idea!' Then they both went for Kostoied. 'You, a syndicalist, an educated man, how could you sit by and let a simple soldier, an ignorant child of nature, act in such a reckless manner! And you a populist!'[1] And Kostoied gave them as good as he got. 'That's interesting,' he says. 'The prisoner has to look after his guard, does he? Well, really, the day that happens the hens will start to crow.' I was shaking you as hard as I could. 'Yura,' I cried, 'get up, there's been an escape.' But nothing doing. If a gun had gone off in your ear you wouldn't have heard it. . . . But I'll tell you more later. . . . Look! Father, Yura, look, isn't the view superb!"

Through the opening in the window they could see the country covered with spring floods as far as eye could reach. Somewhere a river had overflowed its banks and the water had come right up to the embankment. In the foreshortened view from the bunk it looked as if the train were actually gliding on the water.

Only here and there was its smoothness broken by streaks of a metallic blue, but over all the rest of its surface the hot morning sun was chasing glassy patches of light as smooth and oily as melted butter that a cook brushes with a feather on a pie crust.

In this shoreless flood were sunk the shafts of the white clouds, their pediments submerged together with the fields, the hollows, and the bushes.

And somewhere in the middle of the flood there was a narrow strip of land

---

[1] Left-wing idealists who devoted themselves to work among the people.

with a row of doubled trees growing up and down and suspended between earth and sky.

"Look, a family of ducks!" Alexander Alexandrovich cried out.

"Where?"

"Near the island. More to the right. Damn, they've flown. We've frightened them."

"Yes, I see them now," said Yurii Andreievich. "I must have a talk with you, Alexander Alexandrovich. Some other time. . . . As for our labor conscripts and the women, good for them. And I'm sure there wasn't any murder. They just broke free like the water."

### 24

The white northern night was ending. Everything could be seen clearly—the mountain, the thicket, and the ravine—but seemed unreal, as though made up.

The wood, which had several blossoming wild cherries in it, was just coming into leaf. It grew under an overhanging cliff, on a narrow ledge above another precipice.

The waterfall, though not far away, could be seen only from the edge of the ravine beyond the thicket. Vasia was tired from walking to see it, to experience the joy and terror of the spectacle.

The waterfall had no equal anywhere around, nothing that could match it. This uniqueness endowed it with an awesome quality; it was like a living and conscious creature, a local dragon or winged serpent who levied tribute and preyed upon the countryside.

Halfway down, it broke on a sharp rock and divided in two. The top was almost motionless, but the two lower columns weaved slightly from side to side as if the water were continually slipping and righting itself, shaken but always recovering.

Vasia had spread his sheepskin on the ground and was lying at the edge of the thicket. When it grew lighter, a large bird with heavy wings flew down from the mountain, soared in a smooth circle around the wood, and settled on a pine close to where he lay. He looked up enchanted at its dark blue throat and gray-blue breast and whispered its Urals name, *ronzha*. Then he got up, picked up his sheepskin, flung it over his shoulders, and crossed the clearing to speak to his companion.

"Come on, Auntie Polia. Goodness, how cold you are! I can hear your teeth chattering. Well, what are you staring at, why are you so frightened? We've got to go, I'm telling you, we must get to a village. They'll hide us, they won't harm their own kind. If we go on like this we'll die of starvation. We've had nothing to eat for two days. Uncle Voroniuk must have raised a terrible hullabaloo, they must all be out looking for us. We have to go, Auntie; to put it plainly, we've got to run. I don't know what to do with you, Auntie, not a word out of you for two whole days. You worry too much, honest to God, you do. What are you so unhappy about? It isn't as if you'd meant to push Auntie Katia Ogryzkova off the train, you just caught her sideways, by accident, I saw you. She picked herself up off the grass—I saw her with my own eyes—and she got up and ran away. She and Uncle Prokhor, Prokhor Kharitonovich, are sure to catch up with us, we'll all be together again. The main thing is to stop worrying, then you'll find your tongue again."

Tiagunova got up, took Vasia's hand, and said softly:

"All right, let's go, lamb."

### 25

Their timbers creaking, the cars climbed up the steep hill. Below the bank there was a thicket, its top not quite reaching the level of the track. Lower still were fields. The floods had just withdrawn and the grass was strewn with sand and pieces of timber. The boards must have been washed down from somewhere higher up the hill where they had been stacked preparatory to floating them downstream.

The young wood below the embankment was still almost as bare as in winter. Only in the buds that spotted it all over like drops of candle grease there was something not in accord with the rest, something superfluous, some disturbance, perhaps dirt or an inflammation causing them to swell, and the disturbance, superfluity, and dirt were the signs of life, which had already set the most forward of the trees on fire with its green leafy flame.

Here and there a birch stretched itself like a martyr pierced by the barbs and arrows of its opening shoots, and you knew its smell by just looking at it, the smell of its glistening resin, which is used for making varnish.

Soon the tracks drew level with the place where the logs washed down by the flood might have come from. A cutting through the wood showed at a bend of the tracks; it was littered all over with chips and shavings, and there was a pile of timber in the middle. The engine braked and the train shuddered and stopped on the curve of the hill, bending slightly in a wide arc.

A few short barking hoots and shouts came from the engine, but the passengers did not need these signals to know that the engineer had stopped to take in a supply of fuel.

The freight-car doors rolled open, and a crowd the size of the population of a small town poured out. Only the sailors stayed in the front cars; they were excused from all chores.

There was not enough small firewood in the clearing to fill the tender, and

some of the large timber had to be cut down to the right size. The engine crew had saws as part of their equipment and these were issued to volunteers, one to each pair, the doctor and his father-in-law among them.

Grinning sailors stuck their heads out of their doors. They were a curious mixture of middle-aged workingmen, straight from their emergency training, and boys just out of naval college who looked as if they had got in by mistake among the staid fathers of families and who joked and played the fool with the older sailors to keep themselves from thinking. All of them felt that their hour of trial was at hand.

Jokes and guffaws followed the work parties.

"Hey, Grandfather! I'm not shirking, I'm too young to work, my nanny won't let me." "Hey, Marva, don't saw off your skirt, you'll catch cold!" "Hey, young one, don't go to the wood, come and be my wife instead!"

### 26

There were several trestles in the clearing. Yurii Andreievich and Alexander Alexandrovich went up to one of them and began to saw.

This was the moment of spring when the earth emerges from the snow looking much as when the snow had trapped it six months earlier. The wood smelled of damp and was heaped with last year's leaves like an unswept room where people have been tearing up letters, bills, and receipts for years.

"Don't go so fast, you'll tire yourself," said the doctor, giving a slower and more even movement to the saw. "What about a rest?"

The wood echoed to the hoarse ringing of other saws; somewhere, very far away, a nightingale was trying out its voice, and at longer intervals a blackbird whistled as if blowing dust out of a flute. Even the engine steam rose into the sky warbling like milk boiling up on a nursery alcohol stove.

"What did you want to speak to me about?" asked Alexander Alexandrovich. "Do you remember? We were going past the island, the ducks flew away, and you said you wanted to speak to me."

"Oh, yes. . . . Well, I don't quite know how to put it briefly. I was thinking that we are going farther and farther. The whole of this region is in ferment. We don't know what we'll find when we get there. Perhaps we ought to talk things over just in case . . . I don't mean about our convictions—it would be absurd to try to define them in five minutes in a spring wood. Besides, we know each other well. You and I and Tonia and many others like us, we make up our own world these days, the only difference between us is in the degree of our awareness of it. But that's not what I want to talk about. What I meant was that perhaps we ought to agree in advance on how to behave under certain circumstances, so that we need never blush for one another or make each other feel ashamed."

"I know what you mean. I like the way you put it. Now this is what I'll tell you. Do you remember that night you brought me the paper with the first government decrees in the winter, in a snowstorm? You remember how unbelievably uncompromising they were? It was that single-mindedness that carried us away. But such things retain their original purity only in the minds of those who have conceived them, and then only on the day they are first made public. Next day, the casuistry of politics has turned them inside out. What can I say to you? Their philosophy is alien to me, their regime is hostile to us, I have not been asked if I consent to all this change. But I have been trusted, and my own actions,

even if they were not freely chosen, put me under a certain obligation.

"Tonia keeps asking if we'll arrive in time to plant our vegetables. I don't know. I don't know the soil or the climate in the Urals; the summer is so short I can't imagine how anything ever ripens in time.

"But after all, it is not for the sake of gardening that we are going all this enormous distance. No, we had better face things honestly, our object is quite different. We are going to try to subsist in the modern fashion, taking our share in the squandering of old Krueger's properties, his factories and machines. We are not going to rebuild his fortune, but like everyone else and in the same incredibly chaotic way we'll fritter it away and lend a hand in the collective squandering of thousands for the sake of earning a kopek's worth of living. Not that I would take back the estate on the old terms, even if you showered me with gold. That would be as foolish as to start running about naked or trying to forget the alphabet. No, the age of private property in Russia is over, and anyway, we Gromekos lost our acquisitive passion a generation ago."

## 27

It was too hot and stuffy in the car to sleep. The doctor's pillow was soaked in sweat. Carefully, so as not to wake the others, he got down from his bunk and pushed open the car doors.

Sticky damp heat struck him in the face as if he had walked into a cobweb in a cellar. "Mist," he guessed. "Tomorrow will be scorching hot. That's why it is so airless and so heavy and oppressive now."

It was a big station, possibly a junction. Besides the mist and the stillness, there was a feeling of emptiness, of neglect, as if the train had been lost and forgotten. It must be standing at the farthest end of the station, and so great was the maze of tracks separating it from the station buildings that if, at the other end of the yard, the earth were to open and swallow up the station, no one in the train would have noticed it.

Two faint sounds could be heard in the distance.

Behind him, where they had come from, there was a rhythmic splashing, as if clothes were being rinsed or the wind were flapping a heavy, damp flag against a pole.

From ahead there came an even rumbling, which made the doctor, who had been at the front, prick up his ears. "Long-range guns," he decided after listening to the calmly echoing, low, sustained note.

"That's it, we're right at the front." He shook his head and jumped down from the car. He walked a few steps forward. Two cars farther up, the train ended; the rest had been uncoupled and had gone away with the engine.

"So that was why they were so keyed up yesterday," the doctor thought. "They had a feeling they would be thrown in as soon as we arrived."

He walked around the front car, meaning to cross the rails and look for the main part of the station, but a sentry with a rifle rose in his path.

"Where you going? Got a pass?"

"What is this station?"

"Never mind. Who are you?"

"I am a doctor from Moscow. My family and I are passengers on this train. Here are my papers."

"To hell with your papers. I'm not such a fool as to try to read in the dark. There's a mist—can't you see? I don't need any papers to know what kind of doctor you are. Those are more of your doctors shooting twelve-inch guns at us. Put an end to you, I would, but it's too

soon for that. Get back now, while you're still in one piece."

"He's taking me for someone else," thought Zhivago. Clearly, it was no use arguing, better follow his advice before it was too late. He turned and walked the other way.

The gunfire was now at his back. There, behind him, was the east. There the sun had risen in a drift of mist and was peering dully through floating shadows, like a naked man through clouds of steam at the baths.

Zhivago walked down the length of the train and passed the end car. His feet sank deeper and deeper into soft sand.

The even sound of splashing came nearer. The ground sloped down steeply. He stopped, trying to make out the indistinct shapes in front of him; the mist made them unnaturally large. One more step, and the hulls of beached boats came up out of the dark. Before him was a wide river, its lazy ripples splashing slowly, wearily against the sides of the fishing smacks and the planks of landing stages along the shore.

A figure rose from the beach.

"Who gave you permission to prowl around?" asked another sentry with a rifle.

"What is this river?" shot out Yurii Andreievich, though he had firmly resolved not to ask any more questions.

By way of answer the sentry put his whistle to his mouth, but he was saved the trouble, for the first sentry, whom it was meant to summon, had evidently been following the doctor without a sound, and now joined his comrade. They stood talking.

"There's no doubt about it. You can tell this kind of bird at a glance. 'What's this station?' 'What's this river?' There's dust in your eyes! What do you say? Shall we take him straight to the jetty or to the train first?"

"I say to the train. See what the boss says.—Your documents," he barked. Grabbing the bunch of papers in his fist and calling back to someone: "Keep an eye on him," he strode away with the first sentry toward the station.

The third figure, whom Zhivago had not so far made out, was evidently a fisherman. He had been lying on the beach, but he now grunted, stirred, and set about enlightening the doctor on his position.

"It's lucky for you they're taking you to the boss. That may save your skin. But you mustn't blame them. They're only doing their duty. The people are on top nowadays. Perhaps it's even for the best in the long run, though there isn't much to be said for it now. They've made a mistake, you see. They've been hunting, hunting all the time, for a certain man. So they thought it was you. That's him, they thought, that's the enemy of the workers' state, we've got him. A mistake, that's all it is. If anything happens, insist on seeing the boss. Don't you let those two get away with anything. They're politically conscious, it's a misfortune, God help us. They'd think nothing of doing away with you. So, if they say 'Come along,' see you don't go. Say you must see the boss."

From the fisherman Yurii Andreievich learned that the river was the famous waterway, the Rynva, and that the station by the river served Razvilie, an industrial suburb of the town of Yuriatin. He also learned that Yuriatin, which lay a couple of miles upstream, seemed now to have been recaptured from the Whites. And that there had been troubles in Razvilie and that they too seemed to have been put down, the reason for the great stillness all around being that the station area had been cleared of civilians and strictly cordoned off. He learned finally that among the trains at the station which were used as military offices was the special train of Army Commissar Strelnikov, to whom the two sentries had gone to report.

A third sentry now came from the direction in which the two others had gone; he was distinguished from them chiefly by the fact that he pulled his rifle after him, the butt trailing on the ground, or propped it up in front of him like a tipsy friend who needed his support. This guard took the doctor to the commissar.

### 28

Sounds of laughter and movement came from one of the two coupled parlor cars to which the guard, after giving the password to the sentry, took the doctor, but they ceased the moment the two men went in.

The guard led the doctor down a narrow passage to a wide central compartment. It was a clean, comfortable room where tidy, well-dressed people worked in complete silence. The doctor had had a very different idea of the background of Strelnikov, the famous non-Party military expert who was the pride and terror of the region.

But undoubtedly the real center of his activities lay elsewhere, closer to the staff H.Q. and to the field of military operations. This could only be his personal suite, his private office and sleeping quarters.

Hence the stillness, rather like that in a steam bath with cork floors and attendants in soft slippers.

The office was in the former dining car, carpeted and with several desks in it.

"One moment," said a young officer whose desk was by the door. He nodded absent-mindedly, dismissing the guard who left, rattling his rifle butt on the metal strips nailed across the floor of the passage. After this, everyone felt free to

[ 365 ]

forget the doctor and paid no more attention to him.

From where he stood at the entrance he could see his papers lying on a desk at the far end of the room. The desk was occupied by a man who was older than the rest and who looked like an old-style colonel. He was an army statistician of some sort. Mumbling to himself, he consulted reference books, studied field maps, checked, compared, cut out, and pasted things in. After looking around at every window in the room he announced: "It's going to be hot," as though forced to this conclusion only by the examination of all the windows.

An army electrician was crawling about on the floor mending a broken wire. When he reached the desk by the door the young officer got up to make room for him. At the next table a typist in an army leather jacket was struggling with her typewriter; its carriage had slipped and got stuck. The young officer stood above her and examined the cause of the mishap from above while the electrician crawled in under her desk and examined it from below. The old-style colonel got up and joined them, and all four busied themselves with the typewriter.

This made Yurii Andreievich feel better. These people must know his fate better than he did; it was hardly likely that they would be so unconcerned and so busy with trifles in the presence of a man whom they considered doomed.

"And yet who knows?" he reflected. "Why are they so unconcerned? Guns are going off and people are dying, and they calmly prognosticate heat—not the heat of the battle but of the weather. Perhaps, after all, they have seen so much that they have no sensibility left."

To occupy himself, he stared across the room through the window opposite.

29

He could see the edge of the tracks and higher up the hill the station and the suburb of Razvilie.

Three flights of unpainted wooden steps led from the platforms to the station building.

At the end of the tracks there was a large graveyard for old engines. Locomotives without tenders, with smokestacks shaped like the tops of knee boots or like beakers, stood smokestack to smokestack amid piles of scrap.

The engine graveyard below and the human graveyard above, the crumpled iron on the tracks and the rusty iron of the roofs and shop signs of the suburb, composed a single picture of neglect and age under the white sky scalded by the early morning heat.

Living in Moscow, Yurii Andreievich had forgotten how many shop signs there still were in other towns and how much of the façades they covered. Some of those he was seeing now were so large that he could read them easily from where he stood, and they came down so low over the crooked windows of the sagging one-story buildings that the squat little houses were almost hidden by them like the faces of village children in their fathers' caps.

The mist had gone from the west, and now what remained of it in the east stirred, swayed, and parted like the curtain of a stage.

And there, on a hill above Razvilie and a mile or two beyond it, stood a large town, the size of a provincial capital. The sun warmed its colors and the distance simplified its lines. It clung to the summit of the hill in tiers, house by house and street by street, with a big church in the middle on the top, as in a cheap color print of a desert monastery or of Mount Athos.

"Yuriatin," the doctor thought excitedly. "The town I used to hear about so often from Anna Ivanovna and from Nurse Antipova. How strange that I should see it in these circumstances!"

At that moment the attention of the military was diverted from the typewriter to something they could see from one of the other windows, and the doctor looked around.

A group of prisoners was being taken under guard up the station steps. Among them was a boy in a school uniform who was wounded in the head. He had received first aid, but a trickle of blood seeped through the bandage and he kept smudging it with his hand over his dark sweaty face. Walking between two Red Army men at the tail of the procession, he attracted notice not only by his resolute air, his good looks, and the pathos of so young a rebel's plight, but by the utter absurdity of his own and his two companions' gestures. They were doing exactly the opposite of what they should have done.

He was still wearing his school cap. It slithered continually from his bandaged head, and instead of taking it off and carrying it in his hand he rammed it back each time, disturbing the bandage and the wound, and in this his two guards assisted him readily.

In this absurdity, so contrary to common sense, the doctor saw a profound symbol. He longed to rush out and address the boy in words that were impatiently welling up inside him. He longed to shout to him and to the people in the railway coach that salvation lay not in loyalty to forms but in throwing them off.

He turned away. Strelnikov came in with long, vigorous strides and stood in the middle of the room.

How was it possible that he, a doctor, with his countless acquaintances, had never until this day come across anything so definite as this man's personality? How was it that they had never been thrown together, that their paths had not crossed?

In some inexplicable way it was clear at once that this man was entirely a manifestation of the will. So completely was he the self he resolved to be that everything about him seemed inevitable, exact, perfect—his well-proportioned, handsomely set head, his impetuous step, his long legs, his knee boots which may well have been muddy but looked polished, and his gray serge tunic which may have been creased but looked as if it were made of the best linen and had just been pressed.

Such was the irresistible effect of his brilliance, his unaffected ease, and his sense of being at home in any conceivable situation on earth.

He must certainly, Yurii Andreievich thought, be possessed of a remarkable gift, but it was not necessarily the gift of originality. This talent, which showed itself in his every movement, might well be the talent of imitation. In those days everyone modeled himself on someone else—they imitated heroes of history, or the men who had struck their imagination by winning fame in the fighting at the front or in the streets, or those who had great prestige with the people, or this or that comrade who had won distinction, or simply one another.

Strelnikov politely concealed any surprise or annoyance he may have felt at the presence of a stranger. He addressed his staff, treating him as if he belonged among them.

He said: "Congratulations. We have driven them back. It all seems more like playing at war than serious business, because they are as Russian as we are, only stuffed with nonsense—they won't give it up, so we have to beat it out of them. Their commander was my friend. His origin is even more proletarian than mine. We grew up in the same house. He has done a great deal for me in my life and I am deeply indebted to him. And here I am rejoicing that we have thrown them back beyond the river and perhaps even farther. Hurry up with that connection, Gurian, we need the telephone, we can't possibly manage with only mesengers and the telegraph. Have you noticed how hot it is? I managed to get in an hour's sleep, just the same. Oh, yes!" He turned to the doctor, remembering that he had been waked up to deal with some nonsense in connection with this man.

"This man?" Strelnikov thought, looking him over sharply. "Nonsense! He's nothing like him. Fools!" He laughed, and said to Yurii Andreievich:

"My apologies, comrade. They mistook you for someone else. My sentries got mixed up. You are free to go. Where are the comrade's work papers? Ah, here are your documents. May I just have a glance . . . Zhivago . . . Zhivago . . . Doctor Zhivago . . . Moscow . . . How about going to my place for a moment? This is the secretariat, I'm in the next car. This way, I won't keep you long."

### 30

Who, in fact, was Strelnikov?

That he should have reached and held his position was remarkable, for he was a non-Party man. He had been totally unknown because, though born in Moscow, he had gone straight from the university to the provinces as a teacher, and in the war had been taken prisoner, reported missing, believed killed, and had only recently come back from German captivity.

He was recommended and vouched for by Tiverzin, a railway worker of advanced political views in whose family he had lived as a child. Those who controlled appointments were impressed by him: in those days of inordinate rhetoric and political extremism his revolutionary fervor, equally unbridled, was remarkable for its genuineness. His fanaticism was not an imitation but was his own, a natural consequence of all his previous life.

Strelnikov justified the confidence of the authorities.

His fighting record over the past few months included the actions at Nizhni Kelmes and Ust-Nemdinsk, the suppression of the Gubysov peasants who had put up armed resistance to food levies, and of the men of the 14th Infantry who had plundered a food convoy. He had also dealt with Stenka Razin soldiers, who had started an uprising in the town of Turkatui and gone over to the Whites, and with the mutiny at Chirkin Us, where a loyal commander had been killed.

In each case, he had taken his enemies by surprise and had investigated, tried, sentenced, and enforced his sentence with speed, severity, and resolution.

He had brought the epidemic of desertions in this whole region under control and had successfully reorganized the recruiting bodies. As a result, conscription went ahead and the Red Army reception centers were working overtime.

Finally, when the White pressure from the north increased and the position became admittedly grave, Strelnikov was entrusted with new responsibilities, military, strategic, and operational. His interventions produced immediate results.

Strelnikov ("the shooter") knew that rumor had nicknamed him Razstrelnikov, the Executioner. He took this in his stride; he was disturbed by nothing.

He was a native of Moscow, and his father was a worker who had been sent to prison for taking part in the revolution of 1905. He did not participate in the revolutionary movement in those years, first because he was too young, and at the university because young men who come from a poor background value higher education more and work harder than the children of the rich. The ferment among other students left him uninvolved. He absorbed an immense amount of information and after taking his degree in the humanities trained himself later in science and mathematics.

Exempted from the army, he enlisted voluntarily, was commissioned, sent to the front, and captured, and on hearing of the revolution in Russia he escaped in 1917 and came home. He had two characteristic features, two passions: an unusual power of clear and logical reasoning, and a great moral purity and sense of justice; he was ardent and honorable.

But he would not have made a scientist of the sort who break new ground. His intelligence lacked the capacity for bold leaps into the unknown, the sudden flashes of insight that transcend barren, logical deductions.

And if he were really to do good, he would have needed, in addition to his principles, a heart capable of violating them—a heart which knows only of particular, not of general, cases, and which achieves greatness in little actions.

Filled with the loftiest aspirations from his childhood, he had looked upon the world as a vast arena where everyone competed for perfection, keeping scrupulously to the rules. When he found that this was not so, it did not occur to him that his conception of the world order might have been oversimplified. He nursed his grievance and with it the ambition to judge between life and the dark forces that distorted it, and to be life's champion and avenger.

Embittered by his disappointment, he was armed by the revolution.

### 31

"Zhivago," repeated Strelnikov when they were settled in his room. "Zhivago . . . Trade, I think. Or upper class . . . Well, of course, a Moscow doctor . . . Going to Varykino. That's strange, why should you leave Moscow for such a provincial hole?"

"That's just the idea. In search of quiet, seclusion, and obscurity."

"Well, well, how romantic! Varykino? I know most of the places around here. That used to be Krueger's estate. You aren't related to him, by any chance? You don't happen to be his heir?"

"Why the irony? Being his 'heir' has nothing to do with it. Though it is true that my wife . . ."

"Ah, so you see! But if you're feeling nostalgic for the Whites I'm going to disappoint you. You're too late. We've cleared the district."

"You're still making fun of me?"

"And then, a doctor. An army medical officer. And we're at war. That really is my business. You're a deserter. The Greens[1] are also seeking refuge in the woods. Your reasons?"

"I have been wounded twice and discharged as an invalid."

"Next you'll be handing me a reference from the People's Commissariat of Education or Health to prove that you are a Soviet citizen, a 'sympathizer,' 'entirely loyal.' These are apocalyptic times, my dear sir, this is the Last Judgment. This is a time for angels with flaming swords and winged beasts from the abyss, not for sympathizers and loyal doctors. However, I told you you were free, and I won't go back on my word. But remember, it's for this once. I have a feeling

---

[1] Greens: Anarchistic elements, chiefly peasants, who fought both Reds and Whites.

that we'll meet again, and then our conversation will be quite different. Watch out."

Neither the threat nor the challenge disturbed Yurii Andreievich. He said: "I know what you think of me. From your point of view you are right. But the issue you wish me to discuss with you is one I have been arguing with an imaginary accuser all my life, and it would be odd if I had not by now reached some conclusion. Only I could not put it into a couple of words. So if I am really free, permit me to leave without having it out with you. If I am not, then you must decide what to do with me. I have no excuses to make to you."

They were interrupted by the telephone. The line was repaired. Strelnikov picked up the receiver.

"Thanks, Gurian. Now be a good fellow and send somebody along to see Comrade Zhivago to his train; I don't want any more accidents. And give me the Razvilie Cheka Transport Department."

When Zhivago had gone, Strelnikov telephoned the railway station.

"There's a schoolboy they've brought in, keeps pulling his cap over his ears and he's got a bandaged head, it's disgraceful.—That's right.—He's to have medical aid if he needs it.—Certainly.—Yes, like the apple of your eye, you'll be responsible to me personally.—Food, too, if necessary. That's right. Now, let's get down to business. . . . I'm still talking, don't cut me off. Damn, there's somebody else on the line. Gurian! Gurian! They've cut me off."

He gave up trying to finish his conversation for the time being. "It could be one of my former pupils," he thought. "Fighting us, now he's big." He counted up the years since he had stopped teaching to see if the boy could have been his pupil. Then he looked out of the window toward the panorama of the horizon, and searched for the part of Yuriatin where they had lived. Suppose his wife and daughter were still there! Couldn't he go to them? Why not now, this very minute? Yes, but how could he? They belonged to another life. First he must see this one through, this new life, then he could go back to the one that had been interrupted. Someday he would do it. Someday. But when, when?

# A BIOGRAPHICAL SKETCH OF
# BORIS PASTERNAK*

BORIS LEONIDOVICH PASTERNAK (1890–1960), born in Moscow, was the son of talented artists: his father was a painter and illustrator of Tolstoy's works, his mother, a well-known concert pianist. Pasternak's education began in a German school in Moscow and was continued at the University of Moscow. Under the influence of the composer Scriabin, Pasternak took up the study of musical composition for six years from 1904 to 1910. By 1912 he had renounced music as his calling in life and went to the University of Marburg, Germany, to study philosophy. After four months there and a trip to Italy, he returned to Russia and decided to dedicate himself to literature.

Pasternak's first book of verse went unnoticed. With *Sestra moya zhizn* (*My Sister Life,* 1922) and *Temy i variatsii* (*Themes and Variations,* 1923), the latter marked by an extreme but sober style, Pasternak first gained a place as a leading poet among his Russian contemporaries. In 1924 he published *Vysokaya bolezn* (Sublime Malady), which portrayed the 1905 revolt as he saw it, and *Detstvo Lyuvers* (*The Child-*

hood of *Lyuvers*), a lyrical and psychological depiction of a young girl on the threshold of womanhood. A collection of four short stories was published the following year under the title *Vozdushnye puti* (*Aerial Ways*). In 1927 Pasternak again returned to the revolution of 1905 as a subject for two long works: *Leytenant Shmidt,* a poem expressing threnodic sorrow for the fate of Lieutenant Schmidt, the leader of the mutiny at Sevastopol, and *Devyatsot pyaty god* (*The Year 1905*), a powerful but diffuse poem which concentrates on the events related to the revolution of 1905.

Pasternak's reticent autobiography, *Okhrannaya granota* (*Safe Conduct*), appeared in 1931 and was followed the next year by a collection of lyrics, *Vtoroye rozhdenie* (*Second Birth*) (1932). In 1935 he published translations of some Georgian poets and subsequently translated the major dramas of Shakespeare, several works of Goethe, Schiller, Kleist, and Ben Jonson, and poems by Petöfi, Verlaine, Swinburne, Shelley, and others. *Na rannikh poyezdakh* (*In Early Trains*), a collection of poems written since 1936, was published in 1943 and enlarged and reissued in 1945 as *Zemnye prostory* (*Wide Spaces of the Earth*).

In 1957 *Doktor Zhivago,* Pasternak's only novel—except for the earlier "novel in verse" *Spektorsky* (1926)—first appeared in an Italian translation. It has

* *Editor's Note:* Rather than publish an essay on the life and works of Pasternak, we have chosen to present only the following minimum sketch, leaving the author himself to tell us of his life in his masterpiece *I Remember, Sketch for an Autobiography,* finished in November 1957. See page 247.

been acclaimed by some critics as a successful attempt at combining lyrical-descriptive and epic-dramatic styles. An autobiographical sketch, *Biografichesky ocherk* (*I Remember, Sketch for an Autobiography*), was published in 1959, first in Italian and subsequently in English.

Pasternak lived in Peredelkino, near Moscow, until his death in 1960.

# THE 1958 PRIZE

## By KJELL STRÖMBERG

THE award of the Nobel Prize for Literature to Boris Pasternak resulted in worldwide political repercussions. The great Russian poet and novelist first accepted the Prize, then was forced by his government to reject it. Letters and press clippings referring to this literary event, which quickly became a great political scandal, fill a number of large files in the archives of the Nobel Foundation and the Swedish Academy.

Some commentators saw a precedent in the commotion created in 1936, when the Nobel Prize for Peace was awarded to Carl von Ossietsky, a German journalist who lay dying in one of Hitler's prisons. The Nazi dictator thereupon forbade Germans in the future to accept any Prize from the Nobel Foundation. The Foundation did not consider itself in any way bound to respect this position; three years later, the Carolingian Institute of Medicine and Surgery of the University of Stockholm had no qualms about awarding the Nobel Prize for Medicine to a German scientist, Gerhard Domagk. Domagk, however, had to wait for the fall of the Nazi regime before taking possession of his award.

But the Pasternak case was not quite the same. Some argued that the prize had been awarded to him chiefly, if not exclusively, for his more or less autobiographical novel *Doctor Zhivago,* which

for many years he had tried in vain to have published in Soviet Russia. Convinced that the Russian market would remain closed to his work, with its thinly veiled criticism of the regime which had come to power forty years before, the author entrusted a copy of his manuscript to his personal friend and literary agent abroad, the Italian publisher Giangiacomo Feltrinelli. Feltrinelli, generally regarded as a Communist sympathizer, succeeded in getting the manuscript out of the Soviet Union, together with secret instructions authorizing him to publish it abroad without heeding any public protest which the author might eventually be forced to make against him. The first Italian edition in November 1957, was immediately followed by a series of translations in other languages —English, French, German, and, of course, Swedish, since the name of Pasternak had long figured among the most prominent candidates for the Nobel Prize. Although a Russian-language edition was printed in Amsterdam and clandestinely shipped into Russia, it was sold almost openly to employees at the Russian pavilion of the Brussels Exposition of 1958.

No one knows whether the Kremlin was unaware of this or simply closed its eyes. The Soviet press prudently held its tongue. Pasternak himself must have

[ 373 ]

thought the moment of danger safely past when suddenly the announcement of the Nobel Prize burst like a bomb. A few weeks before at his *dacha* outside Moscow, in an interview with his Swedish translator, he had spoken freely of his work and quoted passages in harmony with Soviet doctrine.

This false Soviet forebearance is not easy to explain. That year, Moscow literary circles buzzed with escalating rumors from Stockholm anticipating a Nobel Prize for one of their own authors. Their leading hope was Mikhail Sholokhov, who enjoyed the highest reputation in Soviet literature. The author of *And Quiet Flows the Don,* an unquestionable masterpiece translated into scores of languages, had been a candidate for the Prize for nearly as long as Pasternak. His candidacy was supported abroad at least as enthusiastically as Pasternak's, since he was better known. It should be recalled that in 1933, the Soviets had stomached without a grimace the award of the only Nobel Prize ever won by a Russian writer—not awarded to the illustrious Gorki, who was still alive, but to an emigré, Ivan Bunin. It is easy to understand the deep disappointment in these circles when, twenty-five years later, the Swedish Academy gave the nod to Pasternak rather than Sholokhov, who was the Kremlin's unofficial poet laureate.

One member of the government, Minister for Cultural Affairs Nicholas Mikhailov, was caught by surprise; unbriefed on Pasternak's particular situation, he went so far as to hail the award to Pasternak as a Russian writer. But ironically the ignominious attacks leveled against Pasternak were unleashed by the professional association of Soviet writers, headed by the influential critic Surkov, and by the literary journals controlled by him. Mr. Khruschev's public fulminations, and the threats of other reprisals if

he accepted the Nobel Prize came only after the fierce attacks launched by his old colleagues. Denounced as an enemy of the people, a pig dirtying his own land, a traitor like Judas betraying the fatherland for thirty pieces of silver, Pasternak could have gone into tranquil exile abroad, living well on the profits from his books. Spattered with insults and beaten to the ground by the storm, he decided to renounce the Prize. He expressed his warmest thanks to the Stockholm Academy, then later sent a personal letter to the new master of all the Russias, humbly asking as an undeserved grace to live and die in his native land, which he believed he had served and wished always to serve to the full measure of his talents. To live elsewhere, he wrote, would be like being buried alive.

Although the choice of the laureate was recognized as perfectly justified from the literary point of view, the Academy was accused of having primarily political motives, as if they had mounted a kind of anti-Soviet demonstration in spite of foreseeable consequences for Pasternak. There may be a little truth in such a theory, but it is certainly not the whole truth. And it cannot be denied that once the Swedish Academy had made its decision, it spared no effort to absolve itself from any suspicion of a secret political motivation, conscious or unconscious.

To begin with, it was not *Doctor Zhivago* which called Pasternak to the attention of the Academy. Britons had proposed him as a candidate as early as 1946, and he had become a leading contender since the first report on him was submitted in 1947. This report, a substantial document, was the work of an eminent Slavic specialist, Anton Karlgren. He began by observing that Pasternak, the first Soviet writer to be presented to the Nobel Committee, was the leading Russian author in the view of most discerning Western critics. He added that Pasternak was perhaps the most exclusive of contemporary Russian writers, that is, the least accessible to the average reader. This was particularly true of his poetry, to which Karlgren devoted the bulk of his study. In his narrative prose, Karlgren noted, his extraordinary faculty for seizing upon the most secret movements of the spirit brought him close to certain Western innovators, especially Proust. He concluded by describing Pasternak as the least Russian, the most "Western" of Soviet writers—a trait which had already earned him several scoldings from the official censors, according to whom his books were distressingly lacking in popular appeal.

In Pasternak's writings there is no question of any political divergences before *Doctor Zhivago*. Nothing presaged this vast realistic painting of an entire epoch, an entire society. When it came out in Italian, Anders Österling, permanent secretary of the Swedish Academy, went so far as to compare it to *War and Peace*. "A strong patriotic accent comes through, but with no trace of empty propaganda," he wrote in January 1958. "With its abundant documentation, its intense local color and its psychological frankness, this work bears convincing witness to the fact that the creative faculty in literature is in no sense extinct in Russia. It is hard to believe that the Soviet authorities might seriously envisage forbidding its publication in the land of its birth."

The controversial *Doctor Zhivago*, although it is the laureate's masterpiece, is not mentioned in the brief citation published at the time of the award, contrary to the usage often observed in the past—the writer's chief work is usually cited. The text—and the context, prudently written—of the motivation for Pasternak's award, reads as follows: "This year's Nobel Prize for Literature has

been awarded by the Swedish Academy to the Soviet Russian writer Boris Pasternak for his notable achievement in both contemporary poetry and the field of the great Russian narrative tradition." Such is the text included in the official annual of the Nobel Foundation, but the following words are added, without comment: "As is well known, Pasternak has sent word that he does not wish to accept this distinction."

Not knowing the author's address in the country, the Swedish representative in Moscow had been unable to deliver the announcement of the award, as was normally done. Faced with the high-level reactions which came a few days later, the young chargé d'affaires thought it wiser to avoid any official action. It is clear, however, that the Swedish government was kept informed of developments in this delicate matter once the Soviet leaders had put it on a political plane. A diplomatic gesture was made in Pasternak's favor; Pandit Nehru, Indian chief of state and president of the Hindu Literary Academy, instructed his ambassador in Moscow to intervene with Khrushchev to bring the persecution to a halt. Krishna Menon, then the Indian Ambassador, was received by an Assistant Secretary for Foreign Affairs, who, greatly embarrassed, apparently argued that the Soviet government had been obliged to answer the foreign press and those diplomatic circles in the United States and elsewhere who had used Pasternak's award as a weapon against the Soviets. The Soviet official did, however, recognize the exaggeration and the grossness of language used in the Soviet press in writing about Pasternak.

There is no doubt that the emotion aroused abroad by this "intellectual Budapest," as a leading Paris newspaper called it, had a certain salutary effect. It is even possible, as some claimed, that the pressing appeals made by literary groups in many countries and the vehement reaction of the free press throughout the world saved the life, if not the total freedom, of Pasternak. His relative liberty still had to be bought at the price of his Nobel Prize. He sent a brief telegram to the Swedish Academy, written in French: "Considering the meaning this award has been given in the society to which I belong, I must reject this undeserved Prize which has been presented to me. Please do not receive my voluntary rejection with displeasure."

Österling replied briefly to this distressing message in the name of the Swedish Academy, expressing his regrets, his cordiality, and his respect. The money involved was invested in the Nobel fund, as required by the rules now in force, but the laureate's name remains inscribed in the list of winners in spite of his "voluntary" refusal.

On December 10, at the awards ceremony, Österling simply announced Pasternak's name and read the motivation for his award, adding that although the writer had declined the Prize, the award nevertheless remained valid. He regretted that delivery of the Prize could not be made. A heavy silence greeted the announcement at the end of the ceremony. No allusion to Pasternak was made in the addresses given at the traditional Town Hall banquet in honor of the laureates. The Soviet ambassador attended—not to celebrate the triumph of his masters over the great "undesirable" writer, but to honor the three Soviet scientists who shared the Nobel Prize for Physics.

---

Translated by Dale McAdoo.